Precalculus: Student Solutions Manual

Custom Edition

Ron Larson

CENGAGE
Learning·

Australia • Brazil • Japan • Korea • Mexico • Singapore • Spain • United Kingdom • United States

Precalculus: Student Solutions Manual: Custom Edition , Ninth Edition

Precalculus: Student Solutions Manual, Ninth Edition
Ron Larson

For product information and technology assistance, contact us at
Cengage Learning Customer & Sales Support, 1-800-354-9706

For permission to use material from this text or product,
submit all requests online at **cengage.com/permissions**
Further permissions questions can be emailed to
permissionrequest@cengage.com

This book contains select works from existing Cengage Learning resources and was produced by Cengage Learning Custom Solutions for collegiate use. As such, those adopting and/or contributing to this work are responsible for editorial content accuracy, continuity and completeness.

Compilation © 2015 Cengage Learning

ISBN: 978-1-337-04612-1

WCN: 01-100-101

Cengage Learning
20 Channel Center Street
Boston, MA 02210
USA

Cengage Learning is a leading provider of customized learning solutions with office locations around the globe, including Singapore, the United Kingdom, Australia, Mexico, Brazil, and Japan. Locate your local office at:
www.international.cengage.com/region.

Cengage Learning products are represented in Canada by Nelson Education, Ltd.

For your lifelong learning solutions, visit **www.cengage.com/custom.**

Visit our corporate website at **www.cengage.com.**

Brief Contents

CHAPTER 1
Functions and Their Graphs

Section 1.1   Rectangular Coordinates

1. Cartesian

3. Distance Formula

5.

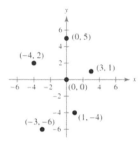

7. $(-3, 4)$

9. $x > 0$ and $y < 0$ in Quadrant IV.

11. $x = -4$ and $y > 0$ in Quadrant II.

13. $(x, -y)$ is in the second Quadrant means that (x, y) is in Quadrant III.

15.

Year, x	Number of Stores, y
2003	4906
2004	5289
2005	6141
2006	6779
2007	7262
2008	7720
2009	8416
2010	8970

Year $(t = 3 \leftrightarrow 2003)$

17. $d = \sqrt{(x_2 - x_1)^2 + (y_2 - y_1)^2}$

$= \sqrt{(3 - (-2))^2 + (-6 - 6)^2}$

$= \sqrt{(5)^2 + (-12)^2}$

$= \sqrt{25 + 144}$

$= 13$ units

19. $d = \sqrt{(x_2 - x_1)^2 + (y_2 - y_1)^2}$

$= \sqrt{(-5 - 1)^2 + (-1 - 4)^2}$

$= \sqrt{(-6)^2 + (-5)^2}$

$= \sqrt{36 + 25}$

$= \sqrt{61}$ units

21. $d = \sqrt{(x_2 - x_1)^2 + (y_2 - y_1)^2}$

$= \sqrt{\left(2 - \dfrac{1}{2}\right)^2 + \left(-1 - \dfrac{4}{3}\right)^2}$

$= \sqrt{\left(\dfrac{3}{2}\right)^2 + \left(-\dfrac{7}{3}\right)^2}$

$= \sqrt{\dfrac{9}{4} + \dfrac{49}{9}}$

$= \sqrt{\dfrac{277}{36}}$

$= \dfrac{\sqrt{277}}{6}$ units

23. (a) $(1, 0), (13, 5)$

Distance $= \sqrt{(13 - 1)^2 + (5 - 0)^2}$

$= \sqrt{12^2 + 5^2} = \sqrt{169} = 13$

$(13, 5), (13, 0)$

Distance $= |5 - 0| = |5| = 5$

$(1, 0), (13, 0)$

Distance $= |1 - 13| = |-12| = 12$

(b) $5^2 + 12^2 = 25 + 144 = 169 = 13^2$

25. $d_1 = \sqrt{(4-2)^2 + (0-1)^2} = \sqrt{4+1} = \sqrt{5}$

$d_2 = \sqrt{(4+1)^2 + (0+5)^2} = \sqrt{25+25} = \sqrt{50}$

$d_3 = \sqrt{(2+1)^2 + (1+5)^2} = \sqrt{9+36} = \sqrt{45}$

$\left(\sqrt{5}\right)^2 + \left(\sqrt{45}\right)^2 = \left(\sqrt{50}\right)^2$

27. $d_1 = \sqrt{(1-3)^2 + (-3-2)^2} = \sqrt{4+25} = \sqrt{29}$

$d_2 = \sqrt{(3+2)^2 + (2-4)^2} = \sqrt{25+4} = \sqrt{29}$

$d_3 = \sqrt{(1+2)^2 + (-3-4)^2} = \sqrt{9+49} = \sqrt{58}$

$d_1 = d_2$

29. (a)

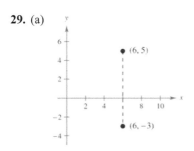

(b) $d = \sqrt{(5-(-3))^2 + (6-6)^2} = \sqrt{64} = 8$

(c) $\left(\dfrac{6+6}{2}, \dfrac{5+(-3)}{2}\right) = (6,1)$

31. (a)

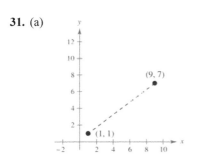

(b) $d = \sqrt{(9-1)^2 + (7-1)^2} = \sqrt{64+36} = 10$

(c) $\left(\dfrac{9+1}{2}, \dfrac{7+1}{2}\right) = (5,4)$

33. (a)

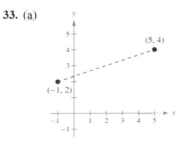

(b) $d = \sqrt{(5+1)^2 + (4-2)^2}$

$= \sqrt{36+4} = 2\sqrt{10}$

(c) $\left(\dfrac{-1+5}{2}, \dfrac{2+4}{2}\right) = (2,3)$

35. (a)

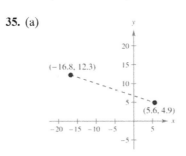

(b) $d = \sqrt{(-16.8-5.6)^2 + (12.3-4.9)^2}$

$= \sqrt{501.76 + 54.76} = \sqrt{556.52}$

(c) $\left(\dfrac{-16.8+5.6}{2}, \dfrac{12.3+4.9}{2}\right) = (-5.6, 8.6)$

37. $d = \sqrt{120^2 + 150^2}$

$= \sqrt{36,900}$

$= 30\sqrt{41}$

≈ 192.09

The plane flies about 192 kilometers.

39. midpoint $= \left(\dfrac{2002+2010}{2}, \dfrac{19,564+35,123}{2}\right)$

$= (2006, 27{,}343.5)$

In 2006, the sales for the Coca-Cola Company were about $27,343.5 million.

41. $(-2+2, -4+5) = (0,1)$

$(2+2, -3+5) = (4,2)$

$(-1+2, -1+5) = (1,4)$

43. $(-7+4, -2+8) = (-3,6)$

$(-2+4, 2+8) = (2,10)$

$(-2+4, -4+8) = (2,4)$

$(-7+4, -4+8) = (-3,4)$

45. (a) The minimum wage had the greatest increase from 2000 to 2010.

    (b) Minimum wage in 1990: $3.80

       Minimum wage in 1995: $4.25

       Percent increase: $\left(\dfrac{4.25 - 3.80}{3.80} \right)(100) \approx 11.8\%$

       Minimum wage in 1995: $4.25

       Minimum wage in 2011: $7.25

       Percent increase: $\left(\dfrac{7.25 - 4.25}{4.25} \right)(100) \approx 70.6\%$

       So, the minimum wage increased 11.8% from 1990 to 1995 and 70.6% from 1995 to 2011.

    (c) $\begin{matrix} \text{Minimum wage} \\ \text{in 2016} \end{matrix} = \begin{matrix} \text{Minimum wage} \\ \text{in 2011} \end{matrix} + \left(\begin{matrix} \text{Percent} \\ \text{increase} \end{matrix} \right)\left(\begin{matrix} \text{Minimum wage} \\ \text{in 2011} \end{matrix} \right) \approx \$7.25 + 0.706(\$7.25) \approx \$12.37$

       So, the minimum wage will be about $12.37 in the year 2016.

    (d) Answer will vary. *Sample answer:* No, the prediction is too high because it is likely that the percent increase over a 4-year period (2011–2016) will be less than the percent increase over a 16-year period (1995–2011).

47. Because $x_m = \dfrac{x_1 + x_2}{2}$ and $y_m = \dfrac{y_1 + y_2}{2}$ we have:

$$2x_m = x_1 + x_2 \qquad\qquad 2y_m = y_1 + y_2$$

$$2x_m - x_1 = x_2 \qquad\qquad 2y_m - y_1 = y_2$$

So, $(x_2, y_2) = (2x_m - x_1, 2y_m - y_1)$.

49. The midpoint of the given line segment is $\left(\dfrac{x_1 + x_2}{2}, \dfrac{y_1 + y_2}{2} \right)$.

The midpoint between (x_1, y_1) and $\left(\dfrac{x_1 + x_2}{2}, \dfrac{y_1 + y_2}{2} \right)$ is $\left(\dfrac{x_1 + \dfrac{x_1 + x_2}{2}}{2}, \dfrac{y_1 + \dfrac{y_1 + y_2}{2}}{2} \right) = \left(\dfrac{3x_1 + x_2}{4}, \dfrac{3y_1 + y_2}{4} \right)$.

The midpoint between $\left(\dfrac{x_1 + x_2}{2}, \dfrac{y_1 + y_2}{2} \right)$ and (x_2, y_2) is $\left(\dfrac{\dfrac{x_1 + x_2}{2} + x_2}{2}, \dfrac{\dfrac{y_1 + y_2}{2} + y_2}{2} \right) = \left(\dfrac{x_1 + 3x_2}{4}, \dfrac{y_1 + 3y_2}{4} \right)$.

So, the three points are $\left(\dfrac{3x_1 + x_2}{4}, \dfrac{3y_1 + y_2}{4} \right), \left(\dfrac{x_1 + x_2}{2}, \dfrac{y_1 + y_2}{2} \right)$, and $\left(\dfrac{x_1 + 3x_2}{4}, \dfrac{y_1 + 3y_2}{4} \right)$.

51.

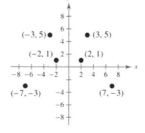

    (a) The point is reflected through the y-axis.

    (b) The point is reflected through the x-axis.

    (c) The point is reflected through the origin.

53. No. It depends on the magnitude of the quantities measured.

55. False, you would have to use the Midpoint Formula 15 times.

57. False. The polygon could be a rhombus. For example, consider the points $(4, 0), (0, 6), (-4, 0),$ and $(0, -6)$.

59. Use the Midpoint Formula to prove the diagonals of the parallelogram bisect each other.

$$\left(\dfrac{b + a}{2}, \dfrac{c + 0}{2} \right) = \left(\dfrac{a + b}{2}, \dfrac{c}{2} \right)$$

$$\left(\dfrac{a + b + 0}{2}, \dfrac{c + 0}{2} \right) = \left(\dfrac{a + b}{2}, \dfrac{c}{2} \right)$$

Section 1.2   Graphs of Equations

1. solution or solution point

3. intercepts

5. circle; (h, k); r

7. (a) $(0, 2)$: $2 \overset{?}{=} \sqrt{0 + 4}$

$2 = 2$

Yes, the point *is* on the graph.

(b) $(5, 3)$: $3 \overset{?}{=} \sqrt{5 + 4}$

$3 \overset{?}{=} \sqrt{9}$

$3 = 3$

Yes, the point *is* on the graph.

9. (a) $(2, 0)$: $(2)^2 - 3(2) + 2 \overset{?}{=} 0$

$4 - 6 + 2 \overset{?}{=} 0$

$0 = 0$

Yes, the point *is* on the graph.

(b) $(-2, 8)$: $(-2)^2 - 3(-2) + 2 \overset{?}{=} 8$

$4 + 6 + 2 \overset{?}{=} 8$

$12 \neq 8$

No, the point *is not* on the graph.

11. (a) $(2, 3)$: $3 \overset{?}{=} |2 - 1| + 2$

$3 \overset{?}{=} 1 + 2$

$3 = 3$

Yes, the point *is* on the graph.

(b) $(-1, 0)$: $0 \overset{?}{=} |-1 - 1| + 2$

$0 \overset{?}{=} 2 + 2$

$0 \neq 4$

No, the point *is not* on the graph.

13. (a) $(3, -2)$: $(3)^2 + (-2)^2 \overset{?}{=} 20$

$9 + 4 \overset{?}{=} 20$

$13 \neq 20$

No, the point *is not* on the graph.

(b) $(-4, 2)$: $(-4)^2 + (2)^2 \overset{?}{=} 20$

$16 + 4 \overset{?}{=} 20$

$20 = 20$

Yes, the point *is* on the graph.

15. $y = -2x + 5$

x	-1	0	1	2	$\frac{5}{2}$
y	7	5	3	1	0
(x, y)	$(-1, 7)$	$(0, 5)$	$(1, 3)$	$(2, 1)$	$\left(\frac{5}{2}, 0\right)$

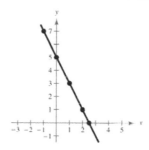

17. $y = x^2 - 3x$

x	-1	0	1	2	3
y	4	0	-2	-2	0
(x, y)	$(-1, 4)$	$(0, 0)$	$(1, -2)$	$(2, -2)$	$(3, 0)$

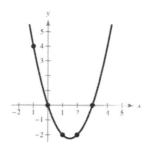

19. x-intercept: $(3, 0)$

y-intercept: $(0, 9)$

21. x-intercept: $(-2, 0)$

y-intercept: $(0, 2)$

23. x-intercept: $(1, 0)$

y-intercept: $(0, 2)$

25. $x^2 - y = 0$

$(-x)^2 - y = 0 \Rightarrow x^2 - y = 0 \Rightarrow y$-axis symmetry

$x^2 - (-y) = 0 \Rightarrow x^2 + y = 0 \Rightarrow$ No x-axis symmetry

$(-x)^2 - (-y) = 0 \Rightarrow x^2 + y = 0 \Rightarrow$ No origin symmetry

27. $y = x^3$

$y = (-x)^3 \Rightarrow y = -x^3 \Rightarrow$ No y-axis symmetry

$-y = x^3 \Rightarrow y = -x^3 \Rightarrow$ No x-axis symmetry

$-y = (-x)^3 \Rightarrow -y = -x^3 \Rightarrow y = x^3 \Rightarrow$ Origin symmetry

29. $y = \dfrac{x}{x^2 + 1}$

$y = \dfrac{-x}{(-x)^2 + 1} \Rightarrow y = \dfrac{-x}{x^2 + 1} \Rightarrow$ No y-axis symmetry

$-y = \dfrac{x}{x^2 + 1} \Rightarrow y = \dfrac{-x}{x^2 + 1} \Rightarrow$ No x-axis symmetry

$-y = \dfrac{-x}{(-x)^2 + 1} \Rightarrow -y = \dfrac{-x}{x^2 + 1} \Rightarrow y = \dfrac{x}{x^2 + 1} \Rightarrow$ Origin symmetry

31. $xy^2 + 10 = 0$

$(-x)y^2 + 10 = 0 \Rightarrow -xy^2 + 10 = 0 \Rightarrow$ No y-axis symmetry

$x(-y)^2 + 10 = 0 \Rightarrow xy^2 + 10 = 0 \Rightarrow x$-axis symmetry

$(-x)(-y)^2 + 10 = 0 \Rightarrow -xy^2 + 10 = 0 \Rightarrow$ No origin symmetry

33.

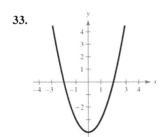

35.

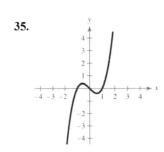

37. $y = -3x + 1$

x-intercept: $\left(\frac{1}{3}, 0\right)$

y-intercept: $(0, 1)$

No symmetry

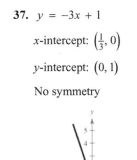

39. $y = x^2 - 2x$

x-intercepts: $(0, 0), (2, 0)$

y-intercept: $(0, 0)$

No symmetry

x	-1	0	1	2	3
y	3	0	-1	0	3

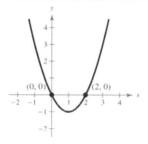

41. $y = x^3 + 3$

x-intercept: $\left(\sqrt[3]{-3}, 0\right)$

y-intercept: $(0, 3)$

No symmetry

x	-2	-1	0	1	2
y	-5	2	3	4	11

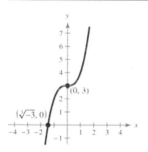

43. $y = \sqrt{x - 3}$

x-intercept: $(3, 0)$

y-intercept: none

No symmetry

x	3	4	7	12
y	0	1	2	3

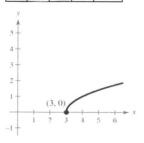

45. $y = |x - 6|$

x-intercept: $(6, 0)$

y-intercept: $(0, 6)$

No symmetry

x	-2	0	2	4	6	8	10
y	8	6	4	2	0	2	4

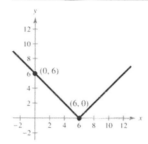

47. $x = y^2 - 1$

x-intercept: $(-1, 0)$

y-intercepts: $(0, -1), (0, 1)$

x-axis symmetry

x	-1	0	3
y	0	± 1	± 2

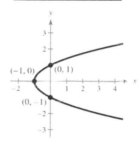

49. $y = 5 - \frac{1}{2}x$

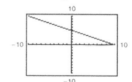

Intercepts: $(10, 0), (0, 5)$

51. $y = x^2 - 4x + 3$

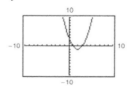

Intercepts: $(3, 0), (1, 0), (0, 3)$

53. $y = \dfrac{2x}{x-1}$

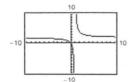

Intercept: $(0, 0)$

55. $y = \sqrt[3]{x} + 2$

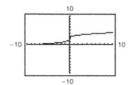

Intercepts: $(-8, 0), (0, 2)$

57. $y = x\sqrt{x+6}$

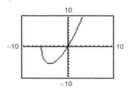

Intercepts: $(0, 0), (-6, 0)$

59. $y = |x + 3|$

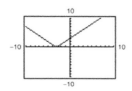

Intercepts: $(-3, 0), (0, 3)$

61. Center: $(0, 0)$; Radius: 4

$$(x - 0)^2 + (y - 0)^2 = 4^2$$
$$x^2 + y^2 = 16$$

63. Center: $(2, -1)$; Radius: 4

$$(x - 2)^2 + (y - (-1))^2 = 4^2$$
$$(x - 2)^2 + (y + 1)^2 = 16$$

65. Center: $(-1, 2)$; Solution point: $(0, 0)$

$$(x - (-1))^2 + (y - 2)^2 = r^2$$
$$(0 + 1)^2 + (0 - 2)^2 = r^2 \Rightarrow 5 = r^2$$
$$(x + 1)^2 + (y - 2)^2 = 5$$

67. Endpoints of a diameter: $(0, 0), (6, 8)$

Center: $\left(\dfrac{0 + 6}{2}, \dfrac{0 + 8}{2}\right) = (3, 4)$

$$(x - 3)^2 + (y - 4)^2 = r^2$$
$$(0 - 3)^2 + (0 - 4)^2 = r^2 \Rightarrow 25 = r^2$$
$$(x - 3)^2 + (y - 4)^2 = 25$$

69. $x^2 + y^2 = 25$

Center: $(0, 0)$, Radius: 5

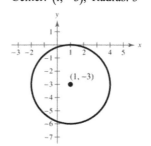

71. $(x - 1)^2 + (y + 3)^2 = 9$

Center: $(1, -3)$, Radius: 3

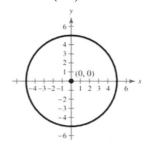

73. $\left(x - \frac{1}{2}\right)^2 + \left(y - \frac{1}{2}\right)^2 = \frac{9}{4}$

Center: $\left(\frac{1}{2}, \frac{1}{2}\right)$, Radius: $\frac{3}{2}$

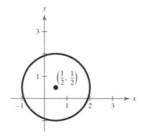

75. $y = 500,000 - 40,000t, \ 0 \le t \le 8$

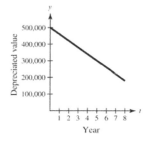

77. (a)

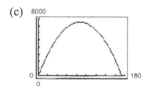

(b) $2x + 2y = \frac{1040}{3}$

$2y = \frac{1040}{3} - 2x$

$y = \frac{520}{3} - x$

$A = xy = x\left(\frac{520}{3} - x\right)$

(c)

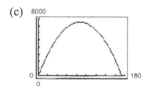

8000

180

(d) When $x = y = 86\frac{2}{3}$ yards, the area is a maximum of $7511\frac{1}{9}$ square yards.

(e) A regulation NFL playing field is 120 yards long and $53\frac{1}{3}$ yards wide. The actual area is 6400 square yards.

79. (a)

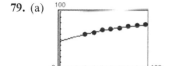

Because the line is close to the points, the model fits the data well.

(b) Graphically: The point $(90, 75.4)$ represents a life expectancy of 75.4 years in 1990.

Algebraically: $y = -0.002t^2 + 0.5t + 46.6$

$= -0.002(90)^2 + 0.5(90) + 46.6$

$= 75.4$

So, the life expectancy in 1990 was about 75.4 years.

(c) Graphically: The point $(94.6, 76.0)$ represents a life expectancy of 76 years during the year 1994.

Algebraically: $y = -0.002t^2 + 0.5t + 46.6$

$76.0 = -0.002t^2 + 0.5t + 46.6$

$0 = -0.002t^2 + 0.5t - 29.4$

Use the quadratic formula to solve.

$t = \dfrac{-b \pm \sqrt{b^2 - 4ac}}{2a}$

$= \dfrac{-(0.5) \pm \sqrt{(0.5)^2 - 4(-0.002)(-29.4)}}{2(-0.002)}$

$= \dfrac{-0.5 \pm \sqrt{0.0148}}{-0.004}$

$= 125 \pm 30.4$

So, $t = 94.6$ or $t = 155.4$. Since 155.4 is not in the domain, the solution is $t = 94.6$, which is the year 1994.

(d) When $t = 115$:

$y = -0.002t^2 + 0.5t + 46.6$

$= -0.002(115)^2 + (0.5)(115) + 46.6$

$= 77.65$

The life expectancy using the model is 77.65 years, which is slightly less than the given projection of 78.9 years.

(e) Answers will vary. *Sample answer:* No. Because the model is quadratic, the life expectancies begin to decrease after a certain point.

81. $y = ax^2 + bx^3$

(a) $y = a(-x)^2 + b(-x)^3$

$\quad = ax^2 - bx^3$

To be symmetric with respect to the y-axis; a can be any non-zero real number, b must be zero.

(b) $-y = a(-x)^2 + b(-x)^3$

$\quad -y = ax^2 - bx^3$

$\quad y = -ax^2 + bx^3$

To be symmetric with respect to the origin; a must be zero, b can be any non-zero real number.

Section 1.3   Linear Equations in Two Variables

1. linear

3. point-slope

5. perpendicular

7. linear extrapolation

9. (a) $m = \frac{2}{3}$. Because the slope is positive, the line rises.

Matches L_2.

(b) m is undefined. The line is vertical. Matches L_3.

(c) $m = -2$. The line falls. Matches L_1.

11.

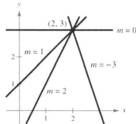

13. Two points on the line: $(0, 0)$ and $(4, 6)$

Slope $= \dfrac{y_2 - y_1}{x_2 - x_1} = \dfrac{6}{4} = \dfrac{3}{2}$

15. $y = 5x + 3$

Slope: $m = 5$

y-intercept: $(0, 3)$

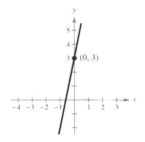

17. $y = -\frac{1}{2}x + 4$

Slope: $m = -\frac{1}{2}$

y-intercept: $(0, 4)$

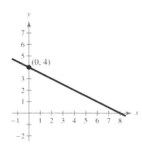

19. $y - 3 = 0$

$\quad y = 3$, horizontal line

Slope: $m = 0$

y-intercept: $(0, 3)$

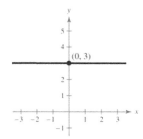

21. $5x - 2 = 0$

$x = \frac{2}{5}$, vertical line

Slope: undefined

No y-intercept

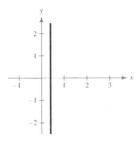

23. $7x - 6y = 30$

$-6y = -7x + 30$

$y = \frac{7}{6}x - 5$

Slope: $m = \frac{7}{6}$

y-intercept: $(0, -5)$

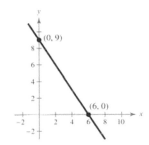

25. $m = \dfrac{0 - 9}{6 - 0} = \dfrac{-9}{6} = -\dfrac{3}{2}$

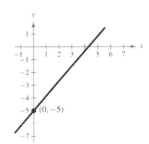

27. $m = \dfrac{6 - (-2)}{1 - (-3)} = \dfrac{8}{4} = 2$

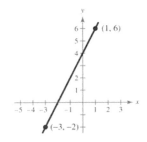

29. $m = \dfrac{-7 - (-7)}{8 - 5} = \dfrac{0}{3} = 0$

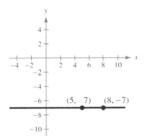

31. $m = \dfrac{4 - (-1)}{-6 - (-6)} = \dfrac{5}{0}$

m is undefined.

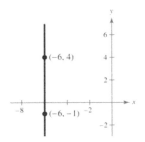

33. $m = \dfrac{1.6 - 3.1}{-5.2 - 4.8} = \dfrac{-1.5}{-10} = 0.15$

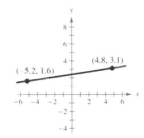

35. Point: $(2, 1)$, Slope: $m = 0$

Because $m = 0$, y does not change. Three points are $(0, 1), (3, 1),$ and $(-1, 1)$.

37. Point: $(-8, 1)$, Slope is undefined.

Because m is undefined, x does not change. Three points are $(-8, 0), (-8, 2),$ and $(-8, 3)$.

39. Point: $(-5, 4)$, Slope: $m = 2$

Because $m = 2 = \frac{2}{1}$, y increases by 2 for every one unit increase in x. Three additional points are $(-4, 6)$, $(-3, 8),$ and $(-2, 10)$.

41. Point: $(-1, -6)$, Slope: $m = -\frac{1}{2}$

Because $m = -\frac{1}{2}$, y decreases by 1 unit for every two unit increase in x. Three additional points are $(1, -7)$, $(3, -8)$, and $(-13, 0)$.

43. Point: $(0, -2)$; $m = 3$

$$y + 2 = 3(x - 0)$$
$$y = 3x - 2$$

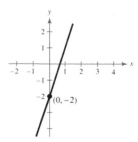

45. Point: $(-3, 6)$; $m = -2$

$$y - 6 = -2(x + 3)$$
$$y = -2x$$

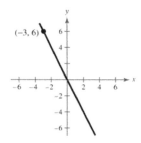

47. Point: $(4, 0)$; $m = -\frac{1}{3}$

$$y - 0 = -\frac{1}{3}(x - 4)$$
$$y = -\frac{1}{3}x + \frac{4}{3}$$

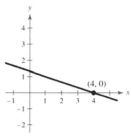

49. Point: $(2, -3)$; $m = -\frac{1}{2}$

$$y - (-3) = -\frac{1}{2}(x - 2)$$
$$y + 3 = -\frac{1}{2}x + 1$$
$$y = -\frac{1}{2}x - 2$$

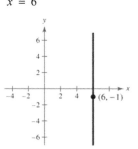

51. Point: $(6, -1)$; m is undefined.

Because the slope is undefined, the line is a vertical line.

$$x = 6$$

53. Point: $\left(4, \frac{5}{2}\right)$; $m = 0$

$$y - \frac{5}{2} = 0(x - 4)$$
$$y - \frac{5}{2} = 0$$
$$y = \frac{5}{2}$$

55. $(5, -1)$, $(-5, 5)$

$$y + 1 = \frac{5 + 1}{-5 - 5}(x - 5)$$
$$y = -\frac{3}{5}(x - 5) - 1$$
$$y = -\frac{3}{5}x + 2$$

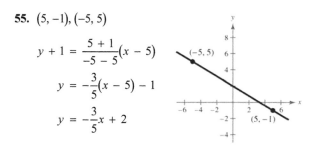

57. $(-8, 1)$, $(-8, 7)$

Because both points have $x = -8$, the slope is undefined, and the line is vertical.

$$x = -8$$

59. $\left(2, \dfrac{1}{2}\right), \left(\dfrac{1}{2}, \dfrac{5}{4}\right)$

$$y - \dfrac{1}{2} = \dfrac{\dfrac{5}{4} - \dfrac{1}{2}}{\dfrac{1}{2} - 2}(x - 2)$$

$$y = -\dfrac{1}{2}(x - 2) + \dfrac{1}{2}$$

$$y = -\dfrac{1}{2}x + \dfrac{3}{2}$$

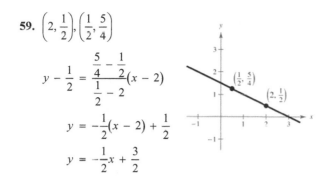

61. $(1, 0.6), (-2, -0.6)$

$$y - 0.6 = \dfrac{-0.6 - 0.6}{-2 - 1}(x - 1)$$

$$y = 0.4(x - 1) + 0.6$$

$$y = 0.4x + 0.2$$

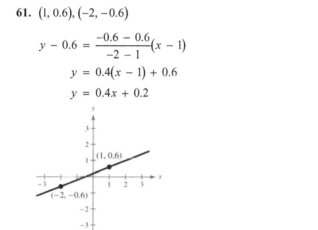

63. $(2, -1), \left(\dfrac{1}{3}, -1\right)$

$$y + 1 = \dfrac{-1 - (-1)}{\dfrac{1}{3} - 2}(x - 2)$$

$$y + 1 = 0$$

$$y = -1$$

The line is horizontal.

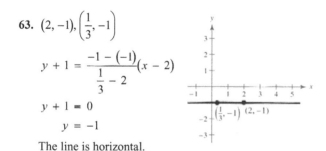

65. $L_1: y = \dfrac{1}{3}x - 2$

$$m_1 = \dfrac{1}{3}$$

$$L_2: y = \dfrac{1}{3}x + 3$$

$$m_2 = \dfrac{1}{3}$$

The lines are parallel.

67. $L_1: y = \dfrac{1}{2}x - 3$

$$m_1 = \dfrac{1}{2}$$

$$L_2: y = -\dfrac{1}{2}x + 1$$

$$m_2 = -\dfrac{1}{2}$$

The lines are neither parallel nor perpendicular.

69. $L_1: (0, -1), (5, 9)$

$$m_1 = \dfrac{9 + 1}{5 - 0} = 2$$

$$L_2: (0, 3), (4, 1)$$

$$m_2 = \dfrac{1 - 3}{4 - 0} = -\dfrac{1}{2}$$

The lines are perpendicular.

71. $L_1: (3, 6), (-6, 0)$

$$m_1 = \dfrac{0 - 6}{-6 - 3} = \dfrac{2}{3}$$

$$L_2: (0, -1), \left(5, \dfrac{7}{3}\right)$$

$$m_2 = \dfrac{\dfrac{7}{3} + 1}{5 - 0} = \dfrac{2}{3}$$

The lines are parallel.

73. $4x - 2y = 3$

$$y = 2x - \dfrac{3}{2}$$

Slope: $m = 2$

(a) $(2, 1), m = 2$

$$y - 1 = 2(x - 2)$$

$$y = 2x - 3$$

(b) $(2, 1), m = -\dfrac{1}{2}$

$$y - 1 = -\dfrac{1}{2}(x - 2)$$

$$y = -\dfrac{1}{2}x + 2$$

75. $3x + 4y = 7$

$$y = -\dfrac{3}{4}x + \dfrac{7}{4}$$

Slope: $m = -\dfrac{3}{4}$

(a) $\left(-\dfrac{2}{3}, \dfrac{7}{8}\right), m = -\dfrac{3}{4}$

$$y - \dfrac{7}{8} = -\dfrac{3}{4}\left(x - \left(-\dfrac{2}{3}\right)\right)$$

$$y = -\dfrac{3}{4}x + \dfrac{3}{8}$$

(b) $\left(-\dfrac{2}{3}, \dfrac{7}{8}\right), m = \dfrac{4}{3}$

$$y - \dfrac{7}{8} = \dfrac{4}{3}\left(x - \left(-\dfrac{2}{3}\right)\right)$$

$$y = \dfrac{4}{3}x + \dfrac{127}{72}$$

77. $y + 3 = 0$

$\qquad y = -3$

Slope: $m = 0$

(a) $(-1, 0), m = 0$

$\qquad y = 0$

(b) $(-1, 0), m$ is undefined.

$\qquad x = -1$

79. $x - y = 4$

$\qquad y = x - 4$

Slope: $m = 1$

(a) $(2.5, 6.8), m = 1$

$\qquad y - 6.8 = 1(x - 2.5)$

$\qquad\qquad y = x + 4.3$

(b) $(2.5, 6.8), m = -1$

$\qquad y - 6.8 = (-1)(x - 2.5)$

$\qquad\qquad y = -x + 9.3$

81. $\dfrac{x}{2} + \dfrac{y}{3} = 1$

$\quad 3x + 2y - 6 = 0$

83. $\dfrac{x}{-1/6} + \dfrac{y}{-2/3} = 1$

$\qquad 6x + \dfrac{3}{2}y = -1$

$\quad 12x + 3y + 2 = 0$

85. $\dfrac{x}{c} + \dfrac{y}{c} = 1, c \ne 0$

$\qquad x + y = c$

$\qquad 1 + 2 = c$

$\qquad\quad 3 = c$

$\qquad x + y = 3$

$\quad x + y - 3 = 0$

87. (a) $m = 135.$ The sales are increasing 135 units per year.

(b) $m = 0.$ There is no change in sales during the year.

(c) $m = -40.$ The sales are decreasing 40 units per year.

89. $y = \frac{6}{100}x$

$\quad y = \frac{6}{100}(200) = 12$ feet

91. $(10, 2540), m = -125$

$\qquad V - 2540 = -125(t - 10)$

$\qquad V - 2540 = -125t + 1250$

$\qquad\qquad V = -125t + 3790, 5 \le t \le 10$

93. The C-intercept measures the fixed costs of manufacturing when zero bags are produced.

The slope measures the cost to produce one laptop bag.

95. Using the points $(0, 875)$ and $(5, 0),$ where the first coordinate represents the year t and the second coordinate represents the value $V,$ you have

$$m = \frac{0 - 875}{5 - 0} = -175$$

$$V = -175t + 875, 0 \le t \le 5.$$

97. Using the points $(0, 32)$ and $(100, 212),$ where the first coordinate represents a temperature in degrees Celsius and the second coordinate represents a temperature in degrees Fahrenheit, you have

$$m = \frac{212 - 32}{100 - 0} = \frac{180}{100} = \frac{9}{5}.$$

Since the point $(0, 32)$ is the F- intercept, $b = 32,$ the equation is $F = \dfrac{9}{5}C + 32.$

99. (a) Total Cost = cost for fuel and maintainance + cost for operator + purchase cost

$\qquad\qquad C = 9.5t + 11.5t + 42,000$

$\qquad\qquad C = 21.0t + 42,000$

(b) Revenue = Rate per hour $\cdot$ Hours

$\qquad\qquad R = 45t$

(c) $P = R - C$

$\qquad P = 45t - (21t + 42,000)$

$\qquad P = 24t - 42,000$

(d) Let $P = 0,$ and solve for $t.$

$\qquad 0 = 24t - 42,000$

$\quad 42,000 = 24t$

$\qquad 1750 = t$

The equipment must be used 1750 hours to yield a profit of 0 dollars.

101. False. The slope with the greatest magnitude corresponds to the steepest line.

103. Find the slope of the line segments between the points A and B, and B and C.

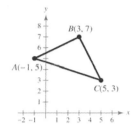

$$m_{AB} = \frac{7 - 5}{3 - (-1)} = \frac{2}{4} = \frac{1}{2}$$

$$m_{BC} = \frac{3 - 7}{5 - 3} = \frac{-4}{2} = -2$$

Since the slopes are negative reciprocals, the line segments are perpendicular and therefore intersect to form a right angle. So, the triangle is a right triangle.

105. No. The slope cannot be determined without knowing the scale on the y-axis. The slopes will be the same if the scale on the y-axis of (a) is $2\frac{1}{2}$ and the scale on the y-axis of (b) is 1. Then the slope of both is $\frac{5}{4}$.

107. No, the slopes of two perpendicular lines have opposite signs. (Assume that neither line is vertical or horizontal.)

109. The line $y = 4x$ rises most quickly.

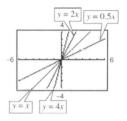

The line $y = -4x$ falls most quickly.

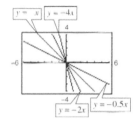

The greater the magnitude of the slope (the absolute value of the slope), the faster the line rises or falls.

111. Set the distance between $(4, -1)$ and (x, y) equal to the distance between $(-2, 3)$ and (x, y).

$$\sqrt{(x - 4)^2 + [y - (-1)]^2} = \sqrt{[x - (-2)]^2 + (y - 3)^2}$$

$$(x - 4)^2 + (y + 1)^2 = (x + 2)^2 + (y - 3)^2$$

$$x^2 - 8x + 16 + y^2 + 2y + 1 = x^2 + 4x + 4 + y^2 - 6y + 9$$

$$-8x + 2y + 17 = 4x - 6y + 13$$

$$0 = 12x - 8y - 4$$

$$0 = 4(3x - 2y - 1)$$

$$0 = 3x - 2y - 1$$

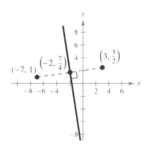

This line is the perpendicular bisector of the line segment connecting $(4, -1)$ and $(-2, 3)$.

113. Set the distance between $\left(3, \frac{5}{2}\right)$ and (x, y) equal to the distance between $(-7, 1)$ and (x, y).

$$\sqrt{(x - 3)^2 + \left(y - \frac{5}{2}\right)^2} = \sqrt{[x - (-7)]^2 + (y - 1)^2}$$

$$(x - 3)^2 + \left(y - \frac{5}{2}\right)^2 = (x + 7)^2 + (y - 1)^2$$

$$x^2 - 6x + 9 + y^2 - 5y + \frac{25}{4} = x^2 + 14x + 49 + y^2 - 2y + 1$$

$$-6x - 5y + \frac{61}{4} = 14x - 2y + 50$$

$$-24x - 20y + 61 = 56x - 8y + 200$$

$$80x + 12y + 139 = 0$$

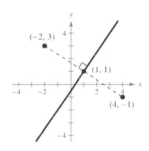

This line is the perpendicular bisector of the line segment connecting $\left(3, \frac{5}{2}\right)$ and $(-7, 1)$.

Section 1.4 Functions

1. domain; range; function

3. implied domain

5. Yes, the relationship is a function. Each domain value is matched with exactly one range value.

7. No, it does not represent a function. The input values of 10 and 7 are each matched with two output values.

9. (a) Each element of A is matched with exactly one element of B, so it does represent a function.

   (b) The element 1 in A is matched with two elements, -2 and 1 of B, so it does not represent a function.

   (c) Each element of A is matched with exactly one element of B, so it does represent a function.

   (d) The element 2 in A is not matched with an element of B, so the relation does not represent a function.

11. $x^2 + y^2 = 4 \Rightarrow y = \pm\sqrt{4 - x^2}$

    No, y *is not* a function of x.

13. $2x + 3y = 4 \Rightarrow y = \frac{1}{3}(4 - 2x)$

    Yes, y *is* a function of x.

15. $y = \sqrt{16 - x^2}$

    Yes, y *is* a function of x.

17. $y = |4 - x|$

    Yes, y *is* a function of x.

19. $y = -75$ or $y = -75 + 0x$

    Yes, y *is* a function of x.

21. $f(x) = 2x - 3$

    (a) $f(1) = 2(1) - 3 = -1$

    (b) $f(-3) = 2(-3) - 3 = -9$

    (c) $f(x - 1) = 2(x - 1) - 3 = 2x - 5$

23. $g(t) = 4t^2 - 3t + 5$

    (a) $g(2) = 4(2)^2 - 3(2) + 5$
    $= 15$

    (b) $g(t - 2) = 4(t - 2)^2 - 3(t - 2) + 5$
    $= 4t^2 - 19t + 27$

    (c) $g(t) - g(2) = 4t^2 - 3t + 5 - 15$
    $= 4t^2 - 3t - 10$

25. $f(y) = 3 - \sqrt{y}$

    (a) $f(4) = 3 - \sqrt{4} = 1$

    (b) $f(0.25) = 3 - \sqrt{0.25} = 2.5$

    (c) $f(4x^2) = 3 - \sqrt{4x^2} = 3 - 2|x|$

27. $q(x) = \dfrac{1}{x^2 - 9}$

    (a) $q(0) = \dfrac{1}{0^2 - 9} = -\dfrac{1}{9}$

    (b) $q(3) = \dfrac{1}{3^2 - 9}$ is undefined.

    (c) $q(y + 3) = \dfrac{1}{(y + 3)^2 - 9} = \dfrac{1}{y^2 + 6y}$

29. $f(x) = \dfrac{|x|}{x}$

    (a) $f(2) = \dfrac{|2|}{2} = 1$

    (b) $f(-2) = \dfrac{|-2|}{-2} = -1$

    (c) $f(x - 1) = \dfrac{|x - 1|}{x - 1} = \begin{cases} -1, & \text{if } x < 1 \\ 1, & \text{if } x > 1 \end{cases}$

31. $f(x) = \begin{cases} 2x + 1, & x < 0 \\ 2x + 2, & x \geq 0 \end{cases}$

    (a) $f(-1) = 2(-1) + 1 = -1$

    (b) $f(0) = 2(0) + 2 = 2$

    (c) $f(2) = 2(2) + 2 = 6$

33. $f(x) = x^2 - 3$

    $f(-2) = (-2)^2 - 3 = 1$

    $f(-1) = (-1)^2 - 3 = -2$

    $f(0) = (0)^2 - 3 = -3$

    $f(1) = (1)^2 - 3 = -2$

    $f(2) = (2)^2 - 3 = 1$

x	-2	-1	0	1	2
$f(x)$	1	-2	-3	-2	1

35. $f(x) = \begin{cases} -\frac{1}{2}x + 4, & x \le 0 \\ (x - 2)^2, & x > 0 \end{cases}$

$f(-2) = -\frac{1}{2}(-2) + 4 = 5$

$f(-1) = -\frac{1}{2}(-1) + 4 = 4\frac{1}{2} = \frac{9}{2}$

$f(0) = -\frac{1}{2}(0) + 4 = 4$

$f(1) = (1 - 2)^2 = 1$

$f(2) = (2 - 2)^2 = 0$

x	-2	-1	0	1	2
$f(x)$	5	$\frac{9}{2}$	4	1	0

37. $15 - 3x = 0$

$3x = 15$

$x = 5$

39. $\dfrac{3x - 4}{5} = 0$

$3x - 4 = 0$

$x = \dfrac{4}{3}$

41. $x^2 - 9 = 0$

$x^2 = 9$

$x = \pm 3$

43. $x^3 - x = 0$

$x(x^2 - 1) = 0$

$x(x + 1)(x - 1) = 0$

$x = 0,\ x = -1,\ \text{or } x = 1$

45. $f(x) = g(x)$

$x^2 = x + 2$

$x^2 - x - 2 = 0$

$(x - 2)(x + 1) = 0$

$x - 2 = 0 \quad x + 1 = 0$

$x = 2 \qquad x = -1$

47. $f(x) = g(x)$

$x^4 - 2x^2 = 2x^2$

$x^4 - 4x^2 = 0$

$x^2(x^2 - 4) = 0$

$x^2(x + 2)(x - 2) = 0$

$x^2 = 0 \Rightarrow x = 0$

$x + 2 = 0 \Rightarrow x = -2$

$x - 2 = 0 \Rightarrow x = 2$

49. $f(x) = 5x^2 + 2x - 1$

Because $f(x)$ is a polynomial, the domain is all real numbers x.

51. $h(t) = \dfrac{4}{t}$

The domain is all real numbers t except $t = 0$.

53. $g(y) = \sqrt{y - 10}$

Domain: $y - 10 \ge 0$

$y \ge 10$

The domain is all real numbers y such that $y \ge 10$.

55. $g(x) = \dfrac{1}{x} - \dfrac{3}{x + 2}$

The domain is all real numbers x except $x = 0,\ x = -2$.

57. $f(s) = \dfrac{\sqrt{s - 1}}{s - 4}$

Domain: $s - 1 \ge 0 \Rightarrow s \ge 1$ and $s \ne 4$

The domain consists of all real numbers s, such that $s \ge 1$ and $s \ne 4$.

59. $f(x) = \dfrac{x - 4}{\sqrt{x}}$

The domain is all real numbers x such that $x > 0$ or $(0, \infty)$.

61. (a)

Height, x	Volume, V
1	484
2	800
3	972
4	1024
5	980
6	864

The volume is maximum when $x = 4$ and $V = 1024$ cubic centimeters.

(b)

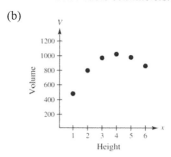

V is a function of x.

(c) $V = x(24 - 2x)^2$

Domain: $0 < x < 12$

63. $A = s^2$ and $P = 4s \Rightarrow \dfrac{P}{4} = s$

$A = \left(\dfrac{P}{4}\right)^2 = \dfrac{P^2}{16}$

65. $\qquad y = -\frac{1}{10}x^2 + 3x + 6$

$y(30) = -\frac{1}{10}(30)^2 + 3(30) + 6 = 6$ feet

If the child holds a glove at a height of 5 feet, then the ball *will* be over the child's head because it will be at a height of 6 feet.

67. $A = \dfrac{1}{2}bh = \dfrac{1}{2}xy$

Because $(0, y), (2, 1),$ and $(x, 0)$ all lie on the same line, the slopes between any pair are equal.

$\dfrac{1 - y}{2 - 0} = \dfrac{0 - 1}{x - 2}$

$\dfrac{1 - y}{2} = \dfrac{-1}{x - 2}$

$y = \dfrac{2}{x - 2} + 1$

$y = \dfrac{x}{x - 2}$

So, $A = \dfrac{1}{2}x\left(\dfrac{x}{x - 2}\right) = \dfrac{x^2}{2(x - 2)}.$

The domain of A includes x-values such that $x^2/[2(x - 2)] > 0.$ By solving this inequality, the domain is $x > 2.$

69. For 2004 through 2007, use

$p(t) = 4.57t + 27.3.$

2004: $p(4) = 4.57(4) + 27.3 = 45.58\%$

2005: $p(5) = 4.57(5) + 27.3 = 50.15\%$

2006: $p(6) = 4.57(6) + 27.3 = 54.72\%$

2007: $p(7) = 4.57(7) + 27.3 = 59.29\%$

For 2008 through 2010, use

$p(t) = 3.35t + 37.6.$

2008: $p(8) = 3.35(8) + 37.6 = 64.4\%$

2009: $p(9) = 3.35(9) + 37.6 = 67.75\%$

2010: $p(10) = 3.35(10) + 37.6 = 71.1\%$

71. (a) Cost = variable costs + fixed costs

$C = 12.30x + 98,000$

(b) Revenue = price per unit × number of units

$R = 17.98x$

(c) Profit = Revenue − Cost

$P = 17.98x - (12.30x + 98,000)$

$P = 5.68x - 98,000$

73. (a)

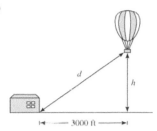

(b) $(3000)^2 + h^2 - d^2$

$$h = \sqrt{d^2 - (3000)^2}$$

Domain: $d \geq 3000$ (because both $d \geq 0$ and $d^2 - (3000)^2 \geq 0$)

75. (a) $R = n(\text{rate}) = n[8.00 - 0.05(n - 80)], n \geq 80$

$$R = 12.00n - 0.05n^2 = 12n - \frac{n^2}{20} = \frac{240n - n^2}{20}, n \geq 80$$

(b)

n	90	100	110	120	130	140	150
$R(n)$	\$675	\$700	\$715	\$720	\$715	\$700	\$675

The revenue is maximum when 120 people take the trip.

77.
$$f(x) = x^2 - x + 1$$
$$f(2 + h) = (2 + h)^2 - (2 + h) + 1$$
$$= 4 + 4h + h^2 - 2 - h + 1$$
$$= h^2 + 3h + 3$$
$$f(2) = (2)^2 - 2 + 1 = 3$$
$$f(2 + h) - f(2) = h^2 + 3h$$
$$\frac{f(2 + h) - f(2)}{h} = \frac{h^2 + 3h}{h} = h + 3, h \neq 0$$

79.
$$f(x) = x^3 + 3x$$
$$f(x + h) = (x + h)^3 + 3(x + h)$$
$$= x^3 + 3x^2h + 3xh^2 + h^3 + 3x + 3h$$
$$\frac{f(x + h) - f(x)}{h} = \frac{(x^3 + 3x^2h + 3xh^2 + h^3 + 3x + 3h) - (x^3 + 3x)}{h}$$
$$= \frac{h(3x^2 + 3xh + h^2 + 3)}{h}$$
$$= 3x^2 + 3xh + h^2 + 3, h \neq 0$$

81.
$$g(x) = \frac{1}{x^2}$$
$$\frac{g(x) - g(3)}{x - 3} = \frac{\frac{1}{x^2} - \frac{1}{9}}{x - 3}$$
$$= \frac{9 - x^2}{9x^2(x - 3)}$$
$$= \frac{-(x + 3)(x - 3)}{9x^2(x - 3)}$$
$$= -\frac{x + 3}{9x^2}, x \neq 3$$

83. $f(x) = \sqrt{5x}$
$$\frac{f(x) - f(5)}{x - 5} = \frac{\sqrt{5x} - 5}{x - 5}, x \neq 5$$

85. By plotting the points, we have a parabola, so $g(x) = cx^2$. Because $(-4, -32)$ is on the graph, you have $-32 = c(-4)^2 \Rightarrow c = -2$. So, $g(x) = -2x^2$.

87. Because the function is undefined at 0, we have $r(x) = c/x$. Because $(-4, -8)$ is on the graph, you have $-8 = c/-4 \Rightarrow c = 32$. So, $r(x) = 32/x$.

89. False. The equation $y^2 = x^2 + 4$ is a relation between x and y. However, $y = \pm\sqrt{x^2 + 4}$ does not represent a function.

91. False. The range is $[-1, \infty)$.

93. $f(x) = \sqrt{x - 1}$ Domain: $x \geq 1$

$g(x) = \dfrac{1}{\sqrt{x - 1}}$ Domain: $x > 1$

The value 1 may be included in the domain of $f(x)$ as it is possible to find the square root of 0. However, 1 cannot be included in the domain of $g(x)$ as it causes a zero to occur in the denominator which results in the function being undefined.

95. No; x is the independent variable, f is the name of the function.

97. (a) Yes. The amount that you pay in sales tax will increase as the price of the item purchased increases.

(b) No. The length of time that you study the night before an exam does not necessarily determine your score on the exam.

Section 1.5 Analyzing Graphs of Functions

1. Vertical Line Test

3. decreasing

5. average rate of change; secant

7. Domain: $(-\infty, \infty)$; Range: $[-4, \infty)$

(a) $f(-2) = 0$

(b) $f(-1) = -1$

(c) $f\left(\frac{1}{2}\right) = 0$

(d) $f(1) = -2$

9. Domain: $(-\infty, \infty)$; Range: $(-2, \infty)$

(a) $f(2) = 0$

(b) $f(1) = 1$

(c) $f(3) = 2$

(d) $f(-1) = 3$

11. $y = \frac{1}{4}x^3$

A vertical line intersects the graph at most once, so y *is* a function of x.

13. $x^2 + y^2 = 25$

A vertical line intersects the graph more than once, so y *is not* a function of x.

15. $f(x) = 2x^2 - 7x - 30$

$2x^2 - 7x - 30 = 0$

$(2x + 5)(x - 6) = 0$

$2x + 5 = 0$ or $x - 6 = 0$

$x = -\frac{5}{2}$ $x = 6$

17. $f(x) = \dfrac{x}{9x^2 - 4}$

$\dfrac{x}{9x^2 - 4} = 0$

$x = 0$

19. $f(x) = \frac{1}{2}x^3 - x$

$\frac{1}{2}x^3 - x = 0$

$x^3 - 2x = 2(0)$

$x(x^2 - 2) = 0$

$x = 0$ or $x^2 - 2 = 0$

$x^2 = 2$

$x = \pm\sqrt{2}$

21. $f(x) = 4x^3 - 24x^2 - x + 6$

$4x^3 - 24x^2 - x + 6 = 0$

$4x^2(x - 6) - 1(x - 6) = 0$

$(x - 6)(4x^2 - 1) = 0$

$(x - 6)(2x + 1)(2x - 1) = 0$

$x - 6 = 0$ or $2x + 1 = 0$ or $2x - 1 = 0$

$x = 6$ $x = -\frac{1}{2}$ $x = \frac{1}{2}$

23. $f(x) = \sqrt{2x} - 1$

$$\sqrt{2x} - 1 = 0$$
$$\sqrt{2x} = 1$$
$$2x = 1$$
$$x = \frac{1}{2}$$

25. (a)

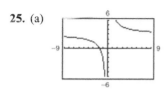

Zero: $x = -\frac{5}{3}$

(b) $f(x) = 3 + \frac{5}{x}$

$$3 + \frac{5}{x} = 0$$
$$3x + 5 = 0$$
$$x = -\frac{5}{3}$$

27. (a)

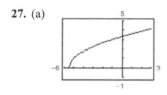

Zero: $x = -\frac{11}{2}$

(b) $f(x) = \sqrt{2x + 11}$

$$\sqrt{2x + 11} = 0$$
$$2x + 11 = 0$$
$$x = -\frac{11}{2}$$

29. (a)

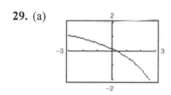

Zero: $x = \frac{1}{3}$

(b) $f(x) = \frac{3x - 1}{x - 6}$

$$\frac{3x - 1}{x - 6} = 0$$
$$3x - 1 = 0$$
$$x = \frac{1}{3}$$

31. $f(x) = \frac{3}{2}x$

The function is increasing on $(-\infty, \infty)$.

33. $f(x) = x^3 - 3x^2 + 2$

The function is increasing on $(-\infty, 0)$ and $(2, \infty)$ and decreasing on $(0, 2)$.

35. $f(x) = |x + 1| + |x - 1|$

The function is increasing on $(1, \infty)$.

The function is constant on $(-1, 1)$.

The function is decreasing on $(-\infty, -1)$.

37. $f(x) = \begin{cases} x + 3, & x \le 0 \\ 3, & 0 < x \le 2 \\ 2x + 1, & x > 2 \end{cases}$

The function is increasing on $(-\infty, 0)$ and $(2, \infty)$.

The function is constant on $(0, 2)$.

39. $f(x) = 3$

(a)

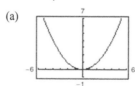

Constant on $(-\infty, \infty)$

(b)

x	-2	-1	0	1	2
$f(x)$	3	3	3	3	3

41. $g(s) = \frac{s^2}{4}$

(a)

Decreasing on $(-\infty, 0)$; Increasing on $(0, \infty)$

(b)

s	-4	-2	0	2	4
$g(s)$	4	1	0	1	4

43. $f(x) = \sqrt{1 - x}$

(a)

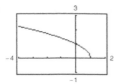

Decreasing on $(-\infty, 1)$

(b)

x	-3	-2	-1	0	1
$f(x)$	2	$\sqrt{3}$	$\sqrt{2}$	1	0

45. $f(x) = x^{3/2}$

(a)

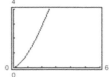

Increasing on $(0, \infty)$

(b)

x	0	1	2	3	4
$f(x)$	0	1	2.8	5.2	8

47. $f(x) = 3x^2 - 2x - 5$

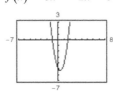

Relative minimum: $\left(\frac{1}{3}, -\frac{16}{3}\right)$ or $(0.33, -5.33)$

49. $f(x) = -2x^2 + 9x$

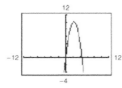

Relative maximum: $(2.25, 10.125)$

51. $f(x) = x^3 - 3x^2 - x + 1$

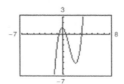

Relative maximum: $(-0.15, 1.08)$

Relative minimum: $(2.15, -5.08)$

53. $h(x) = (x - 1)\sqrt{x}$

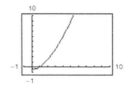

Relative minimum: $(0.33, -0.38)$

55. $f(x) = 4 - x$

$f(x) \geq 0$ on $(-\infty, 4]$

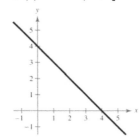

57. $f(x) = 9 - x^2$

$f(x) \geq 0$ on $[-3, 3]$

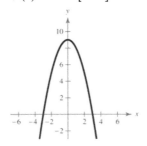

59. $f(x) = \sqrt{x - 1}$

$f(x) \geq 0$ on $[1, \infty)$

$\sqrt{x - 1} \geq 0$

$x - 1 \geq 0$

$x \geq 1$

$[1, \infty)$

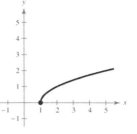

61. $f(x) = -2x + 15$

$$\frac{f(3) - f(0)}{3 - 0} = \frac{9 - 15}{3} = -2$$

The average rate of change from $x_1 = 0$ to $x_2 = 3$ is -2.

63. $f(x) = x^3 - 3x^2 - x$

$$\frac{f(3) - f(1)}{3 - 1} = \frac{-3 - (-3)}{2} = 0$$

The average rate of change from $x_1 = 1$ to $x_2 = 3$ is 0.

65. (a)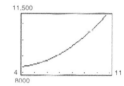

(b) To find the average rate of change of the amount the U.S. Department of Energy spent for research and development from 2005 to 2010, find the average rate of change from $(5, f(5))$ to $(10, f(10))$.

$$\frac{f(10) - f(5)}{10 - 5} = \frac{10{,}925 - 8501.25}{5} = 484.75$$

The amount the U.S. Department of Energy spent for research and development increased by about \$484.75 million each year from 2005 to 2010.

67. $s_0 = 6, v_0 = 64$

(a) $s = -16t^2 + 64t + 6$

(b)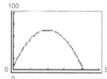

(c) $\dfrac{s(3) - s(0)}{3 - 0} = \dfrac{54 - 6}{3} = 16$

(d) The slope of the secant line is positive.

(e) $s(0) = 6, m = 16$

Secant line: $y - 6 = 16(t - 0)$

$$y = 16t + 6$$

(f)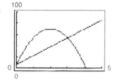

69. $v_0 = 120, s_0 = 0$

(a) $s = -16t^2 + 120t$

(b)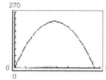

(c) The average rate of change from $t = 3$ to $t = 5$:

$$\frac{s(5) - s(3)}{5 - 3} = \frac{200 - 216}{2} = -\frac{16}{2} = -8 \text{ feet per}$$
second

(d) The slope of the secant line through $(3, s(3))$ and $(5, s(5))$ is negative.

(e) The equation of the secant line: $m = -8$

Using $(5, s(5)) = (5, 200)$ we have

$$y - 200 = -8(t - 5)$$
$$y = -8t + 240.$$

(f)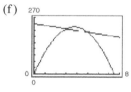

71. $f(x) = x^6 - 2x^2 + 3$

$$f(-x) = (-x)^6 - 2(-x)^2 + 3$$
$$= x^6 - 2x^2 + 3$$
$$= f(x)$$

The function is even. y-axis symmetry.

73. $h(x) = x\sqrt{x + 5}$

$$h(-x) = (-x)\sqrt{-x + 5}$$
$$= -x\sqrt{5 - x}$$
$$\neq h(x)$$
$$\neq -h(x)$$

The function is neither odd nor even. No symmetry.

75. $f(s) = 4s^{3/2}$

$$= 4(-s)^{3/2}$$
$$\neq f(s)$$
$$\neq -f(s)$$

The function is neither odd nor even. No symmetry.

77.

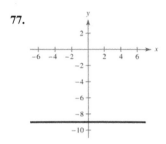

The graph of $f(x) = -9$ is symmetric to the y-axis, which implies $f(x)$ is even.

$$f(-x) = -9$$
$$= f(x)$$

The function is even.

79. $f(x) = -|x - 5|$

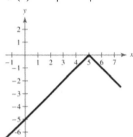

The graph displays no symmetry, which implies $f(x)$ is neither odd nor even.

$$f(x) = -|(-x) - 5|$$
$$= -|-x - 5|$$
$$\neq f(x)$$
$$\neq -f(x)$$

The function is neither even nor odd.

81. $f(x) = \sqrt{1 - x}$

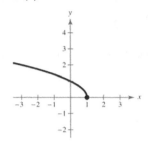

The graph displays no symmetry, which implies $f(x)$ is neither odd nor even.

$$f(-x) = \sqrt{1 - (-x)}$$
$$= \sqrt{1 + x}$$
$$\neq f(x)$$
$$\neq -f(x)$$

The function is neither even nor odd.

83. $h = \text{top} - \text{bottom}$
$$= 3 - (4x - x^2)$$
$$= 3 - 4x + x^2$$

85. $L = \text{right} - \text{left}$
$$= 2 - \sqrt[3]{2y}$$

87. $L = -0.294x^2 + 97.744x - 664.875,\ 20 \le x \le 90$

(a)

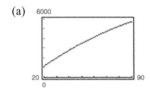

(b) $L = 2000$ when $x \approx 29.9645 \approx 30$ watts.

89. (a) For the average salaries of college professors, a scale of \$10,000 would be appropriate.

(b) For the population of the United States, use a scale of 10,000,000.

(c) For the percent of the civilian workforce that is unemployed, use a scale of 1%.

91. (a) $y = x$

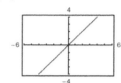

(b) $y = x^2$

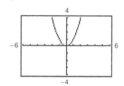

(c) $y = x^3$

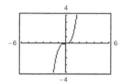

(d) $y = x^4$

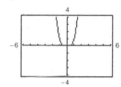

(e) $y = x^5$

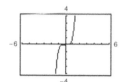

(f) $y = x^6$

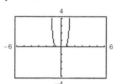

All the graphs pass through the origin. The graphs of the odd powers of x are symmetric with respect to the origin and the graphs of the even powers are symmetric with respect to the y-axis. As the powers increase, the graphs become flatter in the interval $-1 < x < 1$.

93. False. The function $f(x) = \sqrt{x^2 + 1}$ has a domain of all real numbers.

95. $\left(-\frac{5}{3}, -7\right)$

(a) If f is even, another point is $\left(\frac{5}{3}, -7\right)$.

(b) If f is odd, another point is $\left(\frac{5}{3}, 7\right)$.

97.

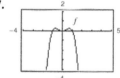

$f(x) = x^2 - x^4$ is even.

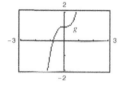

$g(x) = 2x^3 + 1$ is neither.

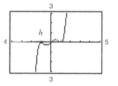

$h(x) = x^5 - 2x^3 + x$ is odd.

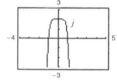

$j(x) = 2 - x^6 - x^8$ is even.

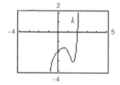

$k(x) = x^5 - 2x^4 + x - 2$ is neither.

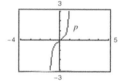

$p(x) = x^9 + 3x^5 - x^3 + x$ is odd.

Equations of odd functions contain only odd powers of x. Equations of even functions contain only even powers of x. A function that has variables raised to even and odd powers is neither odd nor even.

Section 1.6 A Library of Parent Functions

1. $f(x) = [\![x]\!]$

(g) greatest integer function

3. $f(x) = \dfrac{1}{x}$

(h) reciprocal function

5. $f(x) = \sqrt{x}$

(b) square root function

7. $f(x) = |x|$

(f) absolute value function

9. $f(x) = ax + b$

(d) linear function

11. (a) $f(1) = 4, f(0) = 6$

$(1, 4), (0, 6)$

$m = \dfrac{6 - 4}{0 - 1} = -2$

$y - 6 = -2(x - 0)$

$y = -2x + 6$

$f(x) = -2x + 6$

(b)

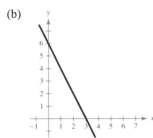

13. (a) $f(-5) = -1, f(5) = -1$

$(-5, -1), (5, -1)$

$m = \dfrac{-1 - (-1)}{5 - (-5)} = \dfrac{0}{10} = 0$

$y - (-1) = 0(x - (-5))$

$y = -1$

$f(x) = -1$

(b)

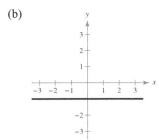

15. $f(x) = 2.5x - 4.25$

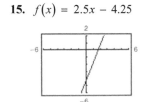

17. $g(x) = -2x^2$

19. $f(x) = x^3 - 1$

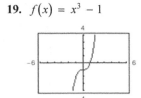

21. $f(x) = 4 - 2\sqrt{x}$

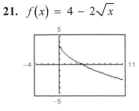

23. $f(x) = 4 + \dfrac{1}{x}$

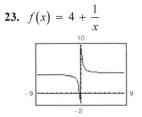

25. $g(x) = |x| - 5$

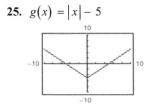

27. $f(x) = [\![x]\!]$

(a) $f(2.1) = 2$

(b) $f(2.9) = 2$

(c) $f(-3.1) = -4$

(d) $f\left(\tfrac{7}{2}\right) = 3$

29. $k(x) = \left[\!\left[\tfrac{1}{2}x + 6\right]\!\right]$

(a) $k(5) = \left[\!\left[\tfrac{1}{2}(5) + 6\right]\!\right] = [\![8.5]\!] = 8$

(b) $k(-6.1) = \left[\!\left[\tfrac{1}{2}(-6.1) + 6\right]\!\right] = [\![2.95]\!] = 2$

(c) $k(0.1) = \left[\!\left[\tfrac{1}{2}(0.1) + 6\right]\!\right] = [\![6.05]\!] = 6$

(d) $k(15) = \left[\!\left[\tfrac{1}{2}(15) + 6\right]\!\right] = [\![13.5]\!] = 13$

31. $g(x) = -[\![x]\!]$

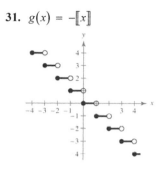

33. $g(x) = [\![x]\!] - 1$

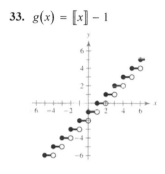

35. $g(x) = \begin{cases} x + 6, & x \le -4 \\ \frac{1}{2}x - 4, & x > -4 \end{cases}$

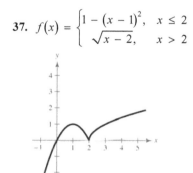

37. $f(x) = \begin{cases} 1 - (x - 1)^2, & x \le 2 \\ \sqrt{x - 2}, & x > 2 \end{cases}$

39. $h(x) = \begin{cases} 4 - x^2, & x < -2 \\ 3 + x, & -2 \le x < 0 \\ x^2 + 1, & x \ge 0 \end{cases}$

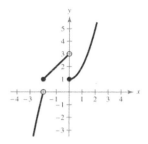

41. $s(x) = 2\left(\frac{1}{4}x - [\![\frac{1}{4}x]\!]\right)$

(a)

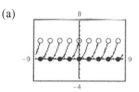

(b) Domain: $(-\infty, \infty)$; Range: $[0, 2)$

43. (a) $W(30) = 14(30) = 420$

   $W(40) = 14(40) = 560$

   $W(45) = 21(45 - 40) + 560 = 665$

   $W(50) = 21(50 - 40) + 560 = 770$

(b) $W(h) = \begin{cases} 14h, & 0 < h \le 45 \\ 21(h - 45) + 630, & h > 45 \end{cases}$

45. Answers will vary. *Sample answer:*

Interval	Input Pipe	Drain Pipe 1	Drain Pipe 2
[0, 5]	Open	Closed	Closed
[5, 10]	Open	Open	Closed
[10, 20]	Closed	Closed	Closed
[20, 30]	Closed	Closed	Open
[30, 40]	Open	Open	Open
[40, 45]	Open	Closed	Open
[45, 50]	Open	Open	Open
[50, 60]	Open	Open	Closed

47. For the first two hours the slope is 1. For the next six hours, the slope is 2. For the final hour, the slope is $\frac{1}{2}$.

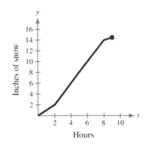

$$f(t) = \begin{cases} t, & 0 \le t \le 2 \\ 2t - 2, & 2 < t \le 8 \\ \frac{1}{2}t + 10, & 8 < t \le 9 \end{cases}$$

To find $f(t) = 2t - 2$, use $m = 2$ and $(2, 2)$.

$y - 2 = 2(t - 2) \Rightarrow y = 2t - 2$

To find $f(t) = \frac{1}{2}t + 10$, use $m = \frac{1}{2}$ and $(8, 14)$.

$y - 14 = \frac{1}{2}(t - 8) \Rightarrow y = \frac{1}{2}t + 10$

Total accumulation = 14.5 inches

49. False. A piecewise-defined function is a function that is defined by two or more equations over a specified domain. That domain may or may not include x- and y-intercepts.

Section 1.7   Transformations of Functions

1. rigid

3. vertical stretch; vertical shrink

5. (a) $f(x) = |x| + c$ ... Vertical shifts

  $c = -1$: $f(x) = |x| - 1$ ... 1 unit down

  $c = 1$: $f(x) = |x| + 1$ ... 1 unit up

  $c = 3$: $f(x) = |x| + 3$ ... 3 units up

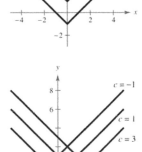

  (b) $f(x) = |x - c|$ ... Horizontal shifts

  $c = -1$: $f(x) = |x + 1|$ ... 1 unit left

  $c = 1$: $f(x) = |x - 1|$ ... 1 unit right

  $c = 3$: $f(x) = |x - 3|$ ... 3 units right

7. (a) $f(x) = [\![x]\!] + c$ Vertical shifts

  $c = -2$: $f(x) = [\![x]\!] - 2$ 2 units down

  $c = 0$: $f(x) = [\![x]\!]$ Parent function

  $c = 2$: $f(x) = [\![x]\!] + 2$ 2 units up

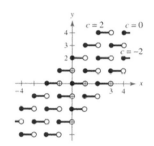

(b) $f(x) = [\![x + c]\!]$ Horizontal shifts

  $c = -2$: $f(x) = [\![x - 2]\!]$ 2 units right

  $c = 0$: $f(x) = [\![x]\!]$ Parent function

  $c = 2$: $f(x) = [\![x + 2]\!]$ 2 units left

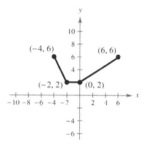

9. (a) $y = f(-x)$

Reflection in the y-axis

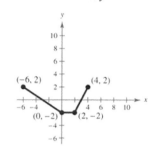

(b) $y = f(x) + 4$

Vertical shift 4 units
upward

(c) $y = 2f(x)$

Vertical stretch (each y-value
is multiplied by 2)

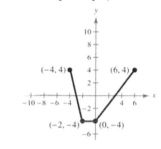

(d) $y = -f(x - 4)$

Reflection in the x-axis and
a horizontal shift 4 units to
the right

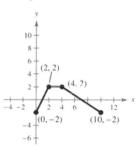

(e) $y = f(x) - 3$

Vertical shift 3 units
downward

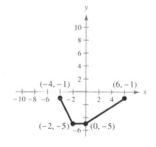

(f) $y = -f(x) - 1$

Reflection in the x-axis and a
vertical shift 1 unit downward

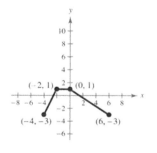

(g) $y = f(2x)$

Horizontal shrink
(each x-value is divided by 2)

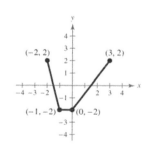

11. Parent function: $f(x) = x^2$

   (a) Vertical shift 1 unit downward

     $g(x) = x^2 - 1$

   (b) Reflection in the x-axis, horizontal shift 1 unit to the left, and a vertical shift 1 unit upward

     $g(x) = -(x + 1)^2 + 1$

13. Parent function: $f(x) = |x|$

   (a) Reflection in the x-axis and a horizontal shift 3 units to the left

     $g(x) = -|x + 3|$

   (b) Horizontal shift 2 units to the right and a vertical shift 4 units downward

     $g(x) = |x - 2| - 4$

15. Parent function: $f(x) = x^3$

   Horizontal shift 2 units to the right

   $y = (x - 2)^3$

17. Parent function: $f(x) = x^2$

   Reflection in the x-axis

   $y = -x^2$

19. Parent function: $f(x) = \sqrt{x}$

   Reflection in the x-axis and a vertical shift 1 unit upward

   $y = -\sqrt{x} + 1$

21. $g(x) = 12 - x^2$

   (a) Parent function: $f(x) = x^2$

   (b) Reflection in the x-axis and a vertical shift 12 units upward

   (c)

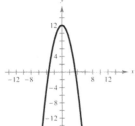

   (d) $g(x) = 12 - f(x)$

23. $g(x) = x^3 + 7$

   (a) Parent function: $f(x) = x^3$

   (b) Vertical shift 7 units upward

   (c)

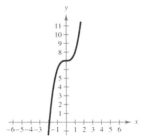

   (d) $g(x) = f(x) + 7$

25. $g(x) = \frac{2}{3}x^2 + 4$

   (a) Parent function: $f(x) = x^2$

   (b) Vertical shrink of two-thirds, and a vertical shift 4 units upward

   (c)

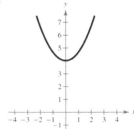

   (d) $g(x) = \frac{2}{3}f(x) + 4$

27. $g(x) = 2 - (x + 5)^2$

   (a) Parent function: $f(x) = x^2$

   (b) Reflection in the x-axis, horizontal shift 5 units to the left, and a vertical shift 2 units upward

   (c)

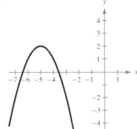

   (d) $g(x) = 2 - f(x + 5)$

29. $g(x) = \sqrt{3x}$

(a) Parent function: $f(x) = \sqrt{x}$

(b) Horizontal shrink by $\frac{1}{3}$

(c)

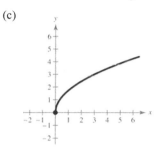

(d) $g(x) = f(3x)$

31. $g(x) = (x - 1)^3 + 2$

(a) Parent function: $f(x) = x^3$

(b) Horizontal shift 1 unit to the right and a vertical shift 2 units upward

(c)

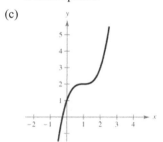

(d) $g(x) = f(x - 1) + 2$

33. $g(x) = 3(x - 2)^3$

(a) Parent function: $f(x) = x^3$

(b) Horizontal shift 2 units to the right, vertical stretch (each y-value is multiplied by 3)

(c)

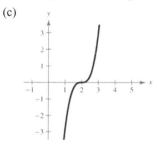

(d) $g(x) = 3f(x - 2)$

35. $g(x) = -|x| - 2$

(a) Parent function: $f(x) = |x|$

(b) Reflection in the x-axis, vertical shift 2 units downward

(c)

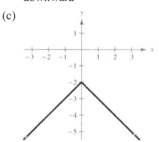

(d) $g(x) = -f(x) - 2$

37. $g(x) = -|x + 4| + 8$

(a) Parent function: $f(x) = |x|$

(b) Reflection in the x-axis, horizontal shift 4 units to the left, and a vertical shift 8 units upward

(c)

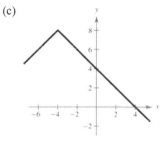

(d) $g(x) = -f(x + 4) + 8$

39. $g(x) = -2|x - 1| - 4$

(a) Parent function: $f(x) = |x|$

(b) Horizontal shift one unit to the right, vertical stretch, reflection in the x-axis, vertical shift four units downward

(c)

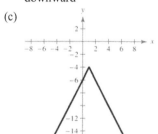

(d) $g(x) = -2f(x - 1) - 4$

41. $g(x) = 3 - [\![x]\!]$

(a) Parent function: $f(x) = [\![x]\!]$

(b) Reflection in the x-axis and a vertical shift 3 units upward

(c)

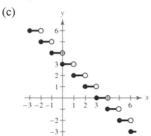

(d) $g(x) = 3 - f(x)$

43. $g(x) = \sqrt{x - 9}$

(a) Parent function: $f(x) = \sqrt{x}$

(b) Horizontal shift 9 units to the right

(c)

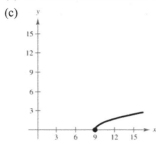

(d) $g(x) = f(x - 9)$

45. $g(x) = \sqrt{7 - x} - 2$ or $g(x) = \sqrt{-(x - 7)} - 2$

(a) Parent function: $f(x) = \sqrt{x}$

(b) Reflection in the y-axis, horizontal shift 7 units to the right, and a vertical shift 2 units downward

(c)

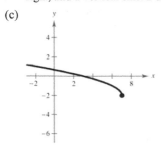

(d) $g(x) = f(7 - x) - 2$

47. $g(x) = (x - 3)^2 - 7$

49. $f(x) = x^3$ moved 13 units to the right

$g(x) = (x - 13)^3$

51. $g(x) = -|x| + 12$

53. $f(x) = \sqrt{x}$ moved 6 units to the left and reflected in both the x- and y-axes

$g(x) = -\sqrt{-x + 6}$

55. $f(x) = x^2$

(a) Reflection in the x-axis and a vertical stretch (each y-value is multiplied by 3)

$g(x) = -3x^2$

(b) Vertical shift 3 units upward and a vertical stretch (each y-value is multiplied by 4)

$g(x) = 4x^2 + 3$

57. $f(x) = |x|$

(a) Reflection in the x-axis and a vertical shrink (each y-value is multiplied by $\frac{1}{2}$)

$g(x) = -\frac{1}{2}|x|$

(b) Vertical stretch (each y-value is multiplied by 3) and a vertical shift 3 units downward

$g(x) = 3|x| - 3$

59. Parent function: $f(x) = x^3$

Vertical stretch (each y-value is multiplied by 2)

$g(x) = 2x^3$

61. Parent function: $f(x) = x^2$

Reflection in the x-axis, vertical shrink (each y-value is multiplied by $\frac{1}{2}$)

$g(x) = -\frac{1}{2}x^2$

63. Parent function: $f(x) = \sqrt{x}$

Reflection in the y-axis, vertical shrink (each y-value is multiplied by $\frac{1}{2}$)

$g(x) = \frac{1}{2}\sqrt{-x}$

65. Parent function: $f(x) = x^3$

Reflection in the x-axis, horizontal shift 2 units to the right and a vertical shift 2 units upward

$g(x) = -(x - 2)^3 + 2$

67. Parent function: $f(x) = \sqrt{x}$

Reflection in the x-axis and a vertical shift 3 units downward

$g(x) = -\sqrt{x} - 3$

69. (a)

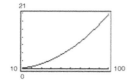

(b) $H(x) = 0.002x^2 + 0.005x - 0.029$

$$H\left(\frac{x}{1.6}\right) = 0.002\left(\frac{x}{1.6}\right)^2 + 0.005\left(\frac{x}{1.6}\right) - 0.029$$

$$= 0.002\left(\frac{x^2}{2.56}\right) + 0.005\left(\frac{x}{1.6}\right) - 0.029$$

$$= 0.00078125x^2 + 0.003125x - 0.029$$

The graph of $H\left(\dfrac{x}{1.6}\right)$ is a horizontal stretch of the

graph of $H(x)$.

71. False. $y = f(-x)$ is a reflection in the *y*-axis.

73. True. Because $|x| - |-x|$, the graphs of

$f(x) = |x| + 6$ and $f(x) = |-x| + 6$ are identical.

75. $y = f(x + 2) - 1$

Horizontal shift 2 units to the left and a vertical shift
1 unit downward

$(0, 1) \rightarrow (0 - 2, 1 - 1) = (-2, 0)$

$(1, 2) \rightarrow (1 - 2, 2 - 1) = (-1, 1)$

$(2, 3) \rightarrow (2 - 2, 3 - 1) = (0, 2)$

77. (a)

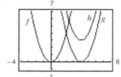

(b)

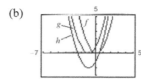

(c)

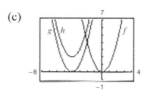

79. (a) The profits were only $\frac{3}{4}$ as large as expected:

$$g(t) = \tfrac{3}{4}f(t)$$

(b) The profits were \$10,000 greater than predicted:

$$g(t) = f(t) + 10,000$$

(c) There was a two-year delay: $g(t) = f(t - 2)$

Section 1.8 Combinations of Functions: Composite Functions

1. addition; subtraction; multiplication; division

3.

x	0	1	2	3
f	2	3	1	2
g	-1	0	$\frac{1}{2}$	0
f + g	1	3	$\frac{3}{2}$	2

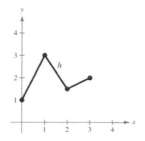

5. $f(x) = x + 2,\ g(x) = x - 2$

(a) $(f + g)(x) = f(x) + g(x)$

$$= (x + 2) + (x - 2)$$

$$= 2x$$

(b) $(f - g)(x) = f(x) - g(x)$

$$= (x + 2) - (x - 2)$$

$$= 4$$

(c) $(fg)(x) = f(x) \cdot g(x)$

$$= (x + 2)(x - 2)$$

$$= x^2 - 4$$

(d) $\left(\dfrac{f}{x}\right)(x) = \dfrac{f(x)}{g(x)} = \dfrac{x + 2}{x - 2}$

Domain: all real numbers x except $x = 2$

7. $f(x) = x^2$, $g(x) = 4x - 5$

   (a) $(f + g)(x) = f(x) + g(x)$

$$= x^2 + (4x - 5)$$

$$= x^2 + 4x - 5$$

   (b) $(f - g)(x) = f(x) - g(x)$

$$= x^2 - (4x - 5)$$

$$= x^2 - 4x + 5$$

   (c) $(fg)(x) = f(x) \cdot g(x)$

$$= x^2(4x - 5)$$

$$= 4x^3 - 5x^2$$

   (d) $\left(\dfrac{f}{g}\right)(x) = \dfrac{f(x)}{g(x)}$

$$= \dfrac{x^2}{4x - 5}$$

      Domain: all real numbers x except $x = \dfrac{5}{4}$

9. $f(x) = x^2 + 6$, $g(x) = \sqrt{1 - x}$

   (a) $(f + g)(x) = f(x) + g(x) = x^2 + 6 + \sqrt{1 - x}$

   (b) $(f - g)(x) = f(x) - g(x) = x^2 + 6 - \sqrt{1 - x}$

   (c) $(fg)(x) = f(x) \cdot g(x) = \left(x^2 + 6\right)\sqrt{1 - x}$

   (d) $\left(\dfrac{f}{g}\right)(x) = \dfrac{f(x)}{g(x)} = \dfrac{x^2 + 6}{\sqrt{1 - x}} = \dfrac{\left(x^2 + 6\right)\sqrt{1 - x}}{1 - x}$

      Domain: $x < 1$

11. $f(x) = \dfrac{1}{x}$, $g(x) = \dfrac{1}{x^2}$

   (a) $(f + g)(x) = f(x) + g(x) = \dfrac{1}{x} + \dfrac{1}{x^2} = \dfrac{x + 1}{x^2}$

   (b) $(f - g)(x) = f(x) - g(x) = \dfrac{1}{x} - \dfrac{1}{x^2} = \dfrac{x - 1}{x^2}$

   (c) $(fg)(x) = f(x) \cdot g(x) = \dfrac{1}{x}\left(\dfrac{1}{x^2}\right) = \dfrac{1}{x^3}$

   (d) $\left(\dfrac{f}{g}\right)(x) = \dfrac{f(x)}{g(x)} = \dfrac{1/x}{1/x^2} = \dfrac{x^2}{x} = x$

      Domain: all real numbers x except $x = 0$

For Exercises 13–23, $f(x) = x^2 + 1$ and $g(x) = x - 4$.

13. $(f + g)(2) = f(2) + g(2) = \left(2^2 + 1\right) + (2 - 4) = 3$

15. $(f - g)(0) = f(0) - g(0)$

$$= \left(0^2 + 1\right) - (0 - 4)$$

$$= 5$$

17. $(f - g)(3t) = f(3t) - g(3t)$

$$= \left[(3t)^2 + 1\right] - (3t - 4)$$

$$= 9t^2 - 3t + 5$$

19. $(fg)(6) = f(6)g(6)$

$$= \left(6^2 + 1\right)(6 - 4)$$

$$= 74$$

21. $\left(\dfrac{f}{g}\right)(5) = \dfrac{f(5)}{g(5)} = \dfrac{5^2 + 1}{5 - 4} = 26$

23. $\left(\dfrac{f}{g}\right)(-1) - g(3) = \dfrac{f(-1)}{g(-1)} - g(3)$

$$= \dfrac{(-1)^2 + 1}{-1 - 4} - (3 - 4)$$

$$= -\dfrac{2}{5} + 1 = \dfrac{3}{5}$$

25. $f(x) = \tfrac{1}{2}x$, $g(x) = x - 1$

   $(f + g)(x) = \tfrac{3}{2}x - 1$

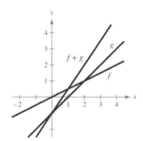

27. $f(x) = 3x$, $g(x) = -\dfrac{x^3}{10}$

   $(f + g)(x) = 3x - \dfrac{x^3}{10}$

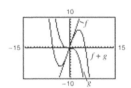

For $0 \le x \le 2$, $f(x)$ contributes most to the magnitude.

For $x > 6$, $g(x)$ contributes most to the magnitude.

29. $f(x) = 3x + 2, g(x) = \sqrt{x + 5}$

$(f + g)x = 3x - \sqrt{x + 5} + 2$

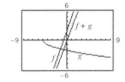

For $0 \le x \le 2$, $f(x)$ contributes most to the magnitude.

For $x > 6$, $f(x)$ contributes most to the magnitude.

31. $f(x) = x^2, g(x) = x - 1$

(a) $(f \circ g)(x) = f(g(x)) = f(x - 1) = (x - 1)^2$

(b) $(g \circ f)(x) = g(f(x)) = g(x^2) = x^2 - 1$

(c) $(g \circ g)(x) = g(g(x)) = g(x - 1) = x - 2$

33. $f(x) = \sqrt[3]{x - 1}, g(x) = x^3 + 1$

(a) $(f \circ g)(x) = f(g(x))$

$= f(x^3 + 1)$

$= \sqrt[3]{(x^3 + 1) - 1}$

$= \sqrt[3]{x^3} = x$

(b) $(g \circ f)(x) = g(f(x))$

$= g(\sqrt[3]{x - 1})$

$= (\sqrt[3]{x - 1})^3 + 1$

$= (x - 1) + 1 = x$

(c) $(g \circ g)(x) = g(g(x))$

$= g(x^3 + 1)$

$= (x^3 + 1)^3 + 1$

$= x^9 + 3x^6 + 3x^3 + 2$

35. $f(x) = \sqrt{x + 4}$ Domain: $x \ge -4$

$g(x) = x^2$ Domain: all real numbers x

(a) $(f \circ g)(x) = f(g(x)) = f(x^2) = \sqrt{x^2 + 4}$

Domain: all real numbers x

(b) $(g \circ f)(x) = g(f(x))$

$= g(\sqrt{x + 4}) = (\sqrt{x + 4})^2 = x + 4$

Domain: $x \ge -4$

37. $f(x) = x^2 + 1$ Domain: all real numbers x

$g(x) = \sqrt{x}$ Domain: $x \ge 0$

(a) $(f \circ g)(x) = f(g(x))$

$= f(\sqrt{x})$

$= (\sqrt{x})^2 + 1$

$= x + 1$

Domain: $x \ge 0$

(b) $(g \circ f)(x) = g(f(x)) = g(x^2 + 1) = \sqrt{x^2 + 1}$

Domain: all real numbers x

39. $f(x) = |x|$ Domain: all real numbers x

$g(x) = x + 6$ Domain: all real numbers x

(a) $(f \circ g)(x) = f(g(x)) = f(x + 6) = |x + 6|$

Domain: all real numbers x

(b) $(g \circ f)(x) = g(f(x)) = g(|x|) = |x| + 6$

Domain: all real numbers x

41. $f(x) = \dfrac{1}{x}$ Domain: all real numbers x except $x = 0$

$g(x) = x + 3$ Domain: all real numbers x

(a) $(f \circ g)(x) = f(g(x)) = f(x + 3) = \dfrac{1}{x + 3}$

Domain: all real numbers x except $x = -3$

(b) $(g \circ f)(x) = g(f(x)) = g\left(\dfrac{1}{x}\right) = \dfrac{1}{x} + 3$

Domain: all real numbers x except $x = 0$

43. (a) $(f + g)(3) = f(3) + g(3) = 2 + 1 = 3$

(b) $\left(\dfrac{f}{g}\right)(2) = \dfrac{f(2)}{g(2)} = \dfrac{0}{2} = 0$

45. (a) $(f \circ g)(2) = f(g(2)) = f(2) = 0$

(b) $(g \circ f)(2) = g(f(2)) = g(0) = 4$

47. $h(x) = (2x^2 + 1)^2$

One possibility: Let $f(x) = x^2$ and $g(x) = 2x + 1$, then $(f \circ g)(x) = h(x)$.

49. $h(x) = \sqrt[3]{x^2 - 4}$

One possibility: Let $f(x) = \sqrt[3]{x}$ and $g(x) = x^2 - 4$, then $(f \circ g)(x) = h(x)$.

51. $h(x) = \dfrac{1}{x + 2}$

One possibility: Let $f(x) = 1/x$ and $g(x) = x + 2$, then $(f \circ g)(x) = h(x)$.

53. $h(x) = \dfrac{-x^2 + 3}{4 - x^2}$

One possibility: Let $f(x) = \dfrac{x + 3}{4 + x}$ and $g(x) = -x^2$, then $(f \circ g)(x) = h(x)$.

55. (a) $T(x) = R(x) + B(x) = \frac{3}{4}x + \frac{1}{15}x^2$

(b)

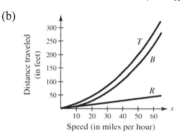

(c) $B(x)$; As x increases, $B(x)$ increases at a faster rate.

63. Let O = oldest sibling, M = middle sibling, Y = youngest sibling. Then the ages of each sibling can be found using the equations:

$O = 2M$

$M = \frac{1}{2}Y + 6$

(a) $O(M(Y)) = 2\left(\frac{1}{2}(Y) + 6\right) = 12 + Y$; Answers will vary.

(b) Oldest sibling is 16: $O = 16$

Middle sibling: $O = 2M$

$16 = 2M$

$M = 8$ years old

Youngest sibling: $M = \frac{1}{2}Y + 6$

$8 = \frac{1}{2}Y + 6$

$2 = \frac{1}{2}Y$

$Y = 4$ years old

65. False. $(f \circ g)(x) = 6x + 1$ and $(g \circ f)(x) = 6x + 6$

57. (a) $p(t) = d(t) + c(t)$

(b) $p(5)$ represents the number of dogs and cats in 2005.

(c) $h(t) = \dfrac{p(t)}{n(t)} = \dfrac{d(t) + c(t)}{n(t)}$

$h(t)$ represents the number of dogs and cats at time t compared to the population at time t or the number of dogs and cats per capita.

59. (a) $r(x) = \dfrac{x}{2}$

(b) $A(r) = \pi r^2$

(c) $(A \circ r)(x) = A(r(x)) = A\left(\dfrac{x}{2}\right) = \pi\left(\dfrac{x}{2}\right)^2$

$(A \circ r)(x)$ represents the area of the circular base of the tank on the square foundation with side length x.

61. (a) $f(g(x)) = f(0.03x) = 0.03x - 500{,}000$

(b) $g(f(x)) = g(x - 500{,}000) = 0.03(x - 500{,}000)$

$g(f(x))$ represents your bonus of 3% of an amount over \$500,000.

67. Let $f(x)$ and $g(x)$ be two odd functions and define $h(x) = f(x)g(x)$. Then

$$h(-x) = f(-x)g(-x)$$
$$= \left[-f(x)\right]\left[-g(x)\right] \quad \text{because } f \text{ and } g \text{ are odd}$$
$$= f(x)g(x)$$
$$= h(x).$$

So, $h(x)$ is even.

Let $f(x)$ and $g(x)$ be two even functions and define $h(x) = f(x)g(x)$. Then

$$h(-x) = f(-x)g(-x)$$
$$= f(x)g(x) \quad \text{because } f \text{ and } g \text{ are even}$$
$$= h(x).$$

So, $h(x)$ is even.

69. Let $f(x)$ be an odd function, $g(x)$ be an even function, and define $h(x) = f(x)g(x)$. Then

$$h(-x) = f(-x)g(-x)$$
$$= \left[-f(x)\right]g(x) \quad \text{because } f \text{ is odd and } g \text{ is even}$$
$$= -f(x)g(x)$$
$$= -h(x).$$

So, h is odd and the product of an odd function and an even function is odd.

Section 1.9   Inverse Functions

1. inverse

3. range; domain

5. one-to-one

7. $f(x) = 6x$

$$f^{-1}(x) = \frac{x}{6} = \frac{1}{6}x$$

$$f\left(f^{-1}(x)\right) = f\left(\frac{x}{6}\right) = 6\left(\frac{x}{6}\right) = x$$

$$f^{-1}\left(f(x)\right) = f^{-1}(6x) = \frac{6x}{6} = x$$

9. $f(x) = 3x + 1$

$$f^{-1}(x) = \frac{x - 1}{3}$$

$$f\left(f^{-1}(x)\right) = f\left(\frac{x-1}{3}\right) = 3\left(\frac{x-1}{3}\right) + 1 = x$$

$$f^{-1}\left(f(x)\right) = f^{-1}(3x + 1) = \frac{(3x+1) - 1}{3} = x$$

11. $f(x) = \sqrt[3]{x}$

$$f^{-1}(x) = x^3$$

$$f\left(f^{-1}(x)\right) = f(x^3) = \sqrt[3]{x^3} = x$$

$$f^{-1}\left(f(x)\right) = f^{-1}\left(\sqrt[3]{x}\right) = \left(\sqrt[3]{x}\right)^3 = x$$

13. $(f \circ g)(x) = f\left(g(x)\right) = f\left(-\dfrac{2x + 6}{7}\right) = -\dfrac{7}{2}\left(-\dfrac{2x + 6}{7}\right) - 3 = x + 3 - 3 = x$

$(g \circ f)(x) = g\left(f(x)\right) = g\left(-\dfrac{7}{2}x - 3\right) = -\dfrac{2\left(-\dfrac{7}{2}x - 3\right) + 6}{7} = \dfrac{-(-7x)}{7} = x$

15. $(f \circ g)(x) = f\left(g(x)\right) = f\left(\sqrt[3]{x - 5}\right) = \left(\sqrt[3]{x - 5}\right)^3 + 5 = x - 5 + 5 = x$

$(g \circ f)(x) = g\left(f(x)\right) = g\left(x^3 + 5\right) = \sqrt[3]{x^3 + 5 - 5} = \sqrt[3]{x^3} = x$

17.

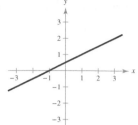

19.

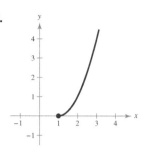

21. $f(x) = 2x, g(x) = \dfrac{x}{2}$

(a) $f(g(x)) = f\left(\dfrac{x}{2}\right) = 2\left(\dfrac{x}{2}\right) = x$

$g(f(x)) = g(2x) = \dfrac{2x}{2} = x$

(b)

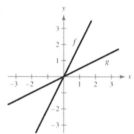

23. $f(x) = 7x + 1, g(x) = \dfrac{x - 1}{7}$

(a) $f(g(x)) = f\left(\dfrac{x - 1}{7}\right) = 7\left(\dfrac{x - 1}{7}\right) + 1 = x$

$g(f(x)) = g(7x + 1) = \dfrac{(7x + 1) - 1}{7} = x$

(b)

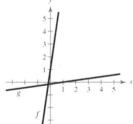

25. $f(x) = \dfrac{x^3}{8}, g(x) = \sqrt[3]{8x}$

(a) $f(g(x)) = f\left(\sqrt[3]{8x}\right) = \dfrac{\left(\sqrt[3]{8x}\right)^3}{8} = \dfrac{8x}{8} = x$

$g(f(x)) = g\left(\dfrac{x^3}{8}\right) = \sqrt[3]{8\left(\dfrac{x^3}{8}\right)} = \sqrt[3]{x^3} = x$

(b)

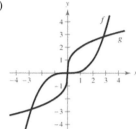

27. $f(x) = \sqrt{x - 4}, g(x) = x^2 + 4, x \geq 0$

(a) $f(g(x)) = f(x^2 + 4), x \geq 0$

$= \sqrt{(x^2 + 4) - 4} = x$

$g(f(x)) = g\left(\sqrt{x - 4}\right)$

$= \left(\sqrt{x - 4}\right)^2 + 4 = x$

(b)

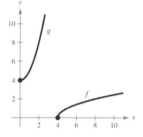

29. $f(x) = 9 - x^2, x \geq 0; g(x) = \sqrt{9 - x}, x \leq 9$

(a) $f(g(x)) = f(\sqrt{9 - x}), x \leq 9 = 9 - (\sqrt{9 - x})^2 = x$

$g(f(x)) = g(9 - x^2), x \geq 0 = \sqrt{9 - (9 - x^2)} = x$

(b)

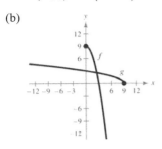

31. $f(x) = \dfrac{x - 1}{x + 5}, g(x) = -\dfrac{5x + 1}{x - 1}$

(a) $f(g(x)) = f\left(-\dfrac{5x + 1}{x - 1}\right) = \dfrac{\left(-\dfrac{5x + 1}{x - 1} - 1\right)}{\left(-\dfrac{5x + 1}{x - 1} + 5\right)} \cdot \dfrac{x - 1}{x - 1} = \dfrac{-(5x + 1) - (x - 1)}{-(5x + 1) + 5(x - 1)} = \dfrac{-6x}{-6} = x$

$g(f(x)) = g\left(\dfrac{x - 1}{x + 5}\right) = -\dfrac{\left[5\left(\dfrac{x - 1}{x + 5}\right) + 1\right]}{\left[\dfrac{x - 1}{x + 5} - 1\right]} \cdot \dfrac{x + 5}{x + 5} = -\dfrac{5(x - 1) + (x + 5)}{(x - 1) - (x + 5)} = -\dfrac{6x}{-6} = x$

(b)

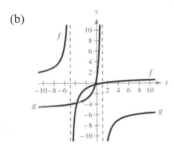

33. No, $\{(-2, -1), (1, 0), (2, 1), (1, 2), (-2, 3), (-6, 4)\}$ does not represent a function. -2 and 1 are paired with two different values.

35.

x	-2	0	2	4	6	8
$f^{-1}(x)$	-2	-1	0	1	2	3

37. Yes, because no horizontal line crosses the graph of f at more than one point, f has an inverse.

39. No, because some horizontal lines cross the graph of f twice, f *does not* have an inverse.

41. $g(x) = (x + 5)^3$

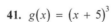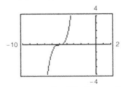

g passes the Horizontal Line Test, so g *has* an inverse.

43. $f(x) = -2x\sqrt{16 - x^2}$

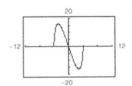

f does not pass the Horizontal Line Test, so f *does not* have an inverse.

45. (a) $f(x) = 2x - 3$ (b)

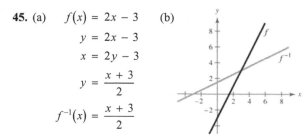

$$y = 2x - 3$$

$$x = 2y - 3$$

$$y = \frac{x + 3}{2}$$

$$f^{-1}(x) = \frac{x + 3}{2}$$

(c) The graph of f^{-1} is the reflection of the graph of f in the line $y = x$.

(d) The domains and ranges of f and f^{-1} are all real numbers.

47. (a) $f(x) = x^5 - 2$ (b)

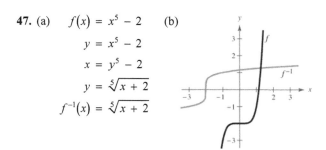

$$y = x^5 - 2$$

$$x = y^5 - 2$$

$$y = \sqrt[5]{x + 2}$$

$$f^{-1}(x) = \sqrt[5]{x + 2}$$

(c) The graph of f^{-1} is the reflection of the graph of f in the line $y = x$.

(d) The domains and ranges of f and f^{-1} are all real numbers.

49. (a) $f(x) = \sqrt{4 - x^2}, 0 \le x \le 2$

$$y = \sqrt{4 - x^2}$$

$$x = \sqrt{4 - y^2}$$

$$x^2 = 4 - y^2$$

$$y^2 = 4 - x^2$$

$$y = \sqrt{4 - x^2}$$

$$f^{-1}(x) = \sqrt{4 - x^2}, 0 \le x \le 2$$

(b)

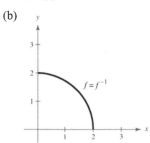

(c) The graph of f^{-1} is the same as the graph of f.

(d) The domains and ranges of f and f^{-1} are all real numbers x such that $0 \le x \le 2$.

51. (a) $f(x) = \dfrac{4}{x}$ (b)

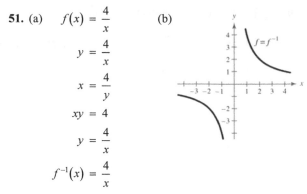

$$y = \frac{4}{x}$$

$$x = \frac{4}{y}$$

$$xy = 4$$

$$y = \frac{4}{x}$$

$$f^{-1}(x) = \frac{4}{x}$$

(c) The graph of f^{-1} is the same as the graph of f.

(d) The domains and ranges of f and f^{-1} are all real numbers except for 0.

53. (a) $f(x) = \dfrac{x + 1}{x - 2}$ (b)

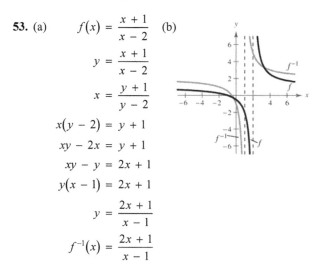

$$y = \frac{x + 1}{x - 2}$$

$$x = \frac{y + 1}{y - 2}$$

$$x(y - 2) = y + 1$$

$$xy - 2x = y + 1$$

$$xy - y = 2x + 1$$

$$y(x - 1) = 2x + 1$$

$$y = \frac{2x + 1}{x - 1}$$

$$f^{-1}(x) = \frac{2x + 1}{x - 1}$$

(c) The graph of f^{-1} is the reflection of graph of f in the line $y = x$.

(d) The domain of f and the range of f^{-1} is all real numbers except 2.

The range of f and the domain of f^{-1} is all real numbers except 1.

55. (a) $f(x) = \sqrt[3]{x - 1}$ (b)

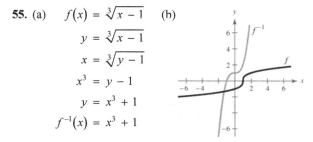

$$y = \sqrt[3]{x - 1}$$

$$x = \sqrt[3]{y - 1}$$

$$x^3 = y - 1$$

$$y = x^3 + 1$$

$$f^{-1}(x) = x^3 + 1$$

(c) The graph of f^{-1} is the reflection of the graph of f in the line $y = x$.

(d) The domains and ranges of f and f^{-1} are all real numbers.

57. $f(x) = x^4$

$y = x^4$

$x = y^4$

$y = \pm\sqrt[4]{x}$

This does not represent y as a function of x. f does not have an inverse.

59. $g(x) = \dfrac{x}{8}$

$y = \dfrac{x}{8}$

$x = \dfrac{y}{8}$

$y = 8x$

This is a function of x, so g has an inverse.

$g^{-1}(x) = 8x$

61. $p(x) = -4$

$y = -4$

Because $y = -4$ for all x, the graph is a horizontal line and fails the Horizontal Line Test. p does not have an inverse.

63. $f(x) = (x + 3)^2, x \geq -3 \Rightarrow y \geq 0$

$y = (x + 3)^2, x \geq -3, y \geq 0$

$x = (y + 3)^2, y \geq -3, x \geq 0$

$\sqrt{x} = y + 3, y \geq -3, x \geq 0$

$y = \sqrt{x} - 3, x \geq 0, y \geq -3$

This is a function of x, so f has an inverse.

$f^{-1}(x) = \sqrt{x} - 3, x \geq 0$

65. $f(x) = \begin{cases} x + 3, & x < 0 \\ 6 - x, & x \geq 0 \end{cases}$

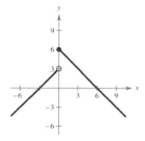

This graph fails the Horizontal Line Test, so f does not have an inverse.

67. $h(x) = -\dfrac{4}{x^2}$

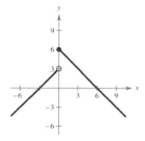

The graph fails the Horizontal Line Test so h does not have an inverse.

69. $f(x) = \sqrt{2x + 3} \Rightarrow x \geq -\dfrac{3}{2}, y \geq 0$

$y = \sqrt{2x + 3}, x \geq -\dfrac{3}{2}, y \geq 0$

$x = \sqrt{2y + 3}, y \geq -\dfrac{3}{2}, x \geq 0$

$x^2 = 2y + 3, x \geq 0, y \geq -\dfrac{3}{2}$

$y = \dfrac{x^2 - 3}{2}, x \geq 0, y \geq -\dfrac{3}{2}$

This is a function of x, so f has an inverse.

$f^{-1}(x) = \dfrac{x^2 - 3}{2}, x \geq 0$

71. $f(x) = \dfrac{6x + 4}{4x + 5}$

$y = \dfrac{6x + 4}{4x + 5}$

$x = \dfrac{6y + 4}{4y + 5}$

$x(4y + 5) = 6y + 4$

$4xy + 5x = 6y + 4$

$4xy - 6y = -5x + 4$

$y(4x - 6) = -5x + 4$

$y = \dfrac{-5x + 4}{4x - 6}$

$= \dfrac{5x - 4}{6 - 4x}$

This is a function of x, so f has an inverse.

$f^{-1}(x) = \dfrac{5x - 4}{6 - 4x}$

73. $f(x) = (x - 2)^2$

domain of $f: x \geq 2$, range of $f: y \geq 0$

$$f(x) = (x - 2)^2$$
$$y = (x - 2)^2$$
$$x = (y - 2)^2$$
$$\sqrt{x} = y - 2$$
$$\sqrt{x} + 2 = y$$

So, $f^{-1}(x) = \sqrt{x} + 2$.

domain of $f^{-1}: x \geq 0$, range of $f^{-1}: x \geq 2$

75. $f(x) = |x + 2|$

domain of $f: x \geq -2$, range of $f: y \geq 0$

$$f(x) = |x + 2|$$
$$y = |x + 2|$$
$$x = y + 2$$
$$x - 2 = y$$

So, $f^{-1}(x) = x - 2$.

domain of $f^{-1}: x \geq 0$, range of $f^{-1}: y \geq -2$

77. $f(x) = (x + 6)^2$

domain of $f: x \geq -6$, range of $f: y \geq 0$

$$f(x) = (x + 6)^2$$
$$y = (x + 6)^2$$
$$x = (y + 6)^2$$
$$\sqrt{x} = y + 6$$
$$\sqrt{x} - 6 = y$$

So, $f^{-1}(x) = \sqrt{x} - 6$.

domain of $f^{-1}: x \geq 0$, range of $f^{-1}: y \geq -6$

79. $f(x) = -2x^2 + 5$

domain of $f: x \geq 0$, range of $f: y \leq 5$

$$f(x) = -2x^2 + 5$$
$$y = -2x^2 + 5$$
$$x = -2y^2 + 5$$
$$x - 5 = -2y^2$$
$$5 - x = 2y^2$$
$$\sqrt{\frac{5 - x}{2}} = y$$
$$\frac{\sqrt{5 - x}}{\sqrt{2}} \cdot \frac{\sqrt{2}}{\sqrt{2}} = y$$
$$\frac{\sqrt{2(5 - x)}}{2} = y$$

So, $f^{-1}(x) = \dfrac{\sqrt{-2(x - 5)}}{2}$.

domain of $f^{-1}(x): x \leq 5$, range of $f^{-1}(x): y \geq 0$

81. $f(x) = |x - 4| + 1$

domain of $f: x \geq 4$, range of $f: y \geq 1$

$$f(x) = |x - 4| + 1$$
$$y = x - 3$$
$$x = y - 3$$
$$x + 3 = y$$

So, $f^{-1}(x) = x + 3$.

domain of $f^{-1}: x \geq 1$, range of $f^{-1}: y \geq 4$

In Exercises 83–87, $f(x) = \frac{1}{8}x - 3$, $f^{-1}(x) = 8(x + 3)$,

$g(x) = x^3$, $g^{-1}(x) = \sqrt[3]{x}$.

83. $(f^{-1} \circ g^{-1})(1) = f^{-1}(g^{-1}(1))$
$$= f^{-1}(\sqrt[3]{1})$$
$$= 8(\sqrt[3]{1} + 3) = 32$$

85. $(f^{-1} \circ f^{-1})(6) = f^{-1}(f^{-1}(6))$
$$= f^{-1}(8[6 + 3])$$
$$= 8[8(6 + 3) + 3] = 600$$

87. $(f \circ g)(x) = f(g(x)) = f(x^3) = \frac{1}{8}x^3 - 3$

$$y = \frac{1}{8}x^3 - 3$$

$$x = \frac{1}{8}y^3 - 3$$

$$x + 3 = \frac{1}{8}y^3$$

$$8(x + 3) = y^3$$

$$\sqrt[3]{8(x + 3)} = y$$

$$(f \circ g)^{-1}(x) = 2\sqrt[3]{x + 3}$$

In Exercises 89–91, $f(x) = x + 4$, $f^{-1}(x) = x - 4$,

$g(x) = 2x - 5$, $g^{-1}(x) = \dfrac{x + 5}{2}$.

89. $(g^{-1} \circ f^{-1})(x) = g^{-1}(f^{-1}(x))$

$$= g^{-1}(x - 4)$$

$$= \frac{(x - 4) + 5}{2}$$

$$= \frac{x + 1}{2}$$

91. $(f \circ g)(x) = f(g(x))$

$$= f(2x - 5)$$

$$= (2x - 5) + 4$$

$$= 2x - 1$$

$$(f \circ g)^{-1}(x) = \frac{x + 1}{2}$$

Note: Comparing Exercises 89 and 91,

$(f \circ g)^{-1}(x) = (g^{-1} \circ f^{-1})(x)$.

93. (a) $y = 10 + 0.75x$

$$x = 10 + 0.75y$$

$$x - 10 = 0.75y$$

$$\frac{x - 10}{0.75} = y$$

So, $f^{-1}(x) = \dfrac{x - 10}{0.75}$.

$x =$ hourly wage, $y =$ number of units produced

(b) $y = \dfrac{24.25 - 10}{0.75} = 19$

So, 19 units are produced.

95. False. $f(x) = x^2$ is even and does not have an inverse.

97.

x	1	3	4	6
f	1	2	6	7

x	1	2	6	7
$f^{-1}(x)$	1	3	4	6

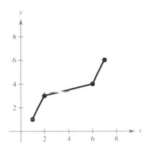

99. Let $(f \circ g)(x) = y$. Then $x = (f \circ g)^{-1}(y)$. Also,

$$(f \circ g)(x) = y \Rightarrow f(g(x)) = y$$

$$g(x) = f^{-1}(y)$$

$$x = g^{-1}(f^{-1}(y))$$

$$x = (g^{-1} \circ f^{-1})(y).$$

Because f and g are both one-to-one

functions, $(f \circ g)^{-1} = g^{-1} \circ f^{-1}$.

101. If $f(x) = k(2 - x - x^3)$ has an inverse and

$f^{-1}(3) = -2$, then $f(-2) = 3$. So,

$$f(-2) = k(2 - (-2) - (-2)^3) = 3$$

$$k(2 + 2 + 8) = 3$$

$$12k = 3$$

$$k = \frac{3}{12} = \frac{1}{4}.$$

So, $k = \frac{1}{4}$.

103.

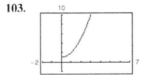

There is an inverse function $f^{-1}(x) = \sqrt{x - 1}$ because

the domain of f is equal to the range of f^{-1} and the

range of f is equal to the domain of f^{-1}.

105. This situation could be represented by a one-to-one function if the runner does not stop to rest. The inverse function would represent the time in hours for a given number of miles completed.

Section 1.10   Mathematical Modeling and Variation

1. variation; regression

3. least squares regression

5. directly proportional

7. directly proportional

9. combined

11.

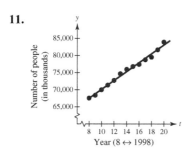

The model fits the data well.

13.

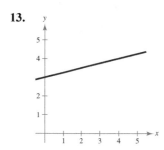

Using the point $(0, 3)$ and $(4, 4)$, $y = \frac{1}{4}x + 3$.

15.

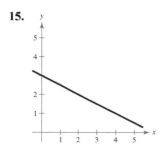

Using the points $(2, 2)$ and $(4, 1)$, $y = -\frac{1}{2}x + 3$.

17. (a)

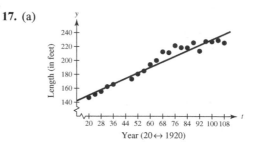

(b) Using the points $(32, 162.3)$ and $(96, 227.7)$:

$$m = \frac{227.7 - 162.3}{96 - 32}$$

$$\approx 1.02$$

$$y - 162.3 = 1.02(t - 32)$$

$$y = 1.02t + 129.66$$

(c) $y \approx 1.01t + 130.82$

(d) The models are similar.

2012 → use $t = 112$

Model from part (b):

$y = 1.02(112) + 129.66 = 243.9$ feet

Model from part (c):

$y = 1.01(112) + 130.82 = 243.94$ feet

19. $y = kx$

$14 = k(2)$

$7 = k$

$y = 7x$

21. $y = kx$

$2050 = k(10)$

$205 = k$

$y = 205x$

23. $y = kx$

$1 = k(5)$

$\frac{1}{5} = k$

$y = \frac{1}{5}x$

25. $y = kx$

$8\pi = k(4)$

$\pi = k$

$y = \frac{\pi}{2}x$

27. $k = 1$

x	2	4	6	8	10
$y = kx^2$	4	16	36	64	100

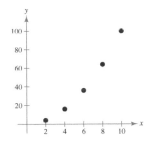

29. $k = \frac{1}{2}$

x	2	4	6	8	10
$y = \frac{1}{2}x^3$	4	32	108	256	500

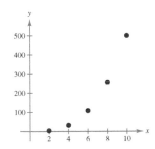

31. $k = 2, n = 1$

x	2	4	6	8	10
$y = \dfrac{2}{x}$	1	$\frac{1}{2}$	$\frac{1}{3}$	$\frac{1}{4}$	$\frac{1}{5}$

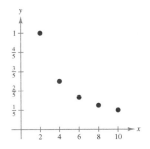

33. $k = 10$

x	2	4	6	8	10
$y = \dfrac{k}{x^2}$	$\frac{5}{2}$	$\frac{5}{8}$	$\frac{5}{18}$	$\frac{5}{32}$	$\frac{1}{10}$

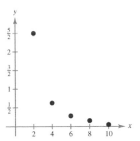

35. The graph appears to represent $y = 4/x$, so y varies inversely as x.

37. $y = \dfrac{k}{x}$

$1 = \dfrac{k}{5}$

$5 = k$

$y = \dfrac{5}{x}$

This equation checks with the other points given in the table.

39. $y = kx$

$-7 = k(10)$

$-\dfrac{7}{10} = k$

$y = -\dfrac{7}{10}x$

This equation checks with the other points given in the table.

41. $A = kr^2$

43. $y = \dfrac{k}{x^2}$

45. $F = \dfrac{kg}{r^2}$

47. $R = k(T - T_e)$

49. $R = kS(S - L)$

51. $S = 4\pi r^2$

The surface area of a sphere varies directly as the square of the radius r.

53. $A = \frac{1}{2}bh$

The area of a triangle is jointly proportional to its base and height.

55. $A = kr^2$

$9\pi = k(3)^2$

$\pi = k$

$A = \pi r^2$

57. $y = \dfrac{k}{x}$

$7 = \dfrac{k}{4}$

$28 = k$

$y = \dfrac{28}{x}$

59. $F = krs^3$

$4158 = k(11)(3)^3$

$k = 14$

$F = 14rs^3$

61. $z = \dfrac{kx^2}{y}$

$6 = \dfrac{k(6)^2}{4}$

$\dfrac{24}{36} = k$

$\dfrac{2}{3} = k$

$z = \dfrac{2/3x^2}{y} = \dfrac{2x^2}{3y}$

63. $I = kP$

$113.75 = k(3250)$

$0.035 = k$

$I = 0.035P$

65. $y = kx$

$33 = k(13)$

$\dfrac{33}{13} = k$

$y = \dfrac{33}{13}x$

When $x = 10$ inches, $y \approx 25.4$ centimeters.

When $x = 20$ inches, $y \approx 50.8$ centimeters.

67. $d = kF$

$0.12 = k(220)$

$\dfrac{3}{5500} = k$

$d = \dfrac{3}{5500}F$

$0.16 = \dfrac{3}{5500}F$

$\dfrac{880}{3} = F$

The required force is $293\frac{1}{3}$ newtons.

69. $d = kF$

$1.9 = k(25) \implies k = 0.076$

$d = 0.076F$

When the distance compressed is 3 inches, we have

$3 = 0.076F$

$F \approx 39.47.$

No child over 39.47 pounds should use the toy.

71. $d = kv^2$

$0.02 = k\left(\dfrac{1}{4}\right)^2$

$k = 0.32$

$d = 0.32v^2$

$0.12 = 0.32v^2$

$v^2 = \dfrac{0.12}{0.32} = \dfrac{3}{8}$

$v = \dfrac{\sqrt{3}}{2\sqrt{2}} = \dfrac{\sqrt{6}}{4} \approx 0.61$ mi/hr

73. $W = kmh$

$2116.8 = k(120)(1.8)$

$k = \dfrac{2116.8}{(120)(1.8)} = 9.8$

$W = 9.8mh$

When $m = 100$ kilograms and $h = 1.5$ meters, we have $W = 9.8(100)(1.5) = 1470$ joules.

75. (a)

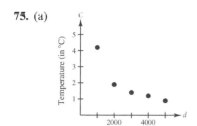

(b) Yes, the data appears to be modeled (approximately) by the inverse proportion model.

$$4.2 = \frac{k_1}{1000} \qquad 1.9 = \frac{k_2}{2000} \qquad 1.4 = \frac{k_3}{3000} \qquad 1.2 = \frac{k_4}{4000} \qquad 0.9 = \frac{k_5}{5000}$$

$$4200 = k_1 \qquad 3800 = k_2 \qquad 4200 = k_3 \qquad 4800 = k_4 \qquad 4500 = k_5$$

(c) Mean: $k = \dfrac{4200 + 3800 + 4200 + 4800 + 4500}{5} = 4300$, Model: $C = \dfrac{4300}{d}$

(d)

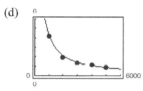

(e) $3 = \dfrac{4300}{d}$

$d = \dfrac{4300}{3} = 1433\dfrac{1}{3}$ meters

77. False. π is a constant, not a variable. So, the area A varies directly as the square of the radius, r.

79. (a) y will change by a factor of one-fourth.

(b) y will change by a factor of four.

Review Exercises for Chapter 1

1. $x^2 - 6x - 27 < 0$

$(x + 3)(x - 9) < 0$

Key numbers: $x = -3, x = 9$

Test intervals: $(-\infty, -3), (-3, 9), (9, \infty)$

Test: Is $(x + 3)(x - 9) < 0$?

By testing an x-value in each test interval in the inequality, we see that the solution set is $(-3, 9)$.

3. $6x^2 + 5x < 4$

$6x^2 + 5x - 4 < 0$

$(3x + 4)(2x - 1) < 0$

Key numbers: $x = -\frac{4}{3}, x = \frac{1}{2}$

Test intervals: $\left(-\infty, -\frac{4}{3}\right), \left(-\frac{4}{3}, \frac{1}{2}\right), \left(\frac{1}{2}, \infty\right)$

Test: Is $(3x + 4)(2x - 1) < 0$?

By testing an x-value in each test interval in the inequality, we see that the solution set is $\left(-\frac{4}{3}, \frac{1}{2}\right)$.

5. $\dfrac{x-5}{3-x} < 0$

Key numbers: $x = 5, x = 3$

Test intervals: $(-\infty, 3), (3, 5), (5, \infty)$

Test: Is $\dfrac{x-5}{3-x} < 0$?

By testing an *x*-value in each test interval in the inequality, we see that the solution set is $(-\infty, 3) \cup (5, \infty)$.

7. $y = 3x - 5$

x	−2	−1	0	1	2
y	−11	−8	−5	−2	1

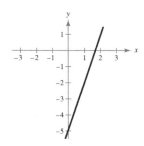

9. $y = x^2 - 3x$

x	−1	0	1	2	3	4
y	4	0	−2	−2	0	4

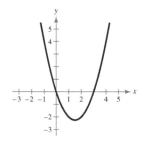

11. $y = 2x + 7$

x-intercept: Let $y = 0$.

$$0 = 2x + 7$$
$$x = -\tfrac{7}{2}$$
$$\left(-\tfrac{7}{2}, 0\right)$$

y-intercept: Let $x = 0$.

$$y = 2(0) + 7$$
$$y = 7$$
$$(0, 7)$$

13. $y = (x - 3)^2 - 4$

x-intercepts: $0 = (x - 3)^2 - 4 \Rightarrow (x - 3)^2 = 4$

$$\Rightarrow x - 3 = \pm 2$$
$$\Rightarrow x = 3 \pm 2$$
$$\Rightarrow x = 5 \text{ or } x = 1$$
$$(5, 0), (1, 0)$$

y-intercept: $y = (0 - 3)^2 - 4$

$$y = 9 - 4$$
$$y = 5$$
$$(0, 5)$$

15. $y = -4x + 1$

Intercepts: $\left(\tfrac{1}{4}, 0\right), (0, 1)$

$y = -4(-x) + 1 \Rightarrow y = 4x + 1 \Rightarrow$ No *y*-axis symmetry

$-y = -4x + 1 \Rightarrow y = 4x - 1 \Rightarrow$ No *x*-axis symmetry

$-y = -4(-x) + 1 \Rightarrow y = -4x - 1 \Rightarrow$ No origin symmetry

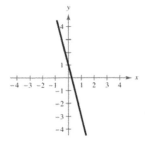

17. $y = 5 - x^2$

Intercepts: $\left(\pm\sqrt{5}, 0 \right), (0, 5)$

$y = 5 - (-x)^2 \Rightarrow y = 5 - x^2 \Rightarrow$ y-axis symmetry

$-y = 5 - x^2 \Rightarrow y = -5 + x^2 \Rightarrow$ No x-axis symmetry

$-y = 5 - (-x)^2 \Rightarrow y = -5 + x^2 \Rightarrow$ No origin symmetry

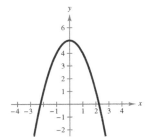

19. $y = x^3 + 3$

Intercepts: $\left(-\sqrt[3]{3}, 0 \right), (0, 3)$

$y = (-x)^3 + 3 \Rightarrow y = -x^3 + 3 \Rightarrow$ No y-axis symmetry

$-y = x^3 + 3 \Rightarrow y = -x^3 - 3 \Rightarrow$ No x-axis symmetry

$-y = (-x)^3 + 3 \Rightarrow y = x^3 - 3 \Rightarrow$ No origin symmetry

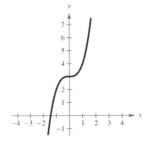

21. $y = \sqrt{x + 5}$

Domain: $[-5, \infty)$

Intercepts: $(-5, 0), \left(0, \sqrt{5} \right)$

$y = \sqrt{-x + 5} \Rightarrow$ No y-axis symmetry

$-y = \sqrt{x + 5} \Rightarrow y = -\sqrt{x + 5} \Rightarrow$ No x-axis symmetry

$-y = \sqrt{-x + 5} \Rightarrow y = -\sqrt{-x + 5} \Rightarrow$ No origin symmetry

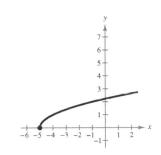

23. $x^2 + y^2 = 9$

Center: $(0, 0)$

Radius: 3

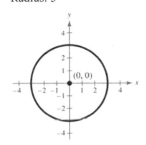

25. $(x + 2)^2 + y^2 = 16$

$\left(x - (-2) \right)^2 + (y - 0)^2 = 4^2$

Center: $(-2, 0)$

Radius: 4

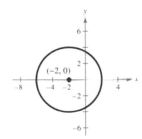

27. Endpoints of a diameter: $(0, 0)$ and $(4, -6)$

Center: $\left(\dfrac{0 + 4}{2}, \dfrac{0 + (-6)}{2}\right) = (2, -3)$

Radius: $r = \sqrt{(2 - 0)^2 + (-3 - 0)^2} = \sqrt{4 + 9} = \sqrt{13}$

Standard form: $(x - 2)^2 + (y - (-3))^2 = \left(\sqrt{13}\right)^2$

$(x - 2)^2 + (y + 3)^2 = 13$

29. $y = 3x + 13$

Slope: $m = 3$

y-intercept: $(0, 13)$

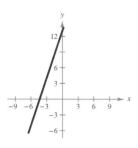

31. $y = 6$

Slope: $m = 0$

y-intercept: $(0, 6)$

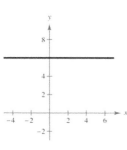

33. $(6, 4), (-3, -4)$

$m = \dfrac{4 - (-4)}{6 - (-3)} = \dfrac{4 + 4}{6 + 3} = \dfrac{8}{9}$

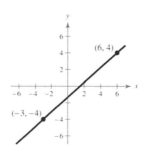

35. $(10, -3), m = -\dfrac{1}{2}$

$y - (-3) = -\dfrac{1}{2}(x - 10)$

$y + 3 = -\dfrac{1}{2}x + 5$

$y = -\dfrac{1}{2}x + 2$

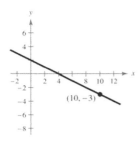

37. $(-1, 0), (6, 2)$

$m = \dfrac{2 - (0)}{6 - (-1)} = \dfrac{2}{7}$

$y - 0 = \dfrac{2}{7}(x - (-1))$

$y = \dfrac{2}{7}(x + 1)$

$y = \dfrac{2}{7}x + \dfrac{2}{7}$

39. Point: $(3, -2)$

$5x - 4y = 8$

$y = \dfrac{5}{4}x - 2$

(a) Parallel slope: $m = \dfrac{5}{4}$

$y - (-2) = \dfrac{5}{4}(x - 3)$

$y + 2 = \dfrac{5}{4}x - \dfrac{15}{4}$

$y = \dfrac{5}{4}x - \dfrac{23}{4}$

(b) Perpendicular slope: $m = -\dfrac{4}{5}$

$y - (-2) = -\dfrac{4}{5}(x - 3)$

$y + 2 = -\dfrac{4}{5}x + \dfrac{12}{5}$

$y = -\dfrac{4}{5}x + \dfrac{2}{5}$

41. *Verbal Model*: Sale price $= \big($List price$\big) - \big($Discount$\big)$

Labels: Sale price $= S$

List price $= L$

Discount $= 20\%$ of $L = 0.2L$

Equation: $S = L - 0.2L$

$S = 0.8L$

43. $16x - y^4 = 0$

$$y^4 = 16x$$

$$y = \pm 2\sqrt[4]{x}$$

No, y is not a function of x. Some x-values correspond to two y-values.

45. $y = \sqrt{1 - x}$

Yes, the equation represents y as a function of x. Each x-value, $x \le 1$, corresponds to only one y-value.

47. $f(x) = x^2 + 1$

(a) $f(2) = (2)^2 + 1 = 5$

(b) $f(-4) = (-4)^2 + 1 = 17$

(c) $f(t^2) = (t^2)^2 + 1 = t^4 + 1$

(d) $f(t + 1) = (t + 1)^2 + 1$

$$= t^2 + 2t + 2$$

49. $f(x) = \sqrt{25 - x^2}$

Domain: $25 - x^2 \ge 0$

$$(5 + x)(5 - x) \ge 0$$

Critical numbers: $x = \pm 5$

Test intervals: $(-\infty, -5), (-5, 5), (5, \infty)$

Test: Is $25 - x^2 \ge 0$?

Solution set: $-5 \le x \le 5$

Domain: all real numbers x such that $-5 \le x \le 5$, or $[-5, 5]$

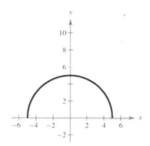

51. $v(t) = -32t + 48$

$v(1) = 16$ feet per second

53. $f(x) = 2x^2 + 3x - 1$

$$\frac{f(x + h) - f(x)}{h} = \frac{\left[2(x + h)^2 + 3(x + h) - 1\right] - \left(2x^2 + 3x - 1\right)}{h}$$

$$= \frac{2x^2 + 4xh + 2h^2 + 3x + 3h - 1 - 2x^2 - 3x + 1}{h}$$

$$= \frac{h(4x + 2h + 3)}{h}$$

$$= 4x + 2h + 3, \quad h \ne 0$$

55. $y = (x - 3)^2$

A vertical line intersects the graph no more than once, so y *is* a function of x.

57. $f(x) = 3x^2 - 16x + 21$

$$3x^2 - 16x + 21 = 0$$

$$(3x - 7)(x - 3) = 0$$

$$3x - 7 = 0 \quad \text{or} \quad x - 3 = 0$$

$$x = \tfrac{7}{3} \quad \text{or} \qquad x = 3$$

59. $f(x) = \dfrac{8x + 3}{11 - x}$

$$\frac{8x + 3}{11 - x} = 0$$

$$8x + 3 = 0$$

$$x = -\tfrac{3}{8}$$

61. $f(x) = |x| + |x + 1|$

f is increasing on $(0, \infty)$.

f is decreasing on $(-\infty, -1)$.

f is constant on $(-1, 0)$.

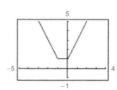

63. $f(x) = -x^2 + 2x + 1$

Relative maximum: $(1, 2)$

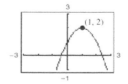

65. $f(x) = -x^2 + 8x - 4$

$$\frac{f(4) - f(0)}{4 - 0} = \frac{12 - (-4)}{4} = 4$$

The average rate of change of f from $x_1 = 0$ to $x_2 = 4$ is 4.

67. $f(x) = x^4 - 20x^2$

$f(-x) = (-x)^4 - 20(-x)^2 = x^4 - 20x^2 = f(x)$

The function is even.

69. (a) $f(2) = -6, f(-1) = 3$

     Points: $(2, -6), (-1, 3)$

$$m = \frac{3 - (-6)}{-1 - 2} = \frac{9}{-3} = -3$$

$$y - (-6) = -3(x - 2)$$
$$y + 6 = -3x + 6$$
$$y = -3x$$
$$f(x) = -3x$$

(b)

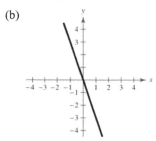

71. $f(x) = 3 - x^2$

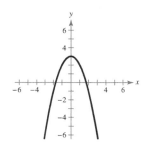

73. $g(x) = \dfrac{1}{x + 5}$

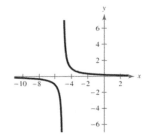

75. (a) $f(x) = x^2$

(b) $h(x) = x^2 - 9$

     Vertical shift 9 units downward

(c)

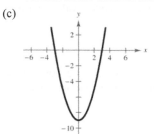

(d) $h(x) = f(x) - 9$

77. (a) $f(x) = \sqrt{x}$

(b) $h(x) = -\sqrt{x} + 4$

     Vertical shift 4 units upward, reflection in the x-axis

(c)

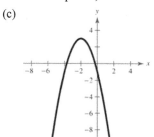

(d) $h(x) = -f(x) + 4$

79. (a) $f(x) = x^2$

(b) $h(x) = -(x + 2)^2 + 3$

     Horizontal shift two units to the left, vertical shift 3 units upward, reflection in the x-axis.

(c)

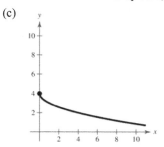

(d) $h(x) = -f(x + 2) + 3$

81. (a) $f(x) = [\![x]\!]$

(b) $h(x) = -[\![x]\!] + 6$

Reflection in the x-axis and a vertical shift 6 units upward

(c)

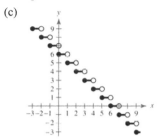

(d) $h(x) = -f(x) + 6$

83. (a) $f(x) = [\![x]\!]$

(b) $h(x) = 5[\![x - 9]\!]$

Horizontal shift 9 units to the right and a vertical stretch (each y-value is multiplied by 5)

(c)

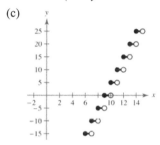

(d) $h(x) = 5f(x - 9)$

85. $f(x) = x^2 + 3, g(x) = 2x - 1$

(a) $(f + g)(x) = (x^2 + 3) + (2x - 1) = x^2 + 2x + 2$

(b) $(f - g)(x) = (x^2 + 3) - (2x - 1) = x^2 - 2x + 4$

(c) $(fg)(x) = (x^2 + 3)(2x - 1) = 2x^3 - x^2 + 6x - 3$

(d) $\left(\dfrac{f}{g}\right)(x) = \dfrac{x^2 + 3}{2x - 1}$, Domain: $x \neq \dfrac{1}{2}$

87. $f(x) = \frac{1}{3}x - 3, g(x) = 3x + 1$

The domains of f and g are all real numbers.

(a) $(f \circ g)(x) = f(g(x))$

$= f(3x + 1)$

$= \frac{1}{3}(3x + 1) - 3$

$= x + \frac{1}{3} - 3$

$= x - \frac{8}{3}$

Domain: all real numbers

(b) $(g \circ f)(x) = g(f(x))$

$= g\left(\frac{1}{3}x - 3\right)$

$= 3\left(\frac{1}{3}x - 3\right) + 1$

$= x - 9 + 1$

$= x - 8$

Domain: all real numbers

89. $N(T(t)) = 25(2t + 1)^2 - 50(2t + 1) + 300, \ 2 \leq t \leq 20$

$= 25(4t^2 + 4t + 1) - 100t - 50 + 300$

$= 100t^2 + 100t + 25 - 100t + 250$

$= 100t^2 + 275$

The composition $N(T(t))$ represents the number of bacteria in the food as a function of time.

91. $f(x) = 3x + 8$

$$y = 3x + 8$$
$$x = 3y + 8$$
$$x - 8 = 3y$$
$$y = \frac{x - 8}{3}$$
$$y = \frac{1}{3}(x - 8)$$

So, $f^{-1}(x) = \frac{1}{3}(x - 8)$

$$f(f^{-1}(x)) = f\left(\frac{1}{3}(x - 8)\right) = 3\left(\frac{1}{3}(x - 8)\right) + 8 = x - 8 + 8 = x$$

$$f^{-1}(f(x)) = f^{-1}(3x + 8) = \frac{1}{3}(3x + 8 - 8) = \frac{1}{3}(3x) = x$$

93. $f(x) = (x - 1)^2$

No, the function does not have an inverse because some horizontal lines intersect the graph twice.

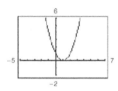

95. (a) $\quad f(x) = \frac{1}{2}x - 3$ (b)

$$y = \frac{1}{2}x - 3$$
$$x = \frac{1}{2}y - 3$$
$$x + 3 = \frac{1}{2}y$$
$$2(x + 3) = y$$
$$f^{-1}(x) = 2x + 6$$

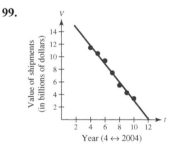

(c) The graph of f^{-1} is the reflection of the graph of f in the line $y = x$.

(d) The domains and ranges of f and f^{-1} are the set of all real numbers.

97. $f(x) = 2(x - 4)^2$ is increasing on $(4, \infty)$.

Let $f(x) = 2(x - 4)^2$, $x > 4$ and $y > 0$.

$$y = 2(x - 4)^2$$
$$x = 2(y - 4)^2, x > 0, y > 4$$
$$\frac{x}{2} = (y - 4)^2$$
$$\sqrt{\frac{x}{2}} = y - 4$$
$$\sqrt{\frac{x}{2}} + 4 = y$$
$$f^{-1}(x) = \sqrt{\frac{x}{2}} + 4, x > 0$$

99.

The model fits the data well.

101.
$$C = khw^2$$
$$28.80 = k(16)(6)^2$$
$$k = 0.05$$
$$C = (0.05)(14)(8)^2 = \$44.80$$

103. True. If $f(x) = x^3$ and $g(x) = \sqrt[3]{x}$, then the domain of g is all real numbers, which is equal to the range of f and vice versa.

Problem Solving for Chapter 1

1. (a) $W_1 = 0.07S + 2000$

(b) $W_2 = 0.05S + 2300$

(c)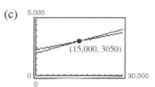

Point of intersection: $(15{,}000, 3050)$

Both jobs pay the same, \$3050, if you sell \$15,000 per month.

(d) No. If you think you can sell \$20,000 per month, keep your current job with the higher commission rate. For sales over \$15,000 it pays more than the other job.

3. (a) Let $f(x)$ and $g(x)$ be two even functions. Then define $h(x) = f(x) \pm g(x)$.

$$h(-x) = f(-x) \pm g(-x)$$
$$= f(x) \pm g(x) \text{ because } f \text{ and } g \text{ are even}$$
$$= h(x)$$

So, $h(x)$ is also even.

(b) Let $f(x)$ and $g(x)$ be two odd functions. Then define $h(x) = f(x) \pm g(x)$.

$$h(-x) = f(-x) \pm g(-x)$$
$$= -f(x) \pm g(x) \text{ because } f \text{ and } g \text{ are odd}$$
$$= -h(x)$$

So, $h(x)$ is also odd. $\left(\text{If } f(x) \neq g(x)\right)$

(c) Let $f(x)$ be odd and $g(x)$ be even. Then define $h(x) = f(x) \pm g(x)$.

$$h(-x) = f(-x) \pm g(-x)$$
$$= -f(x) \pm g(x) \text{ because } f \text{ is odd and } g \text{ is even}$$
$$\neq h(x)$$
$$\neq -h(x)$$

So, $h(x)$ is neither odd nor even.

5. $f(x) = a_{2n}x^{2n} + a_{2n-2}x^{2n-2} + \cdots + a_2x^2 + a_0$

$f(-x) = a_{2n}(-x)^{2n} + a_{2n-2}(-x)^{2n-2} + \cdots + a_2(-x)^2 + a_0 = a_{2n}x^{2n} + a_{2n-2}x^{2n-2} + \cdots + a_2x^2 + a_0 = f(x)$

So, $f(x)$ is even.

7. (a) April 11: 10 hours

April 12: 24 hours

April 13: 24 hours

April 14: $23\frac{2}{3}$ hours

Total: $81\frac{2}{3}$ hours

(b) Speed $= \dfrac{\text{distance}}{\text{time}} = \dfrac{2100}{81\frac{2}{3}} = \dfrac{180}{7} = 25\frac{5}{7}$ mph

(c) $D = -\dfrac{180}{7}t + 3400$

Domain: $0 \le t \le \dfrac{1190}{9}$

Range: $0 \le D \le 3400$

(d)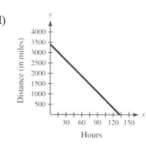

9. (a)–(d) Use $f(x) = 4x$ and $g(x) = x + 6$.

(a) $(f \circ g)(x) = f(x + 6) = 4(x + 6) = 4x + 24$

(b) $(f \circ g)^{-1}(x) = \dfrac{x - 24}{4} = \dfrac{1}{4}x - 6$

(c) $f^{-1}(x) = \dfrac{1}{4}x$

$\ g^{-1}(x) = x - 6$

(d) $(g^{-1} \circ f^{-1})(x) = g^{-1}\left(\dfrac{1}{4}x\right) = \dfrac{1}{4}x - 6$

(e) $f(x) = x^3 + 1$ and $g(x) = 2x$

$\ (f \circ g)(x) = f(2x) = (2x)^3 + 1 = 8x^3 + 1$

$\ (f \circ g)^{-1}(x) = \sqrt[3]{\dfrac{x - 1}{8}} = \dfrac{1}{2}\sqrt[3]{x - 1}$

$\ f^{-1}(x) = \sqrt[3]{x - 1}$

$\ g^{-1}(x) = \dfrac{1}{2}x$

$\ (g^{-1} \circ f^{-1})(x) = g^{-1}\left(\sqrt[3]{x - 1}\right) = \dfrac{1}{2}\sqrt[3]{x - 1}$

(f) Answers will vary.

(g) Conjecture: $(f \circ g)^{-1}(x) = (g^{-1} \circ f^{-1})(x)$

11. $H(x) = \begin{cases} 1, & x \geq 0 \\ 0, & x < 0 \end{cases}$

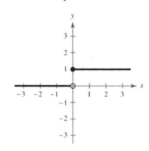

(a) $H(x) - 2$

(b) $H(x - 2)$

(c) $-H(x)$

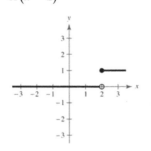

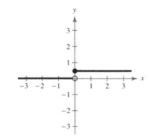

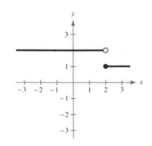

(d) $H(-x)$

(e) $\frac{1}{2}H(x)$

(f) $-H(x - 2) + 2$

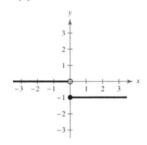

13. $(f \circ (g \circ h))(x) = f((g \circ h)(x)) = f(g(h(x))) = (f \circ g \circ h)(x)$

$((f \circ g) \circ h)(x) = (f \circ g)(h(x)) = f(g(h(x))) = (f \circ g \circ h)(x)$

15.

x	$f(x)$	$f^{-1}(x)$
-4	—	2
-3	4	1
-2	1	0
-1	0	—
0	-2	-1
1	3	-2
2	-4	—
3	—	—
4	—	-3

(a)

x	$f(f^{-1}(x))$
-4	$f(f^{-1}(-4)) = f(2) = -4$
-2	$f(f^{-1}(-2)) = f(0) = -2$
0	$f(f^{-1}(0)) = f(-1) = 0$
4	$f(f^{-1}(4)) = f(-3) = 4$

(b)

x	$(f + f^{-1})(x)$
-3	$f(-3) + f^{-1}(-3) = 4 + 1 = 5$
-2	$f(-2) + f^{-1}(-2) = 1 + 0 = 1$
0	$f(0) + f^{-1}(0) = -2 + (-1) = -3$
1	$f(1) + f^{-1}(1) = -3 + (-2) = -5$

(c)

x	$(f \cdot f^{-1})(x)$
-3	$f(-3)f^{-1}(-3) = (4)(1) = 4$
-2	$f(-2)f^{-1}(-2) = (1)(0) = 0$
0	$f(0)f^{-1}(0) = (-2)(-1) = 2$
1	$f(1)f^{-1}(1) = (-3)(-2) = 6$

(d)

x	$\left| f^{-1}(x) \right|$
-4	$\left| f^{-1}(-4) \right| = \left| 2 \right| = 2$
-3	$\left| f^{-1}(-3) \right| = \left| 1 \right| = 1$
0	$\left| f^{-1}(0) \right| = \left| -1 \right| = 1$
4	$\left| f^{-1}(4) \right| = \left| -3 \right| = 3$

Practice Test for Chapter 1

1. Given the points $(-3, 4)$ and $(5, -6)$, find (a) the midpoint of the line segment joining the points, and (b) the distance between the points.

2. Graph $y = \sqrt{7 - x}$.

3. Write the standard equation of the circle with center $(-3, 5)$ and radius 6.

4. Find the equation of the line through $(2, 4)$ and $(3, -1)$.

5. Find the equation of the line with slope $m = 4/3$ and y-intercept $b = -3$.

6. Find the equation of the line through $(4, 1)$ perpendicular to the line $2x + 3y = 0$.

7. If it costs a company $32 to produce 5 units of a product and $44 to produce 9 units, how much does it cost to produce 20 units? (Assume that the cost function is linear.)

8. Given $f(x) = x^2 - 2x + 1$, find $f(x - 3)$.

9. Given $f(x) = 4x - 11$, find $\dfrac{f(x) - f(3)}{x - 3}$.

10. Find the domain and range of $f(x) = \sqrt{36 - x^2}$.

11. Which equations determine y as a function of x?

    (a) $6x - 5y + 4 = 0$

    (b) $x^2 + y^2 = 9$

    (c) $y^3 = x^2 + 6$

12. Sketch the graph of $f(x) = x^2 - 5$.

13. Sketch the graph of $f(x) = |x + 3|$.

14. Sketch the graph of $f(x) = \begin{cases} 2x + 1, & \text{if } x \geq 0, \\ x^2 - x, & \text{if } x < 0. \end{cases}$

15. Use the graph of $f(x) = |x|$ to graph the following:

    (a) $f(x + 2)$

    (b) $-f(x) + 2$

16. Given $f(x) = 3x + 7$ and $g(x) = 2x^2 - 5$, find the following:

    (a) $(g - f)(x)$

    (b) $(fg)(x)$

17. Given $f(x) = x^2 - 2x + 16$ and $g(x) = 2x + 3$, find $f(g(x))$.

18. Given $f(x) = x^3 + 7$, find $f^{-1}(x)$.

19. Which of the following functions have inverses?

    (a) $f(x) = |x - 6|$

    (b) $f(x) = ax + b, a \neq 0$

    (c) $f(x) = x^3 - 19$

20. Given $f(x) = \sqrt{\dfrac{3 - x}{x}}, 0 < x \leq 3$, find $f^{-1}(x)$.

Exercises 21–23, true or false?

21. $y = 3x + 7$ and $y = \frac{1}{3}x - 4$ are perpendicular.

22. $(f \circ g)^{-1} = g^{-1} \circ f^{-1}$

23. If a function has an inverse, then it must pass both the Vertical Line Test and the Horizontal Line Test.

24. If z varies directly as the cube of x and inversely as the square root of y, and $z = -1$ when $x = -1$ and $y = 25$, find z in terms of x and y.

25. Use your calculator to find the least square regression line for the data.

x	-2	-1	0	1	2	3
y	1	2.4	3	3.1	4	4.7

C H A P T E R 2
Polynomial and Rational Functions

C H A P T E R   2
Polynomial and Rational Functions

Section 2.1   Quadratic Functions and Models

1. polynomial

3. quadratic; parabola

5. positive; minimum

7. $f(x) = (x - 2)^2$ opens upward and has vertex $(2, 0)$. Matches graph (e).

8. $f(x) = (x + 4)^2$ opens upward and has vertex $(-4, 0)$. Matches graph (c).

9. $f(x) = x^2 - 2$ opens upward and has vertex $(0, -2)$. Matches graph (b).

10. $f(x) = (x + 1)^2 - 2$ opens upward and has vertex $(-1, -2)$. Matches graph (a).

11. $f(x) = 4 - (x - 2)^2 = -(x - 2)^2 + 4$ opens downward and has vertex $(2, 4)$. Matches graph (f).

12. $f(x) = -(x - 4)^2$ opens downward and has vertex $(4, 0)$. Matches graph (d).

13. (a) $y = \frac{1}{2}x^2$ (b) $y = -\frac{1}{8}x^2$ (c) $y = \frac{3}{2}x^2$ (d) $y = -3x^2$

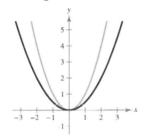
Vertical shrink

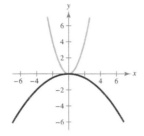
Vertical shrink and reflection in the x-axis

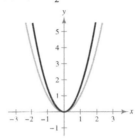
Vertical stretch

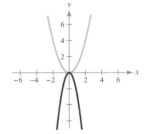
Vertical stretch and reflection in the x-axis

15. (a) $y = (x - 1)^2$ (b) $y = (3x)^2 + 1$ (c) $y = \left(\frac{1}{3}x\right)^2 - 3$ (d) $y = (x + 3)^2$

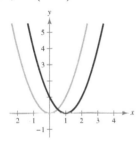
Horizontal shift one unit to the right

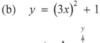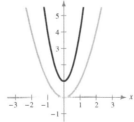
Horizontal shrink and a vertical shift one unit upward

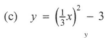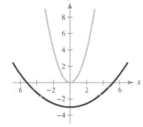
Horizontal stretch and a vertical shift three units downward

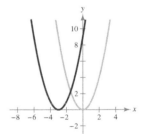
Horizontal shift three units to the left

17. $f(x) = x^2 - 6x$

$\quad = (x^2 - 6x + 9) - 9$

$\quad = (x - 3)^2 - 9$

Vertex: $(3, -9)$

Axis of symmetry: $x = 3$

Find x-intercepts:

$x^2 - 6x = 0$

$x(x - 6) = 0$

$\quad\quad x = 0$

$x - 6 = 0 \Rightarrow x = 6$

x-intercepts: $(0, 0), (6, 0)$

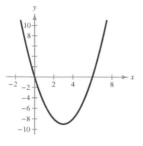

19. $h(x) = x^2 - 8x + 16 = (x - 4)^2$

Vertex: $(4, 0)$

Axis of symmetry: $x = 4$

Find x-intercepts:

$(x - 4)^2 = 0$

$x - 4 = 0$

$\quad\quad x = 4$

x-intercept: $(4, 0)$

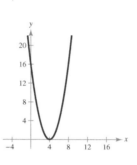

21. $f(x) = x^2 + 8x + 13$

$\quad = (x^2 + 8x + 16) - 16 + 13$

$\quad = (x + 4)^2 - 3$

Vertex: $(-4, -3)$

Axis of symmetry: $x = -4$

Find x-intercepts:

$x^2 + 8x + 13 = 0$

$x^2 + 8x = -13$

$x^2 + 8x + 16 = 16 - 13$

$(x + 4)^2 = 3$

$x + 4 = \pm\sqrt{3}$

$\quad\quad x = -4 \pm \sqrt{3}$

x-intercepts: $\left(-4 \pm \sqrt{3}, 0\right)$

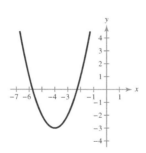

23. $f(x) = x^2 - 14x + 54$

$\quad = (x^2 - 14x + 49) - 49 + 54$

$\quad = (x - 7)^2 + 5$

Vertex: $(7, 5)$

Axis of symmetry: $x = 7$

Find x-intercepts:

$x^2 - 14x + 54 = 0$

$x^2 - 14x = -54$

$x^2 - 14x + 49 = -54 + 49$

$(x - 7)^2 = -5$

$x - 7 = \pm\sqrt{-5}$

$\quad\quad x = 7 \pm \sqrt{5}i$

Not a real number

No x-intercepts

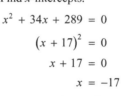

25. $f(x) = x^2 + 34x + 289$

$\quad = (x + 17)^2$

Vertex: $(-17, 0)$

Axis of symmetry: $x = -17$

Find x-intercepts:

$x^2 + 34x + 289 = 0$

$(x + 17)^2 = 0$

$x + 17 = 0$

$\quad\quad x = -17$

x-intercept: $(-17, 0)$

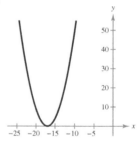

27. $f(x) = x^2 - x + \dfrac{5}{4}$

$\quad = \left(x^2 - x + \dfrac{1}{4}\right) - \dfrac{1}{4} + \dfrac{5}{4}$

$\quad = \left(x - \dfrac{1}{2}\right)^2 + 1$

Vertex: $\left(\dfrac{1}{2}, 1\right)$

Axis of symmetry: $x = \dfrac{1}{2}$

Find x-intercepts:

$x^2 - x + \dfrac{5}{4} = 0$

$x = \dfrac{1 \pm \sqrt{1 - 5}}{2}$

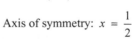

Not a real number

No x-intercepts

29. $f(x) = -x^2 + 2x + 5$

$= -(x^2 - 2x + 1) - (-1) + 5$

$= -(x - 1)^2 + 6$

Vertex: $(1, 6)$

Axis of symmetry: $x = 1$

Find x-intercepts:

$-x^2 + 2x + 5 = 0$

$x^2 - 2x - 5 = 0$

$x = \dfrac{2 \pm \sqrt{4 + 20}}{2}$

$= 1 \pm \sqrt{6}$

x-intercepts: $\left(1 - \sqrt{6}, 0\right), \left(1 + \sqrt{6}, 0\right)$

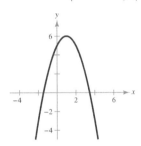

31. $h(x) = 4x^2 - 4x + 21$

$= 4\left(x^2 - x + \dfrac{1}{4}\right) - 4\left(\dfrac{1}{4}\right) + 21$

$= 4\left(x - \dfrac{1}{2}\right)^2 + 20$

Vertex: $\left(\dfrac{1}{2}, 20\right)$

Axis of symmetry: $x = \dfrac{1}{2}$

Find x-intercepts:

$4x^2 - 4x + 21 = 0$

$x = \dfrac{4 \pm \sqrt{16 - 336}}{2(4)}$

Not a real number

No x-intercepts

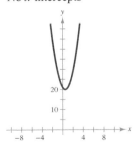

33. $f(x) = \frac{1}{4}x^2 - 2x - 12$

$= \frac{1}{4}(x^2 - 8x + 16) - \frac{1}{4}(16) - 12$

$= \frac{1}{4}(x - 4)^2 - 16$

Vertex: $(4, -16)$

Axis of symmetry: $x = 4$

Find x-intercepts:

$\frac{1}{4}x^2 - 2x - 12 = 0$

$x^2 - 8x - 48 = 0$

$(x + 4)(x - 12) = 0$

$x = -4$ or $x = 12$

x-intercepts: $(-4, 0), (12, 0)$

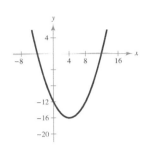

35. $f(x) = -(x^2 + 2x - 3) = -(x + 1)^2 + 4$

Vertex: $(-1, 4)$

Axis of symmetry: $x = -1$

x-intercepts: $(-3, 0), (1, 0)$

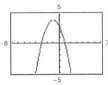

37. $g(x) = x^2 + 8x + 11 = (x + 4)^2 - 5$

Vertex: $(-4, -5)$

Axis of symmetry: $x = -4$

x-intercepts: $\left(-4 \pm \sqrt{5}, 0\right)$

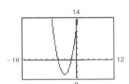

39. $f(x) = 2x^2 - 16x + 32$

$= 2(x^2 - 8x + 16)$

$= 2(x - 4)^2$

Vertex: $(4, 0)$

Axis of symmetry: $x = 4$

x-intercepts: $(4, 0)$

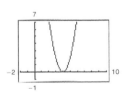

41. $g(x) = \frac{1}{2}(x^2 + 4x - 2) = \frac{1}{2}(x + 2)^2 - 3$

Vertex: $(-2, -3)$

Axis of symmetry: $x = -2$

x-intercepts: $\left(-2 \pm \sqrt{6}, 0\right)$

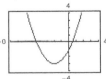

43. $(-1, 4)$ is the vertex.

$y = a(x + 1)^2 + 4$

Because the graph passes through $(1, 0)$,

$0 = a(1 + 1)^2 + 4$

$-4 = 4a$

$-1 = a.$

So, $y = -1(x + 1)^2 + 4 = -(x + 1)^2 + 4.$

45. $(-2, 2)$ is the vertex.

$y = a(x + 2)^2 + 2$

Because the graph passes through $(-1, 0)$,

$0 = a(-1 + 2)^2 + 2$

$-2 = a.$

So, $y = -2(x + 2)^2 + 2.$

47. $(-2, 5)$ is the vertex.

$f(x) = a(x + 2)^2 + 5$

Because the graph passes through $(0, 9)$,

$9 = a(0 + 2)^2 + 5$

$4 = 4a$

$1 = a.$

So, $f(x) = 1(x + 2)^2 + 5 = (x + 2)^2 + 5.$

49. $(1, -2)$ is the vertex.

$f(x) = a(x - 1)^2 - 2$

Because the graph passes through $(-1, 14)$,

$14 = a(-1 - 1)^2 - 2$

$14 = 4a - 2$

$16 = 4a$

$4 = a.$

So, $f(x) = 4(x - 1)^2 - 2.$

51. $(5, 12)$ is the vertex.

$f(x) = a(x - 5)^2 + 12$

Because the graph passes through $(7, 15)$,

$15 = a(7 - 5)^2 + 12$

$3 = 4a \Rightarrow a = \frac{3}{4}.$

So, $f(x) = \frac{3}{4}(x - 5)^2 + 12.$

53. $\left(-\frac{1}{4}, \frac{3}{2}\right)$ is the vertex.

$f(x) = a\left(x + \frac{1}{4}\right)^2 + \frac{3}{2}$

Because the graph passes through $(-2, 0)$,

$0 = a\left(-2 + \frac{1}{4}\right)^2 + \frac{3}{2}$

$-\frac{3}{2} = \frac{49}{16}a \Rightarrow a = -\frac{24}{49}.$

So, $f(x) = -\frac{24}{49}\left(x + \frac{1}{4}\right)^2 + \frac{3}{2}.$

55. $\left(-\frac{5}{2}, 0\right)$ is the vertex.

$f(x) = a\left(x + \frac{5}{2}\right)^2$

Because the graph passes through $\left(-\frac{7}{2}, -\frac{16}{3}\right)$,

$-\frac{16}{3} = a\left(-\frac{7}{2} + \frac{5}{2}\right)^2$

$-\frac{16}{3} = a.$

So, $f(x) = -\frac{16}{3}\left(x + \frac{5}{2}\right)^2.$

57. $y = x^2 - 4x - 5$

x-intercepts: $(5, 0), (-1, 0)$

$0 = x^2 - 4x - 5$

$0 = (x - 5)(x + 1)$

$x = 5$ or $x = -1$

59. $f(x) = x^2 - 4x$

x-intercepts: $(0, 0), (4, 0)$

$0 = x^2 - 4x$

$0 = x(x - 4)$

$x = 0$ or $x = 4$

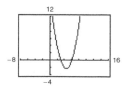

The x-intercepts and the solutions of $f(x) = 0$ are the same.

61. $f(x) = x^2 - 9x + 18$

x-intercepts: $(3, 0), (6, 0)$

$0 = x^2 - 9x + 18$

$0 = (x - 3)(x - 6)$

$x = 3$ or $x = 6$

The x-intercepts and the solutions of $f(x) = 0$ are the same.

63. $f(x) = 2x^2 - 7x - 30$

x-intercepts: $\left(-\frac{5}{2}, 0\right), (6, 0)$

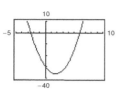

$0 = 2x^2 - 7x - 30$

$0 = (2x + 5)(x - 6)$

$x = -\frac{5}{2}$ or $x = 6$

The x-intercepts and the solutions of $f(x) = 0$ are the same.

65. $f(x) = \left[x - (-1)\right](x - 3)$ opens upward

$\quad = (x + 1)(x - 3)$

$\quad = x^2 - 2x - 3$

$g(x) = -\left[x - (-1)\right](x - 3)$ opens downward

$\quad = -(x + 1)(x - 3)$

$\quad = -(x^2 - 2x - 3)$

$\quad = -x^2 + 2x + 3$

Note: $f(x) = a(x + 1)(x - 3)$ has x-intercepts $(-1, 0)$ and $(3, 0)$ for all real numbers $a \neq 0$.

67. $f(x) = (x - 0)(x - 10)$ opens upward

$\quad = x^2 - 10x$

$g(x) = -(x - 0)(x - 10)$ opens downward

$\quad = -x^2 + 10x$

Note: $f(x) = a(x - 0)(x - 10) = ax(x - 10)$ has x-intercepts $(0, 0)$ and $(10, 0)$ for all real numbers $a \neq 0$.

69. $f(x) = \left[x - (-3)\right]\left[x - \left(-\frac{1}{2}\right)\right](2)$ opens upward

$\quad = (x + 3)\left(x + \frac{1}{2}\right)(2)$

$\quad = (x + 3)(2x + 1)$

$\quad = 2x^2 + 7x + 3$

$g(x) = -(2x^2 + 7x + 3)$ opens downward

$\quad = -2x^2 - 7x - 3$

Note: $f(x) = a(x + 3)(2x + 1)$ has x-intercepts $(-3, 0)$ and $\left(-\frac{1}{2}, 0\right)$ for all real numbers $a \neq 0$.

71. Let $x = $ the first number and $y = $ the second number.

Then the sum is

$x + y = 110 \Rightarrow y = 110 - x.$

The product is $P(x) = xy = x(110 - x) = 110x - x^2.$

$P(x) = -x^2 + 110x$

$\quad = -\left(x^2 - 110x + 3025 - 3025\right)$

$\quad = -\left[(x - 55)^2 - 3025\right]$

$\quad = -(x - 55)^2 + 3025$

The maximum value of the product occurs at the vertex of $P(x)$ and is 3025. This happens when $x = y = 55$.

73. Let $x = $ the first number and $y = $ the second number.

Then the sum is

$x + 2y = 24 \Rightarrow y = \dfrac{24 - x}{2}.$

The product is $P(x) = xy = x\left(\dfrac{24 - x}{2}\right).$

$P(x) = \frac{1}{2}\left(-x^2 + 24x\right)$

$\quad = -\frac{1}{2}\left(x^2 - 24x + 144 - 144\right)$

$\quad = -\frac{1}{2}\left[(x - 12)^2 - 144\right] = -\frac{1}{2}(x - 12)^2 + 72$

The maximum value of the product occurs at the vertex of $P(x)$ and is 72. This happens when $x = 12$ and $y = (24 - 12)/2 = 6$. So, the numbers are 12 and 6.

75. $y = -\dfrac{4}{9}x^2 + \dfrac{24}{9}x + 12$

The vertex occurs at $-\dfrac{b}{2a} = \dfrac{-24/9}{2(-4/9)} = 3$. The maximum height is

$y(3) = -\dfrac{4}{9}(3)^2 + \dfrac{24}{9}(3) + 12 = 16$ feet.

77. $C = 800 - 10x + 0.25x^2 = 0.25x^2 - 10x + 800$

The vertex occurs at $x = -\dfrac{b}{2a} = -\dfrac{-10}{2(0.25)} = 20.$

The cost is minimum when $x = 20$ fixtures.

79. $R(p) = -25p^2 + 1200p$

(a) $R(20) = \$14,000$ thousand $= \$14,000,000$

   $R(25) = \$14,375$ thousand $= \$14,375,000$

   $R(30) = \$13,500$ thousand $= \$13,500,000$

(b) The revenue is a maximum at the vertex.

   $$-\frac{b}{2a} = \frac{-1200}{2(-25)} = 24$$

   $R(24) = 14,400$

   The unit price that will yield a maximum revenue of $14,400 thousand is $24.

81. (a)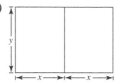

   $$4x + 3y = 200 \Rightarrow y = \frac{1}{3}(200 - 4x) = \frac{4}{3}(50 - x)$$

   $$A = 2xy = 2x\left[\frac{4}{3}(50 - x)\right] = \frac{8}{3}x(50 - x) = \frac{8x(50 - x)}{3}$$

(b)

x	A
5	600
10	$1066\frac{2}{3}$
15	1400
20	1600
25	$1666\frac{2}{3}$
30	1600

This area is maximum when $x = 25$ feet and $y = \dfrac{100}{3} = 33\frac{1}{3}$ feet.

(c)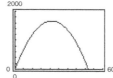

This area is maximum when $x = 25$ feet and $y = \dfrac{100}{3} = 33\frac{1}{3}$ feet.

(d) $A = \dfrac{8}{3}x(50 - x)$

   $= -\dfrac{8}{3}(x^2 - 50x)$

   $= -\dfrac{8}{3}(x^2 - 50x + 625 - 625)$

   $= -\dfrac{8}{3}\left[(x - 25)^2 - 625\right]$

   $= -\dfrac{8}{3}(x - 25)^2 + \dfrac{5000}{3}$

   The maximum area occurs at the vertex and is $5000/3$ square feet. This happens when $x = 25$ feet and $y = \left(200 - 4(25)\right)/3 = 100/3$ feet. The dimensions are $2x = 50$ feet by $33\frac{1}{3}$ feet.

(e) They are all identical.

   $x = 25$ feet and $y = 33\frac{1}{3}$ feet

83. (a)   Revenue $=$ (number of tickets sold)(price per ticket)

Let $y =$ attendance, or the number of tickets sold.

$$m = -100, (20, 1500)$$
$$y - 1500 = -100(x - 20)$$
$$y - 1500 = -100x + 2000$$
$$y = -100x + 3500$$

$$R(x) = (y)(x)$$
$$R(x) = (-100x + 3500)(x)$$
$$R(x) = -100x^2 + 3500x$$

(b) The revenue is at a maximum at the vertex.

$$-\frac{b}{2a} = \frac{-3500}{2(-100)} = 17.5$$

$$R(17.5) = -100(17.5)^2 + 3500(17.5) = \$30{,}625$$

A ticket price of \$17.50 will yield a maximum revenue of \$30,625.

85. (a)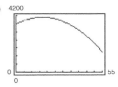

(b) The maximum annual consumption occurs at the point $(16.9, 4074.813)$.

4075 cigarettes

$1966 \rightarrow t = 16$

The maximum consumption occurred in 1966. After that year, the consumption decreases.
It is likely that the warning was responsible for the decrease in consumption.

(c) Annual consumption per smoker $= \dfrac{\text{Annual consumption in 2005} \cdot \text{total population}}{\text{total number of smokers in 2005}} = \dfrac{1487.9(296{,}329{,}000)}{59{,}858{,}458} = 7365.8$

About 7366 cigarettes per smoker annually

Daily consumption per smoker $= \dfrac{\text{Number of cigarettes per year}}{\text{Number of days per year}} = \dfrac{7366}{365} \approx 20.2$

About 20 cigarettes per day

87. True. The equation $-12x^2 - 1 = 0$ has no real solution, so the graph has no x-intercepts.

89. $f(x) = -x^2 + bx - 75$, maximum value: 25

The maximum value, 25, is the y-coordinate of the vertex.

Find the x-coordinate of the vertex:

$$x = -\frac{b}{2a} = -\frac{b}{2(-1)} = \frac{b}{2}$$

$$f(x) = -x^2 + bx - 75$$

$$f\left(\frac{b}{2}\right) = -\left(\frac{b}{2}\right)^2 + b\left(\frac{b}{2}\right) - 75$$

$$25 = -\frac{b^2}{4} + \frac{b^2}{2} - 75$$

$$100 = \frac{b^2}{4}$$

$$400 = b^2$$

$$\pm 20 = b$$

91. $f(x) = x^2 + bx + 26$, minimum value: 10

The minimum value, 10, is the y-coordinate of the vertex.

Find the x-coordinate of the vertex:

$$x = -\frac{b}{2a} = -\frac{b}{2(1)} = -\frac{b}{2}$$

$$f(x) = x^2 + bx + 26$$

$$f\left(-\frac{b}{2}\right) = \left(-\frac{b}{2}\right)^2 + b\left(-\frac{b}{2}\right) + 26$$

$$10 = \frac{b^2}{4} - \frac{b^2}{2} + 26$$

$$-16 = -\frac{b^2}{4}$$

$$64 = b^2$$

$$\pm 8 = b$$

93. $f(x) = ax^2 + bx + c$

$$= a\left(x^2 + \frac{b}{a}x\right) + c$$

$$= a\left(x^2 + \frac{b}{a}x + \frac{b^2}{4a^2} - \frac{b^2}{4a^2}\right) + c$$

$$= a\left(x + \frac{b}{2a}\right)^2 - \frac{b^2}{4a} + c$$

$$= a\left(x + \frac{b}{2a}\right)^2 + \frac{4ac - b^2}{4a}$$

$$f\left(-\frac{b}{2a}\right) = a\left(\frac{b^2}{4a^2}\right) + b\left(-\frac{b}{2a}\right) + c$$

$$= \frac{b^2}{4a} - \frac{b^2}{2a} + c$$

$$= \frac{b^2 - 2b^2 + 4ac}{4a} = \frac{4ac - b^2}{4a}$$

So, the vertex occurs at

$$\left(-\frac{b}{2a}, \frac{4ac - b^2}{4a}\right) = \left(-\frac{b}{2a}, f\left(-\frac{b}{2a}\right)\right).$$

95. If $f(x) = ax^2 + bx + c$ has two real zeros, then by the Quadratic Formula they are

$$x = \frac{-b \pm \sqrt{b^2 - 4ac}}{2a}.$$

The average of the zeros of f is

$$\frac{\dfrac{-b - \sqrt{b^2 - 4ac}}{2a} + \dfrac{-b + \sqrt{b^2 - 4ac}}{2a}}{2} = \frac{\dfrac{-2b}{2a}}{2}$$

$$= -\frac{b}{2a}.$$

This is the x-coordinate of the vertex of the graph.

Section 2.2 Polynomial Functions of Higher Degree

1. continuous

3. n; $n - 1$

5. touches; crosses

7. standard

9. $f(x) = -2x^2 - 5x$ is a parabola with x-intercepts $(0, 0)$ and $\left(-\frac{5}{2}, 0\right)$ and opens downward. Matches graph (h).

10. $f(x) = 2x^3 - 3x + 1$ has intercepts

$(0, 1), (1, 0), \left(-\frac{1}{2} - \frac{1}{2}\sqrt{3}, 0\right)$ and $\left(-\frac{1}{2} + \frac{1}{2}\sqrt{3}, 0\right)$.

Matches graph (f).

11. $f(x) = -\frac{1}{4}x^4 + 3x^2$ has intercepts $(0, 0)$ and $\left(\pm 2\sqrt{3}, 0\right)$. Matches graph (a).

12. $f(x) = -\frac{1}{3}x^3 + x^2 - \frac{4}{3}$ has y-intercept $\left(0, -\frac{4}{3}\right)$. Matches graph (e).

13. $f(x) = x^4 + 2x^3$ has intercepts $(0, 0)$ and $(-2, 0)$. Matches graph (d).

14. $f(x) = \frac{1}{5}x^5 - 2x^3 + \frac{9}{5}x$ has intercepts $(0, 0), (1, 0), (-1, 0), (3, 0), (-3, 0)$. Matches graph (b).

15. $y = x^3$

(a) $f(x) = (x - 4)^3$

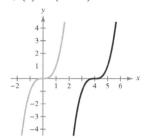

Horizontal shift four units to the right

(b) $f(x) = x^3 - 4$

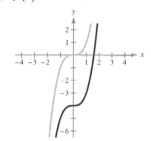

Vertical shift four units downward

(c) $f(x) = -\frac{1}{4}x^3$

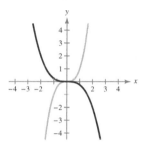

Reflection in the x-axis and a vertical shrink
$\left(\text{each } y\text{-value is multiplied by } \frac{1}{4}\right)$

(d) $f(x) = (x - 4)^3 - 4$

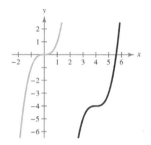

Horizontal shift four units to the right
and vertical shift four units downward

17. $y = x^4$

(a) $f(x) = (x + 3)^4$

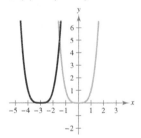

Horizontal shift three
units to the left

(b) $f(x) = x^4 - 3$

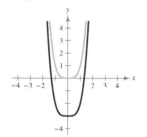

Vertical shift three units
downward

(c) $f(x) = 4 - x^4$

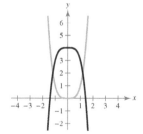

Reflection in the x-axis and then
a vertical shift four units upward

(d) $f(x) = \frac{1}{2}(x - 1)^4$

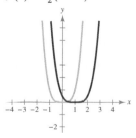

Horizontal shift one unit to
the right and a vertical shrink
$\left(\text{each } y\text{-value is multiplied by } \frac{1}{2}\right)$

(e) $f(x) = (2x)^4 + 1$

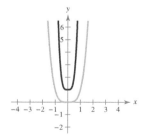

Vertical shift one unit upward
and a horizontal shrink (each
y-value is multiplied by 16)

(f) $f(x) = \left(\frac{1}{2}x\right)^4 - 2$

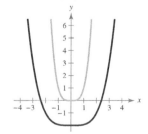

Vertical shift two units downward
and a horizontal stretch (each y-value
is multiplied by $\frac{1}{16}$)

19. $f(x) = \frac{1}{5}x^3 + 4x$

Degree: 3

Leading coefficient: $\frac{1}{5}$

The degree is odd and the leading coefficient is positive. The graph falls to the left and rises to the right.

21. $g(x) = 5 - \frac{7}{2}x - 3x^2$

Degree: 2

Leading coefficient: -3

The degree is even and the leading coefficient is negative. The graph falls to the left and falls to the right.

23. $g(x) = -x^3 + 3x^2$

Degree: 3

Leading coefficient: -1

The degree is odd and the leading coefficient is negative. The graph rises to the left and falls to the right.

25. $f(x) = -2.1x^5 + 4x^3 - 2$

Degree: 5

Leading coefficient: -2.1

The degree is odd and the leading coefficient is negative. The graph rises to the left and falls to the right.

27. $f(x) = 6 - 2x + 4x^2 - 5x^3$

Degree: 3

Leading coefficient: -5

The degree is odd and the leading coefficient is negative. The graph rises to the left and falls to the right.

29. $h(x) = -\frac{3}{4}(t^2 - 3t + 6)$

Degree: 2

Leading coefficient: $-\dfrac{3}{4}$

The degree is even and the leading coefficient is negative. The graph falls to the left and falls to the right.

31. $f(x) = 3x^3 - 9x + 1;\ g(x) = 3x^3$

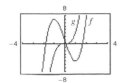

33. $f(x) = -(x^4 - 4x^3 + 16x);\ g(x) = -x^4$

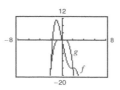

35. $f(x) = x^2 - 36$

(a) $0 = x^2 - 36$

$0 = (x + 6)(x - 6)$

$x + 6 = 0 \qquad x - 6 = 0$

$x = -6 \qquad x = 6$

Zeros: ± 6

(b) Each zero has a multiplicity of one (odd multiplicity).

(c) Turning points: 1 (the vertex of the parabola)

(d)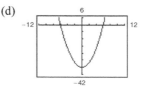

37. $h(t) = t^2 - 6t + 9$

(a) $0 = t^2 - 6t + 9 = (t - 3)^2$

Zero: $t = 3$

(b) $t = 3$ has a multiplicity of 2 (even multiplicity).

(c) Turning points: 1 (the vertex of the parabola)

(d)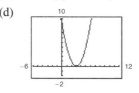

39. $f(x) = \frac{1}{3}x^2 + \frac{1}{3}x - \frac{2}{3}$

(a) $0 = \frac{1}{3}x^2 + \frac{1}{3}x - \frac{2}{3}$

$= \frac{1}{3}(x^2 + x - 2)$

$= \frac{1}{3}(x + 2)(x - 1)$

Zeros: $x = -2,\ x = 1$

(b) Each zero has a multiplicity of 1 (odd multiplicity).

(c) Turning points: 1 (the vertex of the parabola)

(d)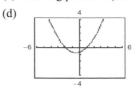

41. $f(x) = 3x^3 - 12x^2 + 3x$

   (a) $0 = 3x^3 - 12x^2 + 3x = 3x(x^2 - 4x + 1)$

      Zeros: $x = 0$, $x = 2 \pm \sqrt{3}$ (by the Quadratic Formula)

   (b) Each zero has a multiplicity of 1 (odd multiplicity).

   (c) Turning points: 2

   (d) 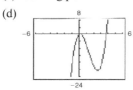

43. $f(t) = t^3 - 8t^2 + 16t$

   (a) $0 = t^3 - 8t^2 + 16t$

      $0 = t(t^2 - 8t + 16)$

      $0 = t(t - 4)(t - 4)$

      $t = 0 \quad t - 4 = 0 \quad t - 4 = 0$

      $t = 0 \quad\quad t = 4 \quad\quad t = 4$

      Zeros: $t = 0$, $t = 4$

   (b) The multiplicity of $t = 0$ is 1 (odd multiplicity).

      The multiplicity of $t = 4$ is 2 (even multiplicity).

   (c) Turning points: 2

   (d) 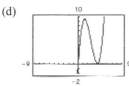

45. $g(t) = t^5 - 6t^3 + 9t$

   (a) $0 = t^5 - 6t^3 + 9t = t(t^4 - 6t^2 + 9) = t(t^2 - 3)^2$

      $= t(t + \sqrt{3})^2(t - \sqrt{3})^2$

      Zeros: $t = 0$, $t = \pm\sqrt{3}$

   (b) $t = 0$ has a multiplicity of 1 (odd multiplicity).

      $t = \pm\sqrt{3}$ each have a multiplicity of 2 (even multiplicity).

   (c) Turning points: 4

   (d) 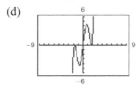

47. $f(x) = 3x^4 + 9x^2 + 6$

   (a) $0 = 3x^4 + 9x^2 + 6$

      $0 = 3(x^4 + 3x^2 + 2)$

      $0 = 3(x^2 + 1)(x^2 + 2)$

   (b) No real zeros

   (c) Turning points: 1

   (d) 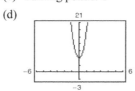

49. $g(x) = x^3 + 3x^2 - 4x - 12$

   (a) $0 = x^3 + 3x^2 - 4x - 12 = x^2(x + 3) - 4(x + 3)$

      $= (x^2 - 4)(x + 3) = (x - 2)(x + 2)(x + 3)$

      Zeros: $x = \pm 2$, $x = -3$

   (b) Each zero has a multiplicity of 1 (odd multiplicity).

   (c) Turning points: 2

   (d) 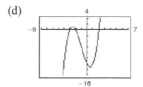

51. $y = 4x^3 - 20x^2 + 25x$

   (a) 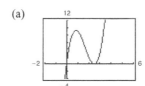

   (b) x-intercepts: $(0, 0)$, $\left(\frac{5}{2}, 0\right)$

   (c) $0 = 4x^3 - 20x^2 + 25x$

      $0 = x(4x^2 - 20x + 25)$

      $0 = x(2x - 5)^2$

      $x = 0, \frac{5}{2}$

   (d) The solutions are the same as the x-coordinates of the x-intercepts.

53. $y = x^5 - 5x^3 + 4x$

(a)

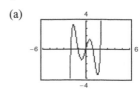

(b) x-intercepts: $(0, 0), (\pm 1, 0), (\pm 2, 0)$

(c) $0 = x^5 - 5x^3 + 4x$

$0 = x(x^2 - 1)(x^2 - 4)$

$0 = x(x + 1)(x - 1)(x + 2)(x - 2)$

$x = 0, \pm 1, \pm 2$

(d) The solutions are the same as the x-coordinates of the x-intercepts.

55. $f(x) = (x - 0)(x - 8)$

$= x^2 - 8x$

Note: $f(x) = ax(x - 8)$ has zeros 0 and 8 for all real numbers $a \neq 0$.

57. $f(x) = (x - 2)(x + 6)$

$= x^2 + 4x - 12$

Note: $f(x) = a(x - 2)(x + 6)$ has zeros 2 and -6 for all real numbers $a \neq 0$.

59. $f(x) = (x - 0)(x + 4)(x + 5)$

$= x(x^2 + 9x + 20)$

$= x^3 + 9x^2 + 20x$

Note: $f(x) = ax(x + 4)(x + 5)$ has zeros $0, -4$, and -5 for all real numbers $a \neq 0$.

61. $f(x) = (x - 4)(x + 3)(x - 3)(x - 0)$

$= (x - 4)(x^2 - 9)x$

$= x^4 - 4x^3 - 9x^2 + 36x$

Note: $f(x) = a(x^4 - 4x^3 - 9x^2 + 36x)$ has zeros $4, -3, 3$, and 0 for all real numbers $a \neq 0$.

63. $f(x) = \left[x - \left(1 + \sqrt{3}\right)\right]\left[x - \left(1 - \sqrt{3}\right)\right]$

$= \left[(x - 1) - \sqrt{3}\right]\left[(x - 1) + \sqrt{3}\right]$

$= (x - 1)^2 - \left(\sqrt{3}\right)^2$

$= x^2 - 2x + 1 - 3$

$= x^2 - 2x - 2$

Note: $f(x) = a(x^2 - 2x - 2)$ has zeros $1 + \sqrt{3}$ and $1 - \sqrt{3}$ for all real numbers

65. $f(x) = (x + 3)(x + 3) = x^2 + 6x + 9$

Note: $f(x) = a(x^2 + 6x + 9), a \neq 0$, has degree 2 and zero $x = -3$.

67. $f(x) = (x - 0)(x + 5)(x - 1)$

$= x(x^2 + 4x - 5)$

$= x^3 + 4x^2 - 5x$

Note: $f(x) = ax(x^2 + 4x - 5), a \neq 0$, has degree 3 and zeros $x = 0, -5$, and 1.

69. $f(x) = (x - 0)\left(x - \sqrt{3}\right)\left(x - \left(-\sqrt{3}\right)\right)$

$= x\left(x - \sqrt{3}\right)\left(x + \sqrt{3}\right) = x^3 - 3x$

Note: $f(x) = a(x^3 - 3x), a \neq 0$, has degree 3 and zeros $x = 0, \sqrt{3}$, and $-\sqrt{3}$.

71. $f(x) = \left(x - (-5)\right)^2(x - 1)(x - 2) = x^4 + 7x^3 - 3x^2 - 55x + 50$

or $f(x) = \left(x - (-5)\right)(x - 1)^2(x - 2) = x^4 + x^3 - 15x^2 + 23x - 10$

or $f(x) = \left(x - (-5)\right)(x - 1)(x - 2)^2 = x^4 - 17x^2 + 36x - 20$

Note: Any nonzero scalar multiple of these functions would also have degree 4 and zeros $x = -5, 1$, and 2.

73. $f(x) = x^4(x + 4) = x^5 + 4x^4$

or $f(x) = x^3(x + 4)^2 = x^5 + 8x^4 + 16x^3$

or $f(x) = x^2(x + 4)^3 = x^5 + 12x^4 + 48x^3 + 64x^2$

or $f(x) = x(x + 4)^4 = x^5 + 16x^4 + 96x^3 + 256x^2 + 256x$

Note: Any nonzero scalar multiple of these functions would also have degree 5 and zeros $x = 0$ and -4.

75. $f(x) = x^3 - 25x = x(x + 5)(x - 5)$

(a) Falls to the left; rises to the right

(b) Zeros: $0, -5, 5$

(c)

x	-2	-1	0	1	2
$f(x)$	42	24	0	-24	-42

(d)

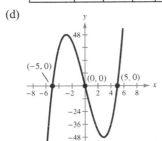

77. $f(t) = \frac{1}{4}(t^2 - 2t + 15) = \frac{1}{4}(t - 1)^2 + \frac{7}{2}$

(a) Rises to the left; rises to the right

(b) No real zeros (no x-intercepts)

(c)

t	-1	0	1	2	3
$f(t)$	4.5	3.75	3.5	3.75	4.5

(d) The graph is a parabola with vertex $\left(1, \frac{7}{2}\right)$.

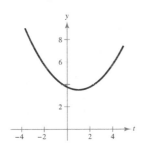

79. $f(x) = x^3 - 2x^2 = x^2(x - 2)$

(a) Falls to the left; rises to the right

(b) Zeros: $0, 2$

(c)

x	-1	0	$\frac{1}{2}$	1	2	3
$f(x)$	-3	0	$-\frac{3}{8}$	-1	0	9

(d)

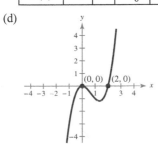

81. $f(x) = 3x^3 - 15x^2 + 18x = 3x(x - 2)(x - 3)$

(a) Falls to the left; rises to the right

(b) Zeros: $0, 2, 3$

(c)

x	0	1	2	2.5	3	3.5
$f(x)$	0	6	0	-1.875	0	7.875

(d)

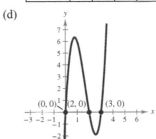

83. $f(x) = -5x^2 - x^3 = -x^2(5 + x)$

(a) Rises to the left; falls to the right

(b) Zeros: $0, -5$

(c)

x	-5	-4	-3	-2	-1	0	1
$f(x)$	0	-16	-18	-12	-4	0	-6

(d)

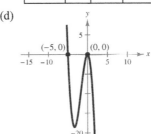

85. $f(x) = x^2(x - 4)$

(a) Falls to the left; rises to the right

(b) Zeros: $0, 4$

(c)

x	-1	0	1	2	3	4	5
$f(x)$	5	0	-3	-8	-9	0	25

(d)

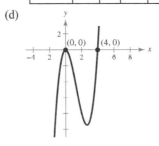

87. $g(t) = -\frac{1}{4}(t - 2)^2(t + 2)^2$

(a) Falls to the left; falls to the right

(b) Zeros: 2, −2

(c)

t	−3	−2	−1	0	1	2	3
$g(t)$	$-\frac{25}{4}$	0	$-\frac{9}{4}$	−4	$-\frac{9}{4}$	0	$-\frac{25}{4}$

(d)
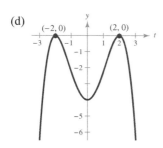

89. $f(x) = x^3 - 16x = x(x - 4)(x + 4)$

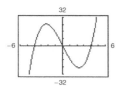

Zeros: 0 of multiplicity 1; 4 of multiplicity 1; and −4 of multiplicity 1

91. $g(x) = \frac{1}{5}(x + 1)^2(x - 3)(2x - 9)$

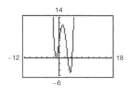

Zeros: −1 of multiplicity 2; 3 of multiplicity 1; $\frac{9}{2}$ of multiplicity 1

93. $f(x) = x^3 - 3x^2 + 3$

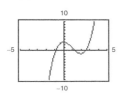

x	y
−3	−51
−2	−17
−1	−1
0	3
1	1
2	−1
3	3
4	19

The function has three zeros. They are in the intervals $[-1, 0], [1, 2],$ and $[2, 3]$. They are $x \approx -0.879, 1.347, 2.532$.

95. $g(x) = 3x^4 + 4x^3 - 3$

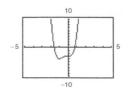

x	y
−4	509
−3	132
−2	13
−1	−4
0	−3
1	4
2	77
3	348

The function has two zeros. They are in the intervals $[-2, -1]$ and $[0, 1]$. They are $x \approx -1.585, 0.779$.

97. (a) Volume = $l \cdot w \cdot h$

height = x

length = width = $36 - 2x$

So, $V(x) = (36 - 2x)(36 - 2x)(x) = x(36 - 2x)^2$.

(b) Domain: $0 < x < 18$

The length and width must be positive.

(c)

Box Height	Box Width	Box Volume, V
1	$36 - 2(1)$	$1[36 - 2(1)]^2 = 1156$
2	$36 - 2(2)$	$2[36 - 2(2)]^2 = 2048$
3	$36 - 2(3)$	$3[36 - 2(3)]^2 = 2700$
4	$36 - 2(4)$	$4[36 - 2(4)]^2 = 3136$
5	$36 - 2(5)$	$5[36 - 2(5)]^2 = 3380$
6	$36 - 2(6)$	$6[36 - 2(6)]^2 = 3456$
7	$36 - 2(7)$	$7[36 - 2(7)]^2 = 3388$

The volume is a maximum of 3456 cubic inches when the height is 6 inches and the length and width are each 24 inches. So the dimensions are $6 \times 24 \times 24$ inches.

(d)
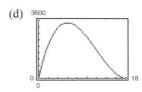

The maximum point on the graph occurs at $x = 6$. This agrees with the maximum found in part (c).

99. (a) $A = l \cdot w = (12 - 2x)(x) = -2x^2 + 12x$

(b) 16 feet = 192 inches

$V = l \cdot w \cdot h$

$\quad = (12 - 2x)(x)(192)$

$\quad = -384x^2 + 2304x$

(c) Because x and $12 - 2x$ cannot be negative, we have $0 < x < 6$ inches for the domain.

(d)

x	V
0	0
1	1920
2	3072
3	3456
4	3072
5	1920
6	0

When $x = 3$, the volume is a maximum with $V = 3456$ in.^{3}. The dimensions of the gutter cross-section are 3 inches × 6 inches × 3 inches.

(e)

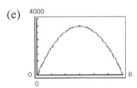

Maximum: (3, 3456)

The maximum value is the same.

(f) No. The volume is a product of the constant length and the cross-sectional area. The value of x would remain the same; only the value of V would change if the length was changed.

101. (a)

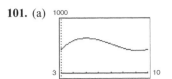

Relative maximum: (5.01, 655.75)

Relative minimum: (9.25, 417.42)

(b) The revenue is increasing over (3, 5.01) and decreasing over (5.01, 9.25), and then increasing over (9.25, 10).

(c) The revenue for this company is increasing from 2003 to 2005, when it reached a (relative) maximum of $655.75 million. From 2005 to 2009, revenue was decreasing when it dropped to $417.42 million. From 2009 to 2010, revenue began to increase again.

103. $R = \dfrac{1}{100,000}\left(-x^3 + 600x^2\right)$

The point of diminishing returns (where the graph changes from curving upward to curving downward) occurs when $x = 200$. The point is (200, 160) which corresponds to spending $2,000,000 on advertising to obtain a revenue of $160 million.

105. False. A fifth-degree polynomial can have at most four turning points.

107. False. The function $f(x) = (x - 2)^2$ has one turning point and two real (repeated) zeros.

109. False. $f(x) = -x^3$ rises to the left.

111. True. A polynomial of degree 7 with a negative leading coefficient rises to the left and falls to the right.

113. Answers will vary. *Sample answers:*

$a_4 < 0$ $\qquad\qquad\qquad\qquad$ $a_4 > 0$

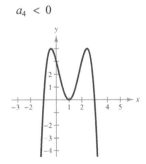 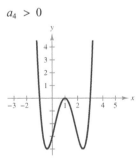

115. $f(x) = x^4$; $f(x)$ is even.

(a) $g(x) = f(x) + 2$

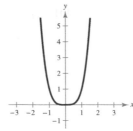

Vertical shift two units upward

$g(-x) = f(-x) + 2$

$\qquad = f(x) + 2$

$\qquad = g(x)$

Even

(b) $g(x) = f(x + 2)$

Horizontal shift two units to the left

Neither odd nor even

(c) $g(x) = f(-x) = (-x)^4 = x^4$

Reflection in the y-axis. The graph looks the same.

Even

(d) $g(x) = -f(x) = -x^4$

Reflection in the x-axis

Even

(e) $g(x) = f\left(\frac{1}{2}x\right) = \frac{1}{16}x^4$

Horizontal stretch

Even

(f) $g(x) = \frac{1}{2}f(x) = \frac{1}{2}x^4$

Vertical shrink

Even

(g) $g(x) = f\left(x^{3/4}\right) = \left(x^{3/4}\right)^4 = x^3, x \geq 0$

Neither odd nor even

(h) $g(x) = (f \circ f)(x) = f(f(x)) = f(x^4) = (x^4)^4 = x^{16}$

Even

117. (a)

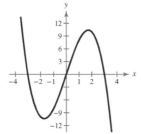

Zeros: 3

Relative minimum: 1

Relative maximum: 1

The number of zeros is the same as the degree and the number of extrema is one less than the degree.

(b)

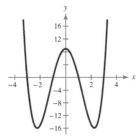

Zeros: 4

Relative minima: 2

Relative maximum: 1

The number of zeros is the same as the degree and the number of extrema is one less than the degree.

(c)

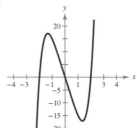

Zeros: 3

Relative minimum: 1

Relative maximum: 1

The number of zeros and the number of extrema are both less than the degree.

Section 2.3 Polynomial and Synthetic Division

1. $f(x)$ is the dividend; $d(x)$ is the divisor: $q(x)$ is the quotient: $r(x)$ is the remainder

3. improper

5. Factor

7. $y_1 = \dfrac{x^2}{x+2}$ and $y_2 = x - 2 + \dfrac{4}{x+2}$

$$\begin{array}{r} x - 2 \\ x+2\overline{)x^2 + 0x + 0} \\ \underline{x^2 + 2x} \\ -2x + 0 \\ \underline{-2x - 4} \\ 4 \end{array}$$

So, $\dfrac{x^2}{x+2} = x - 2 + \dfrac{4}{x+2}$ and $y_1 = y_2$.

9. $y_1 = \dfrac{x^2 + 2x - 1}{x+3}, y_2 = x - 1 + \dfrac{2}{x+3}$

(a) and (b)

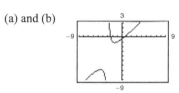

(c) $\begin{array}{r} x - 1 \\ x+3\overline{)x^2 + 2x - 1} \\ \underline{x^2 + 3x} \\ -x - 1 \\ \underline{-x - 3} \\ 2 \end{array}$

So, $\dfrac{x^2 + 2x - 1}{x+3} = x - 1 + \dfrac{2}{x+3}$ and $y_1 = y_2$.

11. $\begin{array}{r} 2x + 4 \\ x+3\overline{)2x^2 + 10x + 12} \\ \underline{2x^2 + 6x} \\ 4x + 12 \\ \underline{4x + 12} \\ 0 \end{array}$

$\dfrac{2x^2 + 10x + 12}{x+3} = 2x + 4, x \neq 3$

13. $\begin{array}{r} x^2 - 3x + 1 \\ 4x+5\overline{)4x^3 - 7x^2 - 11x + 5} \\ \underline{4x^3 + 5x^2} \\ -12x^2 - 11x \\ \underline{-12x^2 - 15x} \\ 4x + 5 \\ \underline{4x + 5} \\ 0 \end{array}$

$\dfrac{4x^3 - 7x^2 - 11x + 5}{4x+5} = x^2 - 3x + 1, x \neq -\dfrac{5}{4}$

15. $\begin{array}{r} x^3 + 3x^2 \qquad -1 \\ x+2\overline{)x^4 + 5x^3 + 6x^2 - x - 2} \\ \underline{x^4 + 2x^3} \\ 3x^3 + 6x^2 \\ \underline{3x^3 + 6x^2} \\ -x - 2 \\ \underline{-x - 2} \\ 0 \end{array}$

$\dfrac{x^4 + 5x^3 + 6x^2 - x - 2}{x+2} = x^3 + 3x^2 - 1, x \neq -2$

17. $\begin{array}{r} x^2 + 3x + 9 \\ x-3\overline{)x^3 + 0x^2 + 0x - 27} \\ \underline{x^3 - 3x^2} \\ 3x^2 + 0x \\ \underline{3x^2 - 9x} \\ 9x - 27 \\ \underline{9x - 27} \\ 0 \end{array}$

$\dfrac{x^3 - 27}{x-3} = x^2 + 3x + 9, x \neq 3$

19. $\begin{array}{r} 7 \\ x+2\overline{)7x + 3} \\ \underline{7x + 14} \\ -11 \end{array}$

$\dfrac{7x + 3}{x+2} = 7 - \dfrac{11}{x+2}$

21. $\begin{array}{r} x \\ x^2 + 0x + 1\overline{)x^3 + 0x^2 + 0x - 9} \\ \underline{x^3 + 0x^2 + x} \\ -x - 9 \end{array}$

$\dfrac{x^3 - 9}{x^2 + 1} = x - \dfrac{x + 9}{x^2 + 1}$

23.
$$
\begin{array}{r}
2x - 8 \\
x^2 + 0x + 1\overline{)2x^3 - 8x^2 + 3x - 9} \\
\underline{2x^3 + 0x^2 + 2x} \\
-8x^2 + x - 9 \\
\underline{-8x^2 - 0x - 8} \\
x - 1
\end{array}
$$

$$\frac{2x^3 - 8x^2 + 3x - 9}{x^2 + 1} = 2x - 8 + \frac{x - 1}{x^2 + 1}$$

25.
$$
\begin{array}{r}
x + 3 \\
x^3 - 3x^2 + 3x - 1\overline{)x^4 + 0x^3 + 0x^2 + 0x + 0} \\
\underline{x^4 - 3x^3 + 3x^2 - x} \\
3x^3 - 3x^2 + x + 0 \\
\underline{3x^3 - 9x^2 + 9x - 3} \\
6x^2 - 8x + 3
\end{array}
$$

$$\frac{x^4}{(x - 1)^3} = x + 3 + \frac{6x^2 - 8x + 3}{(x - 1)^3}$$

27.
$$
\begin{array}{r|rrrr}
5 & 3 & -17 & 15 & -25 \\
 & & 15 & -10 & 25 \\
\hline
 & 3 & -2 & 5 & 0
\end{array}
$$

$$\frac{3x^3 - 17x^2 + 15x - 25}{x - 5} = 3x^2 - 2x + 5,\, x \neq 5$$

35.
$$
\begin{array}{r|rrrr}
4 & 5 & -6 & 0 & 8 \\
 & & 20 & 56 & 224 \\
\hline
 & 5 & 14 & 56 & 232
\end{array}
$$

$$\frac{5x^3 - 6x^2 + 8}{x - 4} = 5x^2 + 14x + 56 + \frac{232}{x - 4}$$

37.
$$
\begin{array}{r|rrrrr}
6 & 10 & -50 & 0 & 0 & -800 \\
 & & 60 & 60 & 360 & 2160 \\
\hline
 & 10 & 10 & 60 & 360 & 1360
\end{array}
$$

$$\frac{10x^4 - 50x^3 - 800}{x - 6} = 10x^3 + 10x^2 + 60x + 360 + \frac{1360}{x - 6}$$

39.
$$
\begin{array}{r|rrrr}
-8 & 1 & 0 & 0 & 512 \\
 & & -8 & 64 & -512 \\
\hline
 & 1 & -8 & 64 & 0
\end{array}
$$

$$\frac{x^3 + 512}{x + 8} = x^2 - 8x + 64,\, x \neq -8$$

41.
$$
\begin{array}{r|rrrrr}
2 & -3 & 0 & 0 & 0 & 0 \\
 & & -6 & -12 & -24 & -48 \\
\hline
 & -3 & -6 & -12 & -24 & -48
\end{array}
$$

$$\frac{-3x^4}{x - 2} = -3x^3 - 6x^2 - 12x - 24 - \frac{48}{x - 2}$$

29.
$$
\begin{array}{r|rrrr}
3 & 6 & 7 & -1 & 26 \\
 & & 18 & 75 & 222 \\
\hline
 & 6 & 25 & 74 & 248
\end{array}
$$

$$\frac{6x^3 + 7x^2 - x + 26}{x - 3} = 6x^2 + 25x + 74 + \frac{248}{x - 3}$$

31.
$$
\begin{array}{r|rrrr}
-2 & 4 & 8 & -9 & -18 \\
 & & -8 & 0 & 18 \\
\hline
 & 4 & 0 & -9 & 0
\end{array}
$$

$$\frac{4x^3 + 8x^2 - 9x - 18}{x + 2} = 4x^2 - 9,\, x \neq -2$$

33.
$$
\begin{array}{r|rrrr}
-10 & -1 & 0 & 75 & -250 \\
 & & 10 & -100 & 250 \\
\hline
 & -1 & 10 & -25 & 0
\end{array}
$$

$$\frac{-x^3 + 75x - 250}{x + 10} = -x^2 + 10x - 25,\, x \neq -10$$

43.
$$
\begin{array}{r|rrrrr}
6 & -1 & 0 & 0 & 180 & 0 \\
 & & -6 & -36 & -216 & -216 \\
\hline
 & -1 & -6 & -36 & -36 & -216
\end{array}
$$

$$\frac{180x - x^4}{x - 6} = -x^3 - 6x^2 - 36x - 36 - \frac{216}{x - 6}$$

45.
$$
\begin{array}{r|rrrr}
-\dfrac{1}{2} & 4 & 16 & -23 & -15 \\
 & & -2 & -7 & 15 \\
\hline
 & 4 & 14 & -30 & 0
\end{array}
$$

$$\frac{4x^3 + 16x^2 - 23x - 15}{x + \dfrac{1}{2}} = 4x^2 + 14x - 30,\, x \neq -\frac{1}{2}$$

47. $f(x) = x^3 - x^2 - 14x + 11, k = 4$

$$\begin{array}{r|rrrr} 4 & 1 & -1 & -14 & 11 \\ & & 4 & 12 & -8 \\ \hline & 1 & 3 & -2 & 3 \end{array}$$

$f(x) = (x - 4)(x^2 + 3x - 2) + 3$

$f(4) = 4^3 - 4^2 - 14(4) + 11 = 3$

49. $f(x) = 15x^4 + 10x^3 - 6x^2 + 14, k = -\frac{2}{3}$

$$\begin{array}{r|rrrrr} -\frac{2}{3} & 15 & 10 & -6 & 0 & 14 \\ & & -10 & 0 & 4 & -\frac{8}{3} \\ \hline & 15 & 0 & -6 & 4 & \frac{34}{3} \end{array}$$

$f(x) = \left(x + \frac{2}{3}\right)\left(15x^3 - 6x + 4\right) + \frac{34}{3}$

$f\left(-\frac{2}{3}\right) = 15\left(-\frac{2}{3}\right)^4 + 10\left(-\frac{2}{3}\right)^3 - 6\left(-\frac{2}{3}\right)^2 + 14 = \frac{34}{3}$

51. $f(x) = x^3 + 3x^2 - 2x - 14, k = \sqrt{2}$

$$\begin{array}{r|rrrr} \sqrt{2} & 1 & 3 & -2 & -14 \\ & & \sqrt{2} & 2 + 3\sqrt{2} & 6 \\ \hline & 1 & 3 + \sqrt{2} & 3\sqrt{2} & -8 \end{array}$$

$f(x) = \left(x - \sqrt{2}\right)\left[x^2 + \left(3 + \sqrt{2}\right)x + 3\sqrt{2}\right] - 8$

$f\left(\sqrt{2}\right) = \left(\sqrt{2}\right)^3 + 3\left(\sqrt{2}\right)^2 - 2\sqrt{2} - 14 = -8$

53. $f(x) = -4x^3 + 6x^2 + 12x + 4, k = 1 - \sqrt{3}$

$$\begin{array}{r|rrrr} 1 - \sqrt{3} & -4 & 6 & 12 & 4 \\ & & -4 + 4\sqrt{3} & -10 + 2\sqrt{3} & -4 \\ \hline & -4 & 2 + 4\sqrt{3} & 2 + 2\sqrt{3} & 0 \end{array}$$

$f(x) = \left(x - 1 + \sqrt{3}\right)\left[-4x^2 + \left(2 + 4\sqrt{3}\right)x + \left(2 + 2\sqrt{3}\right)\right]$

$f\left(1 - \sqrt{3}\right) = -4\left(1 - \sqrt{3}\right)^3 + 6\left(1 - \sqrt{3}\right)^2 + 12\left(1 - \sqrt{3}\right) + 4 = 0$

55. $f(x) = 2x^3 - 7x + 3$

(a) Using the Remainder Theorem:

$f(1) = 2(1)^3 - 7(1) + 3 = -2$

Using synthetic division:

$$
\begin{array}{r|rrrr}
1 & 2 & 0 & -7 & 3 \\
  &   & 2 & 2 & -5 \\
\hline
  & 2 & 2 & -5 & -2 \\
\end{array}
$$

Verify using long division:

$$
\begin{array}{r}
2x^2 + 2x - 5 \\
x - 1 \overline{)\,2x^3 + 0x^2 - 7x + 3\,} \\
\underline{2x^3 - 2x^2} \\
2x^2 - 7x \\
\underline{2x^2 - 2x} \\
-5x + 3 \\
\underline{-5x + 5} \\
-2
\end{array}
$$

(b) Using the Remainder Theorem:

$f(-2) = 2(-2)^3 - 7(-2) + 3 = 1$

Using synthetic division:

$$
\begin{array}{r|rrrr}
-2 & 2 & 0 & -7 & 3 \\
   &   & -4 & 8 & -2 \\
\hline
   & 2 & -4 & 1 & 1 \\
\end{array}
$$

Verify using long division:

$$
\begin{array}{r}
2x^2 - 4x + 1 \\
x + 2 \overline{)\,2x^3 + 0x^2 - 7x + 3\,} \\
\underline{2x^3 + 4x^2} \\
-4x^2 - 7x \\
\underline{-4x^2 - 8x} \\
x + 3 \\
\underline{x + 2} \\
1
\end{array}
$$

(c) Using the Remainder Theorem:

$$f\left(\frac{1}{2}\right) = 2\left(\frac{1}{2}\right)^3 - 7\left(\frac{1}{2}\right) + 3 = -\frac{1}{4}$$

Using synthetic division:

$$
\begin{array}{r|rrrr}
\frac{1}{2} & 2 & 0 & -7 & 3 \\
  &   & 1 & \frac{1}{2} & -\frac{13}{4} \\
\hline
  & 2 & 1 & -\frac{13}{2} & -\frac{1}{4} \\
\end{array}
$$

Verify using long division:

$$
\begin{array}{r}
2x^2 + x - \frac{13}{2} \\
x - \frac{1}{2} \overline{)\,2x^3 + 0x^2 - 7x + 3\,} \\
\underline{2x^3 - x^2} \\
x^2 - 7x \\
\underline{x^2 - \frac{1}{2}x} \\
-\frac{13}{2}x + 3 \\
\underline{-\frac{13}{2}x + \frac{13}{4}} \\
-\frac{1}{4}
\end{array}
$$

(d) Using the Remainder Theorem:

$f(2) = 2(2)^3 - 7(2) + 3 = 5$

Using synthetic division:

$$
\begin{array}{r|rrrr}
2 & 2 & 0 & -7 & 3 \\
  &   & 4 & 8 & 2 \\
\hline
  & 2 & 4 & 1 & 5 \\
\end{array}
$$

Verify using long division:

$$
\begin{array}{r}
2x^2 + 4x + 1 \\
x - 2 \overline{)\,2x^3 + 0x^2 - 7x + 3\,} \\
\underline{2x^3 - 4x^2} \\
4x^2 - 7x \\
\underline{4x^2 - 8x} \\
x + 3 \\
\underline{x - 2} \\
5
\end{array}
$$

57. $h(x) = x^3 - 5x^2 - 7x + 4$

(a) Using the Remainder Theorem:
$$h(3) = (3)^3 - 5(3)^2 - 7(3) + 4 = -35$$
Using synthetic division:

$$
\begin{array}{r|rrrr}
3 & 1 & -5 & -7 & 4 \\
  &   & 3 & -6 & -39 \\
\hline
  & 1 & -2 & -13 & -35
\end{array}
$$

Verify using long division:

$$
\require{enclose}
\begin{array}{r}
x^2 - 2x - 13 \\
x - 3 \enclose{longdiv}{x^3 - 5x^2 - 7x + 4} \\
\underline{x^3 - 3x^2} \\
2x^2 \quad 7x \\
\underline{-2x^2 + 6x} \\
-13x + 4 \\
\underline{-13x + 39} \\
-35
\end{array}
$$

(b) Using the Remainder Theorem:
$$h(2) = (2)^3 - 5(2)^2 - 7(2) + 4 = -22$$
Using synthetic division:

$$
\begin{array}{r|rrrr}
2 & 1 & -5 & -7 & 4 \\
  &   & 2 & -6 & -26 \\
\hline
  & 1 & -3 & -13 & -22
\end{array}
$$

Verify using long division:

$$
\begin{array}{r}
x^2 - 3x - 13 \\
x - 2 \enclose{longdiv}{x^3 - 5x^2 - 7x + 4} \\
\underline{x^3 - 2x^2} \\
-3x^2 - 7x \\
\underline{-3x^2 + 6x} \\
-13x + 4 \\
\underline{-13x + 26} \\
-22
\end{array}
$$

(c) Using the Remainder Theorem:
$$h(-2) = (-2)^3 - 5(-2)^2 - 7(-2) + 4 = -10$$
Using synthetic division:

$$
\begin{array}{r|rrrr}
-2 & 1 & -5 & -7 & 4 \\
   &   & -2 & 14 & -14 \\
\hline
   & 1 & -7 & 7 & -10
\end{array}
$$

Verify using long division:

$$
\begin{array}{r}
x^2 - 7x + 7 \\
x + 2 \enclose{longdiv}{x^3 - 5x^2 - 7x + 4} \\
\underline{x^3 + 2x^2} \\
-7x^2 - 7x \\
\underline{-7x^2 - 14x} \\
7x + 4 \\
\underline{7x + 14} \\
-10
\end{array}
$$

(d) Using the Remainder Theorem:
$$h(-5) = (-5)^3 - 5(-5)^2 - 7(-5) + 4 = -211$$
Using synthetic division:

$$
\begin{array}{r|rrrr}
-5 & 1 & -5 & -7 & 4 \\
   &   & -5 & 50 & -215 \\
\hline
   & 1 & -10 & 43 & -211
\end{array}
$$

Verify using long division:

$$
\begin{array}{r}
x^2 - 10x + 43 \\
x + 5 \enclose{longdiv}{x^3 - 5x^2 - 7x + 4} \\
\underline{x^3 + 5x^2} \\
-10x^2 - 7x \\
\underline{-10x^2 - 50x} \\
43x + 4 \\
\underline{43x + 215} \\
-211
\end{array}
$$

59.

$$
\begin{array}{r|rrrr}
2 & 1 & 0 & -7 & 6 \\
  &   & 2 & 4 & -6 \\
\hline
  & 1 & 2 & -3 & 0
\end{array}
$$

$$
\begin{aligned}
x^3 - 7x + 6 &= (x - 2)(x^2 + 2x - 3) \\
&= (x - 2)(x + 3)(x - 1)
\end{aligned}
$$

Zeros: $2, -3, 1$

61.

$$
\begin{array}{r|rrrr}
\frac{1}{2} & 2 & -15 & 27 & -10 \\
            &   & 1 & -7 & 10 \\
\hline
            & 2 & -14 & 20 & 0
\end{array}
$$

$$
\begin{aligned}
2x^3 - 15x^2 + 27x - 10 &= \left(x - \tfrac{1}{2}\right)(2x^2 - 14x + 20) \\
&= (2x - 1)(x - 2)(x - 5)
\end{aligned}
$$

Zeros: $\frac{1}{2}, 2, 5$

63.

$$
\begin{array}{r|rrrr}
\sqrt{3} & 1 & 2 & -3 & -6 \\
         &   & \sqrt{3} & 3 + 2\sqrt{3} & 6 \\
\hline
         & 1 & 2 + \sqrt{3} & 2\sqrt{3} & 0
\end{array}
$$

$$
\begin{array}{r|rrr}
-\sqrt{3} & 1 & 2 + \sqrt{3} & 2\sqrt{3} \\
          &   & -\sqrt{3} & -2\sqrt{3} \\
\hline
          & 1 & 2 & 0
\end{array}
$$

$$x^3 + 2x^2 - 3x - 6 = (x - \sqrt{3})(x + \sqrt{3})(x + 2)$$

Zeros: $-\sqrt{3}, \sqrt{3}, -2$

65.

$$1 + \sqrt{3} \begin{array}{|ccccc} 1 & -3 & 0 & 2 \\ & 1 + \sqrt{3} & 1 - \sqrt{3} & -2 \\ \hline 1 & -2 + \sqrt{3} & 1 - \sqrt{3} & 0 \end{array}$$

$$1 - \sqrt{3} \begin{array}{|ccc} 1 & -2 + \sqrt{3} & 1 - \sqrt{3} \\ & 1 - \sqrt{3} & -1 + \sqrt{3} \\ \hline 1 & -1 & 0 \end{array}$$

$x^3 - 3x^2 + 2 = \left[x - \left(1 + \sqrt{3}\right) \right]\left[x - \left(1 - \sqrt{3}\right) \right](x - 1)$

$\qquad = (x - 1)\left(x - 1 - \sqrt{3}\right)\left(x - 1 + \sqrt{3}\right)$

Zeros: $1, 1 - \sqrt{3}, 1 + \sqrt{3}$

67. $f(x) = 2x^3 + x^2 - 5x + 2$; Factors: $(x + 2), (x - 1)$

(a)
$$-2 \begin{array}{|cccc} 2 & 1 & -5 & 2 \\ & -4 & 6 & -2 \\ \hline 2 & -3 & 1 & 0 \end{array}$$

$$1 \begin{array}{|ccc} 2 & -3 & 1 \\ & 2 & -1 \\ \hline 2 & -1 & 0 \end{array}$$

Both are factors of $f(x)$ because the remainders
are zero.

(b) The remaining factor of $f(x)$ is $(2x - 1)$.

(c) $f(x) = (2x - 1)(x + 2)(x - 1)$

(d) Zeros: $\frac{1}{2}, -2, 1$

(e)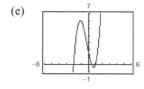

69. $f(x) = x^4 - 4x^3 - 15x^2 + 58x - 40$;

Factors: $(x - 5), (x + 4)$

(a)
$$5 \begin{array}{|ccccc} 1 & -4 & -15 & 58 & -40 \\ & 5 & 5 & -50 & 40 \\ \hline 1 & 1 & -10 & 8 & 0 \end{array}$$

$$-4 \begin{array}{|cccc} 1 & 1 & -10 & 8 \\ & -4 & 12 & -8 \\ \hline 1 & -3 & 2 & 0 \end{array}$$

Both are factors of $f(x)$ because the remainders
are zero.

(b) $x^2 - 3x + 2 = (x - 1)(x - 2)$

The remaining factors are $(x - 1)$ and $(x - 2)$.

(c) $f(x) = (x - 1)(x - 2)(x - 5)(x + 4)$

(d) Zeros: $1, 2, 5, -4$

(e)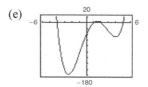

71. $f(x) = 6x^3 + 41x^2 - 9x - 14$;

Factors: $(2x + 1), (3x - 2)$

(a)
$$-\frac{1}{2} \begin{array}{|cccc} 6 & 41 & -9 & -14 \\ & -3 & -19 & 14 \\ \hline 6 & 38 & -28 & 0 \end{array}$$

$$\frac{2}{3} \begin{array}{|ccc} 6 & 38 & -28 \\ & 4 & 28 \\ \hline 6 & 42 & 0 \end{array}$$

Both are factors of $f(x)$ because the remainders
are zero.

(b) $6x + 42 = 6(x + 7)$

This shows that $\dfrac{f(x)}{\left(x + \dfrac{1}{2}\right)\left(x - \dfrac{2}{3}\right)} = 6(x + 7)$,

so $\dfrac{f(x)}{(2x + 1)(3x - 2)} = x + 7$.

The remaining factor is $(x + 7)$.

(c) $f(x) = (x + 7)(2x + 1)(3x - 2)$

(d) Zeros: $-7, -\dfrac{1}{2}, \dfrac{2}{3}$

(e)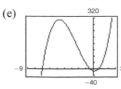

73. $f(x) = 2x^3 - x^2 - 10x + 5;$

Factors: $(2x - 1), (x + \sqrt{5})$

(a)
$$\frac{1}{2} \begin{array}{|rrrr} 2 & -1 & -10 & 5 \\ & 1 & 0 & -5 \\ \hline 2 & 0 & -10 & 0 \end{array}$$

$$-\sqrt{5} \begin{array}{|rrr} 2 & 0 & -10 \\ & -2\sqrt{5} & 10 \\ \hline 2 & -2\sqrt{5} & 0 \end{array}$$

Both are factors of $f(x)$ because the remainders are zero.

(b) $2x - 2\sqrt{5} = 2(x - \sqrt{5})$

This shows that $\dfrac{f(x)}{\left(x - \dfrac{1}{2}\right)(x + \sqrt{5})} = 2(x - \sqrt{5})$,

so $\dfrac{f(x)}{(2x - 1)(x + \sqrt{5})} = x - \sqrt{5}.$

The remaining factor is $(x - \sqrt{5})$.

(c) $f(x) = (x + \sqrt{5})(x - \sqrt{5})(2x - 1)$

(d) Zeros: $-\sqrt{5}, \sqrt{5}, \dfrac{1}{2}$

(e)
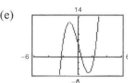

75. $f(x) = x^3 - 2x^2 - 5x + 10$

(a) The zeros of f are $x = 2$ and $x \approx \pm 2.236.$

(b) An exact zero is $x = 2.$

(c)
$$2 \begin{array}{|rrrr} 1 & -2 & -5 & 10 \\ & 2 & 0 & -10 \\ \hline 1 & 0 & -5 & 0 \end{array}$$

$f(x) = (x - 2)(x^2 - 5)$

$\quad\quad = (x - 2)(x - \sqrt{5})(x + \sqrt{5})$

77. $h(t) = t^3 - 2t^2 - 7t + 2$

(a) The zeros of h are $t = -2, t \approx 3.732, t \approx 0.268.$

(b) An exact zero is $t = -2.$

(c)
$$-2 \begin{array}{|rrrr} 1 & -2 & -7 & 2 \\ & -2 & 8 & -2 \\ \hline 1 & -4 & 1 & 0 \end{array}$$

$h(t) = (t + 2)(t^2 - 4t + 1)$

By the Quadratic Formula, the zeros of $t^2 - 4t + 1$ are $2 \pm \sqrt{3}$. Thus,

$h(t) = (t + 2)\left[t - \left(2 + \sqrt{3}\right)\right]\left[t - \left(2 - \sqrt{3}\right)\right].$

79. $h(x) = x^5 - 7x^4 + 10x^3 + 14x^2 - 24x$

(a) The zeros of h are $x = 0, x = 3, x = 4,$
$x \approx 1.414, x \approx -1.414.$

(b) An exact zero is $x = 4.$

(c)
$$4 \begin{array}{|rrrrr} 1 & -7 & 10 & 14 & -24 \\ & 4 & -12 & -8 & 24 \\ \hline 1 & -3 & -2 & 6 & 0 \end{array}$$

$h(x) = (x - 4)(x^4 - 3x^3 - 2x^2 + 6x)$

$\quad\quad = x(x - 4)(x - 3)(x + \sqrt{2})(x - \sqrt{2})$

81. $\dfrac{4x^3 - 8x^2 + x + 3}{2x - 3}$

$$\frac{3}{2} \begin{array}{|rrrr} 4 & 8 & 1 & 3 \\ & 6 & -3 & -3 \\ \hline 4 & -2 & -2 & 0 \end{array}$$

$\dfrac{4x^3 - 8x^2 + x + 3}{x - \dfrac{3}{2}} = 4x^2 - 2x - 2 = 2(2x^2 - x - 1)$

So, $\dfrac{4x^3 - 8x^2 + x + 3}{2x - 3} = 2x^2 - x - 1, x \neq \dfrac{3}{2}.$

83. $\dfrac{x^4 + 6x^3 + 11x^2 + 6x}{x^2 + 3x + 2} = \dfrac{x^4 + 6x^3 + 11x^2 + 6x}{(x + 1)(x + 2)}$

$$
\begin{array}{r|rrrrr}
-1 & 1 & 6 & 11 & 6 & 0 \\
   &   & -1 & -5 & -6 & 0 \\
\hline
   & 1 & 5 & 6 & 0 & 0
\end{array}
$$

$$
\begin{array}{r|rrrr}
-2 & 1 & 5 & 6 & 0 \\
   &   & -2 & -6 & 0 \\
\hline
   & 1 & 3 & 0 & 0
\end{array}
$$

$\dfrac{x^4 + 6x^3 + 11x^2 + 6x}{(x + 1)(x + 2)} = x^2 + 3x,\ x \ne -2, -1$

85. (a)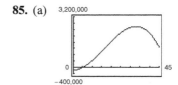

(b) Using the trace and zoom features, when $x = 25$, an advertising expense of about \$250,000 would produce
the same profit of \$2,174,375.

(c) $x = 25$

$$
\begin{array}{r|rrrr}
25 & -152 & 7545 & 0 & -169{,}625 \\
   &   & -3800 & 93{,}625 & 2{,}340{,}625 \\
\hline
   & -152 & 3745 & 93{,}625 & 2{,}171{,}000
\end{array}
$$

So, an advertising expense of \$250,000 yields a profit of \$2,171,000, which is close to \$2,174,375.

Section 2.4   Complex Numbers

1. real

3. pure imaginary

5. principal square

7. $a + bi = -12 + 7i$

    $a = -12$

    $b = 7$

9. $(a - 1) + (b + 3)i = 5 + 8i$

    $a - 1 = 5 \Rightarrow a = 6$

    $b + 3 = 8 \Rightarrow b = 5$

11. $8 + \sqrt{-25} = 8 + 5i$

27. $\left(-2 + \sqrt{-8}\right) + \left(5 - \sqrt{-50}\right) = -2 + 2\sqrt{2}i + 5 - 5\sqrt{2}i$

                                       $= 3 - 3\sqrt{2}i$

87. False. If $(7x + 4)$ is a factor of f, then $-\frac{4}{7}$ is a zero of f.

89. True. The degree of the numerator is greater than the degree of the denominator.

91.

$$
\begin{array}{r}
x^{2n} + 6x^n + 9 \\
x^n + 3 \overline{\smash{\big)}\ x^{3n} + 9x^{2n} + 27x^n + 27} \\
\underline{x^{3n} + 3x^{2n}} \\
6x^{2n} + 27x^n \\
\underline{6x^{2n} + 18x^n} \\
9x^n + 27 \\
\underline{9x^n + 27} \\
0
\end{array}
$$

$\dfrac{x^{3n} + 9x^{2n} + 27x^n + 27}{x^n + 3} = x^{2n} + 6x^n + 9,\ x^n \ne -3$

13. $2 - \sqrt{-27} = 2 - \sqrt{27}i$

                  $= 2 - 3\sqrt{3}i$

15. $\sqrt{-80} = 4\sqrt{5}i$

17. $14 = 14 + 0i = 14$

19. $-10i + i^2 = -10i - 1 = -1 - 10i$

21. $\sqrt{-0.09} = \sqrt{0.09}i$

            $= 0.3i$

23. $(7 + i) + (3 - 4i) = 10 - 3i$

25. $(9 - i) - (8 - i) = 1$

29. $13i - (14 - 7i) = 13i - 14 + 7i$
$$= -14 + 20i$$

31. $-\left(\frac{3}{2} + \frac{5}{2}i\right) + \left(\frac{5}{3} + \frac{11}{3}i\right) = -\frac{3}{2} - \frac{5}{2}i + \frac{5}{3} + \frac{11}{3}i$
$$= -\frac{9}{6} - \frac{15}{6}i + \frac{10}{6} + \frac{22}{6}i$$
$$= \frac{1}{6} + \frac{7}{6}i$$

33. $(1 + i)(3 - 2i) = 3 - 2i + 3i - 2i^2$
$$= 3 + i + 2 = 5 + i$$

35. $12i(1 - 9i) = 12i - 108i^2$
$$= 12i + 108$$
$$= 108 + 12i$$

37. $\left(\sqrt{14} + \sqrt{10}i\right)\left(\sqrt{14} - \sqrt{10}i\right) = 14 - 10i^2$
$$= 14 + 10 = 24$$

39. $(6 + 7i)^2 = 36 + 84i + 49i^2$
$$= 36 + 84i - 49$$
$$= -13 + 84i$$

41. $(2 + 3i)^2 + (2 - 3i)^2 = 4 + 12i + 9i^2 + 4 - 12i + 9i^2$
$$= 4 + 12i - 9 + 4 - 12i - 9$$
$$= -10$$

43. The complex conjugate of $9 + 2i$ is $9 - 2i$.
$$(9 + 2i)(9 - 2i) = 81 - 4i^2$$
$$= 81 + 4$$
$$= 85$$

45. The complex conjugate of $-1 - \sqrt{5}i$ is $-1 + \sqrt{5}i$.
$$\left(-1 - \sqrt{5}i\right)\left(-1 + \sqrt{5}i\right) = 1 - 5i^2$$
$$= 1 + 5 = 6$$

47. The complex conjugate of $\sqrt{-20} = 2\sqrt{5}i$ is $-2\sqrt{5}i$.
$$\left(2\sqrt{5}i\right)\left(-2\sqrt{5}i\right) = 20i^2 = 20$$

49. The complex conjugate of $\sqrt{6}$ is $\sqrt{6}$.
$$\left(\sqrt{6}\right)\left(\sqrt{6}\right) = 6$$

51. $\frac{3}{i} \cdot \frac{-i}{-i} = \frac{-3i}{-i^2} = -3i$

53. $\frac{2}{4 - 5i} = \frac{2}{4 - 5i} \cdot \frac{4 + 5i}{4 + 5i}$
$$= \frac{2(4 + 5i)}{16 + 25} = \frac{8 + 10i}{41} = \frac{8}{41} + \frac{10}{41}i$$

55. $\frac{5 + i}{5 - i} \cdot \frac{(5 + i)}{(5 + i)} = \frac{25 + 10i + i^2}{25 - i^2}$
$$= \frac{24 + 10i}{26} = \frac{12}{13} + \frac{5}{13}i$$

57. $\frac{9 - 4i}{i} \cdot \frac{-i}{-i} = \frac{-9i + 4i^2}{-i^2} = -4 - 9i$

59. $\frac{3i}{(4 - 5i)^2} = \frac{3i}{16 - 40i + 25i^2} = \frac{3i}{-9 - 40i} \cdot \frac{-9 + 40i}{-9 + 40i}$
$$= \frac{-27i + 120i^2}{81 + 1600} = \frac{-120 - 27i}{1681}$$
$$= -\frac{120}{1681} - \frac{27}{1681}i$$

61. $\frac{2}{1 + i} - \frac{3}{1 - i} = \frac{2(1 - i) - 3(1 + i)}{(1 + i)(1 - i)}$
$$= \frac{2 - 2i - 3 - 3i}{1 + 1}$$
$$= \frac{-1 - 5i}{2}$$
$$= -\frac{1}{2} - \frac{5}{2}i$$

63. $\frac{i}{3 - 2i} + \frac{2i}{3 + 8i} = \frac{i(3 + 8i) + 2i(3 - 2i)}{(3 - 2i)(3 + 8i)}$
$$= \frac{3i + 8i^2 + 6i - 4i^2}{9 + 24i - 6i - 16i^2}$$
$$= \frac{4i^2 + 9i}{9 + 18i + 16}$$
$$= \frac{-4 + 9i}{25 + 18i} \cdot \frac{25 - 18i}{25 - 18i}$$
$$= \frac{-100 + 72i + 225i - 162i^2}{625 + 324}$$
$$= \frac{62 + 297i}{949} = \frac{62}{949} + \frac{297}{949}i$$

65. $\sqrt{-6} \cdot \sqrt{-2} = \left(\sqrt{6}i\right)\left(\sqrt{2}i\right) = \sqrt{12}i^2 = \left(2\sqrt{3}\right)(-1)$
$$= -2\sqrt{3}$$

67. $\left(\sqrt{-15}\right)^2 = \left(\sqrt{15}i\right)^2 = 15i^2 = -15$

69. $\left(3 + \sqrt{-5}\right)\left(7 - \sqrt{-10}\right) = \left(3 + \sqrt{5}i\right)\left(7 - \sqrt{10}i\right)$

$$= 21 - 3\sqrt{10}i + 7\sqrt{5}i - \sqrt{50}i^2$$
$$= \left(21 + \sqrt{50}\right) + \left(7\sqrt{5} - 3\sqrt{10}\right)i$$
$$= \left(21 + 5\sqrt{2}\right) + \left(7\sqrt{5} - 3\sqrt{10}\right)i$$

71. $x^2 - 2x + 2 = 0;\ a = 1,\ b = -2,\ c = 2$

$$x = \frac{-(-2) \pm \sqrt{(-2)^2 - 4(1)(2)}}{2(1)}$$
$$= \frac{2 \pm \sqrt{-4}}{2}$$
$$= \frac{2 \pm 2i}{2}$$
$$= 1 \pm i$$

73. $4x^2 + 16x + 17 = 0;\ a = 4,\ b = 16,\ c = 17$

$$x = \frac{-16 \pm \sqrt{(16)^2 - 4(4)(17)}}{2(4)}$$
$$= \frac{-16 \pm \sqrt{-16}}{8}$$
$$= \frac{-16 \pm 4i}{8}$$
$$= -2 \pm \frac{1}{2}i$$

75. $4x^2 + 16x + 15 = 0;\ a = 4,\ b = 16,\ c = 15$

$$x = \frac{-16 \pm \sqrt{(16)^2 - 4(4)(15)}}{2(4)}$$
$$= \frac{-16 \pm \sqrt{16}}{8} = \frac{-16 \pm 4}{8}$$
$$x = -\frac{12}{8} = -\frac{3}{2} \text{ or } x = -\frac{20}{8} = -\frac{5}{2}$$

77. $\frac{3}{2}x^2 - 6x + 9 = 0$ Multiply both sides by 2.

$3x^2 - 12x + 18 = 0;\ a = 3,\ b = -12,\ c = 18$

$$x = \frac{-(-12) \pm \sqrt{(-12)^2 - 4(3)(18)}}{2(3)}$$
$$= \frac{12 \pm \sqrt{-72}}{6}$$
$$= \frac{12 \pm 6\sqrt{2}i}{6} = 2 \pm \sqrt{2}i$$

79. $1.4x^2 - 2x - 10 = 0$ Multiply both sides by 5.

$7x^2 - 10x - 50 = 0;\ a = 7,\ b = -10,\ c = -50$

$$x = \frac{-(-10) \pm \sqrt{(-10)^2 - 4(7)(-50)}}{2(7)}$$
$$= \frac{10 \pm \sqrt{1500}}{14}$$
$$= \frac{10 \pm 10\sqrt{15}}{14}$$
$$= \frac{5}{7} \pm \frac{5\sqrt{15}}{7}$$

81. $-6i^3 + i^2 = -6i^2i + i^2$

$$= -6(-1)i + (-1)$$
$$= 6i - 1$$
$$= -1 + 6i$$

83. $-14i^5 = -14i^2i^2i = -14(-1)(-1)(i) = -14i$

85. $\left(\sqrt{-72}\right)^3 = \left(6\sqrt{2}i\right)^3$

$$= 6^3\left(\sqrt{2}\right)^3 i^3$$
$$= 216\left(2\sqrt{2}\right)i^2i$$
$$= 432\sqrt{2}(-1)i$$
$$= -432\sqrt{2}i$$

87. $\dfrac{1}{i^3} = \dfrac{1}{i^2i} = \dfrac{1}{-i} = \dfrac{1}{-i} \cdot \dfrac{i}{i} = \dfrac{i}{-i^2} = i$

89. $(3i)^4 = 81i^4 = 81i^2i^2 = 81(-1)(-1) = 81$

91. (a) $z_1 = 9 + 16i, z_2 = 20 - 10i$

(b) $\dfrac{1}{z} = \dfrac{1}{z_1} + \dfrac{1}{z_2} = \dfrac{1}{9 + 16i} + \dfrac{1}{20 - 10i} = \dfrac{20 - 10i + 9 + 16i}{(9 + 16i)(20 - 10i)} = \dfrac{29 + 6i}{340 + 230i}$

$z = \left(\dfrac{340 + 230i}{29 + 6i}\right)\left(\dfrac{29 - 6i}{29 - 6i}\right) = \dfrac{11{,}240 + 4630i}{877} = \dfrac{11{,}240}{877} + \dfrac{4630}{877}i$

93. False.

If $b = 0$ then $a + bi = a - bi = a$.

That is, if the complex number is real, the number equals its conjugate.

95. False.

$$i^{44} + i^{150} - i^{74} - i^{109} + i^{61} = \left(i^2\right)^{22} + \left(i^2\right)^{75} - \left(i^2\right)^{37} - \left(i^2\right)^{54}i + \left(i^2\right)^{30}i$$
$$= (-1)^{22} + (-1)^{75} - (-1)^{37} - (-1)^{54}i + (-1)^{30}i$$
$$= 1 - 1 + 1 - i + i = 1$$

97. $i = i$

$i^2 = -1$

$i^3 = -i$

$i^4 = 1$

$i^5 = i^4 i = i$

$i^6 = i^4 i^2 = -1$

$i^7 = i^4 i^3 = -i$

$i^8 = i^4 i^4 = 1$

$i^9 = i^4 i^4 i = i$

$i^{10} = i^4 i^4 i^2 = -1$

$i^{11} = i^4 i^4 i^3 = -i$

$i^{12} = i^4 i^4 i^4 = 1$

The pattern $i, -1, -i, 1$ repeats. Divide the exponent by 4.

If the remainder is 1, the result is i .

If the remainder is 2, the result is -1 .

If the remainder is 3, the result is $-i$.

If the remainder is 0, the result is 1.

99. $\sqrt{-6}\sqrt{-6} = \sqrt{6}i\sqrt{6}i = 6i^2 = -6$

101. $\left(a_1 + b_1 i\right) + \left(a_2 + b_2 i\right) = \left(a_1 + a_2\right) + \left(b_1 + b_2\right)i$

The complex conjugate of this sum is $\left(a_1 + a_2\right) - \left(b_1 + b_2\right)i$.

The sum of the complex conjugates is $\left(a_1 - b_1 i\right) + \left(a_2 - b_2 i\right) = \left(a_1 + a_2\right) - \left(b_1 + b_2\right)i$.

So, the complex conjugate of the sum of two complex numbers is the sum of their complex conjugates.

Section 2.5   Zeros of Polynomial Functions

1. Fundamental Theorem of Algebra

5. linear; quadratic; quadratic

3. Rational Zero

7. Descartes's Rule of Signs

9. Since f is a 1st degree polynomial function, there is one zero.

11. Since f is a 3rd degree polynomial function, there are three zeros.

13. Since f is a 2nd degree polynomial function, there are two zeros.

15. $f(x) = x^3 + 2x^2 - x - 2$

    Possible rational zeros: $\pm 1, \pm 2$

    Zeros shown on graph: $-2, -1, 1, 2$

17. $f(x) = 2x^4 - 17x^3 + 35x^2 + 9x - 45$

    Possible rational zeros: $\pm 1, \pm 3, \pm 5, \pm 9, \pm 15, \pm 45,$
    $$\pm\tfrac{1}{2}, \pm\tfrac{3}{2}, \pm\tfrac{5}{2}, \pm\tfrac{9}{2}, \pm\tfrac{15}{2}, \pm\tfrac{45}{2}$$

    Zeros shown on graph: $-1, \tfrac{3}{2}, 3, 5$

19. $f(x) = x^3 - 7x - 6$

    Possible rational zeros: $\pm 1, \pm 2, \pm 3, \pm 6$

    $$
    \begin{array}{r|rrrr}
    3 & 1 & 0 & -7 & -6 \\
      &   & 3 & 9 & 6 \\
    \hline
      & 1 & 3 & 2 & 0
    \end{array}
    $$

    $f(x) = (x - 3)(x^2 + 3x + 2)$

    $ = (x - 3)(x + 2)(x + 1)$

    So, the rational zeros are $-2, -1,$ and 3.

21. $g(x) = x^3 - 4x^2 - x + 4$

    $ = x^2(x - 4) - 1(x - 4)$

    $ = (x - 4)(x^2 - 1)$

    $ = (x - 4)(x - 1)(x + 1)$

    So, the rational zeros are $4, 1,$ and -1.

23. $h(t) = t^3 + 8t^2 + 13t + 6$

    Possible rational zeros: $\pm 1, \pm 2, \pm 3, \pm 6$

    $$
    \begin{array}{r|rrrr}
    -6 & 1 & 8 & 13 & 6 \\
       &   & -6 & -12 & -6 \\
    \hline
       & 1 & 2 & 1 & 0
    \end{array}
    $$

    $t^3 + 8t^2 + 13t + 6 = (t + 6)(t^2 + 2t + 1)$

    $ = (t + 6)(t + 1)(t + 1)$

    So, the rational zeros are -1 and -6.

25. $C(x) = 2x^3 + 3x^2 - 1$

    Possible rational zeros: $\pm 1, \pm \tfrac{1}{2}$

    $$
    \begin{array}{r|rrrr}
    -1 & 2 & 3 & 0 & -1 \\
       &   & -2 & -1 & 1 \\
    \hline
       & 2 & 1 & -1 & 0
    \end{array}
    $$

    $2x^3 + 3x^2 - 1 = (x + 1)(2x^2 + x - 1)$

    $ = (x + 1)(x + 1)(2x - 1)$

    $ = (x + 1)^2(2x - 1)$

    So, the rational zeros are -1 and $\tfrac{1}{2}$.

27. $f(x) = 9x^4 - 9x^3 - 58x^2 + 4x + 24$

    Possible rational zeros:
    $\pm 1, \pm 2, \pm 3, \pm 4, \pm 6, \pm 8, \pm 12, \pm 24,$
    $$\pm\tfrac{1}{3}, \pm\tfrac{2}{3}, \pm\tfrac{4}{3}, \pm\tfrac{8}{3}, \pm\tfrac{1}{9}, \pm\tfrac{2}{9}, \pm\tfrac{4}{9}, \pm\tfrac{8}{9}$$

    $$
    \begin{array}{r|rrrrr}
    -2 & 9 & -9 & -58 & 4 & 24 \\
       &   & -18 & 54 & 8 & -24 \\
    \hline
       & 9 & -27 & -4 & 12 & 0
    \end{array}
    $$

    $$
    \begin{array}{r|rrrr}
    3 & 9 & -27 & -4 & 12 \\
      &   & 27 & 0 & -12 \\
    \hline
      & 9 & 0 & -4 & 0
    \end{array}
    $$

    $f(x) = (x + 2)(x - 3)(9x^2 - 4)$

    $ = (x + 2)(x - 3)(3x - 2)(3x + 2)$

    So, the rational zeros are $-2, 3, \tfrac{2}{3},$ and $-\tfrac{2}{3}$.

29. $z^4 + z^3 + z^2 + 3z - 6 = 0$

    Possible rational zeros: $\pm 1, \pm 2, \pm 3, \pm 6$

    $$
    \begin{array}{r|rrrrr}
    1 & 1 & 1 & 1 & 3 & -6 \\
      &   & 1 & 2 & 3 & 6 \\
    \hline
      & 1 & 2 & 3 & 6 & 0
    \end{array}
    $$

    $(z - 1)(z^3 + 2z^2 + 3z + 6) = 0$

    $(z - 1)(z^2 + 3)(z + 2) = 0$

    So, the real zeros are -2 and 1.

31. $2y^4 + 3y^3 - 16y^2 + 15y - 4 = 0$

Possible rational zeros: $\pm\frac{1}{2}, \pm1, \pm2, \pm4$

$$
\begin{array}{r|rrrrr}
1 & 2 & 3 & -16 & 15 & -4 \\
  &   & 2 & 5 & -11 & 4 \\
\hline
  & 2 & 5 & -11 & 4 & 0
\end{array}
$$

$$
\begin{array}{r|rrrr}
1 & 2 & 5 & -11 & 4 \\
  &   & 2 & 7 & -4 \\
\hline
  & 2 & 7 & -4 & 0
\end{array}
$$

$(y - 1)(y - 1)(2y^2 + 7y - 4) = 0$

$(y - 1)(y - 1)(2y - 1)(y + 4) = 0$

So, the real zeros are $-4, \frac{1}{2}$ and 1.

33. $f(x) = x^3 + x^2 - 4x - 4$

(a) Possible rational zeros: $\pm1, \pm2, \pm4$

(b)
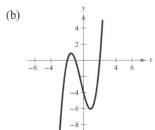

(c) Real zeros: $-2, -1, 2$

35. $f(x) = -4x^3 + 15x^2 - 8x - 3$

(a) Possible rational zeros: $\pm1, \pm3, \pm\frac{1}{2}, \pm\frac{3}{2}, \pm\frac{1}{4}, \pm\frac{3}{4}$

(b)
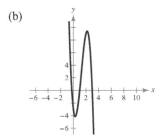

(c) Real zeros: $-\frac{1}{4}, 1, 3$

37. $f(x) = -2x^4 + 13x^3 - 21x^2 + 2x + 8$

(a) Possible rational zeros: $\pm1, \pm2, \pm4, \pm8, \pm\frac{1}{2}$

(b)
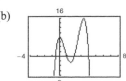

(c) Real zeros: $-\frac{1}{2}, 1, 2, 4$

39. $f(x) = 32x^3 - 52x^2 + 17x + 3$

(a) Possible rational zeros: $\pm1, \pm3, \pm\frac{1}{2}, \pm\frac{3}{2}, \pm\frac{1}{4}, \pm\frac{3}{4},$

$\pm\frac{1}{8}, \pm\frac{3}{8}, \pm\frac{1}{16}, \pm\frac{3}{16}, \pm\frac{1}{32}, \pm\frac{3}{32}$

(b)
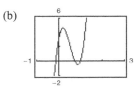

(c) Real zeros: $-\frac{1}{8}, \frac{3}{4}, 1$

41. $f(x) = x^4 - 3x^2 + 2$

(a) $x = \pm1$, about ±1.414

(b) An exact zero is $x = 1$.

$$
\begin{array}{r|rrrrr}
1 & 1 & 0 & -3 & 0 & 2 \\
  &   & 1 & 1 & -2 & -2 \\
\hline
  & 1 & 1 & -2 & -2 & 0
\end{array}
$$

(c)
$$
\begin{array}{r|rrrr}
-1 & 1 & 1 & -2 & -2 \\
   &   & -1 & 0 & 2 \\
\hline
   & 1 & 0 & -2 & 0
\end{array}
$$

$f(x) = (x - 1)(x + 1)(x^2 - 2)$

$\qquad = (x - 1)(x + 1)(x - \sqrt{2})(x + \sqrt{2})$

43. $h(x) = x^5 - 7x^4 + 10x^3 + 14x^2 - 24x$

(a) $h(x) = x(x^4 - 7x^3 + 10x^2 + 14x - 24)$

$x = 0, 3, 4$, about ±1.414

(b) An exact zero is $x = 3$.

$$
\begin{array}{r|rrrrr}
3 & 1 & -7 & 10 & 14 & -24 \\
  &   & 3 & -12 & -6 & 24 \\
\hline
  & 1 & -4 & -2 & 8 & 0
\end{array}
$$

(c)
$$
\begin{array}{r|rrrr}
4 & 1 & -4 & -2 & 8 \\
  &   & 4 & 0 & -8 \\
\hline
  & 1 & 0 & -2 & 0
\end{array}
$$

$h(x) = x(x - 3)(x - 4)(x^2 - 2)$

$\qquad = x(x - 3)(x - 4)(x - \sqrt{2})(x + \sqrt{2})$

45. $f(x) = (x - 1)(x - 5i)(x + 5i)$

$\quad\quad = (x - 1)(x^2 + 25)$

$\quad\quad = x^3 - x^2 + 25x - 25$

Note: $f(x) = a(x^3 - x^2 + 25x - 25)$, where a is any nonzero real number, has the zeros 1 and $\pm 5i$.

47. If $5 + i$ is a zero, so is its conjugate, $5 - i$.

$\quad f(x) = (x - 2)(x - (5 + i))(x - (5 - i))$

$\quad\quad = (x - 2)(x^2 - 10x + 26)$

$\quad\quad = x^3 - 12x^2 + 46x - 52$

Note: $f(x) = a(x^3 - 12x^2 + 46x - 52)$, where a is any nonzero real number, has the zeros 2 and $5 \pm i$.

49. If $3 + \sqrt{2}i$ is a zero, so is its conjugate, $3 - \sqrt{2}i$.

$\quad f(x) = (3x - 2)(x + 1)\left[x - \left(3 + \sqrt{2}i\right)\right]\left[x - \left(3 - \sqrt{2}i\right)\right]$

$\quad\quad = (3x - 2)(x + 1)\left[(x - 3) - \sqrt{2}i\right]\left[(x - 3) + \sqrt{2}i\right]$

$\quad\quad = (3x^2 + x - 2)\left[(x - 3)^2 - \left(\sqrt{2}i\right)^2\right]$

$\quad\quad = (3x^2 + x - 2)(x^2 - 6x + 9 + 2)$

$\quad\quad = (3x^2 + x - 2)(x^2 - 6x + 11)$

$\quad\quad = 3x^4 - 17x^3 + 25x^2 + 23x - 22$

Note: $f(x) = a(3x^4 - 17x^3 + 25x^2 + 23x - 22)$, where a is any nonzero real number, has the zeros $\frac{2}{3}, -1$, and $3 \pm \sqrt{2}i$.

51. $f(x) = x^4 + 6x^2 - 27$

(a) $f(x) = (x^2 + 9)(x^2 - 3)$

(b) $f(x) = (x^2 + 9)(x + \sqrt{3})(x - \sqrt{3})$

(c) $f(x) = (x + 3i)(x - 3i)(x + \sqrt{3})(x - \sqrt{3})$

53. $f(x) = x^4 - 4x^3 + 5x^2 - 2x - 6$

$$
\begin{array}{r}
x^2 - 2x + 3 \\
x^2 - 2x - 2 \overline{\smash{)}\, x^4 - 4x^3 + 5x^2 - 2x - 6} \\
\underline{x^4 - 2x^3 - 2x^2} \\
-2x^3 + 7x^2 - 2x \\
\underline{-2x^3 + 4x^2 + 4x} \\
3x^2 - 6x - 6 \\
\underline{3x^2 - 6x - 6} \\
0
\end{array}
$$

(a) $f(x) = (x^2 - 2x - 2)(x^2 - 2x + 3)$

(b) $f(x) = (x - 1 + \sqrt{3})(x - 1 - \sqrt{3})(x^2 - 2x + 3)$

(c) $f(x) = (x - 1 + \sqrt{3})(x - 1 - \sqrt{3})(x - 1 + \sqrt{2}i)(x - 1 - \sqrt{2}i)$

Note: Use the Quadratic Formula for (b) and (c).

55. $f(x) = x^3 - x^2 + 4x - 4$

Because $2i$ is a zero, so is $-2i$.

$$
\begin{array}{r|rrrr}
2i & 1 & -1 & 4 & -4 \\
   &   & 2i & -4-2i & 4 \\
\hline
   & 1 & 2i-1 & -2i & 0
\end{array}
$$

$$
\begin{array}{r|rrr}
-2i & 1 & 2i-1 & -2i \\
    &   & -2i & 2i \\
\hline
    & 1 & -1 & 0
\end{array}
$$

$f(x) = (x - 2i)(x + 2i)(x - 1)$

The zeros of $f(x)$ are $x = 1, \pm 2i$.

Alternate Solution:

Because $x = \pm 2i$ are zeros of $f(x)$,

$(x + 2i)(x - 2i) = x^2 + 4$ is a factor of $f(x)$.

By long division, you have:

$$
\begin{array}{r}
x - 1 \\
x^2 + 0x + 4 \overline{)\,x^3 - x^2 + 4x - 4} \\
\underline{x^3 + 0x^2 + 4x} \\
-x^2 + 0x - 4 \\
\underline{-x^2 + 0x - 4} \\
0
\end{array}
$$

$f(x) = (x^2 + 4)(x - 1)$

The zeros of $f(x)$ are $x = 1, \pm 2i$.

57. $f(x) = 2x^4 - x^3 + 49x^2 - 25x - 25$

Because $5i$ is a zero, so is $-5i$.

$$
\begin{array}{r|rrrrr}
5i & 2 & -1 & 49 & 25 & -25 \\
   &   & 10i & -5i-50 & -5i+25 & 25 \\
\hline
   & 2 & -1+10i & -1-5i & -5i & 0
\end{array}
$$

$$
\begin{array}{r|rrrr}
-5i & 2 & -1+10i & -1-5i & -5i \\
    &   & -10i & 5i & 5i \\
\hline
    & 2 & -1 & -1 & 0
\end{array}
$$

$f(x) = (x - 5i)(x + 5i)(2x^2 - x - 1)$

$ = (x - 5i)(x + 5i)(2x + 1)(x - 1)$

The zeros of $f(x)$ are $x = \pm 5i, -\frac{1}{2}, 1$.

Alternate Solution:

Because $x = \pm 5i$ are zeros of $f(x)$, $(x - 5i)(x + 5i) = x^2 + 25$ is a factor of $f(x)$.

By long division, you have:

$$
\begin{array}{r}
2x^2 - x - 1 \\
x^2 + 0x + 25 \overline{)\,2x^4 - x^3 + 49x^2 - 25x - 25} \\
\underline{2x^4 + 0x^3 + 50x^2} \\
-x^3 - x^2 - 25x \\
\underline{-x^3 + 0x^2 + 25x} \\
-x^2 + 0x - 25 \\
\underline{-x^2 + 0x - 25} \\
0
\end{array}
$$

$f(x) = (x^2 + 25)(2x^2 - x - 1)$

The zeros of $f(x)$ are $x = \pm 5i, -\frac{1}{2}, 1$.

59. $g(x) = 4x^3 + 23x^2 + 34x - 10$

Because $-3 + i$ is a zero, so is $-3 - i$.

$$
\begin{array}{r|rrrr}
-3+i & 4 & 23 & 34 & -10 \\
 & & -12+4i & -37-i & 10 \\
\hline
 & 4 & 11+4i & -3-i & 0
\end{array}
$$

$$
\begin{array}{r|rrr}
-3-i & 4 & 11+4i & -3-i \\
 & & -12-4i & 3+i \\
\hline
 & 4 & -1 & 0
\end{array}
$$

The zero of $4x - 1$ is $x = \frac{1}{4}$. The zeros of

$g(x)$ are $x = -3 \pm i, \frac{1}{4}$.

Alternate Solution

Because $-3 \pm i$ are zeros of $g(x)$,

$$\left[x - (-3 + i)\right]\left[x - (-3 - i)\right] = \left[(x + 3) - i\right]\left[(x + 3) + i\right]$$
$$= (x + 3)^2 - i^2$$
$$= x^2 + 6x + 10$$

is a factor of $g(x)$. By long division, you have:

$$
\begin{array}{r}
4x - 1 \\
x^2 + 6x + 10 \overline{\smash{\big)}\ 4x^3 + 23x^2 + 34x - 10} \\
\underline{4x^3 + 24x^2 + 40x} \\
-x^2 - 6x - 10 \\
\underline{-x^2 - 6x - 10} \\
0
\end{array}
$$

$$g(x) = (x^2 + 6x + 10)(4x - 1)$$

The zeros of $g(x)$ are $x = -3 \pm i, \frac{1}{4}$.

61. $f(x) = x^4 + 3x^3 - 5x^2 - 21x + 22$

Because $-3 + \sqrt{2}i$ is a zero, so is $-3 - \sqrt{2}i$, and

$$\left[x - \left(-3 + \sqrt{2}i\right)\right]\left[x - \left(-3 - \sqrt{2}i\right)\right] = \left[(x + 3) - \sqrt{2}i\right]\left[(x + 3) + \sqrt{2}i\right]$$
$$= (x + 3)^2 - \left(\sqrt{2}i\right)^2$$
$$= x^2 + 6x + 11$$

is a factor of $f(x)$. By long division, you have:

$$
\begin{array}{r}
x^2 - 3x + 2 \\
x^2 + 6x + 11 \overline{\smash{\big)}\ x^4 + 3x^3 - 5x^2 - 21x + 22} \\
\underline{x^4 + 6x^3 + 11x^2} \\
-3x^3 - 16x^2 - 21x \\
\underline{-3x^3 - 18x^2 - 33x} \\
2x^2 + 12x + 22 \\
\underline{2x^2 + 12x + 22} \\
0
\end{array}
$$

$$f(x) = (x^2 + 6x + 11)(x^2 - 3x + 2)$$
$$= (x^2 + 6x + 11)(x - 1)(x - 2)$$

The zeros of $f(x)$ are $x = -3 \pm \sqrt{2}i, 1, 2$.

63. $f(x) = x^2 + 36$

$\qquad = (x + 6i)(x - 6i)$

The zeros of $f(x)$ are $x = \pm 6i$.

65. $h(x) = x^2 - 2x + 17$

By the Quadratic Formula, the zeros of $f(x)$ are

$$x = \frac{2 \pm \sqrt{4 - 68}}{2} = \frac{2 \pm \sqrt{-64}}{2} = 1 \pm 4i.$$

$$f(x) = \left(x - (1 + 4i)\right)\left(x - (1 - 4i)\right)$$
$$= (x - 1 - 4i)(x - 1 + 4i)$$

67. $f(x) = x^4 - 16$

$\quad = (x^2 - 4)(x^2 + 4)$

$\quad = (x - 2)(x + 2)(x - 2i)(x + 2i)$

Zeros: $\pm 2, \pm 2i$

69. $f(z) = z^2 - 2z + 2$

By the Quadratic Formula, the zeros of $f(z)$ are

$z = \dfrac{2 \pm \sqrt{4 - 8}}{2} = 1 \pm i.$

$f(z) = \left[z - (1 + i) \right]\left[z - (1 - i) \right]$

$\quad = (z - 1 - i)(z - 1 + i)$

71. $g(x) = x^3 - 3x^2 + x + 5$

Possible rational zeros: $\pm 1, \pm 5$

$$
\begin{array}{r|rrrr}
-1 & 1 & -3 & 1 & 5 \\
   &   & -1 & 4 & -5 \\
\hline
   & 1 & -4 & 5 & 0
\end{array}
$$

By the Quadratic Formula, the zeros of $x^2 - 4x + 5$

are: $x = \dfrac{4 \pm \sqrt{16 - 20}}{2} = 2 \pm i$

Zeros: $-1, 2 \pm i$

$g(x) = (x + 1)(x - 2 - i)(x - 2 + i)$

73. $h(x) = x^3 - x + 6$

Possible rational zeros: $\pm 1, \pm 2, \pm 3, \pm 6$

$$
\begin{array}{r|rrrr}
-2 & 1 & 0 & -1 & 6 \\
   &   & -2 & 4 & -6 \\
\hline
   & 1 & -2 & 3 & 0
\end{array}
$$

By the Quadratic Formula, the zeros of $x^2 - 2x + 3$ are

$x = \dfrac{2 \pm \sqrt{4 - 12}}{2} = 1 \pm \sqrt{2}i.$

Zeros: $-2, 1 \pm \sqrt{2}i$

$h(x) = (x + 2)\left[x - \left(1 + \sqrt{2}i \right) \right]\left[x - \left(1 - \sqrt{2}i \right) \right]$

$\quad = (x + 2)(x - 1 - \sqrt{2}i)(x - 1 + \sqrt{2}i)$

75. $f(x) = 5x^3 - 9x^2 + 28x + 6$

Possible rational zeros:

$\pm 1, \pm 2, \pm 3, \pm 6, \pm \dfrac{1}{5}, \pm \dfrac{2}{5}, \pm \dfrac{3}{5}, \pm \dfrac{6}{5}$

$$
\begin{array}{r|rrrr}
-\frac{1}{5} & 5 & -9 & 28 & 6 \\
   &   & -1 & 2 & -6 \\
\hline
   & 5 & -10 & 30 & 0
\end{array}
$$

By the Quadratic Formula, the zeros of

$5x^2 - 10x + 30 = 5(x^2 - 2x + 6)$ are

$x = \dfrac{2 \pm \sqrt{4 - 24}}{2} = 1 \pm \sqrt{5}i.$

Zeros: $-\dfrac{1}{5}, 1 \pm \sqrt{5}i$

$f(x) = \left[x - \left(-\dfrac{1}{5} \right) \right](5)\left[x - \left(1 + \sqrt{5}i \right) \right]\left[x - \left(1 - \sqrt{5}i \right) \right]$

$\quad = (5x + 1)(x - 1 - \sqrt{5}i)(x - 1 + \sqrt{5}i)$

77. $g(x) = x^4 - 4x^3 + 8x^2 - 16x + 16$

Possible rational zeros: $\pm 1, \pm 2, \pm 4, \pm 8, \pm 16$

$$
\begin{array}{r|rrrrr}
2 & 1 & -4 & 8 & -16 & 16 \\
  &   & 2 & -4 & 8 & -16 \\
\hline
  & 1 & -2 & 4 & -8 & 0
\end{array}
$$

$$
\begin{array}{r|rrrr}
2 & 1 & -2 & 4 & -8 \\
  &   & 2 & 0 & 8 \\
\hline
  & 1 & 0 & 4 & 0
\end{array}
$$

$g(x) = (x - 2)(x - 2)(x^2 + 4)$

$\quad = (x - 2)^2(x + 2i)(x - 2i)$

Zeros: $2, \pm 2i$

79. $f(x) = x^4 + 10x^2 + 9$

$\quad = (x^2 + 1)(x^2 + 9)$

$\quad = (x + i)(x - i)(x + 3i)(x - 3i)$

Zeros: $\pm i, \pm 3i$

81. $f(x) = x^3 + 24x^2 + 214x + 740$

Possible rational zeros: $\pm 1, \pm 2, \pm 4, \pm 5, \pm 10, \pm 20, \pm 37,$
$$\pm 74, \pm 148, \pm 185, \pm 370, \pm 740$$

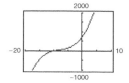

Based on the graph, try $x = -10$.

$$
\begin{array}{r|rrrr}
-10 & 1 & 24 & 214 & 740 \\
    &   & -10 & -140 & -740 \\
\hline
    & 1 & 14 & 74 & 0 \\
\end{array}
$$

By the Quadratic Formula, the zeros of $x^2 + 14x + 74$

are $x = \dfrac{-14 \pm \sqrt{196 - 296}}{2} = -7 \pm 5i$.

The zeros of $f(x)$ are $x = -10$ and $x = -7 \pm 5i$.

83. $f(x) = 16x^3 - 20x^2 - 4x + 15$

Possible rational zeros:

$\pm 1, \pm 3, \pm 5, \pm 15, \pm \dfrac{1}{2}, \pm \dfrac{3}{2}, \pm \dfrac{5}{2}, \pm \dfrac{15}{2}, \pm \dfrac{1}{4}, \pm \dfrac{3}{4},$

$\pm \dfrac{5}{4}, \pm \dfrac{15}{4}, \pm \dfrac{1}{8}, \pm \dfrac{3}{8}, \pm \dfrac{5}{8}, \pm \dfrac{15}{8}, \pm \dfrac{1}{16}, \pm \dfrac{3}{16}, \pm \dfrac{5}{16}, \pm \dfrac{15}{16}$

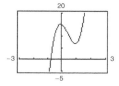

Based on the graph, try $x = -\dfrac{3}{4}$.

$$
\begin{array}{r|rrrr}
-\frac{3}{4} & 16 & -20 & -4 & 15 \\
             &   & -12 & 24 & -15 \\
\hline
             & 16 & -32 & 20 & 0 \\
\end{array}
$$

By the Quadratic Formula, the zeros of
$16x^2 - 32x + 20 = 4(4x^2 - 8x + 5)$ are

$x = \dfrac{8 \pm \sqrt{64 - 80}}{8} = 1 \pm \dfrac{1}{2}i$.

The zeros of $f(x)$ are $x = -\dfrac{3}{4}$ and $x = 1 \pm \dfrac{1}{2}i$.

85. $f(x) = 2x^4 + 5x^3 + 4x^2 + 5x + 2$

Possible rational zeros: $\pm 1, \pm 2, \pm \dfrac{1}{2}$

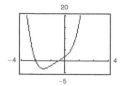

Based on the graph, try $x = -2$ and $x = -\dfrac{1}{2}$.

$$
\begin{array}{r|rrrrr}
-2 & 2 & 5 & 4 & 5 & 2 \\
   &   & -4 & -2 & -4 & -2 \\
\hline
   & 2 & 1 & 2 & 1 & 0 \\
\end{array}
$$

$$
\begin{array}{r|rrrr}
-\frac{1}{2} & 2 & 1 & 2 & 1 \\
             &   & -1 & 0 & -1 \\
\hline
             & 2 & 0 & 2 & 0 \\
\end{array}
$$

The zeros of $2x^2 + 2 = 2(x^2 + 1)$ are $x = \pm i$.

The zeros of $f(x)$ are $x = -2$, $x = -\dfrac{1}{2}$, and $x = \pm i$.

87. $g(x) = 2x^3 - 3x^2 - 3$

Sign variations: 1, positive zeros: 1

$g(-x) = -2x^3 - 3x^2 - 3$

Sign variations: 0, negative zeros: 0

89. $h(x) = 2x^3 + 3x^2 + 1$

Sign variations: 0, positive zeros: 0

$h(-x) = -2x^3 + 3x^2 + 1$

Sign variations: 1, negative zeros: 1

91. $g(x) = 5x^5 - 10x = 5x(x^4 - 2)$

Let $g(x) = x^4 - 2$.

Sign variations: 1, positive zeros: 1

$g(-x) = x^4 - 2$

Sign variations: 1, negative zeros: 1

93. $f(x) = -5x^3 + x^2 - x + 5$

Sign variations: 3, positive zeros: 3 or 1

$f(-x) = 5x^3 + x^2 + x + 5$

Sign variations: 0, negative zeros: 0

95. $f(x) = x^3 + 3x^2 - 2x + 1$

(a)

$$\begin{array}{r|rrrr} 1 & 1 & 3 & -2 & 1 \\ & & 1 & 4 & 2 \\ \hline & 1 & 4 & 2 & 3 \end{array}$$

1 is an upper bound.

(b)

$$\begin{array}{r|rrrr} -4 & 1 & 3 & -2 & 1 \\ & & -4 & 4 & -8 \\ \hline & 1 & -1 & 2 & -7 \end{array}$$

−4 is a lower bound.

97. $f(x) = x^4 - 4x^3 + 16x - 16$

(a)

$$\begin{array}{r|rrrrr} 5 & 1 & -4 & 0 & 16 & -16 \\ & & 5 & 5 & 25 & 205 \\ \hline & 1 & 1 & 5 & 41 & 189 \end{array}$$

5 is an upper bound.

(b)

$$\begin{array}{r|rrrrr} -3 & 1 & -4 & 0 & 16 & -16 \\ & & -3 & 21 & -63 & 141 \\ \hline & 1 & -7 & 21 & -47 & 125 \end{array}$$

−3 is a lower bound.

99. $f(x) = 4x^3 - 3x - 1$

Possible rational zeros: $\pm 1, \pm\frac{1}{2}, \pm\frac{1}{4}$

$$\begin{array}{r|rrrr} 1 & 4 & 0 & -3 & -1 \\ & & 4 & 4 & 1 \\ \hline & 4 & 4 & 1 & 0 \end{array}$$

$$4x^3 - 3x - 1 = (x - 1)(4x^2 + 4x + 1)$$
$$= (x - 1)(2x + 1)^2$$

So, the zeros are 1 and $-\dfrac{1}{2}$.

101. $f(y) = 4y^3 + 3y^2 + 8y + 6$

Possible rational zeros: $\pm 1, \pm 2, \pm 3, \pm 6, \pm\frac{1}{2}, \pm\frac{3}{2}, \pm\frac{1}{4}, \pm\frac{3}{4}$

$$\begin{array}{r|rrrr} -\frac{3}{4} & 4 & 3 & 8 & 6 \\ & & -3 & 0 & -6 \\ \hline & 4 & 0 & 8 & 0 \end{array}$$

$$4y^3 + 3y^2 + 8y + 6 = \left(y + \tfrac{3}{4}\right)(4y^2 + 8)$$
$$= \left(y + \tfrac{3}{4}\right)4(y^2 + 2)$$
$$= (4y + 3)(y^2 + 2)$$

So, the only real zero is $-\dfrac{3}{4}$.

103. $P(x) = x^4 - \frac{25}{4}x^2 + 9$

$$= \tfrac{1}{4}(4x^4 - 25x^2 + 36)$$
$$= \tfrac{1}{4}(4x^2 - 9)(x^2 - 4)$$
$$= \tfrac{1}{4}(2x + 3)(2x - 3)(x + 2)(x - 2)$$

The rational zeros are $\pm\frac{3}{2}$ and ± 2.

105. $f(x) = x^3 - \frac{1}{4}x^2 - x + \frac{1}{4}$

$$= \tfrac{1}{4}(4x^3 - x^2 - 4x + 1)$$
$$= \tfrac{1}{4}\left[x^2(4x - 1) - 1(4x - 1)\right]$$
$$= \tfrac{1}{4}(4x - 1)(x^2 - 1)$$
$$= \tfrac{1}{4}(4x - 1)(x + 1)(x - 1)$$

The rational zeros are $\frac{1}{4}$ and ± 1.

107. $f(x) = x^3 - 1 = (x - 1)(x^2 + x + 1)$

Rational zeros: $1\,(x = 1)$

Irrational zeros: 0

Matches (d).

108. $f(x) = x^3 - 2$

$$= \left(x - \sqrt[3]{2}\right)\left(x^2 + \sqrt[3]{2}x + \sqrt[3]{4}\right)$$

Rational zeros: 0

Irrational zeros: $1\left(x = \sqrt[3]{2}\right)$

Matches (a).

109. $f(x) = x^3 - x = x(x + 1)(x - 1)$

Rational zeros: $3\,(x = 0, \pm 1)$

Irrational zeros: 0

Matches (b).

110. $f(x) = x^3 - 2x$

$$= x(x^2 - 2)$$
$$= x(x + \sqrt{2})(x - \sqrt{2})$$

Rational zeros: $1\,(x = 0)$

Irrational zeros: $2\left(x = \pm\sqrt{2}\right)$

Matches (c).

111. (a)

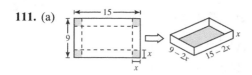

(b) $V = l \cdot w \cdot h = (15 - 2x)(9 - 2x)x$

$$= x(9 - 2x)(15 - 2x)$$

Because length, width, and height must be positive, you have $0 < x < \frac{9}{2}$ for the domain.

(c)

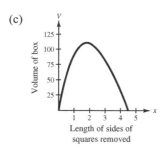

Length of sides of squares removed

The volume is maximum when $x \approx 1.82$.

The dimensions are: length $\approx 15 - 2(1.82) = 11.36$

width $\approx 9 - 2(1.82) = 5.36$

height $= x \approx 1.82$

1.82 cm $\times$ 5.36 cm $\times$ 11.36 cm

(d) $56 = x(9 - 2x)(15 - 2x)$

$56 = 135x - 48x^2 + 4x^3$

$0 = 4x^3 - 48x^2 + 135x - 56$

The zeros of this polynomial are $\frac{1}{2}$, $\frac{7}{2}$, and 8.

x cannot equal 8 because it is not in the domain of V. [The length cannot equal -1 and the width cannot equal -7. The product of $(8)(-1)(-7) = 56$ so it showed up as an extraneous solution.]

So, the volume is 56 cubic centimeters when $x = \frac{1}{2}$ centimeter or $x = \frac{7}{2}$ centimeters.

113. (a) Current bin: $V = 2 \times 3 \times 4 = 24$ cubic feet

New bin: $V = 5(24) = 120$ cubic feet

$$V(x) = (2 + x)(3 + x)(4 + x) = 120$$

(b) $x^3 + 9x^2 + 26x + 24 = 120$

$x^3 + 9x^2 + 26x - 96 = 0$

The only real zero of this polynomial is $x = 2$. All the dimensions should be increased by 2 feet, so the new bin will have dimensions of 4 feet by 5 feet by 6 feet.

115. False. The most complex zeros it can have is two, and the Linear Factorization Theorem guarantees that there are three linear factors, so one zero must be real.

117. $g(x) = -f(x)$. This function would have the same zeros as $f(x)$, so $r_1, r_2,$ and r_3 are also zeros of $g(x)$.

119. $g(x) = f(x - 5)$. The graph of $g(x)$ is a horizontal shift of the graph of $f(x)$ five units of the right, so the zeros of $g(x)$ are $5 + r_1, 5 + r_2,$ and $5 + r_3$.

121. $g(x) = 3 + f(x)$. Because $g(x)$ is a vertical shift of the graph of $f(x)$, the zeros of $g(x)$ cannot be determined.

123. Zeros: $-2, \frac{1}{2}, 3$

$$f(x) = -(x + 2)(2x - 1)(x - 3)$$

$$= -2x^3 + 3x^2 + 11x - 6$$

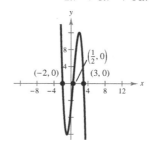

Any nonzero scalar multiple of f would have the same three zeros. Let $g(x) = af(x), a > 0$. There are infinitely many possible functions for f.

Section 2.6 Rational Functions

1. rational functions

3. horizontal asymptote

5. Because the denominator is zero when $x - 1 = 0$, the domain of f is all real numbers except $x = 1$.

x	0	0.5	0.9	0.99	$\to 1$
$f(x)$	−1	−2	−10	−100	$\to -\infty$

x	$1 \leftarrow$	1.01	1.1	1.5	2
$f(x)$	$\infty \leftarrow$	100	10	2	1

As x approaches 1 from the left, $f(x)$ decreases without bound. As x approaches 1 from the right, $f(x)$ increases without bound.

7. Because the denominator is zero when $x^2 - 1 = 0$, the domain of f is all real numbers except $x = -1$ and $x = 1$.

x	−2	−1.5	−1.1	−1.01	$\to -1$
$f(x)$	4	5.4	17.3	152.3	$-\infty$

x	$-1 \leftarrow$	−0.99	−0.9	−0.5	0
$f(x)$	$-\infty \leftarrow$	−147.8	−12.8	−1	0

As x approaches −1 from the left, $f(x)$ increases without bound. As x approaches −1 from the right, $f(x)$ decreases without bound.

x	0	0.5	0.9	0.99	$\to 1$
$f(x)$	0	−1	−12.8	−147.8	$\to -\infty$

x	$1 \leftarrow$	1.01	1.1	1.5	2
$f(x)$	$\infty \leftarrow$	152.3	17.3	5.4	4

As x approaches 1 from the left, $f(x)$ increases without bound. As x approaches 1 from the right, $f(x)$ decreases without bound.

9. $f(x) = \dfrac{4}{x^2}$

Domain: all real numbers except $x = 0$

Vertical asymptote: $x = 0$

Horizontal asymptote: $y = 0$

$\left[\text{Degree of } N(x) < \text{degree of } D(x)\right]$

11. $f(x) = \dfrac{5 + x}{5 - x} = \dfrac{x + 5}{-x + 5}$

Domain: all real numbers except $x = 5$

Vertical asymptote: $x = 5$

Horizontal asymptote: $y = -1$

$\left[\text{Degree of } N(x) = \text{degree of } D(x)\right]$

13. $f(x) = \dfrac{x^3}{x^2 - 1}$

Domain: all real numbers except $x = \pm 1$

Vertical asymptotes: $x = \pm 1$

Horizontal asymptote: None

$\left[\text{Degree of } N(x) > \text{degree of } D(x)\right]$

15. $f(x) = \dfrac{3x^2 + 1}{x^2 + x + 9}$

Domain: All real numbers. The denominator has no real zeros. [Try the Quadratic Formula on the denominator.]

Vertical asymptote: None

Horizontal asymptote: $y = 3$

$\left[\text{Degree of } N(x) = \text{degree of } D(x)\right]$

17. $f(x) = \dfrac{1}{x + 2}$

(a) Domain: all real numbers x except $x = -2$

(b) y-intercept: $\left(0, \dfrac{1}{2}\right)$

(c) Vertical asymptote: $x = -2$

Horizontal asymptote: $y = 0$

(d)

x	−4	−3	−1	0	1
$f(x)$	$-\dfrac{1}{2}$	−1	1	$\dfrac{1}{2}$	$\dfrac{1}{3}$

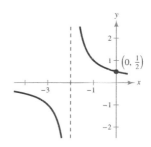

19. $h(x) = \dfrac{-1}{x+4}$

   (a) Domain: all real numbers x except $x = -4$

   (b) y-intercept: $\left(0, -\dfrac{1}{4}\right)$

   (c) Vertical asymptote: $x = -4$

       Horizontal asymptote: $y = 0$

   (d)

x	-6	-5	-3	-2	-1	0
$h(x)$	$\dfrac{1}{2}$	1	-1	$-\dfrac{1}{2}$	$-\dfrac{1}{3}$	$-\dfrac{1}{4}$

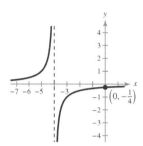

21. $C(x) = \dfrac{7+2x}{2+x}$

   (a) Domain: all real numbers x except $x = -2$

   (b) x-intercept: $\left(-\dfrac{7}{2}, 0\right)$

       y-intercept: $\left(0, \dfrac{7}{2}\right)$

   (c) Vertical asymptote: $x = -2$

       Horizontal asymptote: $y = 2$

   (d)

x	-4	-3	-1	0	1
$C(x)$	$\dfrac{1}{2}$	-1	5	$\dfrac{7}{2}$	3

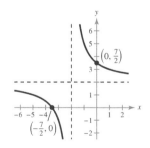

23. $f(x) = \dfrac{x^2}{x^2+9}$

   (a) Domain: all real numbers x

   (b) Intercept: $(0, 0)$

   (c) Horizontal asymptote: $y = 1$

   (d)

x	± 1	± 2	± 3
$f(x)$	$\dfrac{1}{10}$	$\dfrac{4}{13}$	$\dfrac{1}{2}$

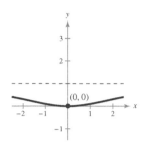

25. $f(t) = \dfrac{1-2t}{t} = -\dfrac{2t-1}{t}$

   (a) Domain: all real numbers t except $t = 0$

   (b) t-intercept: $\left(\dfrac{1}{2}, 0\right)$

   (c) Vertical asymptote: $t = 0$

       Horizontal asymptote: $y = -2$

   (d)

t	-2	-1	$\dfrac{1}{2}$	1	2
$f(t)$	$-\dfrac{5}{2}$	-3	0	-1	$-\dfrac{3}{2}$

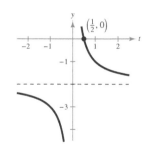

27. $h(x) = \dfrac{x^2 - 5x + 4}{x^2 - 4} = \dfrac{(x - 1)(x - 4)}{(x + 2)(x - 2)}$

  (a) Domain: all real numbers x except $x = \pm 2$

  (b) x-intercepts: $(1, 0), (4, 0)$

     y-intercept: $(0, -1)$

  (c) Vertical asymptotes: $x = -2, x = 2$

     Horizontal asymptote: $y = 1$

  (d)

x	-4	-3	-1	0	1	3	4
$h(x)$	$\dfrac{10}{3}$	$\dfrac{28}{5}$	$-\dfrac{10}{3}$	-1	0	$-\dfrac{2}{5}$	0

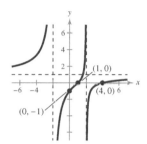

29. $f(x) = \dfrac{x - 4}{x^2 - 16} = \dfrac{x - 4}{(x - 4)(x + 4)} = \dfrac{1}{x + 4}, \ x \neq 4$

Domain: all real numbers x except $x = \pm 4$

Vertical asymptote: $x = -4$ (Because $x - 4$ is a common factor of $N(x)$ and $D(x)$, $x = 4$ is not a vertical asymptote of $f(x)$.)

Horizontal asymptote: $y = 0$

$\left[\text{Degree of } N(x) < \text{degree of } D(x)\right]$

35. $f(x) = \dfrac{x^2 + 3x}{x^2 + x - 6} = \dfrac{x(x + 3)}{(x + 3)(x - 2)} = \dfrac{x}{x - 2}, \ x \neq -3$

  (a) Domain: all real numbers x except $x = -3$ and $x = 2$

  (b) Intercept: $(0, 0)$

  (c) Vertical asymptote: $x = 2$

     Horizontal asymptote: $y = 1$

  (d)

x	-1	0	1	3	4
$f(x)$	$\dfrac{1}{3}$	0	-1	3	2

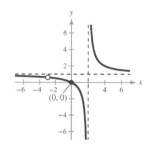

31. $f(t) = \dfrac{t^2 - 1}{t - 1} = \dfrac{(t + 1)(t - 1)}{t - 1} = t + 1, \ t \neq 1$

  (a) Domain: all real numbers t except $t = 1$

  (b) t-intercept: $(-1, 0)$

     y-intercept: $(0, 1)$

  (c) No asymptotes

  (d)

t	-3	-2	-1	0	1	2
$f(t)$	-2	-1	0	1	Undef.	3

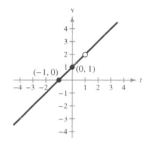

33. $f(x) = \dfrac{x^2 - 25}{x^2 - 4x - 5} = \dfrac{(x + 5)(x - 5)}{(x - 5)(x + 1)} = \dfrac{x + 5}{x + 1}, \ x \neq 5$

Domain: all real numbers x except $x = 5$ and $x = -1$

Vertical asymptote: $x = -1$ (Because $x - 5$ is a common factor of $N(x)$ and $D(x)$, $x = 5$ is not a vertical asymptote of $f(x)$.)

Horizontal asymptote: $y = 1$

$\left[\text{Degree of } N(x) = \text{degree of } D(x)\right]$

37. $f(x) = \dfrac{x^2 - 3x - 4}{2x^2 + x - 1}$

$= \dfrac{(x + 1)(x - 4)}{(2x - 1)(x + 1)} = \dfrac{x - 4}{2x - 1},\ x \neq -1$

Domain: all real numbers x except $x = \dfrac{1}{2}$ and $x = -1$

Vertical asymptote: $x = \dfrac{1}{2}$ (Because $x + 1$ is a common factor of $N(x)$ and $D(x)$, $x = -1$ is not a vertical asymptote of $f(x)$.)

Horizontal asymptote: $y = \dfrac{1}{2}$

$\left[\text{Degree of } N(x) = \text{degree of } D(x)\right]$

39. $f(x) = \dfrac{2x^2 - 5x - 3}{x^3 - 2x^2 - x + 2} = \dfrac{(2x + 1)(x - 3)}{(x - 2)(x + 1)(x - 1)}$

(a) Domain: all real numbers x except $x = 2,\ x = \pm 1$

(b) x-intercepts: $\left(-\dfrac{1}{2}, 0\right), (3, 0)$

y-intercept: $\left(0, -\dfrac{3}{2}\right)$

(c) Vertical asymptotes: $x = 2,\ x = -1,$ and $x = 1$

Horizontal asymptote: $y = 0$

(d)

x	-3	-2	0	$\dfrac{3}{2}$	3	4
$f(x)$	$-\dfrac{3}{4}$	$-\dfrac{5}{4}$	$-\dfrac{3}{2}$	$\dfrac{48}{5}$	0	$\dfrac{3}{10}$

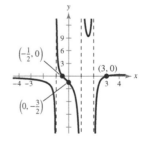

49. $h(x) = \dfrac{x^2 - 9}{x} = x - \dfrac{9}{x}$

(a) Domain: all real numbers x except $x = 0$

(b) x-intercepts: $(-3, 0), (3, 0)$

(c) Vertical asymptote: $x = 0$

Slant asymptote: $y = x$

(d)

x	-6	-4	-3	-2	2	3	4	6
$h(x)$	$-\dfrac{9}{2}$	$-\dfrac{7}{4}$	0	$\dfrac{5}{2}$	$-\dfrac{5}{2}$	0	$\dfrac{7}{4}$	$\dfrac{9}{2}$

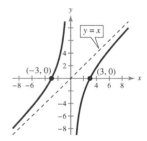

41. g

42. e

43. a

44. f

45. (a) Domain of f: all real numbers x except $x = -1$

Domain of g: all real numbers x

(b)

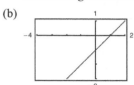

(c) Because there are only finitely many pixels, the graphing utility may not attempt to evaluate the function where it does not exist.

47. (a) Domain of f: all real numbers x except $x = 0, 2$

Domain of g: all real numbers $x = 0$

(b)

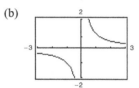

(c) Because there are only finitely many pixels, the graphing utility may not attempt to evaluate the function where it does not exist.

51. $f(x) = \dfrac{2x^2 + 1}{x} = 2x + \dfrac{1}{x}$

   (a) Domain: all real numbers x except $x = 0$

   (b) No intercepts

   (c) Vertical asymptote: $x = 0$

   Slant asymptote: $y = 2x$

   (d)

x	-4	-2	2	4	6
$f(x)$	$-\dfrac{33}{4}$	$-\dfrac{9}{2}$	$\dfrac{9}{2}$	$\dfrac{33}{4}$	$\dfrac{73}{6}$

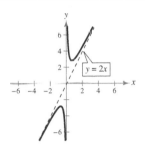

53. $g(x) = \dfrac{x^2 + 1}{x} = x + \dfrac{1}{x}$

   (a) Domain: all real numbers x except $x = 0$

   (b) No intercepts

   (c) Vertical asymptote: $x = 0$

   Slant asymptote: $y = x$

   (d)

x	-4	-2	2	4	6
$g(x)$	$-\dfrac{17}{4}$	$-\dfrac{5}{2}$	$\dfrac{5}{2}$	$\dfrac{17}{4}$	$\dfrac{37}{6}$

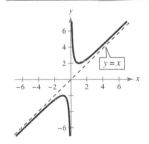

55. $f(t) = \dfrac{t^2 + 1}{t + 5} = -t + 5 - \dfrac{26}{t + 5}$

   (a) Domain: all real numbers t except $t = -5$

   (b) Intercept: $\left(0, -\dfrac{1}{5}\right)$

   (c) Vertical asymptote: $t = -5$

   Slant asymptote: $y = -t + 5$

   (d)

t	-7	-6	-4	-3	0
$f(t)$	25	37	-17	-5	$-\dfrac{1}{5}$

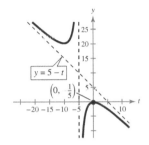

57. $f(x) = \dfrac{x^3}{x^2 - 4} = x + \dfrac{4x}{x^2 - 4}$

   (a) Domain: all real numbers x except $x = \pm 2$

   (b) Intercept: $(0, 0)$

   (c) Vertical asymptotes: $x = \pm 2$

   Slant asymptote: $y = x$

   (d)

x	-6	-4	-1	0	1	4	6
$f(x)$	$-\dfrac{27}{4}$	$-\dfrac{16}{3}$	$\dfrac{1}{3}$	0	$-\dfrac{1}{3}$	$\dfrac{16}{3}$	$\dfrac{27}{4}$

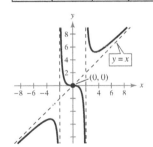

59. $f(x) = \dfrac{x^2 - x + 1}{x - 1} = x + \dfrac{1}{x - 1}$

(a) Domain: all real numbers x except $x = 1$

(b) y-intercept: $(0, -1)$

(c) Vertical asymptote: $x = 1$

Slant asymptote: $y = x$

(d)

x	-4	-2	0	2	4
$f(x)$	$-\dfrac{21}{5}$	$-\dfrac{7}{3}$	-1	3	$\dfrac{13}{3}$

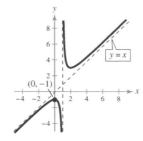

61. $f(x) = \dfrac{2x^3 - x^2 - 2x + 1}{x^2 + 3x + 2} = \dfrac{(2x - 1)(x + 1)(x - 1)}{(x + 1)(x + 2)} = \dfrac{(2x - 1)(x - 1)}{x + 2}, \quad x \neq -1$

$= \dfrac{2x^2 - 3x + 1}{x + 2} = 2x - 7 + \dfrac{15}{x + 2}, \quad x \neq -1$

(a) Domain: all real numbers x except $x = -1$ and $x = -2$

(b) y-intercept: $\left(0, \dfrac{1}{2}\right)$

x-intercepts: $\left(\dfrac{1}{2}, 0\right), (1, 0)$

(c) Vertical asymptote: $x = -2$

Slant asymptote: $y = 2x - 7$

(d)

x	-4	-3	$-\dfrac{3}{2}$	0	1
$f(x)$	$-\dfrac{45}{2}$	-28	20	$\dfrac{1}{2}$	0

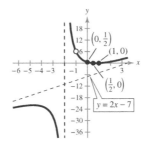

63. $f(x) = \dfrac{x^2 + 5x + 8}{x + 3} = x + 2 + \dfrac{2}{x + 3}$

Domain: all real numbers x except $x = -3$

y-intercept: $\left(0, \dfrac{8}{3}\right)$

Vertical asymptote: $x = -3$

Slant asymptote: $y = x + 2$

Line: $y = x + 2$

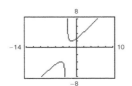

65. $g(x) = \dfrac{1 + 3x^2 - x^3}{x^2} = \dfrac{1}{x^2} + 3 - x = -x + 3 + \dfrac{1}{x^2}$

Domain: all real numbers x except $x = 0$

Vertical asymptote: $x = 0$

Slant asymptote: $y = -x + 3$

Line: $y = -x + 3$

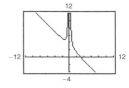

67. $y = \dfrac{x + 1}{x - 3}$

(a) x-intercept: $(-1, 0)$

(b) $\quad 0 = \dfrac{x + 1}{x - 3}$

$0 = x + 1$

$-1 = x$

69. $y = \dfrac{1}{x} - x$

(a) x-intercepts: $(-1, 0), (1, 0)$

(b) $0 = \dfrac{1}{x} - x$

$x = \dfrac{1}{x}$

$x^2 = 1$

$x = \pm 1$

71. $C = \dfrac{25{,}000p}{100 - p}, \; 0 \le p < 100$

(a)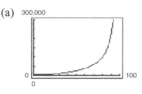

(b) $C = \dfrac{25{,}000(15)}{100 - 15} \approx \$4411.76$

$C = \dfrac{25{,}000(50)}{100 - 50} = \$25{,}000$

$C = \dfrac{25{,}000(90)}{100 - 90} = \$225{,}000$

(c) $C \to \infty$ as $x \to 100$. No, it would not be possible to supply bins to 100% of the residents because the model is undefined for $p = 100$.

73. (a) $A = xy$ and

$(x - 4)(y - 2) = 30$

$y - 2 = \dfrac{30}{x - 4}$

$y = 2 + \dfrac{30}{x - 4} = \dfrac{2x + 22}{x - 4}$

Thus, $A = xy = x\left(\dfrac{2x + 22}{x - 4}\right) = \dfrac{2x(x + 11)}{x - 4}$.

(b) Domain: Since the margins on the left and right are each 2 inches, $x > 4$. In interval notation, the domain is $(4, \infty)$.

(c)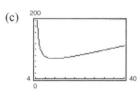

The area is minimum when $x \approx 11.75$ inches and $y \approx 5.87$ inches.

x	5	6	7	8	9	10	11	12	13	14	15
y_1 (Area)	160	102	84	76	72	70	69.143	69	69.333	70	70.909

The area is minimum when x is approximately 12.

75. (a) Let t_1 = time from Akron to Columbus and t_2 = time from Columbus back to Akron.

$$xt_1 = 100 \Rightarrow t_1 = \frac{100}{x}$$

$$yt_2 = 100 \Rightarrow t_2 = \frac{100}{y}$$

$$50(t_1 + t_2) = 200$$
$$t_1 + t_2 = 4$$
$$\frac{100}{x} + \frac{100}{y} = 4$$
$$100y + 100x = 4xy$$
$$25y + 25x = xy$$
$$25x = xy - 25y$$
$$25x = y(x - 25)$$

Thus, $y = \dfrac{25x}{x - 25}$.

(b) Vertical asymptote: $x = 25$

Horizontal asymptote: $y = 25$

(c)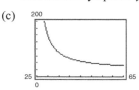

(d)

x	30	35	40	45	50	55	60
y	150	87.5	66.7	56.3	50	45.8	42.9

(e) Sample answer: No. You might expect the average speed for the round trip to be the average of the average speeds for the two parts of the trip.

(f) No. At 20 miles per hour you would use more time in one direction than is required for the round trip at an average speed of 50 miles per hour.

77. False. Polynomial functions do not have vertical asymptotes.

79. False. A graph can have a vertical asymptote and a horizontal asymptote or a vertical asymptote and a slant asymptote, but a graph cannot have both a horizontal asymptote and a slant asymptote.

A horizontal asymptote occurs when the degree of $N(x)$ is equal to the degree of $D(x)$ or when the degree of $N(x)$ is less than the degree of $D(x)$. A slant asymptote occurs when the degree of $N(x)$ is greater than the degree of $D(x)$ by one.

Because the degree of a polynomial is constant, it is impossible to have both relationships at the same time.

81. b

Section 2.7 Nonlinear Inequalities

1. positive; negative

3. zeros; undefined values

5. $x^2 - 3 < 0$

(a) $x = 3$

$$(3)^2 - 3 \overset{?}{<} 0$$
$$6 \not< 0$$

No, $x = 3$ *is not* a solution.

(b) $x = 0$

$$(0)^2 - 3 \overset{?}{<} 0$$
$$-3 < 0$$

Yes, $x = 0$ *is* a solution.

(c) $x = \frac{3}{2}$

$$\left(\frac{3}{2}\right)^2 - 3 \overset{?}{<} 0$$
$$-\frac{3}{4} < 0$$

Yes, $x - \frac{3}{2}$ *is* a solution.

(d) $x = -5$

$$(-5)^2 - 3 \overset{?}{<} 0$$
$$22 \not< 0$$

No, $x = -5$ *is not* a solution.

7. $\dfrac{x+2}{x-4} \geq 3$

(a) $x = 5$

$$\dfrac{5+2}{5-4} \overset{?}{\geq} 3$$

$$7 \geq 3$$

Yes, $x = 5$ *is*
a solution.

(b) $x = 4$

$$\dfrac{4+2}{4-4} \overset{?}{\geq} 3$$

$\dfrac{6}{0}$ is undefined.

No, $x = 4$ *is not*
a solution.

(c) $x = -\dfrac{9}{2}$

$$\dfrac{-\dfrac{9}{2}+2}{-\dfrac{9}{2}-4} \overset{?}{\geq} 3$$

$$\dfrac{5}{17} \not\geq 3$$

No, $x = -\dfrac{9}{2}$ *is not*
a solution.

(d) $x = \dfrac{9}{2}$

$$\dfrac{\dfrac{9}{2}+2}{\dfrac{9}{2}-4} \overset{?}{\geq} 3$$

$$13 \geq 3$$

Yes, $x = \dfrac{9}{2}$ *is*
a solution.

9. $3x^2 - x - 2 = (3x+2)(x-1)$

$$3x+2 = 0 \Rightarrow x = -\tfrac{2}{3}$$

$$x - 1 = 0 \Rightarrow x = 1$$

The key numbers are $-\tfrac{2}{3}$ and 1.

11. $\dfrac{1}{x-5} + 1 = \dfrac{1 + 1(x-5)}{x-5}$

$$= \dfrac{x-4}{x-5}$$

$$x - 4 = 0 \Rightarrow x = 4$$

$$x - 5 = 0 \Rightarrow x = 5$$

The key numbers are 4 and 5.

13. $\qquad x^2 < 9$

$$x^2 - 9 < 0$$

$$(x+3)(x-3) < 0$$

Key numbers: $x = \pm 3$

Test intervals: $(-\infty, -3), (-3, 3), (3, \infty)$

Test: Is $(x+3)(x-3) < 0$?

Interval	x-Value	Value of $x^2 - 9$	Conclusion
$(-\infty, -3)$	-4	7	Positive
$(-3, 3)$	0	-9	Negative
$(3, \infty)$	4	7	Positive

Solution set: $(-3, 3)$

15. $\qquad (x+2)^2 \leq 25$

$$x^2 + 4x + 4 \leq 25$$

$$x^2 + 4x - 21 \leq 0$$

$$(x+7)(x-3) \leq 0$$

Key numbers: $x = -7, x = 3$

Test intervals: $(-\infty, -7), (-7, 3), (3, \infty)$

Test: Is $(x+7)(x-3) \leq 0$?

Interval	x-Value	Value of $(x+7)(x-3)$	Conclusion
$(-\infty, -7)$	-8	$(-1)(-11) = 11$	Positive
$(-7, 3)$	0	$(7)(-3) = -21$	Negative
$(3, \infty)$	4	$(11)(1) = 11$	Positive

Solution set: $[-7, 3]$

17. $x^2 + 4x + 4 \geq 9$

$$x^2 + 4x - 5 \geq 0$$

$$(x+5)(x-1) \geq 0$$

Key numbers: $x = -5, x = 1$

Test intervals: $(-\infty, -5), (-5, 1), (1, \infty)$

Test: Is $(x+5)(x-1) \geq 0$?

Interval	x-Value	Value of $(x+5)(x-1)$	Conclusion
$(-\infty, -5)$	-6	$(-1)(-7) = 7$	Positive
$(-5, 1)$	0	$(5)(-1) = -5$	Negative
$(1, \infty)$	2	$(7)(1) = 7$	Positive

Solution set: $(-\infty, -5] \cup [1, \infty)$

19.
$$x^2 + x < 6$$
$$x^2 + x - 6 < 0$$
$$(x + 3)(x - 2) < 0$$

Key numbers: $x = -3, x = 2$

Test intervals: $(-\infty, -3), (-3, 2), (2, \infty)$

Test: Is $(x + 3)(x - 2) < 0$?

Interval	x-Value	Value of $(x + 3)(x - 2)$	Conclusion
$(-\infty, -3)$	-4	$(-1)(-6) = 6$	Positive
$(-3, 2)$	0	$(3)(-2) = -6$	Negative
$(2, \infty)$	3	$(6)(1) = 6$	Positive

Solution set: $(-3, 2)$

21. $x^2 + 2x - 3 < 0$
$$(x + 3)(x - 1) < 0$$

Key numbers: $x = -3, x = 1$

Test intervals: $(-\infty, -3), (-3, 1), (1, \infty)$

Test: Is $(x + 3)(x - 1) < 0$?

Interval	x-Value	Value of $(x + 3)(x - 1)$	Conclusion
$(-\infty, -3)$	-4	$(-1)(-5) = 5$	Positive
$(-3, 1)$	0	$(3)(-1) = -3$	Negative
$(1, \infty)$	2	$(5)(1) = 5$	Positive

Solution set: $(-3, 1)$

23.
$$3x^2 - 11x > 20$$
$$3x^2 - 11x - 20 > 0$$
$$(3x + 4)(x - 5) > 0$$

Key numbers: $x = 5, x = -\frac{4}{3}$

Test intervals: $\left(-\infty, -\frac{4}{3}\right), \left(-\frac{4}{3}, 5\right), (5, \infty)$

Test: Is $(3x + 4)(x - 5) > 0$?

Interval	x-Value	Value of $(3x + 4)(x - 5)$	Conclusion
$\left(-\infty, -\frac{4}{3}\right)$	-3	$(-5)(-8) = 40$	Positive
$\left(-\frac{4}{3}, 5\right)$	0	$(4)(-5) = -20$	Negative
$(5, \infty)$	6	$(22)(1) = 22$	Positive

Solution set: $\left(-\infty, -\frac{4}{3}\right) \cup (5, \infty)$

25. $x^2 - 3x - 18 > 0$
$$(x + 3)(x - 6) > 0$$

Key numbers: $x = -3, x = 6$

Test intervals: $(-\infty, -3), (-3, 6), (6, \infty)$

Test: Is $(x + 3)(x - 6) > 0$?

Interval	x-Value	Value of $(x + 3)(x - 6)$	Conclusion
$(-\infty, -3)$	-4	$(-1)(-10) = 10$	Positive
$(-3, 6)$	0	$(3)(-6) = -18$	Negative
$(6, \infty)$	7	$(10)(1) = 10$	Positive

Solution set: $(-\infty, -3) \cup (6, \infty)$

27.
$$x^3 - 3x^2 - x > -3$$
$$x^3 - 3x^2 - x + 3 > 0$$
$$x^2(x - 3) - (x - 3) > 0$$
$$(x - 3)(x^2 - 1) > 0$$
$$(x - 3)(x + 1)(x - 1) > 0$$

Key numbers: $x = -1, x = 1, x = 3$

Test intervals: $(-\infty, -1), (-1, 1), (1, 3), (3, \infty)$

Test: Is $(x - 3)(x + 1)(x - 1) > 0$?

Interval	x-Value	Value of $(x - 3)(x + 1)(x - 1)$	Conclusion
$(-\infty, -1)$	-2	$(-5)(-1)(-3) = -15$	Negative
$(-1, 1)$	0	$(-3)(1)(-1) = 3$	Positive
$(1, 3)$	2	$(-1)(3)(1) = -3$	Negative
$(3, \infty)$	4	$(1)(5)(3) = 15$	Positive

Solution set: $(-1, 1) \cup (3, \infty)$

29.
$$4x^3 - 6x^2 < 0$$
$$2x^2(2x - 3) < 0$$

Key numbers: $x = 0, x = \frac{3}{2}$

Test intervals: $(-\infty, 0) \Rightarrow 2x^2(2x - 3) < 0$
$$\left(0, \frac{3}{2}\right) \Rightarrow 2 \Rightarrow 2x^2(2x - 3) < 0$$
$$\left(\frac{3}{2}, \infty\right) \Rightarrow 2x^2(2x - 3) > 0$$

Solution set: $(-\infty, 0) \cup \left(0, \frac{3}{2}\right)$

31.
$$x^3 - 4x \geq 0$$
$$x(x + 2)(x - 2) \geq 0$$

Key numbers: $x = 0, x = \pm 2$

Test intervals: $(-\infty, -2) \Rightarrow x(x + 2)(x - 2) < 0$
$$(-2, 0) \Rightarrow x(x + 2)(x - 2) > 0$$
$$(0, 2) \Rightarrow x(x + 2)(x - 2) < 0$$
$$(2, \infty) \Rightarrow x(x + 2)(x - 2) > 0$$

Solution set: $[-2, 0] \cup [2, \infty)$

33. $(x - 1)^2(x + 2)^3 \geq 0$

Key numbers: $x = 1, x = -2$

Test intervals: $(-\infty, -2) \Rightarrow (x - 1)^2(x + 2)^3 < 0$
$$(-2, 1) \Rightarrow (x - 1)^2(x + 2)^3 > 0$$
$$(1, \infty) \Rightarrow (x - 1)^2(x + 2)^3 > 0$$

Solution set: $[-2, \infty)$

35. $4x^2 - 4x + 1 \le 0$

$(2x - 1)^2 \le 0$

Key number: $x = \dfrac{1}{2}$

Test Interval	x-Value	Polynomial Value	Conclusion
$\left(-\infty, \dfrac{1}{2}\right]$	$x = 0$	$[2(0) - 1]^2 = 1$	Positive
$\left(\dfrac{1}{2}, \infty\right)$	$x = 1$	$[2(1) - 1]^2 = 1$	Positive

The solution set consists of the single real number $\dfrac{1}{2}$.

37. $x^2 - 6x + 12 \le 0$

Using the Quadratic Formula, you can determine that the key numbers are $x = 3 \pm \sqrt{3}i$.

Test Interval	x-Value	Polynomial Value	Conclusion
$(-\infty, \infty)$	$x = 0$	$(0)^2 - 6(0) + 12 = 12$	Positive

The solution set is empty, that is there are no real solutions.

39. $\dfrac{4x - 1}{x} > 0$

Key numbers: $x = 0, \; x = \dfrac{1}{4}$

Test intervals: $(-\infty, 0), \left(0, \dfrac{1}{4}\right), \left(\dfrac{1}{4}, \infty\right)$

Test: Is $\dfrac{4x - 1}{x} > 0$?

Interval	x-Value	Value of $\dfrac{4x - 1}{x}$	Conclusion
$(-\infty, 0)$	-1	$\dfrac{-5}{-1} = 5$	Positive
$\left(0, \dfrac{1}{4}\right)$	$\dfrac{1}{8}$	$\dfrac{-\frac{1}{2}}{\frac{1}{8}} = -4$	Negative
$\left(\dfrac{1}{4}, \infty\right)$	1	$\dfrac{3}{1} = 3$	Positive

Solution set: $(-\infty, 0) \cup \left(\dfrac{1}{4}, \infty\right)$

41. $\dfrac{3x - 5}{x - 5} \geq 0$

Key numbers: $x = \dfrac{5}{3}, x = 5$

Test intervals: $\left(-\infty, \dfrac{5}{3}\right), \left(\dfrac{5}{3}, 5\right), (5, \infty)$

Test: Is $\dfrac{3x - 5}{x - 5} \geq 0$?

Interval	x-Value	Value of $\dfrac{3x - 5}{x - 5}$	Conclusion
$\left(-\infty, \dfrac{5}{3}\right)$	0	$\dfrac{-5}{-5} = 1$	Positive
$\left(\dfrac{5}{3}, 5\right)$	2	$\dfrac{6 - 5}{2 - 5} = -\dfrac{1}{3}$	Negative
$(5, \infty)$	6	$\dfrac{18 - 5}{6 - 5} = 13$	Positive

Solution set: $\left(-\infty, \dfrac{5}{3}\right] \cup (5, \infty)$

43. $\dfrac{x + 6}{x + 1} - 2 < 0$

$\dfrac{x + 6 - 2(x + 1)}{x + 1} < 0$

$\dfrac{4 - x}{x + 1} < 0$

Key numbers: $x = -1, x = 4$

Test intervals: $(-\infty, -1) \Rightarrow \dfrac{4 - x}{x + 1} < 0$

$(-1, 4) \Rightarrow \dfrac{4 - x}{x + 1} > 0$

$(4, \infty) \Rightarrow \dfrac{4 - x}{x + 1} < 0$

Solution set: $(-\infty, -1) \cup (4, \infty)$

45. $\dfrac{2}{x + 5} > \dfrac{1}{x - 3}$

$\dfrac{2}{x + 5} - \dfrac{1}{x - 3} > 0$

$\dfrac{2(x - 3) - 1(x + 5)}{(x + 5)(x - 3)} > 0$

$\dfrac{x - 11}{(x + 5)(x - 3)} > 0$

Key numbers: $x = -5, x = 3, x = 11$

Test intervals: $(-\infty, -5) \Rightarrow \dfrac{x - 11}{(x + 5)(x - 3)} < 0$

$(-5, 3) \Rightarrow \dfrac{x - 11}{(x + 5)(x - 3)} > 0$

$(3, 11) \Rightarrow \dfrac{x - 11}{(x + 5)(x - 3)} < 0$

$(11, \infty) \Rightarrow \dfrac{x - 11}{(x + 5)(x - 3)} > 0$

Solution set: $(-5, 3) \cup (11, \infty)$

47. $\dfrac{1}{x - 3} \leq \dfrac{9}{4x + 3}$

$\dfrac{1}{x - 3} - \dfrac{9}{4x + 3} \leq 0$

$\dfrac{4x + 3 - 9(x - 3)}{(x - 3)(4x + 3)} \leq 0$

$\dfrac{30 \quad 5x}{(x - 3)(4x + 3)} \leq 0$

Key numbers: $x = 3, x = -\dfrac{3}{4}, x = 6$

Test intervals: $\left(-\infty, -\dfrac{3}{4}\right) \Rightarrow \dfrac{30 - 5x}{(x - 3)(4x + 3)} > 0$

$\left(-\dfrac{3}{4}, 3\right) \Rightarrow \dfrac{30 - 5x}{(x - 3)(4x + 3)} < 0$

$(3, 6) \Rightarrow \dfrac{30 - 5x}{(x - 3)(4x + 3)} > 0$

$(6, \infty) \Rightarrow \dfrac{30 - 5x}{(x - 3)(4x + 3)} < 0$

Solution set: $\left(-\dfrac{3}{4}, 3\right) \cup [6, \infty)$

49. $\dfrac{x^2 + 2x}{x^2 - 9} \le 0$

$\dfrac{x(x + 2)}{(x + 3)(x - 3)} \le 0$

Key numbers: $x = 0, x = -2, x = \pm 3$

Test intervals: $(-\infty, -3) \Rightarrow \dfrac{x(x + 2)}{(x + 3)(x - 3)} > 0$

$(-3, -2) \Rightarrow \dfrac{x(x + 2)}{(x + 3)(x - 3)} < 0$

$(-2, 0) \Rightarrow \dfrac{x(x + 2)}{(x + 3)(x - 3)} > 0$

$(0, 3) \Rightarrow \dfrac{x(x + 2)}{(x + 3)(x - 3)} < 0$

$(3, \infty) \Rightarrow \dfrac{x(x + 2)}{(x + 3)(x - 3)} > 0$

Solution set: $(-3, -2] \cup [0, 3)$

51. $\dfrac{3}{x - 1} + \dfrac{2x}{x + 1} > -1$

$\dfrac{3(x + 1) + 2x(x - 1) + 1(x + 1)(x - 1)}{(x - 1)(x + 1)} > 0$

$\dfrac{3x^2 + x + 2}{(x - 1)(x + 1)} > 0$

Key numbers: $x = -1, x = 1$

Test intervals: $(-\infty, -1) \Rightarrow \dfrac{3x^2 + x + 2}{(x - 1)(x + 1)} > 0$

$(-1, 1) \Rightarrow \dfrac{3x^2 + x + 2}{(x - 1)(x + 1)} < 0$

$(1, \infty) \Rightarrow \dfrac{3x^2 + x + 2}{(x - 1)(x + 1)} > 0$

Solution set: $(-\infty, -1) \cup (1, \infty)$

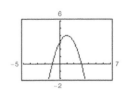

53. $y = -x^2 + 2x + 3$

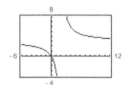

(a) $y \le 0$ when $x \le -1$ or $x \ge 3$.

(b) $y \ge 3$ when $0 \le x \le 2$.

55. $y = \frac{1}{8}x^3 - \frac{1}{2}x$

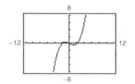

(a) $y \ge 0$ when $-2 \le x \le 0$ or $2 \le x < \infty$.

(b) $y \le 6$ when $x \le 4$.

57. $y = \dfrac{3x}{x - 2}$

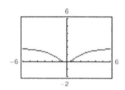

(a) $y \le 0$ when $0 \le x < 2$.

(b) $y \ge 6$ when $2 < x \le 4$.

59. $y = \dfrac{2x^2}{x^2 + 4}$

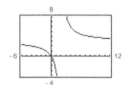

(a) $y \ge 1$ when $x \le -2$ or $x \ge 2$.

This can also be expressed as $|x| \ge 2$.

(b) $y \le 2$ for all real numbers x.

This can also be expressed as $-\infty < x < \infty$.

61. $4 - x^2 \ge 0$

$(2 + x)(2 - x) \ge 0$

Key numbers: $x = \pm 2$

Test intervals: $(-\infty, -2) \Rightarrow 4 - x^2 < 0$

$(-2, 2) \Rightarrow 4 - x^2 > 0$

$(2, \infty) \Rightarrow 4 - x^2 < 0$

Domain: $[-2, 2]$

63. $x^2 - 9x + 20 \geq 0$

$(x - 4)(x - 5) \geq 0$

Key numbers: $x = 4$, $x = 5$

Test intervals: $(-\infty, 4)$, $(4, 5)$, $(5, \infty)$

Interval	x-Value	Value of $(x - 4)(x - 5)$	Conclusion
$(-\infty, 4)$	0	$(-4)(-5) = 20$	Positive
$(4, 5)$	$\frac{9}{2}$	$\left(\frac{1}{2}\right)\left(-\frac{1}{2}\right) = -\frac{1}{4}$	Negative
$(5, \infty)$	6	$(2)(1) = 2$	Positive

Domain: $(-\infty, 4] \cup [5, \infty)$

65. $\dfrac{x}{x^2 - 2x - 35} \geq 0$

$\dfrac{x}{(x + 5)(x - 7)} \geq 0$

Key numbers: $x = 0$, $x = -5$, $x = 7$

Test intervals: $(-\infty, -5) \Rightarrow \dfrac{x}{(x + 5)(x - 7)} < 0$

$(-5, 0) \Rightarrow \dfrac{x}{(x + 5)(x - 7)} > 0$

$(0, 7) \Rightarrow \dfrac{x}{(x + 5)(x - 7)} < 0$

$(7, \infty) \Rightarrow \dfrac{x}{(x + 5)(x - 7)} > 0$

Domain: $(-5, 0] \cup (7, \infty)$

67. $0.4x^2 + 5.26 < 10.2$

$0.4x^2 - 4.94 < 0$

$0.4(x^2 - 12.35) < 0$

Key numbers: $x \approx \pm 3.51$

Test intervals: $(-\infty, -3.51)$, $(-3.51, 3.51)$, $(3.51, \infty)$

Solution set: $(-3.51, 3.51)$

69. $-0.5x^2 + 12.5x + 1.6 > 0$

Key numbers: $x \approx -0.13$, $x \approx 25.13$

Test intervals: $(-\infty, -0.13)$, $(-0.13, 25.13)$, $(25.13, \infty)$

Solution set: $(-0.13, 25.13)$

71. $\dfrac{1}{2.3x - 5.2} > 3.4$

$\dfrac{1}{2.3x - 5.2} - 3.4 > 0$

$\dfrac{1 - 3.4(2.3x - 5.2)}{2.3x - 5.2} > 0$

$\dfrac{-7.82x + 18.68}{2.3x - 5.2} > 0$

Key numbers: $x \approx 2.39$, $x \approx 2.26$

Test intervals: $(-\infty, 2.26)$, $(2.26, 2.39)$, $(2.39, \infty)$

Solution set: $(2.26, 2.39)$

73. $s = -16t^2 + v_0 t + s_0 = -16t^2 + 160t$

(a) $-16t^2 + 160t = 0$

$-16t(t - 10) = 0$

$t = 0, t = 10$

It will be back on the ground in 10 seconds.

(b) $-16t^2 + 160t > 384$

$-16t^2 + 160t - 384 > 0$

$-16(t^2 - 10t + 24) > 0$

$t^2 - 10t + 24 < 0$

$(t - 4)(t - 6) < 0$

Key numbers: $t = 4, t = 6$

Test intervals: $(-\infty, 4)$, $(4, 6)$, $(6, \infty)$

Solution set: 4 seconds $< t <$ 6 seconds

75. $2L + 2W = 100 \Rightarrow W = 50 - L$

$LW \geq 500$

$L(50 - L) \geq 500$

$-L^2 + 50L - 500 \geq 0$

By the Quadratic Formula you have:

Key numbers: $L = 25 \pm 5\sqrt{5}$

Test: Is $-L^2 + 50L - 500 \geq 0$?

Solution set: $25 - 5\sqrt{5} \leq L \leq 25 + 5\sqrt{5}$

13.8 meters $\leq L \leq$ 36.2 meters

77. $R = x(75 - 0.0005x)$ and $C = 30x + 250,000$

$$P = R - C$$
$$= (75x - 0.0005x^2) - (30x + 250,000)$$
$$= -0.0005x^2 + 45x - 250,000$$
$$P \geq 750,000$$
$$-0.0005x^2 + 45x - 250,000 \geq 750,000$$
$$-0.0005x^2 + 45x - 1,000,000 \geq 0$$

Key numbers: $x = 40,000$, $x = 50,000$

(These were obtained by using the Quadratic Formula.)

Test intervals: $(0, 40,000), (40,000, 50,000), (50,000, \infty)$

The solution set is $[40,000, 50,000]$ or $40,000 \leq x \leq 50,000.$ The price per unit is

$$p = \frac{R}{x} = 75 - 0.0005x.$$

For $x = 40,000$, $p = \$55.$ For $x = 50,000$, $p = \$50.$ So, for $40,000 \leq x \leq 50,000$, $\$50.00 \leq p \leq \$55.00.$

79. (a)

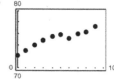

(b) $N = 0.00406t^4 - 0.0564t^3 + 0.147t^2 + 0.86t + 72.2$

(c)

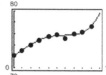

The model fits the data well.

(d) Using the zoom and trace features, the number of students enrolled in schools exceeded 74 million in the year 2001.

(e) No. The model can be used to predict enrollments for years close to those in its domain but when you project too far into the future, the numbers predicted by the model increase too rapidly to be considered reasonable.

81.
$$\frac{1}{R} = \frac{1}{R_1} + \frac{1}{2}$$

$$2R_1 = 2R + RR_1$$

$$2R_1 = R(2 + R_1)$$

$$\frac{2R_1}{2 + R_1} = R$$

Because $R \geq 1$,

$$\frac{2R_1}{2 + R_1} \geq 1$$

$$\frac{2R_1}{2 + R_1} - 1 \geq 0$$

$$\frac{R_1 \quad 2}{2 + R_1} \geq 0.$$

Because $R_1 > 0$, the only key number is $R_1 = 2$. The inequality is satisfied when $R_1 \geq 2$ ohms.

83. True.

$$x^3 - 2x^2 - 11x + 12 = (x + 3)(x - 1)(x - 4)$$

The test intervals are $(-\infty, -3), (-3, 1), (1, 4),$ and $(4, \infty).$

85. $x^2 + bx + 4 = 0$

(a) To have at least one real solution, $b^2 - 4ac \geq 0.$

$$b^2 - 4(1)(4) \geq 0$$

$$b^2 - 16 \geq 0$$

Key numbers: $b = -4, b = 4$

Test intervals: $(-\infty, -4) \Rightarrow b^2 - 16 > 0$

$$(-4, 4) \Rightarrow b^2 - 16 < 0$$

$$(4, \infty) \Rightarrow b^2 - 16 > 0$$

Solution set: $(-\infty, -4] \cup [4, \infty]$

(b) $b^2 - 4ac \geq 0$

Key numbers: $b = -2\sqrt{ac}, b = 2\sqrt{ac}$

Similar to part (a), if $a > 0$ and $c > 0$,

$b \leq -2\sqrt{ac}$ or $b \geq 2ac.$

87. $3x^2 + bx + 10 = 0$

(a) To have at least one real solution, $b^2 - 4ac \geq 0.$

$$b^2 - 4(3)(10) \geq 0$$

$$b^2 - 120 \geq 0$$

Key numbers: $b = -2\sqrt{30}, b = 2\sqrt{30}$

Test intervals: $\left(-\infty, -2\sqrt{30}\right) \Rightarrow b^2 - 120 > 0$

$$\left(-2\sqrt{30}, 2\sqrt{30}\right) \Rightarrow b^2 - 120 < 0$$

$$\left(2\sqrt{30}, \infty\right) \Rightarrow b^2 - 120 > 0$$

Solution set: $\left(-\infty, -2\sqrt{30}\,\right] \cup \left[2\sqrt{30}, \infty\right]$

(b) $b^2 - 4ac \geq 0$

Similar to part (a), if $a > 0$ and $c > 0$,

$b \leq -2\sqrt{ac}$ or $b \geq 2ac.$

89.

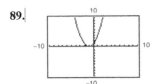

For part (b), the y-values that are less than or equal to 0 occur only at $x = -1$.

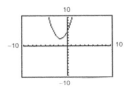

For part (c), there are no y-values that are less than 0.

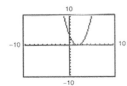

For part (d), the y-values that are greater than 0 occur for all values of x except 2

Review Exercises for Chapter 2

1. (a) $y = 2x^2$

Vertical stretch

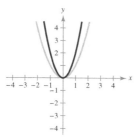

(b) $y = x^2 + 2$

Vertical shift two units upward

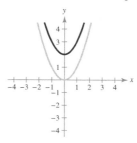

3. $g(x) = x^2 - 2x$

$\quad = x^2 - 2x + 1 - 1$

$\quad = (x - 1)^2 - 1$

Vertex: $(1, -1)$

Axis of symmetry: $x = 1$

$0 = x^2 - 2x = x(x - 2)$

x-intercepts: $(0, 0), (2, 0)$

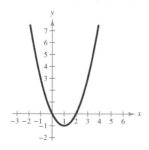

5. $h(x) = 3 + 4x - x^2$

$\quad = -(x^2 - 4x - 3)$

$\quad = -(x^2 - 4x + 4 - 4 - 3)$

$\quad = -\left[(x - 2)^2 - 7\right]$

$\quad = -(x - 2)^2 + 7$

Vertex: $(2, 7)$

Axis of symmetry: $x = 2$

$0 = 3 + 4x - x^2$

$0 = x^2 - 4x - 3$

$x = \dfrac{-(-4) \pm \sqrt{(-4)^2 - 4(1)(-3)}}{2(1)}$

$\quad = \dfrac{4 \pm \sqrt{28}}{2} = 2 \pm \sqrt{7}$

x-intercepts: $\left(2 \pm \sqrt{7}, 0\right)$

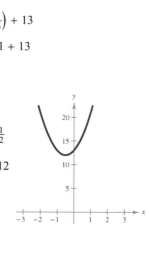

7. $h(x) = 4x^2 + 4x + 13$

$\quad = 4(x^2 + x) + 13$

$\quad = 4\left(x^2 + x + \frac{1}{4} - \frac{1}{4}\right) + 13$

$\quad = 4\left(x^2 + x + \frac{1}{4}\right) - 1 + 13$

$\quad = 4\left(x + \frac{1}{2}\right)^2 + 12$

Vertex: $\left(-\frac{1}{2}, 12\right)$

Axis of symmetry: $x = -\frac{1}{2}$

$\quad 0 = 4\left(x + \frac{1}{2}\right)^2 + 12$

$\left(x + \frac{1}{2}\right)^2 = -3$

No real zeros

x-intercepts: none

9. (a) $x + x + y + y = P$

$$2x + 2y = 1000$$
$$y = 500 - x$$

$$A = xy$$
$$= x(500 - x)$$
$$= 500x - x^2$$

(b) $A = 500x - x^2$

$$= -\left(x^2 - 500x + 62{,}500\right) + 62{,}500$$

$$= -(x - 250)^2 + 62{,}500$$

The maximum area occurs at the vertex when $x = 250$ and $y = 500 - 250 = 250$.

The dimensions with the maximum area are $x = 250$ meters and $y = 250$ meters.

11. $y = x^4$, $f(x) = 6 - x^4$

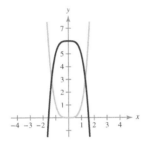

Transformation: Reflection in the x-axis and a vertical shift six units upward

13. $f(x) = -2x^2 - 5x + 12$

The degree is even and the leading coefficient is negative. The graph falls to the left and falls to the right.

15. $g(x) = \frac{3}{4}\left(x^4 + 3x^2 + 2\right)$

The degree is even and the leading coefficient is positive. The graph rises to the left and rises to the right.

17. $g(x) = 2x^3 + 4x^2$

(a) The degree is odd and the leading coefficient, 2, is positive. The graph falls to the left and rises to the right.

(b) $g(x) = 2x^3 + 4x^2$

$$0 = 2x^3 + 4x^2$$
$$0 = 2x^2(x + 2)$$
$$0 = x^2(x + 2)$$

Zeros: $x = -2, 0$

(c)

x	-3	-2	-1	0	1
$g(x)$	-18	0	2	0	6

(d)

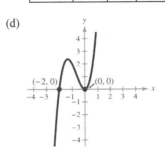

19. $f(x) = -x^3 + x^2 - 2$

(a) The degree is odd and the leading coefficient is negative. The graph rises to the left and falls to the right.

(b) Zero: $x = -1$

(c)

x	-3	-2	-1	0	1	2
$f(x)$	34	10	0	-2	-2	-6

(d)

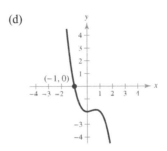

21. (a) $f(x) = 3x^3 - x^2 + 3$

x	-3	-2	-1	0	1	2	3
$f(x)$	-87	-25	-1	3	5	23	75

The zero is in the interval $[-1, 0]$.

(b) Zero: $x \approx -0.900$

23.
$$5x - 3 \overline{)\begin{array}{r} 6x + 3 \\ 30x^2 - 3x + 8 \end{array}}$$
$$\underline{30x^2 - 18x}$$
$$15x + 8$$
$$\underline{15x - 9}$$
$$17$$

$$\frac{30x^2 - 3x + 8}{5x - 3} = 6x + 3 + \frac{17}{5x - 3}$$

25. $f(x) = 20x^4 + 9x^3 - 14x^2 - 3x$

(a)
$$\begin{array}{r|rrrrr} -1 & 20 & 9 & -14 & -3 & 0 \\ & & -20 & 11 & 3 & 0 \\ \hline & 20 & -11 & -3 & 0 & 0 \end{array}$$

Yes, $x = -1$ is a zero of f.

(b)
$$\begin{array}{r|rrrrr} \frac{3}{4} & 20 & 9 & -14 & -3 & 0 \\ & & 15 & 18 & 3 & 0 \\ \hline & 20 & 24 & 4 & 0 & 0 \end{array}$$

Yes, $x = \frac{3}{4}$ is a zero of f.

(c)
$$\begin{array}{r|rrrrr} 0 & 20 & 9 & -14 & -3 & 0 \\ & & 0 & 0 & 0 & 0 \\ \hline & 20 & 9 & -14 & -3 & 0 \end{array}$$

Yes, $x = 0$ is a zero of f.

(d)
$$\begin{array}{r|rrrrr} 1 & 20 & 9 & -14 & -3 & 0 \\ & & 20 & 29 & 15 & 12 \\ \hline & 20 & 29 & 15 & 12 & 12 \end{array}$$

No, $x = 1$ is not a zero of f.

27. $f(x) = 2x^3 + 11x^2 - 21x - 90$; Factor: $(x + 6)$

(a)
$$\begin{array}{r|rrrr} -6 & 2 & 11 & -21 & -90 \\ & & -12 & 6 & 90 \\ \hline & 2 & -1 & -15 & 0 \end{array}$$

Yes, $(x + 6)$ is a factor of $f(x)$.

(b) $2x^2 - x - 15 = (2x + 5)(x - 3)$

The remaining factors are $(2x + 5)$ and $(x - 3)$.

(c) $f(x) = (2x + 5)(x - 3)(x + 6)$

(d) Zeros: $x = -\frac{5}{2}, 3, -6$

(e)
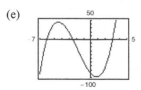

29. $8 + \sqrt{-100} = 8 + 10i$

31. $(7 + 5i) + (-4 + 2i) = (7 - 4) + (5i + 2i) = 3 + 7i$

33. $7i(11 - 9i) = 77i - 63i^2 = 63 + 77i$

35. $\dfrac{6 + i}{4 - i} = \dfrac{6 + i}{4 - i} \cdot \dfrac{4 + i}{4 + i}$

$= \dfrac{24 + 10i + i^2}{16 + 1}$

$= \dfrac{23 + 10i}{17}$

$= \dfrac{23}{17} + \dfrac{10}{17}i$

37. $x^2 - 2x + 10 = 0$

$x = \dfrac{-b \pm \sqrt{b^2 - 4ac}}{2a}$

$= \dfrac{-(-2) \pm \sqrt{(-2)^2 - 4(1)(10)}}{2(1)}$

$= \dfrac{2 \pm \sqrt{-36}}{2}$

$= \dfrac{2 \pm 6i}{2}$

$= 1 \pm 3i$

39. Since $g(x) = x^2 - 2x - 8$ is a 2nd degree polynomial function, it has two zeros.

41. $f(x) = x^3 + 3x^2 - 28x - 60$

Possible rational zeros:
$\pm 1, \pm 2, \pm 3, \pm 4, \pm 5, \pm 6, \pm 10, \pm 12, \pm 15, \pm 20, \pm 30, \pm 60$

$$\begin{array}{r|rrrr} -2 & 1 & 3 & -28 & -60 \\ & & -2 & -2 & 60 \\ \hline & 1 & 1 & -30 & 0 \end{array}$$

$x^3 + 3x^2 - 28x - 60 = (x + 2)(x^2 + x - 30)$
$\qquad\qquad\qquad\qquad = (x + 2)(x + 6)(x - 5)$

The zeros of $f(x)$ are $x = -2$, $x = -6$, and $x = 5$.

43. $g(x) = x^3 - 7x^2 + 36$

$$-2 \begin{array}{|cccc} 1 & -7 & 0 & 36 \\ & -2 & 18 & -36 \\ \hline 1 & -9 & 18 & 0 \end{array}$$

The zeros of $x^2 - 9x + 18 = (x - 3)(x - 6)$ are

$x = 3, 6$. The zeros of $g(x)$ are $x = -2, 3, 6$.

$g(x) = (x + 2)(x - 3)(x - 6)$

45. $h(x) = -2x^5 + 4x^3 - 2x^2 + 5$

$h(x)$ has three variations in sign, so h has either three or one positive real zeros.

$$\begin{aligned} h(-x) &= -2(-x)^5 + 4(-x)^3 - 2(-x)^2 + 5 \\ &= 2x^5 - 4x^3 - 2x^2 + 5 \end{aligned}$$

$h(-x)$ has two variations in sign, so h has either two or no negative real zeros.

47. Because the denominator is zero when $x + 10 = 0$, the domain of f is all real numbers except $x = -10$.

x	-11	-10.5	-10.1	-10.01	-10.001	$\rightarrow -10$
$f(x)$	33	63	303	3003	30,003	$\rightarrow \infty$

x	$-10 \leftarrow$	-9.999	-9.99	-9.9	-9.5	-9
$f(x)$	$-\infty$	$-29,997$	-2997	-297	-57	-27

As x approaches -10 from the left, $f(x)$ increases without bound.

As x approaches -10 from the right, $f(x)$ decreases without bound.

49. $f(x) = \dfrac{4}{x}$

(a) Domain: all real numbers x except $x = 0$

(b) No intercepts

(c) Vertical asymptote: $x = 0$

Horizontal asymptote: $y = 0$

(d)

x	-3	-2	-1	1	2	3
$f(x)$	$-\dfrac{4}{3}$	-2	-4	4	2	$\dfrac{4}{3}$

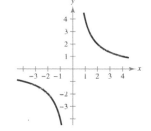

51. $f(x) = \dfrac{x}{x^2 + 1}$

(a) Domain: all real numbers x

(b) Intercept: $(0, 0)$

(c) Horizontal asymptote: $y = 0$

(d)

x	-2	-1	0	1	2
$f(x)$	$-\dfrac{2}{5}$	$-\dfrac{1}{2}$	0	$\dfrac{1}{2}$	$\dfrac{2}{5}$

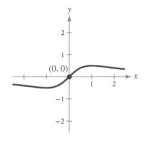

53. $f(x) = \dfrac{6x^2 - 11x + 3}{3x^2 - x}$

$= \dfrac{(3x - 1)(2x - 3)}{x(3x - 1)} = \dfrac{2x - 3}{x}, \; x \neq \dfrac{1}{3}$

(a) Domain: all real numbers x except $x = 0$ and
   $x = \dfrac{1}{3}$

(b) x-intercept: $\left(\dfrac{3}{2}, 0\right)$

(c) Vertical asymptote: $x = 0$
   Horizontal asymptote: $y = 2$

(d)

x	-2	-1	1	2	3	4
$f(x)$	$\dfrac{7}{2}$	5	-1	$\dfrac{1}{2}$	1	$\dfrac{5}{4}$

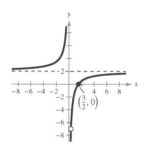

55. $f(x) = \dfrac{2x^3}{x^2 + 1} = 2x - \dfrac{2x}{x^2 + 1}$

(a) Domain: all real numbers x

(b) Intercept: $(0, 0)$

(c) Slant asymptote: $y = 2x$

(d)

x	-2	-1	0	1	2
$f(x)$	$-\dfrac{16}{5}$	-1	0	1	$\dfrac{16}{5}$

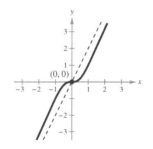

57. $C = \dfrac{528p}{100 - p}, \; 0 \leq p < 100$

(a)
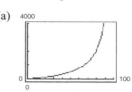

(b) When $p = 25, C = \dfrac{528(25)}{100 - 25} = \$176\,\text{million}.$

When $p = 50, C = \dfrac{528(50)}{100 - 50} = \$528\,\text{million}.$

When $p = 75, C = \dfrac{528(75)}{100 - 75} = \$1584\,\text{million}.$

(c) As $p \to 100, C \to \infty.$ No, it is not possible.

59. $12x^2 + 5x < 2$

$12x^2 + 5x - 2 < 0$

$(4x - 1)(3x + 2) < 0$

Key numbers: $x = -\dfrac{2}{3}, x = \dfrac{1}{4}$

Test intervals: $\left(-\infty, -\dfrac{2}{3}\right), \left(-\dfrac{2}{3}, \dfrac{1}{4}\right), \left(\dfrac{1}{4}, \infty\right)$

Test: Is $(4x - 1)(3x + 2) < 0?$

By testing an x-value in each test interval in the

inequality, you see that the solution set is $\left(-\dfrac{2}{3}, \dfrac{1}{4}\right).$

61. $\dfrac{2}{x + 1} \leq \dfrac{3}{x - 1}$

$\dfrac{2(x - 1) - 3(x + 1)}{(x + 1)(x - 1)} \leq 0$

$\dfrac{2x - 2 - 3x - 3}{(x + 1)(x - 1)} \leq 0$

$\dfrac{-(x + 5)}{(x + 1)(x - 1)} \leq 0$

Key numbers: $x = -5, x = \pm 1$

Test intervals: $(-\infty, -5), (-5, -1), (-1, 1), (1, \infty)$

Test: Is $\dfrac{-(x + 5)}{(x + 1)(x - 1)} \leq 0?$

By testing an x-value in each test interval in the inequality,
you see that the solution set is $[-5, -1) \cup (1, \infty).$

63.
$$P = \frac{1000(1 + 3t)}{5 + t}$$

$$2000 \le \frac{1000(1 + 3t)}{5 + t}$$

$$2000(5 + t) \le 1000(1 + 3t)$$

$$10{,}000 + 2000t \le 1000 + 3000t$$

$$-1000t \le -9000$$

$$t \ge 9 \text{ days}$$

65. False. A fourth-degree polynomial can have at most four zeros, and complex zeros occur in conjugate pairs.

Problem Solving for Chapter 2

1. $f(x) = ax^3 + bx^2 + cx + d$

$$
\begin{array}{r}
ax^2 + (ak + b)x + (ak^2 + bk + c) \\
x - k \overline{)\,ax^3 + bx^2 \quad\;\; + cx \quad\quad\; + d} \\
\underline{ax^3 - akx^2} \\
(ak + b)x^2 + cx \\
\underline{(ak + b)x^2 - (ak^2 + bk)x} \\
(ak^2 + bk + c)x + d \\
\underline{(ak^2 + bk + c)x - (ak^3 + bk^2 + ck)} \\
(ak^3 + bk^2 + ck + d)
\end{array}
$$

So, $f(x) = ax^3 + bx^2 + cx + d = (x - k)\left[ax^2 + (ak + b)x + (ak^2 + bx + c)\right] + ak^3 + bk^2 + ck + d$ and

$f(x) = ak^3 + bk^2 + ck + d$. Because the remainder is $r = ak^3 + bk^2 + ck + d$, $f(k) = r$.

3. $V = l \cdot w \cdot h = x^2(x + 3)$

$$x^2(x + 3) = 20$$

$$x^3 + 3x^2 - 20 = 0$$

Possible rational zeros: $\pm 1, \pm 2, \pm 4, \pm 5, \pm 10, \pm 20$

$$
\begin{array}{c|cccc}
2 & 1 & 3 & 0 & -20 \\
  &   & 2 & 10 & 20 \\
\hline
  & 1 & 5 & 10 & 0
\end{array}
$$

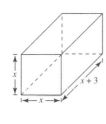

$$(x - 2)(x^2 + 5x + 10) = 0$$

$$x = 2 \text{ or } x = \frac{-5 \pm \sqrt{15}i}{2}$$

Choosing the real positive value for x we have:
$x = 2$ and $x + 3 = 5$.

 The dimensions of the mold are
 2 inches $\times$ 2 inches $\times$ 5 inches.

5. (a) $y = ax^2 + bx + c$

$$(0, -4): \; -4 = a(0)^2 + b(0) + c$$

$$-4 = c$$

$$(4, 0): \; 0 = a(4)^2 + b(4) - 4$$

$$0 = 16a + 4b - 4 = 4(4a + b - 1)$$

$$0 = 4a + b - 1 \quad \text{or} \quad b = 1 - 4a$$

$$(1, 0): \; 0 = a(1)^2 + b(1) - 4$$

$$4 = a + b$$

$$4 = a + (1 - 4a)$$

$$4 = 1 - 3a$$

$$3 = -3a$$

$$a = -1$$

$$b = 1 - 4(-1) = 5$$

$$y = -x^2 + 5x - 4$$

(b) Enter the data points $(0, -4)$, $(1, 0)$, $(2, 2)$, $(4, 0)$, $(6, -10)$ and use the regression feature to obtain

$$y = -x^2 + 5x - 4.$$

7. $f(x) = (x - k)q(x) + r$

(a) Cubic, passes through $(2, 5)$, rises to the right

One possibility:

$$f(x) = (x - 2)x^2 + 5$$
$$= x^3 - 2x^2 + 5$$

(b) Cubic, passes through $(-3, 1)$, falls to the right

One possibility:

$$f(x) = -(x + 3)x^2 + 1$$
$$= -x^3 - 3x^2 + 1$$

9. $(a + bi)(a - bi) = a^2 - abi + abi - b^2i^2 = a^2 + b^2$

Since a and b are real numbers, $a^2 + b^2$ is also a real number.

11. $f(x) = \dfrac{ax}{(x - b)^2}$

(a) $b \neq 0 \Rightarrow x = b$ is a vertical asymptote.

a causes a vertical stretch if $|a| > 1$ and a vertical shrink if $0 < |a| < 1$. For $|a| > 1$, the graph becomes wider as $|a|$ increases. When a is negative, the graph is reflected about the x-axis.

(b) $a \neq 0$. Varying the value of b varies the vertical asymptote of the graph of f. For $b > 0$, the graph is translated to the right. For $b < 0$, the graph is reflected in the x-axis and is translated to the left.

13. Because complex zeros always occur in conjugate pairs, and a cubic equation has three zeros and not four, a cubic equation with real coefficients can not have two real zeros and one complex zero.

Practice Test for Chapter 2

1. Sketch the graph of $f(x) = x^2 - 6x + 5$ and identify the vertex and the intercepts.

2. Find the number of units x that produce a minimum cost C if
   $$C = 0.01x^2 - 90x + 15,000.$$

3. Find the quadratic function that has a maximum at $(1, 7)$ and passes through the point $(2, 5)$.

4. Find two quadratic functions that have x-intercepts $(2, 0)$ and $\left(\frac{4}{3}, 0\right)$.

5. Use the leading coefficient test to determine the right and left end behavior of the graph of the polynomial function
   $f(x) = -3x^5 + 2x^3 - 17$.

6. Find all the real zeros of $f(x) = x^5 - 5x^3 + 4x$.

7. Find a polynomial function with 0, 3, and -2 as zeros.

8. Sketch $f(x) = x^3 - 12x$.

9. Divide $3x^4 - 7x^2 + 2x - 10$ by $x - 3$ using long division.

10. Divide $x^3 - 11$ by $x^2 + 2x - 1$.

11. Use synthetic division to divide $3x^5 + 13x^4 + 12x - 1$ by $x + 5$.

12. Use synthetic division to find $f(-6)$ given $f(x) = 7x^3 + 40x^2 - 12x + 15$.

13. Find the real zeros of $f(x) = x^3 - 19x - 30$.

14. Find the real zeros of $f(x) = x^4 + x^3 - 8x^2 - 9x - 9$.

15. List all possible rational zeros of the function $f(x) = 6x^3 - 5x^2 + 4x - 15$.

16. Find the rational zeros of the polynomial $f(x) = x^3 - \frac{20}{3}x^2 + 9x - \frac{10}{3}$.

17. Write $f(x) = x^4 + x^3 + 5x - 10$ as a product of linear factors.

18. Find a polynomial with real coefficients that has $2, 3 + i$, and $3 - 2i$ as zeros.

19. Use synthetic division to show that $3i$ is a zero of $f(x) = x^3 + 4x^2 + 9x + 36$.

20. Sketch the graph of $f(x) = \dfrac{x - 1}{2x}$ and label all intercepts and asymptotes.

21. Find all the asymptotes of $f(x) = \dfrac{8x^2 - 9}{x^2 + 1}$.

22. Find all the asymptotes of $f(x) = \dfrac{4x^2 - 2x + 7}{x - 1}$.

23. Given $z_1 = 4 - 3i$ and $z_2 = -2 + i$, find the following:

  (a) $z_1 - z_2$

  (b) $z_1 z_2$

  (c) z_1/z_2

24. Solve the inequality: $x^2 - 49 \leq 0$

25. Solve the inequality: $\dfrac{x + 3}{x - 7} \geq 0$

C H A P T E R 3
Exponential and Logarithmic Functions

C H A P T E R   3
Exponential and Logarithmic Functions

Section 3.1   Exponential Functions and Their Graphs

1. algebraic

3. One-to-One

5. $A = P\left(1 + \dfrac{r}{n}\right)^{nt}$

7. $f(1.4) = (0.9)^{1.4} \approx 0.863$

9. $f(-\pi) = 5^{-\pi} \approx 0.006$

11. $g(x) = 5000(2^x) = 5000(2^{-1.5})$
≈ 1767.767

13. $f(x) = 2^x$

Increasing

Asymptote: $y = 0$

Intercept: $(0, 1)$

Matches graph (d).

14. $f(x) = 2^x + 1$

Increasing

Asymptote: $y = 1$

Intercept: $(0, 2)$

Matches graph (c).

15. $f(x) = 2^{-x}$

Decreasing

Asymptote: $y = 0$

Intercept: $(0, 1)$

Matches graph (a).

16. $f(x) = 2^{x-2}$

Increasing

Asymptote: $y = 0$

Intercept: $\left(0, \frac{1}{4}\right)$

Matches graph (b).

17. $f(x) = \left(\frac{1}{2}\right)^x$

x	-2	-1	0	1	2
$f(x)$	4	2	1	0.5	0.25

Asymptote: $y = 0$

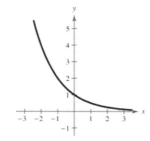

19. $f(x) = 6^{-x}$

x	-2	-1	0	1	2
$f(x)$	36	6	1	0.167	0.028

Asymptote: $y = 0$

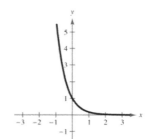

21. $f(x) = 2^{x-1}$

x	-2	-1	0	1	2
$f(x)$	0.125	0.25	0.5	1	2

Asymptote: $y = 0$

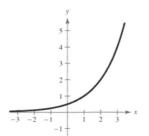

23. $3^{x+1} = 27$

   $3^{x+1} = 3^3$

   $x + 1 = 3$

   $x = 2$

25. $\left(\frac{1}{2}\right)^x = 32$

   $\left(\frac{1}{2}\right)^x = \left(\frac{1}{2}\right)^{-5}$

   $x = -5$

27. $f(x) = 3^x$, $g(x) = 3^x + 1$

   Because $g(x) = f(x) + 1$, the graph of g can be obtained by shifting the graph of f one unit upward.

29. $f(x) = \left(\frac{7}{2}\right)^x$, $g(x) = -\left(\frac{7}{2}\right)^{-x}$

   Because $g(x) = -f(-x)$, the graph of g can be obtained by reflecting the graph of f in the x-axis and y-axis.

31. $y = 2^{-x^2}$

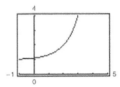

33. $f(x) = 3^{x-2} + 1$

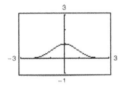

35. $f(x) = e^x = e^{3.2} \approx 24.533$

37. $f(6) = 5000e^{0.06(6)} \approx 7166.647$

39. $f(x) = e^x$

x	-2	-1	0	1	2
$f(x)$	0.135	0.368	1	2.718	7.389

Asymptote: $y = 0$

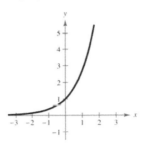

41. $f(x) = 3e^{x+4}$

x	-8	-7	-6	-5	-4
$f(x)$	0.055	0.149	0.406	1.104	3

Asymptote: $y = 0$

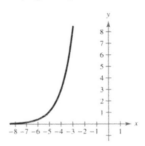

43. $f(x) = 2e^{x-2} + 4$

x	-2	-1	0	1	2
$f(x)$	4.037	4.100	4.271	4.736	6

Asymptote: $y = 4$

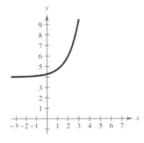

45. $y = 1.08e^{-5x}$

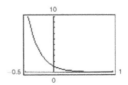

47. $s(t) = 2e^{0.12t}$

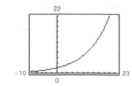

49. $g(x) = 1 + e^{-x}$

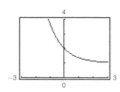

51. $e^{3x+2} = e^3$

$3x + 2 = 3$

$3x = 1$

$x = \frac{1}{3}$

53. $e^{x^2-3} = e^{2x}$

$x^2 - 3 = 2x$

$x^2 - 2x - 3 = 0$

$(x - 3)(x + 1) = 0$

$x = 3$ or $x = -1$

55. $P = \$1500, r = 2\%, t = 10$ years

Compounded n times per year: $A = P\left(1 + \dfrac{r}{n}\right)^{nt} = 1500\left(1 + \dfrac{0.02}{n}\right)^{10n}$

Compounded continuously: $A = Pe^{rt} = 1500e^{0.02(10)}$

n	1	2	4	12	365	Continuous
A	\$1828.49	\$1830.29	\$1831.19	\$1831.80	\$1832.09	\$1832.10

57. $P = \$2500, r = 4\%, t = 20$ years

Compounded n times per year: $A = P\left(1 + \dfrac{r}{n}\right)^{nt} = 2500\left(1 + \dfrac{0.04}{n}\right)^{20n}$

Compounded continuously: $A = Pe^{rt} = 2500e^{0.04(20)}$

n	1	2	4	12	365	Continuous
A	\$5477.81	\$5520.10	\$5541.79	\$5556.46	\$5563.61	\$5563.85

59. $A = Pe^{rt} = 12,000e^{0.04t}$

t	10	20	30	40	50
A	\$17,901.90	\$26,706.49	\$39,841.40	\$59,436.39	\$88,668.67

61. $A = Pe^{rt} = 12,000e^{0.065t}$

t	10	20	30	40	50
A	\$22,986.49	\$44,031.56	\$84,344.25	\$161,564.86	\$309,484.08

63. $A = 30,000e^{(0.05)(25)} \approx \$104,710.29$

65. $C(10) = 23.95(1.04)^{10} \approx \$35.45$

67. (a)

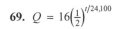

(b)

t	20	21	22	23
P (in millions)	342.748	345.604	348.485	351.389

t	24	25	26	27
P (in millions)	354.318	357.271	360.249	363.251

t	28	29	30	31
P (in millions)	366.279	369.331	372.410	375.513

t	32	33	34	35
P (in millions)	378.643	381.799	384.981	388.190

t	36	37	38	39
P (in millions)	391.425	394.687	397.977	401.294

t	40	41	42	43
P (in millions)	404.639	408.011	411.412	414.840

t	44	45	46	47
P (in millions)	418.298	421.784	425.300	428.844

t	48	49	50
P (in millions)	432.419	436.023	439.657

(c) Using the table of values created by the model, the population will exceed 400 million in 2038.

69. $Q = 16\left(\frac{1}{2}\right)^{t/24{,}100}$

(a) $Q(0) = 16$ grams

(b) $Q(75{,}000) \approx 1.85$ grams

(c)

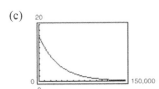

71. (a) $V(t) = 49{,}810\left(\frac{7}{8}\right)^t$ where t is the number of years since it was purchased.

(b) $V(4) = 49{,}810\left(\frac{7}{8}\right)^4 \approx 29{,}197.71$

After 4 years, the value of the van is about $29,198.

73. True. The line $y = -2$ is a horizontal asymptote for the graph of $f(x) = 10^x - 2$.

75. $f(x) = 3^{x-2}$

$= 3^x 3^{-2}$

$= 3^x\left(\frac{1}{3^2}\right)$

$= \frac{1}{9}(3^x)$

$= h(x)$

So, $f(x) \neq g(x)$, but $f(x) = h(x)$.

77. $f(x) = 16(4^{-x})$ and $f(x) = 16(4^{-x})$

$\qquad = 4^2(4^{-x}) \qquad\qquad = 16(2^2)^{-x}$

$\qquad = 4^{2-x} \qquad\qquad\quad = 16(2^{-2x})$

$\qquad = \left(\frac{1}{4}\right)^{-(2-x)} \qquad\quad = h(x)$

$\qquad = \left(\frac{1}{4}\right)^{x-2}$

$\qquad = g(x)$

So, $f(x) = g(x) = h(x)$.

79. $y = 3^x$ and $y = 4^x$

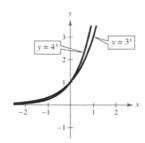

x	-2	-1	0	1	2
3^x	$\frac{1}{9}$	$\frac{1}{3}$	1	3	9
4^x	$\frac{1}{16}$	$\frac{1}{4}$	1	4	16

(a) $4^x < 3^x$ when $x < 0$.

(b) $4^x > 3^x$ when $x > 0$.

81.

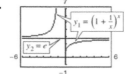

As x increases, the graph of y_1 approaches e, which is y_2.

83. (a)

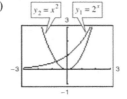

At $x = 2$, both functions have a value of 4. The function y_1 increases for all values of x. The function y_2 is symmetric with respect to the y-axis.

(b)

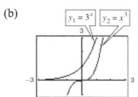

Both functions are increasing for all values of x. For $x > 0$, both functions have a similar shape. The function y_2 is symmetric with respect to the origin.

85. The functions (c) 3^x and (d) 2^{-x} are exponential.

Section 3.2 Logarithmic Functions and Their Graphs

1. logarithmic

3. natural; e

5. $x = y$

7. $\log_4 16 = 2 \Rightarrow 4^2 = 16$

9. $\log_{32} 4 = \frac{2}{5} \Rightarrow 32^{2/5} = 4$

11. $5^3 = 125 \Rightarrow \log_5 125 = 3$

13. $4^{-3} = \frac{1}{64} \Rightarrow \log_4 \frac{1}{64} = -3$

15. $f(x) = \log_2 x$

$\quad f(64) = \log_2 64 = 6$ because $2^6 = 64$

17. $f(x) = \log_8 x$

$\quad f(1) = \log_8 1 = 0$ because $8^0 = 1$

19. $g(x) = \log_a x$

$\quad g(a^2) = \log_a a^2$

$\qquad\quad = 2$ by the Inverse Property

21. $f(x) = \log x$

$\quad f\left(\frac{7}{8}\right) = \log\left(\frac{7}{8}\right) \approx -0.058$

23. $\quad f(x) = \log x$

$\quad f(12.5) = \log 12.5 \approx 1.097$

25. $\log_{11} 11^7 = 7$ because $11^7 = 11^7$

27. $\log_\pi \pi = 1$ because $\pi^1 = \pi$.

29. $\log_5(x + 1) = \log_5 6$

$\qquad\quad x + 1 = 6$

$\qquad\qquad\quad x = 5$

31. $\log(2x + 1) = \log 15$

$2x + 1 = 15$

$x = 7$

33.

x		-2	-1	0	1	2
$f(x) = 7^x$		$\frac{1}{49}$	$\frac{1}{7}$	1	7	49

x		$\frac{1}{49}$	$\frac{1}{7}$	1	7	49
$g(x) = \log_7 x$		-2	-1	0	1	2

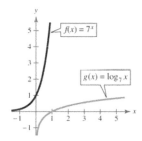

35.

x		-2	-1	0	1	2
$f(x) = 5^x$		$\frac{1}{25}$	$\frac{1}{5}$	1	5	25

x		$\frac{1}{36}$	$\frac{1}{6}$	1	6	36
$g(x) = \log_6 x$		-2	-1	0	1	2

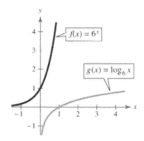

37. $f(x) = -\log_3(x + 2)$

Asymptote: $x = -2$

Point on graph: $(-1, 0)$

Matches graph (c).

The graph of $f(x)$ is obtained by reflecting the graph of $g(x)$ in the x-axis and shifting the graph two units to the left.

38. $f(x) = \log_3(x - 1)$

Asymptote: $x = 1$

Point on graph: $(2, 0)$

Matches graph (d).

$f(x)$ shifts $g(x)$ one unit to the right.

39. $f(x) = \log_3(1 - x) = \log_3\left[-(x - 1)\right]$

Asymptote: $x = 1$

Point on graph: $(0, 0)$

Matches graph (b).

The graph of $f(x)$ is obtained by reflecting the graph of $g(x)$ in the y-axis and shifting the graph one unit to the right.

40. $f(x) = -\log_3(-x)$

Asymptote: $x = 0$

Point on graph: $(-1, 0)$

Matches graph (a).

$f(x)$ reflects $g(x)$ in the x-axis the reflects that graph in the y-axis.

41. $f(x) = \log_4 x$

Domain: $(0, \infty)$

x-intercept: $(1, 0)$

Vertical asymptote: $x = 0$

$y - \log_4 x \Rightarrow 4^y = x$

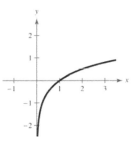

x	$\frac{1}{4}$	1	4	2
$f(x)$	-1	0	1	$\frac{1}{2}$

43. $y = -\log_3 x + 2$

Domain: $(0, \infty)$

x-intercept:

$-\log_3 x + 2 = 0$

$2 = \log_3 x$

$3^2 = x$

$9 = x$

The x-intercept is $(9, 0)$.

Vertical asymptote: $x = 0$

$y = -\log_3 x + 2$

$\log_3 x = 2 - y \Rightarrow 3^{2-y} = x$

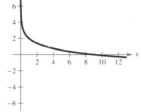

x	27	9	3	1	$\frac{1}{3}$
y	-1	0	1	2	3

45. $f(x) = -\log_6(x + 2)$

Domain: $x + 2 > 0 \Rightarrow x > -2$

The domain is $(-2, \infty)$.

x-intercept:

$0 = -\log_6(x + 2)$

$0 = \log_6(x + 2)$

$6^0 = x + 2$

$1 = x + 2$

$-1 = x$

The x-intercept is $(-1, 0)$.

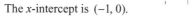

Vertical asymptote: $x + 2 = 0 \Rightarrow x = -2$

$y = -\log_6(x + 2)$

$-y = \log_6(x + 2)$

$6^{-y} - 2 = x$

x	4	-1	$-1\frac{5}{6}$	$-1\frac{35}{36}$
$f(x)$	-1	0	1	2

47. $y = \log\left(\dfrac{x}{7}\right)$

Domain: $\dfrac{x}{7} > 0 \Rightarrow x > 0$

The domain is $(0, \infty)$.

x-intercept: $\log\left(\dfrac{x}{7}\right) = 0$

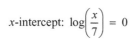

$\dfrac{x}{7} = 10^0$

$\dfrac{x}{7} = 1$

$x = 7$

The x-intercept is $(7, 0)$.

Vertical asymptote: $\dfrac{x}{7} = 0 \Rightarrow x = 0$

The vertical asymptote is the y-axis.

x	1	2	3	4	5
y	-0.85	-0.54	-0.37	-0.24	-0.15

x	6	7	8
y	-0.069	0	0.06

49. $\ln \frac{1}{2} = -0.693\ldots \Rightarrow e^{-0.693\ldots} = \frac{1}{2}$

51. $\ln 250 = 5.521\ldots \Rightarrow e^{5.521\ldots} = 250$

53. $e^2 = 7.3890\ldots \Rightarrow \ln 7.3890\ldots = 2$

55. $e^{-0.9} = 0.406\ldots \Rightarrow \ln 0.406\ldots = -0.9$

57. $f(x) = \ln x$

$f(18.42) = \ln 18.42 \approx 2.913$

59. $g(x) = 8 \ln x$

$g(0.05) = 8 \ln 0.05 \approx -23.966$

61. $g(x) = \ln x$

$g(e^5) = \ln e^5 = 5$ by the Inverse Property

63. $g(x) = \ln x$

$g(e^{-5/6}) = \ln e^{-5/6} = -\frac{5}{6}$ by the Inverse Property

65. $f(x) = \ln(x - 4)$

Domain: $x - 4 > 0 \Rightarrow x > 4$

The domain is $(4, \infty)$.

x-intercept: $0 = \ln(x - 4)$

$e^0 = x - 4$

$5 = x$

The x-intercept is $(5, 0)$.

Vertical asymptote: $x - 4 = 0 \Rightarrow x = 4$

x	4.5	5	6	7
$f(x)$	-0.69	0	0.69	1.10

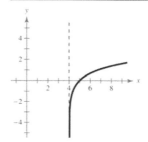

67. $g(x) = \ln(-x)$

Domain: $-x > 0 \Rightarrow x < 0$

The domain is $(-\infty, 0)$.

x-intercept:

$0 = \ln(-x)$

$e^0 = -x$

$-1 = x$

The x-intercept is $(-1, 0)$.

Vertical asymptote: $-x = 0 \Rightarrow x = 0$

x	-0.5	-1	-2	-3
$g(x)$	-0.69	0	0.69	1.10

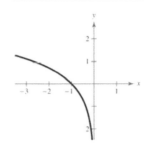

69. $f(x) = \ln(x - 1)$

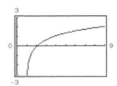

71. $f(x) = \ln x + 8$

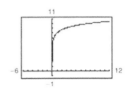

73. $\ln(x + 4) = \ln 12$

$x + 4 = 12$

$x = 8$

75. $\ln(x^2 - 2) = \ln 23$

$x^2 - 2 = 23$

$x^2 = 25$

$x = \pm 5$

77. $t = 16.625 \ln\left(\dfrac{x}{x - 750}\right)$, $x > 750$

(a) When $x = \$897.72$: $t = 16.625 \ln\left(\dfrac{897.72}{897.72 - 750}\right) \approx 30$ years

When $x = \$1659.24$: $t = 16.625 \ln\left(\dfrac{1659.24}{1659.24 - 750}\right) \approx 10$ years

(b) Total amounts: $(897.72)(12)(30) = \$323,179.20 \approx \$323,179$

$(1659.24)(12)(10) = \$199,108.80 \approx \$199,109$

(c) Interest charges: $323,179.20 - 150,000 = \$173,179.20 \approx \$173,179$

$199,108.80 - 150,000 = \$49,108.80 \approx \$49,109$

(d) The vertical asymptote is $x = 750$. The closer the payment is to $750 per month, the longer the length of the mortgage will be. Also, the monthly payment must be greater than $750.

79. $t = \dfrac{\ln 2}{r}$

(a)

r	0.005	0.010	0.015	0.020	0.025	0.030
t	138.6	69.3	46.2	34.7	27.7	23.1

(b)

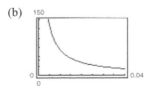

81. $f(t) = 80 - 17 \log(t + 1)$, $0 \le t \le 12$

(a)

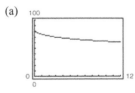

(b) $f(0) = 80 - 17 \log 1 = 80.0$

(c) $f(4) = 80 - 17 \log 5 \approx 68.1$

(d) $f(10) = 80 - 17 \log 11 \approx 62.3$

83. False. Reflecting $g(x)$ about the line $y = x$ will determine the graph of $f(x)$.

85. (a) $f(x) = \ln x, g(x) = \sqrt{x}$

The natural log function grows at a slower rate than the square root function.

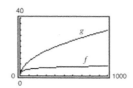

(b) $f(x) = \ln x, g(x) = \sqrt[4]{x}$

The natural log function grows at a slower rate than the fourth root function.

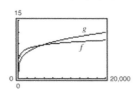

87. (a) False. If y were an exponential function of x, then $y = a^x$, but $a^1 = a$, not 0. Because one point is $(1, 0)$, y is not an exponential function of x.

(b) True. $y = \log_a x$

For $a = 2, y = \log_2 x$.

$x = 1, \log_2 1 = 0$

$x = 2, \log_2 2 = 1$

$x = 8, \log_2 8 = 3$

(c) True. $x = a^y$

For $a = 2, x = 2^y$.

$y = 0, 2^0 = 1$

$y = 1, 2^1 = 2$

$y = 3, 2^3 = 8$

(d) False. If y were a linear function of x, the slope between $(1, 0)$ and $(2, 1)$ and the slope between $(2, 1)$ and $(8, 3)$ would be the same. However,

$$m_1 = \frac{1 - 0}{2 - 1} = 1 \text{ and } m_2 = \frac{3 - 1}{8 - 2} = \frac{2}{6} = \frac{1}{3}.$$

So, y is not a linear function of x.

89. $y = \log_a x \Rightarrow a^y = x$, so, for example, if $a = -2$, there is no value of y for which $(-2)^y = -4$. If $a = 1$, then every power of a is equal to 1, so x could only be 1. So, $\log_a x$ is defined only for $0 < a < 1$ and $a > 1$.

Section 3.3 Properties of Logarithms

1. change-of-base

3. $\dfrac{1}{\log_b a}$

4. $\log_a(uv) = \log_a u + \log_a v$

This is the Product Property. Matches (c).

5. $\ln u^n = n \ln u$

This is the Power Property. Matches (a).

6. $\log_a \dfrac{u}{v} = \log_a u - \log_a v$

This is the Quotient Property. Matches (b).

7. (a) $\log_5 16 = \dfrac{\log 16}{\log 5}$

(b) $\log_5 16 = \dfrac{\ln 16}{\ln 5}$

9. (a) $\log_x \dfrac{3}{10} = \dfrac{\log(3/10)}{\log x}$

(b) $\log_x \dfrac{3}{10} = \dfrac{\ln(3/10)}{\ln x}$

11. $\log_3 7 = \dfrac{\log 7}{\log 3} = \dfrac{\ln 7}{\ln 3} \approx 1.771$

13. $\log_9 0.1 = \dfrac{\log 0.1}{\log 9} = \dfrac{\ln 0.1}{\ln 9} \approx -1.048$

15. $\log_4 8 = \dfrac{\log_2 8}{\log_2 4} = \dfrac{\log_2 2^3}{\log_2 2^2} = \dfrac{3}{2}$

17. $\log_5 \frac{1}{250} = \log_5\left(\frac{1}{125} \cdot \frac{1}{2}\right)$

$= \log_5 \frac{1}{125} + \log_5 \frac{1}{2}$

$= \log_5 5^{-3} + \log_5 2^{-1}$

$= -3 - \log_5 2$

19. $\ln\left(5e^6\right) = \ln 5 + \ln e^6$

$\qquad = \ln 5 + 6$

$\qquad = 6 + \ln 5$

21. $\log_3 9 = 2 \log_3 3 = 2$

23. $\log_2 \sqrt[4]{8} = \frac{1}{4} \log_2 2^3 = \frac{3}{4} \log_2 2 = \frac{3}{4}(1) = \frac{3}{4}$

25. $\log_4 16^2 = 2 \log_4 16 = 2 \log_4 4^2 = 2(2) = 4$

27. $\log_2(-2)$ is undefined. -2 is not in the domain of $\log_2 x$.

29. $\ln e^{4.5} = 4.5$

31. $\ln \dfrac{1}{\sqrt{e}} = \ln 1 - \ln \sqrt{e}$

$\qquad = 0 - \frac{1}{2} \ln e$

$\qquad = 0 - \frac{1}{2}(1)$

$\qquad = -\frac{1}{2}$

33. $\ln e^2 + \ln e^5 = 2 + 5 = 7$

35. $\log_5 75 - \log_5 3 = \log_5 \frac{75}{3}$

$\qquad = \log_5 25$

$\qquad = \log_5 5^2$

$\qquad = 2 \log_5 5$

$\qquad = 2$

37. $\ln 4x = \ln 4 + \ln x$

39. $\log_8 x^4 = 4 \log_8 x$

41. $\log_5 \dfrac{5}{x} = \log_5 5 - \log_5 x$

$\qquad = 1 - \log_5 x$

43. $\ln \sqrt{z} = \ln z^{1/2} = \frac{1}{2} \ln z$

45. $\ln xyz^2 = \ln x + \ln y + \ln z^2$

$\qquad = \ln x + \ln y + 2 \ln z$

47. $\ln z(z-1)^2 = \ln z + \ln(z-1)^2$

$\qquad = \ln z + 2 \ln(z-1), \; z > 1$

49. $\log_2 \dfrac{\sqrt{a-1}}{9} = \log_2 \sqrt{a-1} - \log_2 9$

$\qquad = \frac{1}{2} \log_2 (a-1) - \log_2 3^2$

$\qquad = \frac{1}{2} \log_2 (a-1) - 2 \log_2 3, \; a > 1$

51. $\ln \sqrt[3]{\dfrac{x}{y}} = \frac{1}{3} \ln \dfrac{x}{y}$

$\qquad = \frac{1}{3}\left[\ln x - \ln y\right]$

$\qquad = \frac{1}{3} \ln x - \frac{1}{3} \ln y$

53. $\ln x^2 \sqrt{\dfrac{y}{z}} = \ln x^2 + \ln \sqrt{\dfrac{y}{z}}$

$\qquad = \ln x^2 + \frac{1}{2} \ln \dfrac{y}{z}$

$\qquad = \ln x^2 + \frac{1}{2}\left[\ln y - \ln z\right]$

$\qquad = 2 \ln x + \frac{1}{2} \ln y - \frac{1}{2} \ln z$

55. $\log_5 \left(\dfrac{x^2}{y^2 z^3}\right) = \log_5 x^2 - \log_5 y^2 z^3$

$\qquad = \log_5 x^2 - \left(\log_5 y^2 + \log_5 z^3\right)$

$\qquad = 2 \log_5 x - 2 \log_5 y - 3 \log_5 z$

57. $\ln \sqrt[4]{x^3(x^2+3)} = \frac{1}{4} \ln x^3(x^2+3)$

$\qquad = \frac{1}{4}\left[\ln x^3 + \ln(x^2+3)\right]$

$\qquad = \frac{1}{4}\left[3 \ln x + \ln(x^2+3)\right]$

$\qquad = \frac{3}{4} \ln x + \frac{1}{4} \ln(x^2+3)$

59. $\log_b 10 = \log_b 2 \cdot 5$

$\qquad = \log_b 2 + \log_b 5$

$\qquad \approx 0.3562 + 0.8271$

$\qquad = 1.1833$

61. $\log_b 8 = \log_b 2^3$

$\qquad = 3 \log_b 2$

$\qquad \approx 3(0.3562)$

$\qquad = 1.0686$

63. $\log_b 45 = \log_b 9.5$

$\qquad = \log_b 9 + \log_b 5$

$\qquad = \log_b 3^2 + \log_b 5$

$\qquad = 2\log_b 3 + \log_b 5$

$\qquad \approx 2(0.5646) + 0.8271$

$\qquad = 1.9563$

65. $\log_b 3b^2 = \log_b 3 + \log_b b^2$

$\qquad = \log_b 3 + 2\log_b b$

$\qquad = \log_b 3 + 2(1)$

$\qquad \approx 0.5646 + 2$

$\qquad = 2.5646$

67. $\ln 2 + \ln x = \ln 2x$

69. $2\log_2 x + 4\log_2 y = \log_2 x^2 + \log_2 y^4 = \log_2 x^2 y^4$

71. $\frac{1}{4}\log_3 5x = \log_3(5x)^{1/4} = \log_3 \sqrt[4]{5x}$

73. $\log x - 2\log(x+1) = \log x - \log(x+1)^2$

$\qquad\qquad = \log \dfrac{x}{(x+1)^2}$

75. $\log x - 2\log y + 3\log z = \log x - \log y^2 + \log z^3$

$\qquad\qquad = \log \dfrac{x}{y^2} + \log z^3$

$\qquad\qquad = \log \dfrac{xz^3}{y^2}$

77. $\ln x - \left[\ln(x+1) + \ln(x-1)\right] = \ln x - \ln(x+1)(x-1) = \ln \dfrac{x}{(x+1)(x-1)}$

79. $\frac{1}{3}\left[2\ln(x+3) + \ln x - \ln(x^2-1)\right] = \frac{1}{3}\left[\ln(x+3)^2 + \ln x - \ln(x^2-1)\right]$

$\qquad\qquad = \frac{1}{3}\left[\ln x(x+3)^2 - \ln(x^2-1)\right]$

$\qquad\qquad = \frac{1}{3}\ln \dfrac{x(x+3)^2}{x^2-1}$

$\qquad\qquad = \ln \sqrt[3]{\dfrac{x(x+3)^2}{x^2-1}}$

81. $\frac{1}{3}\left[\log_8 y + 2\log_8(y+4)\right] - \log_8(y-1) = \frac{1}{3}\left[\log_8 y + \log_8(y+4)^2\right] - \log_8(y-1)$

$\qquad\qquad = \frac{1}{3}\log_8 y(y+4)^2 - \log_8(y-1)$

$\qquad\qquad = \log_8 \sqrt[3]{y(y+4)^2} - \log_8(y-1)$

$\qquad\qquad = \log_8 \left(\dfrac{\sqrt[3]{y(y+4)^2}}{y-1}\right)$

83. $\log_2 \dfrac{32}{4} = \log_2 32 - \log_2 4 \neq \dfrac{\log_2 32}{\log_2 4}$

The second and third expressions are equal by Property 2.

85. $\beta = 10\log\left(\dfrac{I}{10^{-12}}\right) = 10\left[\log I - \log 10^{-12}\right] = 10\left[\log I + 12\right] = 120 + 10\log I$

When $I = 10^{-6}$:

$\beta = 120 + 10\log 10^{-6} = 120 + 10(-6) = 60$ decibels

87. $\beta = 10 \log\left(\dfrac{I}{10^{-12}}\right)$

$$\text{Difference} = 10 \log\left(\dfrac{10^{-4}}{10^{-12}}\right) - 10 \log\left(\dfrac{10^{-11}}{10^{-12}}\right)$$

$$= 10\left[\log 10^8 - \log 10\right]$$

$$= 10(8 - 1)$$

$$= 10(7)$$

$$= 70 \text{ dB}$$

89.

x	1	2	3	4	5	6
y	1.000	1.189	1.316	1.414	1.495	1.565
$\ln x$	0	0.693	1.099	1.386	1.609	1.792
$\ln y$	0	0.173	0.275	0.346	0.402	0.448

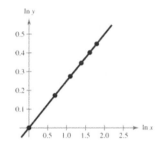

The slope of the line is $\frac{1}{4}$. So, $\ln y = \frac{1}{4} \ln x$

91.

x	1	2	3	4	5	6
y	2.500	2.102	1.900	1.768	1.672	1.597
$\ln x$	0	0.693	1.099	1.386	1.609	1.792
$\ln y$	0.916	0.743	0.642	0.570	0.514	0.468

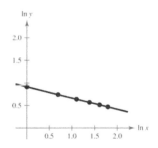

The slope of the line is $-\frac{1}{4}$. So, $\ln y = -\frac{1}{4} \ln x + \ln \frac{5}{2}$.

93.

Weight, x	25	35	50	75	500	1000
Galloping Speed, y	191.5	182.7	173.8	164.2	125.9	114.2
ln x		3.219	3.555	3.912	4.317	6.215	6.908
ln y		5.255	5.208	5.158	5.101	4.835	4.738

$y = 256.24 - 20.8 \ln x$

95. (a)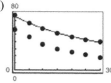

(b) $T - 21 = 54.4(0.964)^t$

$T = 54.4(0.964)^t + 21$

See graph in (a).

(c)

t (in minutes)	$T\,(°C)$	$T - 21\,(°C)$	$\ln(T - 21)$	$1/(T - 21)$
0	78	57	4.043	0.0175
5	66	45	3.807	0.0222
10	57.5	36.5	3.597	0.0274
15	51.2	30.2	3.408	0.0331
20	46.3	25.3	3.231	0.0395
25	42.5	21.5	3.068	0.0465
30	39.6	18.6	2.923	0.0538

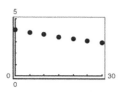

$\ln(T - 21) = -0.037t + 4$

$T = e^{-0.037t + 3.997} + 21$

This graph is identical to T in (b).

(d) $\dfrac{1}{T - 21} = 0.0012t + 0.016$

$T = \dfrac{1}{0.001t + 0.016} + 21$

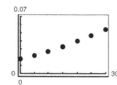 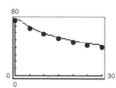

(e) Taking logs of temperatures led to a linear scatter plot because the log function increases very slowly as the x-values increase. Taking the reciprocals of the temperatures led to a linear scatter plot because of the asymptotic nature of the reciprocal function.

97. $f(x) = \ln x$

False, $f(0) \neq 0$ because 0 is not in the domain of $f(x)$.

$f(1) = \ln 1 = 0$

99. False.

$f(x) - f(2) = \ln x - \ln 2 = \ln \dfrac{x}{2} \neq \ln(x - 2)$

101. False.

$f(u) = 2f(v) \Rightarrow \ln u = 2 \ln v \Rightarrow \ln u = \ln v^2 \Rightarrow u = v^2$

103. $f(x) = \log_2 x = \dfrac{\log x}{\log 2} = \dfrac{\ln x}{\ln 2}$

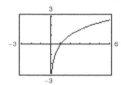

105. $f(x) = \log_{1/4} x$

$= \dfrac{\log x}{\log(1/4)} = \dfrac{\ln x}{\ln(1/4)}$

107. *Sample answers:*

(a) $\ln(1 + 3) \stackrel{?}{=} \ln 1 + \ln 3$

$1.39 \neq 0 + 1.10$

$\ln(u + v) = \ln(uv)$, but $\ln(u + v) \neq \ln u + \ln v$.

(b) $\ln(3 - 1) \stackrel{?}{=} \ln 3 - \ln 1$

$0.69 \neq 1.10 - 0$

$\ln u - \ln v = \ln \dfrac{u}{v}$, but $\ln(u - v) \neq \ln u - \ln v$.

(c) $(\ln 2)^3 \stackrel{?}{=} 3(\ln 2)$

$0.33 \neq 2.08$

$n(\ln u) = \ln u^n$, but $(\ln u)^n \neq n(\ln u)$.

109. $\ln 2 \approx 0.6931$, $\ln 3 \approx 1.0986$, $\ln 5 \approx 1.6094$

$\ln 1 = 0$

$\ln 2 \approx 0.6931$

$\ln 3 \approx 1.0986$

$\ln 4 = \ln(2 \cdot 2) = \ln 2 + \ln 2 \approx 0.6931 + 0.6931 = 1.3862$

$\ln 5 \approx 1.6094$

$\ln 6 = \ln(2 \cdot 3) = \ln 2 + \ln 3 \approx 0.6931 + 1.0986 = 1.7917$

$\ln 8 = \ln 2^3 = 3 \ln 2 \approx 3(0.6931) = 2.0793$

$\ln 9 = \ln 3^2 = 2 \ln 3 \approx 2(1.0986) = 2.1972$

$\ln 10 = \ln(5 \cdot 2) = \ln 5 + \ln 2 \approx 1.6094 + 0.6931 = 2.3025$

$\ln 12 = \ln(2^2 \cdot 3) = \ln 2^2 + \ln 3 = 2 \ln 2 + \ln 3 \approx 2(0.6931) + 1.0986 = 2.4848$

$\ln 15 = \ln(5 \cdot 3) = \ln 5 + \ln 3 \approx 1.6094 + 1.0986 = 2.7080$

$\ln 16 = \ln 2^4 = 4 \ln 2 \approx 4(0.6931) = 2.7724$

$\ln 18 = \ln(3^2 \cdot 2) = \ln 3^2 + \ln 2 = 2 \ln 3 + \ln 2 \approx 2(1.0986) + 0.6931 = 2.8903$

$\ln 20 = \ln(5 \cdot 2^2) = \ln 5 + \ln 2^2 = \ln 5 + 2 \ln 2 \approx 1.6094 + 2(0.6931) = 2.9956$

Section 3.4 Exponential and Logarithmic Equations

1. (a) $x = y$

(b) $x = y$

(c) x

(d) x

3. $4^{2x-7} = 64$

(a) $x = 5$

$4^{2(5)-7} = 4^3 = 64$

Yes, $x = 5$ *is* a solution.

(b) $x = 2$

$4^{2(2)-7} = 4^{-3} = \frac{1}{64} \neq 64$

No, $x = 2$ *is not* a solution.

5. $\log_2(x + 3) = 10$

(a) $x = 1021$

$\log_2(1021 + 3) = \log_2(1024)$

Because $2^{10} = 1024$, $x = 1021$ *is* a solution.

(b) $x = 17$

$\log_2(17 + 3) = \log_2(20)$

Because $2^{10} \neq 20$, $x = 17$ *is not* a solution.

(c) $x = 10^2 - 3 = 97$

$\log_2(97 + 3) = \log_2(100)$

Because $2^{10} \neq 100$, $10^2 - 3$ *is not* a solution.

7. $4^x = 16$

$\quad 4^x = 4^2$

$\qquad x = 2$

9. $\ln x - \ln 2 = 0$

$\qquad \ln x = \ln 2$

$\qquad\quad x = 2$

11. $\ln x = -1$

$\quad e^{\ln x} = e^{-1}$

$\qquad\ x = e^{-1}$

$\qquad\ x \approx 0.368$

13. $\log_4 x = 3$

$\quad 4^{\log_4 x} = 4^3$

$\qquad\quad x = 4^3$

$\qquad\quad x = 64$

15. $f(x) = g(x)$

$\quad 2^x = 8$

$\quad 2^x = 2^3$

$\qquad x = 3$

Point of intersection:

$(3, 8)$

17. $e^x = e^{x^2 - 2}$

$\quad x = x^2 - 2$

$\quad 0 = x^2 - x - 2$

$\quad 0 = (x + 1)(x - 2)$

$\quad x = -1, x = 2$

19. $4(3^x) = 20$

$\qquad 3^x = 5$

$\quad \log_3 3^x = \log_3 5$

$\qquad x = \log_3 5 = \dfrac{\log 5}{\log 3} \text{ or } \dfrac{\ln 5}{\ln 3}$

$\qquad x \approx 1.465$

21. $e^x - 9 = 19$

$\qquad e^x = 28$

$\quad \ln e^x = \ln 28$

$\qquad x = \ln 28 \approx 3.332$

23. $\qquad 3^{2x} = 80$

$\quad \ln 3^{2x} = \ln 80$

$\quad 2x \ln 3 = \ln 80$

$\qquad\quad x = \dfrac{\ln 80}{2 \ln 3} \approx 1.994$

25. $\qquad\qquad 2^{3-x} = 565$

$\qquad\quad \ln 2^{3-x} = \ln 565$

$\qquad (3 - x) \ln 2 = \ln 565$

$\quad 3 \ln 2 - x \ln 2 = \ln 565$

$\qquad\quad -x \ln 2 = \ln 565 - 3 \ln 2$

$\qquad\quad\ x \ln 2 = 3 \ln 2 - \ln 565$

$\qquad\qquad\ x = \dfrac{3 \ln 2 - \ln 565}{\ln 2}$

$\qquad\qquad\ x = 3 - \dfrac{\ln 565}{\ln 2} \approx -6.142$

27. $8(10^{3x}) = 12$

$\qquad 10^{3x} = \dfrac{12}{8}$

$\quad \log 10^{3x} = \log\left(\dfrac{3}{2}\right)$

$\qquad\quad 3x = \log\left(\dfrac{3}{2}\right)$

$\qquad\qquad x = \tfrac{1}{3} \log\left(\dfrac{3}{2}\right)$

$\qquad\qquad x \approx 0.059$

29. $e^{3x} = 12$

$\quad 3x = \ln 12$

$\qquad x = \dfrac{\ln 12}{3} \approx 0.828$

31. $7 - 2e^x = 5$

$\qquad -2e^x = -2$

$\qquad\quad e^x = 1$

$\qquad\qquad x = \ln 1 = 0$

33. $6(2^{3x-1}) - 7 = 9$

$\qquad 6(2^{3x-1}) = 16$

$\qquad\quad 2^{3x-1} = \dfrac{8}{3}$

$\quad \log_2 2^{3x-1} = \log_2\left(\dfrac{8}{3}\right)$

$\qquad 3x - 1 = \log_2\left(\dfrac{8}{3}\right) = \dfrac{\log(8/3)}{\log 2} \text{ or } \dfrac{\ln(8/3)}{\ln 2}$

$\qquad\qquad x = \dfrac{1}{3}\left[\dfrac{\log(8/3)}{\log 2} + 1\right] \approx 0.805$

35.
$$2^x = 3^{x+1}$$
$$\ln 2^x = \ln 3^{x+1}$$
$$x \ln 2 = (x + 1) \ln 3$$
$$x \ln 2 = x \ln 3 + \ln 3$$
$$x \ln 2 - x \ln 3 - \ln 3$$
$$x(\ln 2 - \ln 3) = \ln 3$$
$$x = \frac{\ln 3}{\ln 2 - \ln 3} \approx -2.710$$

37.
$$4^x = 5^{x^2}$$
$$\ln 4^x = \ln 5^{x^2}$$
$$x \ln 4 = x^2 \ln 5$$
$$x^2 \ln 5 - x \ln 4 = 0$$
$$x(x \ln 5 - \ln 4) = 0$$
$$x = 0$$
$$x \ln 5 - \ln 4 = 0 \Rightarrow x = \frac{\ln 4}{\ln 5} \approx 0.861$$

39.
$$e^{2x} - 4e^x - 5 = 0$$
$$(e^x + 1)(e^x - 5) = 0$$
$$e^x = -1 \quad \text{or} \quad e^x = 5$$
(No solution) $x = \ln 5 \approx 1.609$

41.
$$\frac{500}{100 - e^{x/2}} = 20$$
$$500 = 20(100 - e^{x/2})$$
$$25 = 100 - e^{x/2}$$
$$e^{x/2} = 75$$
$$\frac{x}{2} = \ln 75$$
$$x = 2 \ln 75 \approx 8.635$$

43.
$$\left(1 + \frac{0.065}{365}\right)^{365t} = 4$$
$$\ln\left(1 + \frac{0.065}{365}\right)^{365t} = \ln 4$$
$$365t \ln\left(1 + \frac{0.065}{365}\right) = \ln 4$$
$$t = \frac{\ln 4}{365 \ln\left(1 + \frac{0.065}{365}\right)} \approx 21.330$$

45. $\ln x = -3$
$$x = e^{-3} \approx 0.050$$

47.
$$2.1 = \ln 6x$$
$$e^{2.1} = 6x$$
$$\frac{e^{2.1}}{6} = x$$
$$1.361 \approx x$$

49. $3 \ln 5x = 10$
$$\ln 5x = \frac{10}{3}$$
$$5x = e^{10/3}$$
$$x = \frac{e^{10/3}}{5} \approx 5.606$$

51. $2 - 6 \ln x = 10$
$$-6 \ln x = 8$$
$$\ln x = -\frac{4}{3}$$
$$e^{\ln x} = e^{-4/3}$$
$$x = e^{-4/3}$$
$$x \approx 0.264$$

53. $6 \log_3(0.5x) = 11$
$$\log_3(0.5x) = \frac{11}{6}$$
$$3^{\log_3(0.5x)} = 3^{11/6}$$
$$0.5x = 3^{11/6}$$
$$x = 2(3^{11/6}) \approx 14.988$$

55. $\ln x - \ln(x + 1) = 2$
$$\ln\left(\frac{x}{x + 1}\right) = 2$$
$$\frac{x}{x + 1} = e^2$$
$$x = e^2(x + 1)$$
$$x = e^2 x + e^2$$
$$x - e^2 x = e^2$$
$$x(1 - e^2) - e^2$$
$$x = \frac{e^2}{1 - e^2} \approx -1.157$$

This negative value is extraneous. The equation has no solution.

57.
$$\ln(x + 5) = \ln(x - 1) - \ln(x + 1)$$
$$\ln(x + 5) = \ln\left(\frac{x - 1}{x + 1}\right)$$
$$x + 5 = \frac{x - 1}{x + 1}$$
$$(x + 5)(x + 1) = x - 1$$
$$x^2 + 6x + 5 = x - 1$$
$$x^2 + 5x + 6 = 0$$
$$(x + 2)(x + 3) = 0$$
$$x = -2 \quad \text{or} \quad x = -3$$

Both of these solutions are extraneous, so the equation has no solution.

59. $\log(3x + 4) = \log(x - 10)$
$$3x + 4 = x - 10$$
$$2x = -14$$
$$x = -7$$

The negative value is extraneous.
The equation has no solution.

61. $\log_4 x - \log_4(x - 1) = \frac{1}{2}$
$$\log_4\left(\frac{x}{x - 1}\right) = \frac{1}{2}$$
$$4^{\log_4[x/(x-1)]} = 4^{1/2}$$
$$\frac{x}{x - 1} = 4^{1/2}$$
$$x = 2(x - 1)$$
$$x = 2x - 2$$
$$-x = -2$$
$$x = 2$$

63. $f(x) = 5^x - 212$

Algebraically:
$$5^x = 212$$
$$\ln 5^x = \ln 212$$
$$x \ln 5 = \ln 212$$
$$x = \frac{\ln 212}{\ln 5}$$
$$x \approx 3.328$$

The zero is $x \approx 3.328$.

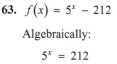

65. $g(x) = 8e^{-2x/3} - 11$

Algebraically:
$$8e^{-2x/3} = 11$$
$$e^{-2x/3} = 1.375$$
$$-\frac{2x}{3} = \ln 1.375$$
$$x = -1.5 \ln 1.375$$
$$x \approx -0.478$$

The zero is $x \approx -0.478$.

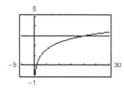

67. $y_1 = 3$
$$y_2 = \ln x$$

From the graph,
$x \approx 20.086$ when $y = 3$.

Algebraically:
$$3 - \ln x = 0$$
$$\ln x = 3$$
$$x = e^3 \approx 20.086$$

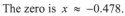

69. $y_1 = 2\ln(x + 3)$
$$y_2 = 3$$

From the graph, $x \approx 1.482$ when $y = 3$.

Algebraically:
$$2\ln(x + 3) = 3$$
$$\ln(x + 3) = \frac{3}{2}$$
$$x + 3 = e^{3/2}$$
$$x = e^{3/2} - 3 \approx 1.482$$

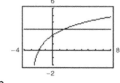

71. (a) $r = 0.025$
$$A = Pe^{rt}$$
$$5000 = 2500e^{0.025t}$$
$$2 = e^{0.025t}$$
$$\ln 2 = 0.025t$$
$$\frac{\ln 2}{0.025} = t$$
$$t \approx 27.73 \text{ years}$$

(b) $r = 0.025$
$$A = Pe^{rt}$$
$$7500 = 2500e^{0.025t}$$
$$3 = e^{0.025t}$$
$$\ln 3 = 0.025t$$
$$\frac{\ln 3}{0.025} = t$$
$$t \approx 43.94 \text{ years}$$

73. $2x^2 e^{2x} + 2x e^{2x} = 0$

$\quad (2x^2 + 2x)e^{2x} = 0$

$\quad\quad 2x^2 + 2x = 0 \quad$ (because $e^{2x} \neq 0$)

$\quad\quad 2x(x + 1) = 0$

$\quad x = 0, -1$

75. $-x e^{-x} + e^{-x} = 0$

$\quad (-x + 1)e^{-x} = 0$

$\quad\quad -x + 1 = 0 \quad$ (because $e^{-x} \neq 0$)

$\quad\quad x = 1$

77. $2x \ln x + x = 0$

$\quad x(2 \ln x + 1) = 0$

$\quad\quad 2 \ln x + 1 = 0 \quad$ (because $x > 0$)

$\quad\quad \ln x = -\frac{1}{2}$

$\quad\quad x = e^{-1/2} \approx 0.607$

79. $\dfrac{1 + \ln x}{2} = 0$

$\quad 1 + \ln x = 0$

$\quad\quad \ln x = -1$

$\quad\quad x = e^{-1} = \dfrac{1}{e} \approx 0.368$

81. (a)

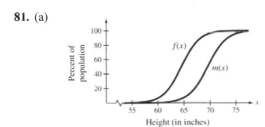

Height (in inches)

From the graph you see horizontal asymptotes at $y = 0$ and $y = 100$.

These represent the lower and upper percent bounds; the range falls between 0% and 100%.

(b) Males:
$$50 = \frac{100}{1 + e^{-0.5536(x - 69.51)}}$$

$$1 + e^{-0.5536(x - 69.51)} = 2$$

$$e^{-0.5536(x - 69.51)} = 1$$

$$-0.5536(x - 69.51) = \ln 1$$

$$-0.5536(x - 69.51) = 0$$

$$x = 69.51$$

The average height of an American male is 69.51 inches.

Females:
$$50 = \frac{100}{1 + e^{-0.5834(x - 64.49)}}$$

$$1 + e^{-0.5834(x - 64.49)} = 2$$

$$e^{-0.5834(x - 64.49)} = 1$$

$$-0.5834(x - 64.49) = \ln 1$$

$$-0.5834(x - 64.49) = 0$$

$$x = 64.49$$

The average height of an American female is 64.49 inches.

83. $N = 68\left(10^{-0.04x}\right)$

When $N = 21$:

$$21 = 68\left(10^{-0.04x}\right)$$

$$\frac{21}{68} = 10^{-0.04x}$$

$$\log_{10} \frac{21}{68} = -0.04x$$

$$x = -\frac{\log_{10}(21/68)}{0.04} \approx 12.76 \text{ inches}$$

85. $y = -3.00 + 11.88 \ln x + \dfrac{36.94}{x}$

(a)

x	0.2	0.4	0.6	0.8	1.0
y	162.6	78.5	52.5	40.5	33.9

(b)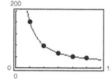

The model seems to fit the data well.

(c) When $y = 30$:

$$30 = -3.00 + 11.88 \ln x + \frac{36.94}{x}$$

Add the graph of $y = 30$ to the graph in part (a) and estimate the point of intersection of the two graphs.

You find that $x \approx 1.20$ meters.

(d) No, it is probably not practical to lower the number of gs experienced during impact to less than 23 because the required distance traveled at $y = 23$ is $x \approx 2.27$ meters. It is probably not practical to design a car allowing a passenger to move forward 2.27 meters (or 7.45 feet) during an impact.

87. $\log_a(uv) = \log_a u + \log_a v$

True by Property 1 in Section 3.3.

89. $\log_a(u - v) = \log_a u - \log_a v$

False.

$$1.95 = \log(100 - 10)$$

$$\neq \log 100 - \log 10 = 1$$

91. Yes, a logarithmic equation can have more than one extraneous solution. See Exercise 103.

93. $A = Pe^{rt}$

(a) $A = (2P)e^{rt} = 2\left(Pe^{rt}\right)$ This doubles your money.

(b) $A = Pe^{(2r)t} = Pe^{rt}e^{rt} = e^{rt}\left(Pe^{rt}\right)$

(c) $A = Pe^{r(2t)} = Pe^{rt}e^{rt} = e^{rt}\left(Pe^{rt}\right)$

Doubling the interest rate yields the same result as doubling the number of years.

If $2 > e^{rt}$ (i.e., $rt < \ln 2$), then doubling your investment would yield the most money. If $rt > \ln 2$, then doubling either the interest rate or the number of years would yield more money.

95. (a) $P = 1000, r = 0.07$, compounded annually, $n = 1$

Effective yield: $A = P\left(1 + \dfrac{r}{n}\right)^{nt} = 1000\left(1 + \dfrac{0.07}{1}\right)^{1} = \$1070$

$\dfrac{1070 - 1000}{1000} = 7\%$

The effective yield is 7%.

Balance after 5 years: $A = P\left(1 + \dfrac{r}{n}\right)^{nt} = 1000\left(1 + \dfrac{0.07}{1}\right)^{1(5)} \approx \$1402.55$

(b) $P = 1000, r = 0.07$, compounded continuously

Effective yield: $A = Pe^{rt} = 1000e^{0.07(1)} \approx \$1072.51$

$\dfrac{1072.51 - 1000}{1000} = 7.25\%$

The effective yield is about 7.25%.

Balance after 5 years: $A = Pe^{rt} = 1000e^{0.07(5)} \approx \$1419.07$

(c) $P = 1000, r = 0.07$, compounded quarterly, $n = 4$

Effective yield: $A = P\left(1 + \dfrac{r}{n}\right)^{nt} = 1000\left(1 + \dfrac{0.07}{4}\right)^{4(1)} \approx \$1071.86$

$\dfrac{1071.86 - 1000}{1000} = 7.19\%$

The effective yield is about 7.19%.

Balance after 5 years: $A = P\left(1 + \dfrac{r}{n}\right)^{nt} = 1000\left(1 + \dfrac{0.07}{4}\right)^{4(5)} \approx \$1414.78$

(d) $P = 1000, r = 0.0725$, compounded quarterly, $n = 4$

Effective yield: $A = P\left(1 + \dfrac{r}{n}\right)^{nt} = 1000\left(1 + \dfrac{0.0725}{4}\right)^{4(1)} \approx \$1074.50$

$\dfrac{1074.50 - 1000}{1000} \approx 7.45\%$

The effective yield is about 7.45%.

Balance after 5 years: $A = P\left(1 + \dfrac{r}{n}\right)^{nt} = 1000\left(1 + \dfrac{0.0725}{4}\right)^{4(5)} \approx \$1432.26$

Savings plan (d) has the greatest effective yield and the highest balance after 5 years.

Section 3.5   Exponential and Logarithmic Models

1. $y = ae^{bx}; y = ae^{-bx}$

3. normally distributed

5. (a) $A = Pe^{rt}$

$\dfrac{A}{e^{rt}} = P$

(b)

$A = Pe^{rt}$

$\dfrac{A}{P} = e^{rt}$

$\ln \dfrac{A}{P} = \ln e^{rt}$

$\ln \dfrac{A}{P} = rt$

$\dfrac{\ln(A/P)}{r} = t$

7. Because $A = 1000e^{0.035t}$, the time to double is given by $2000 = 1000e^{0.035t}$ and you have

$$2 = e^{0.035t}$$

$$\ln 2 = \ln e^{0.035t}$$

$$\ln 2 = 0.035t$$

$$t = \frac{\ln 2}{0.035} \approx 19.8 \text{ years.}$$

Amount after 10 years: $A = 1000e^{0.35} \approx \$1419.07$

9. Because $A = 750e^{rt}$ and $A = 1500$ when $t = 7.75$, you have

$$1500 = 750e^{7.75r}$$

$$2 = e^{7.75r}$$

$$\ln 2 = \ln e^{7.75r}$$

$$\ln 2 = 7.75r$$

$$r = \frac{\ln 2}{7.75} \approx 0.089438 = 8.9438\%.$$

Amount after 10 years: $A = 750e^{0.089438(10)} \approx \$1834.37$

11. Because $A = Pe^{0.045t}$ and $A = 10,000.00$ when $t = 10$, you have

$$10,000.00 = Pe^{0.045(10)}$$

$$\frac{10,000.00}{e^{0.045(10)}} = P = \$6376.28.$$

The time to double is given by

$$t = \frac{\ln 2}{0.045} \approx 15.40 \text{ years.}$$

13. $A = 500,000, r = 0.05, n = 12, t = 10$

$$A = P\left(1 + \frac{r}{n}\right)^{nt}$$

$$500,000 = P\left(1 + \frac{0.05}{12}\right)^{12(10)}$$

$$P = \frac{500,000}{\left(1 + \frac{0.05}{12}\right)^{12(10)}}$$

$$\approx \$303,580.52$$

15. $P = 1000, r = 0.1, A = 2000$

$$A = P\left(1 + \frac{r}{n}\right)^{nt}$$

$$2000 = 1000\left(1 + \frac{0.1}{n}\right)^{nt}$$

$$2 = \left(1 + \frac{0.1}{n}\right)^{nt}$$

(a) $n = 1$

$$(1 + 0.1)^t = 2$$

$$(1.1)^t = 2$$

$$\ln(1.1)^t = \ln 2$$

$$t \ln 1.1 = \ln 2$$

$$t = \frac{\ln 2}{\ln 1.1} \approx 7.27 \text{ years}$$

(b) $n = 12$

$$\left(1 + \frac{0.1}{12}\right)^{12t} = 2$$

$$\ln\left(\frac{12.1}{12}\right)^{12t} = \ln 2$$

$$12t \ln\left(\frac{12.1}{12}\right) = \ln 2$$

$$12t = \frac{\ln 2}{\ln(12.1/12)}$$

$$t = \frac{\ln 2}{12 \ln(12.1/12)} \approx 6.96 \text{ years}$$

(c) $n = 365$

$$\left(1 + \frac{0.1}{365}\right)^{365t} = 2$$

$$\ln\left(\frac{365.1}{365}\right)^{365t} = \ln 2$$

$$365t \ln\left(\frac{365.1}{365}\right) = \ln 2$$

$$365t = \frac{\ln 2}{\ln(365.1/365)}$$

$$t = \frac{\ln 2}{365 \ln(365.1/365)} \approx 6.93 \text{ years}$$

(d) Compounded continuously

$$A = Pe^{rt}$$

$$2000 = 1000e^{0.1t}$$

$$2 = e^{0.1t}$$

$$\ln 2 = \ln e^{0.1t}$$

$$0.1t = \ln 2$$

$$t = \frac{\ln 2}{0.1} \approx 6.93 \text{ years}$$

17. (a) $3P = Pe^{rt}$

$3 = e^{rt}$

$\ln 3 = rt$

$\dfrac{\ln 3}{r} = t$

r	2%	4%	6%	8%	10%	12%
$t = \dfrac{\ln 3}{r}$ (years)	54.93	27.47	18.31	13.73	10.99	9.16

(b) $3P = P(1 + r)^t$

$3 = (1 + r)^t$

$\ln 3 = \ln (1 + r)^t$

$\dfrac{\ln 3}{\ln (1 + r)} = t$

r	2%	4%	6%	8%	10%	12%
$t = \dfrac{\ln 3}{\ln (1 + r)}$ (years)	55.48	28.01	18.85	14.27	11.53	9.69

19. Continuous compounding results in faster growth.

$A = 1 + 0.075[\![t]\!]$ and $A = e^{0.07t}$

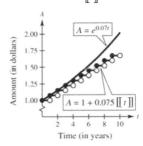

Time (in years)

21. $a = 10, y = \dfrac{1}{2}(10) = 5, t = 1599$

$y = ae^{-bt}$

$5 = 10e^{-b(1599)}$

$0.5 = e^{-1599b}$

$\ln 0.5 = \ln e^{-1599b}$

$\ln 0.5 = -1599b$

$b = -\dfrac{\ln 0.5}{1599}$

Given an initial quantity of 10 grams, after 1000 years, you have

$y = 10e^{-[-(\ln 0.5)/1599](1000)} \approx 6.48$ grams.

23. $y = 2, a = 2(2) = 4, t = 5715$

$y = ae^{-bt}$

$2 = 4e^{-b(5715)}$

$0.5 = e^{-5715b}$

$\ln 0.5 = \ln e^{-5715b}$

$\ln 0.5 = -5715b$

$b = -\dfrac{\ln 0.5}{5715}$

Given 2 grams after 1000 years, the initial amount is

$2 = ae^{-[-(\ln 0.5)/5715](1000)}$

$a \approx 2.26$ grams.

25. $y = ae^{bx}$

$1 = ae^{b(0)} \Rightarrow 1 = a$

$10 = e^{b(3)}$

$\ln 10 = 3b$

$\dfrac{\ln 10}{3} = b \Rightarrow b \approx 0.7675$

So, $y = e^{0.7675x}$.

27. $y = ae^{bx}$

$5 = ae^{b(0)} \Rightarrow 5 = a$

$1 = 5e^{b(4)}$

$\dfrac{1}{5} = e^{4b}$

$\ln\left(\dfrac{1}{5}\right) = 4b$

$\dfrac{\ln(1/5)}{4} = b \Rightarrow b \approx -0.4024$

So, $y = 5e^{-0.4024x}$.

29. (a)

Year	1980	1990	2000	2010
Population	106.1	143.15	196.25	272.37

(b) Let $P = 350$, and solve for t.

$350 = 20.6 + 85.5e^{0.0360t}$

$329.4 = 85.5e^{0.0360t}$

$\dfrac{329.4}{85.5} = e^{0.0360t}$

$\ln\left(\dfrac{329.4}{85.5}\right) = 0.0360t$

$\dfrac{1}{0.0360}\ln\left(\dfrac{329.4}{85.5}\right) = t$

$37.4 \approx t$

(c) No; The population will not continue to grow at such a quick rate.

The population will reach 350,000 people in the year 2017.

31. $y = 4080e^{kt}$

When $t = 3$, $y = 10,000$:

$$10,000 = 4080e^{k(3)}$$

$$\frac{10,000}{4080} = e^{3k}$$

$$\ln\left(\frac{10,000}{4080}\right) = 3k$$

$$k = \frac{\ln(10,000/4080)}{3} \approx 0.2988$$

When $t = 24$: $y = 4080e^{0.2988(24)} \approx 5,309,734$ hits

33. $y = ae^{bt}$

When $t = 3$, $y = 100$:   When $t = 5$, $y = 400$:

$$100 = ae^{3b} \qquad\qquad 400 = ae^{5b}$$

$$\frac{100}{e^{3b}} = a$$

Substitute $\dfrac{100}{e^{3b}}$ for a in the equation on the right.

$$400 = \frac{100}{e^{3b}}e^{5b}$$

$$400 = 100e^{2b}$$

$$4 = e^{2b}$$

$$\ln 4 = 2b$$

$$\ln 2^2 = 2b$$

$$2\ln 2 = 2b$$

$$\ln 2 = b$$

$$a = \frac{100}{e^{3b}} = \frac{100}{e^{3\ln 2}} = \frac{100}{e^{\ln 2^3}} = \frac{100}{2^3} = \frac{100}{8} = 12.5$$

$$y = 12.5e^{(\ln 2)t}$$

After 6 hours, there are $y = 12.5e^{(\ln 2)(6)} = 800$ bacteria.

35. $(0, 1150), (2, 550)$

(a) $m = \dfrac{550 - 1150}{2 - 0} = -300$

$$V = -300t + 1150$$

(b) $550 = 1150e^{k(2)}$

$$\ln\left(\frac{550}{1150}\right) = 2k \Rightarrow k \approx -0.369$$

$$V = 1150e^{-0.368799t}$$

(c)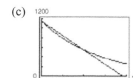

The exponential model depreciates faster in the first two years.

(d)

t	1	3
$V = -300t + 1100$	$850	$250
$V = 1150e^{-0.369t}$	$795	$380

(e) The slope of the linear model means that the computer depreciates $300 per year, then loses all value in the third year. The exponential model depreciates faster in the first two years but maintains value longer.

37. $R = \dfrac{1}{10^{12}}e^{-t/8223}$

(a) $\qquad R = \dfrac{1}{8^{14}}$

$$\frac{1}{10^{12}}e^{-t/8223} = \frac{1}{8^{14}}$$

$$e^{-t/8223} = \frac{10^{12}}{8^{14}}$$

$$-\frac{t}{8223} = \ln\left(\frac{10^{12}}{8^{14}}\right)$$

$$t = -8223\ln\left(\frac{10^{12}}{8^{14}}\right) \approx 12,180 \text{ years old}$$

(b) $\dfrac{1}{10^{12}}e^{-t/8223} = \dfrac{1}{13^{11}}$

$$e^{-t/8223} = \frac{10^{12}}{13^{11}}$$

$$-\frac{t}{8223} = \ln\left(\frac{10^{12}}{13^{11}}\right)$$

$$t = -8223\ln\left(\frac{10^{12}}{13^{11}}\right) \approx 4797 \text{ years old}$$

39. $y = 0.0266e^{-(x-100)^2/450}, \ 70 \le x \le 116$

(a)

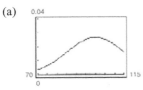

(b) The average IQ score of an adult student is 100.

41. (a) 1998: $t = 18, \ y = \dfrac{269,573}{1 + 985e^{-0.308(18)}}$

$\approx 55,557$ sites

2003: $t = 23, \ y = \dfrac{269,573}{1 + 985e^{-0.308(23)}}$

$\approx 147,644$ sites

2006: $t = 26, \ y = \dfrac{269,573}{1 + 985e^{-0.308(26)}}$

$\approx 203,023$ sites

(b) and (c)

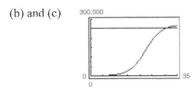

Because the lines intersect at $(30.6, 250,000)$, the number of cell sites will reach 250,000 in the year 2010.

(d) Let $y = 250,000$ and solve for t.

$$250,000 = \dfrac{269,573}{1 + 985e^{-0.308t}}$$

$$1 + 985e^{-0.308t} = \dfrac{269,573}{250,000}$$

$$985e^{-0.308t} = 0.078292$$

$$e^{-0.308t} \approx 0.000079484$$

$$-0.308t \approx \ln(0.00007948)$$

$$t \approx 30.6$$

The number of cell sites will reach 250,000 during the year 2010.

43. $p(t) = \dfrac{1000}{1 + 9e^{-0.1656t}}$

(a) $p(5) = \dfrac{1000}{1 + 9e^{-0.1656(5)}} \approx 203$ animals

(b) $500 = \dfrac{1000}{1 + 9e^{-0.1656t}}$

$1 + 9e^{-0.1656t} = 2$

$9e^{-0.1656t} = 1$

$e^{-0.1656t} = \dfrac{1}{9}$

$t = \dfrac{\ln(1/9)}{0.1656} \approx 13$ months

(c)

The horizontal asymptotes are $p = 0$ and $p = 1000$.

The asymptote with the larger p-value, $p = 1000$, indicates that the population size will approach 1000 as time increases.

45. $R = \log \dfrac{I}{I_0} = \log I$ because $I_0 = 1$.

(a) $R = 6.6$

$6.6 = \log I$

$10^{6.6} = 10^{\log I}$

$3,981,072 \approx I$

(b) $R = 5.6$

$5.6 = \log I$

$10^{5.6} = 10^{\log I}$

$10^{5.6} = I$

$398,107 \approx I$

(c) $R = 7.1$

$7.1 = \log I$

$10^{7.1} = 10^{\log I}$

$10^{7.1} = I$

$12,589,254 \approx I$

47. $\beta = 10 \log \dfrac{I}{I_0}$ where $I_0 = 10^{-12}$ watt/m^2.

(a) $\beta = 10 \log \dfrac{10^{-10}}{10^{-12}} = 10 \log 10^2 = 20$ decibels

(b) $\beta = 10 \log \dfrac{10^{-5}}{10^{-12}} = 10 \log 10^7 = 70$ decibels

(c) $\beta = 10 \log \dfrac{10^{-8}}{10^{-12}} = 10 \log 10^4 = 40$ decibels

(d) $\beta = 10 \log \dfrac{1}{10^{-12}} = 10 \log 10^{12} = 120$ decibels

49.
$$\beta = 10 \log \dfrac{I}{I_0}$$

$$\dfrac{\beta}{10} = \log \dfrac{I}{I_0}$$

$$10^{\beta/10} = 10^{\log I/I_0}$$

$$10^{\beta/10} = \dfrac{I}{I_0}$$

$$I = I_0 10^{\beta/10}$$

$$\% \text{ decrease} = \dfrac{I_0 10^{9.3} - I_0 10^{8.0}}{I_0 10^{9.3}} \times 100 \approx 95\%$$

51. $\mathrm{pH} = -\log\left[\mathrm{H}^+\right]$

$-\log\left(2.3 \times 10^{-5}\right) \approx 4.64$

53. $5.8 = -\log\left[\mathrm{H}^+\right]$

$-5.8 = \log\left[\mathrm{H}^+\right]$

$10^{-5.8} = 10^{\log\left[\mathrm{H}^+\right]}$

$10^{-5.8} = \left[\mathrm{H}^+\right]$

$\left[\mathrm{H}^+\right] \approx 1.58 \times 10^{-6}$ moles per liter

55. $2.9 = -\log\left[\mathrm{H}^+\right]$

$-2.9 = \log\left[\mathrm{H}^+\right]$

$\left[\mathrm{H}^+\right] = 10^{-2.9}$ for the apple juice

$8.0 = -\log\left[\mathrm{H}^+\right]$

$-8.0 = \log\left[\mathrm{H}^+\right]$

$\left[\mathrm{H}^+\right] = 10^{-8}$ for the drinking water

$\dfrac{10^{-2.9}}{10^{-8}} = 10^{5.1}$ times the hydrogen ion concentration of drinking water

57. $t = -10 \ln \dfrac{T - 70}{98.6 - 70}$

At 9:00 A.M. you have:

$t = -10 \ln \dfrac{85.7 - 70}{98.6 - 70} \approx 6$ hours

From this you can conclude that the person died at 3:00 A.M.

59. $u = 120{,}000 \left[\dfrac{0.075t}{1 - \left(\dfrac{1}{1 + 0.075/12}\right)^{12t}} - 1 \right]$

(a)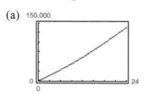

(b) From the graph, $u = \$120{,}000$ when $t \approx 21$ years.

It would take approximately 37.6 years to pay $\$240{,}000$ in interest. Yes, it is possible to pay twice as much in interest charges as the size of the mortgage. It is especially likely when the interest rates are higher.

61. False. The domain can be the set of real numbers for a logistic growth function.

63. False. The graph of $f(x)$ is the graph of $g(x)$ shifted upward five units.

65. Answers will vary.

Review Exercises for Chapter 3

1. $f(x) = 0.3^x$

$f(1.5) = 0.3^{1.5} \approx 0.164$

3. $f(x) = 2^{-0.5x}$

$f(\pi) = 2^{-0.5(\pi)} \approx 0.337$

5. $f(x) = 7(0.2^x)$

$f(-\sqrt{11}) = 7(0.2^{-\sqrt{11}})$

≈ 1456.529

7. $f(x) = 5^x, \ g(x) = 5^x + 1$

Because $g(x) = f(x) + 1$, the graph of g can be obtained by shifting the graph of f one unit upward.

9. $f(x) = 3^x, \ g(x) = 1 - 3^x$

Because $g(x) = 1 - f(x)$, the graph of g can be obtained by reflecting the graph of f in the x-axis and shifting the graph one unit upward. (**Note:** This is equivalent to shifting the graph of f one unit upward and then reflecting the graph in the x-axis.)

11. $f(x) = 4^{-x} + 4$

Horizontal asymptote: $y = 4$

x	-1	0	1	2	3
$f(x)$	8	5	4.25	4.063	4.016

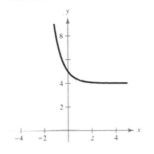

13. $f(x) = 5^{x-2} + 4$

Horizontal asymptote: $y = 4$

x	-1	0	1	2	3
$f(x)$	4.008	4.04	4.2	5	9

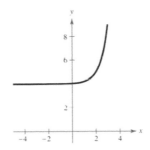

15. $f(x) = \left(\frac{1}{2}\right)^{-x} + 3 = 2^x + 3$

Horizontal asymptote: $y = 3$

x	-2	-1	0	1	2
$f(x)$	3.25	3.5	4	5	7

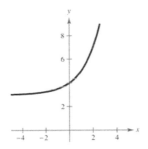

17. $\left(\frac{1}{3}\right)^{x-3} = 9$

$\left(\frac{1}{3}\right)^{x-3} = 3^2$

$\left(\frac{1}{3}\right)^{x-3} = \left(\frac{1}{3}\right)^{-2}$

$x - 3 = -2$

$x = 1$

19. $e^{3x-5} = e^7$

$3x - 5 = 7$

$3x = 12$

$x = 4$

21. $e^8 \approx 2980.958$

23. $e^{-1.7} \approx 0.183$

25. $h(x) = e^{-x/2}$

x	-2	-1	0	1	2
$h(x)$	2.72	1.65	1	0.61	0.37

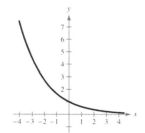

27. $f(x) = e^{x+2}$

x	-3	-2	-1	0	1
$f(x)$	0.37	1	2.72	7.39	20.09

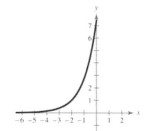

29. $F(t) = 1 - e^{-t/3}$

(a) $F\left(\frac{1}{2}\right) \approx 0.154$

(b) $F(2) \approx 0.487$

(c) $F(5) \approx 0.811$

31. $P = \$5000, r = 3\%, t = 10$ years

Compounded n times per year: $A = P\left(1 + \dfrac{r}{n}\right)^{nt} = 5000\left(1 + \dfrac{0.03}{n}\right)^{10n}$

Compounded continuously: $A = Pe^{rt} = 5000e^{0.03(10)}$

n	1	2	4	12	365	Continuous
A	\$6719.58	\$6734.28	\$6741.74	\$6746.77	\$6749.21	\$6749.29

33. $3^3 = 27$

$\log_3 27 = 3$

35. $e^{0.8} = 2.2255...$

$\ln 2.2255... = 0.8$

37. $f(x) = \log x$

$f(1000) = \log 1000$

$= \log 10^3 = 3$

39. $g(x) = \log_2 x$

$g\left(\frac{1}{4}\right) = \log_2 \frac{1}{4}$

$= \log_2 2^{-2} = -2$

41. $\log_4(x + 7) = \log_4 14$

$x + 7 = 14$

$x = 7$

43. $\ln(x + 9) = \ln 4$

$x + 9 = 4$

$x = -5$

45. $g(x) = \log_7 x \Rightarrow x = 7^y$

Domain: $(0, \infty)$

x-intercept: $(1, 0)$

Vertical asymptote: $x = 0$

x	$\frac{1}{7}$	1	7	49
$g(x)$	-1	0	1	2

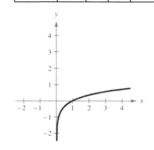

47. $f(x) = 4 - \log(x + 5)$

Domain: $(-5, \infty)$

Because
$$4 - \log(x + 5) = 0 \Rightarrow \log(x + 5) = 4$$
$$x + 5 = 10^4$$
$$x = 10^4 - 5$$
$$= 9995.$$

x-intercept: $(9995, 0)$

Vertical asymptote: $x = -5$

x	-4	-3	-2	-1	0	1
$f(x)$	4	3.70	3.52	3.40	3.30	3.22

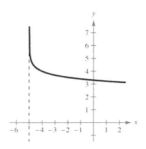

49. $f(22.6) = \ln 22.6 \approx 3.118$

51. $f(\sqrt{e}) = \frac{1}{2} \ln \sqrt{e} = 0.25$

53. $f(x) = \ln x + 3$

Domain: $(0, \infty)$

$$\ln x + 3 = 0$$
$$\ln x = -3$$
$$x = e^{-3}$$

x-intercept: $(e^{-3}, 0)$

Vertical asymptote: $x = 0$

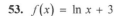

x	1	2	3	$\frac{1}{2}$	$\frac{1}{4}$
$f(x)$	3	3.69	4.10	2.31	1.61

55. $h(x) = \ln(x^2) = 2 \ln|x|$

Domain: $(-\infty, 0) \cup (0, \infty)$

x-intercepts: $(\pm 1, 0)$

Vertical asymptote: $x = 0$

x	± 0.5	± 1	± 2	± 3	± 4
$h(x)$	-1.39	0	1.39	2.20	2.77

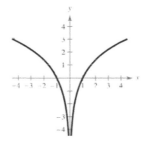

57. $h = 116 \log(a + 40) - 176$
$$h(55) = 116 \log(55 + 40) - 176$$
$$\approx 53.4 \text{ inches}$$

59. (a) $\log_2 6 = \dfrac{\log 6}{\log 2} \approx 2.585$

(b) $\log_2 6 = \dfrac{\ln 6}{\ln 2} \approx 2.585$

61. (a) $\log_{1/2} 5 = \dfrac{\log 5}{\log(1/2)} \approx -2.322$

(b) $\log_{1/2} 5 = \dfrac{\ln 5}{\ln(1/2)} \approx -2.322$

63. $\log 18 = \log(2 \cdot 3^2)$
$$= \log 2 + 2 \log 3$$
$$\approx 1.255$$

65. $\ln 20 = \ln(2^2 \cdot 5)$
$$= 2 \ln 2 + \ln 5 \approx 2.996$$

67. $\log_5 5x^2 = \log_5 5 + \log_5 x^2$
$$= 1 + 2 \log_5 x$$

69. $\log_3 \dfrac{9}{\sqrt{x}} = \log_3 9 - \log_3 \sqrt{x}$
$$= \log_3 3^2 - \log_3 x^{1/2}$$
$$= 2 - \frac{1}{2} \log_3 x$$

71. $\ln x^2 y^2 z = \ln x^2 + \ln y^2 + \ln z$
$$= 2 \ln x + 2 \ln y + \ln z$$

73. $\log_2 5 + \log_2 x = \log_2 5x$

75. $\ln x - \dfrac{1}{4} \ln y = \ln x - \ln \sqrt[4]{y} = \ln \dfrac{x}{\sqrt[4]{y}}$

77. $\dfrac{1}{2} \log_3 x - 2 \log_3 (y + 8) = \log_3 x^{1/2} - \log_3 (y + 8)^2$
$$= \log_3 \sqrt{x} - \log_3 (y + 8)^2$$
$$= \log_3 \dfrac{\sqrt{x}}{(y + 8)^2}$$

79. $t = 50 \log \dfrac{18{,}000}{18{,}000 - h}$

(a) Domain: $0 \le h < 18{,}000$

(b)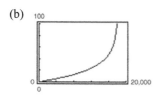

Vertical asymptote: $h = 18{,}000$

(c) As the plane approaches its absolute ceiling, it climbs at a slower rate, so the time required increases.

(d) $50 \log \dfrac{18{,}000}{18{,}000 - 4000} \approx 5.46$ minutes

81. $5^x = 125$
$$5^x = 5^3$$
$$x = 3$$

83. $e^x = 3$
$$x = \ln 3 \approx 1.099$$

85. $\ln x = 4$
$$x = e^4 \approx 54.598$$

87. $e^{4x} = e^{x^2 + 3}$
$$4x = x^2 + 3$$
$$0 = x^2 - 4x + 3$$
$$0 = (x - 1)(x - 3)$$
$$x = 1, \ x = 3$$

89. $2^x - 3 = 29$
$$2^x = 32$$
$$2^x = 2^5$$
$$x = 5$$

91. $25e^{-0.3x} = 12$

Graph $y_1 = 25e^{-0.3x}$ and $y_2 = 12$.

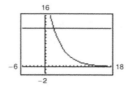

The graphs intersect at $x \approx 2.447$.

93. $\ln 3x = 8.2$
$$e^{\ln 3x} = e^{8.2}$$
$$3x = e^{8.2}$$
$$x = \dfrac{e^{8.2}}{3} \approx 1213.650$$

95. $\ln x - \ln 3 = 2$
$$\ln \dfrac{x}{3} = 2$$
$$e^{\ln (x/3)} = e^2$$
$$\dfrac{x}{3} = e^2$$
$$x = 3e^2 \approx 22.167$$

97. $\log_8 (x - 1) = \log_8 (x - 2) - \log_8 (x + 2)$
$$\log_8 (x - 1) = \log_8 \left(\dfrac{x - 2}{x + 2} \right)$$
$$x - 1 = \dfrac{x - 2}{x + 2}$$
$$(x - 1)(x + 2) = x - 2$$
$$x^2 + x - 2 = x - 2$$
$$x^2 = 0$$
$$x = 0$$

Because $x = 0$ is not in the domain of $\log_8 (x - 1)$ or of $\log_8 (x - 2)$, it is an extraneous solution. The equation has no solution.

99. $\log (1 - x) = -1$
$$1 - x = 10^{-1}$$
$$1 - \tfrac{1}{10} = x$$
$$x = 0.900$$

101. $2 \ln(x + 3) - 3 = 0$

Graph $y_1 = 2 \ln(x + 3) - 3$.

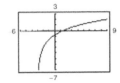

The x-intercept is at $x \approx 1.482$.

103. $6 \log(x^2 + 1) - x = 0$

Graph $y_1 = 6 \log(x^2 + 1) - x$.

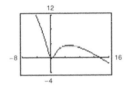

The x-intercepts are at $x = 0$, $x \approx 0.416$, and $x \approx 13.627$.

105. $P = 8500$, $A = 3(8500) = 25{,}500$, $r = 3.5\%$

$$A = Pe^{rt}$$
$$25{,}500 = 8500e^{0.035t}$$
$$3 = e^{0.035t}$$
$$\ln 3 = 0.035t$$
$$t = \frac{\ln 3}{0.035} \approx 31.4 \text{ years}$$

107. $y = 3e^{-2x/3}$

Exponential decay model

Matches graph (e).

108. $y = 4e^{2x/3}$

Exponential growth model

Matches graph (b).

109. $y = \ln(x + 3)$

Logarithmic model

Vertical asymptote: $x = -3$

Graph includes $(-2, 0)$

Matches graph (f).

110. $y = 7 - \log(x + 3)$

Logarithmic model

Vertical asymptote: $x = -3$

Matches graph (d).

111. $y = 2e^{-(x+4)^2/3}$

Gaussian model

Matches graph (a).

112. $y = \dfrac{6}{1 + 2e^{-2x}}$

Logistics growth model

Matches graph (c).

113. $y = ae^{bx}$

Using the point $(0, 2)$, you have

$$2 = ae^{b(0)}$$
$$2 = ae^0$$
$$2 = a(1)$$
$$2 = a$$

Then, using the point $(4, 3)$, you have

$$3 = 2e^{b(4)}$$
$$3 = 2e^{4b}$$
$$\tfrac{3}{2} = e^{4b}$$
$$\ln \tfrac{3}{2} = 4b$$
$$\tfrac{1}{4} \ln\left(\tfrac{3}{2}\right) = b$$

So, $y = 2e^{\frac{1}{4}\ln\left(\frac{3}{2}\right)x}$

or

$$y = 2e^{0.1014x}$$

115. $y = 0.0499e^{-(x-71)^2/128}$, $40 \le x \le 100$

Graph $y_1 = 0.0499e^{-(x-71)^2/128}$.

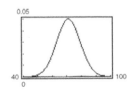

The average test score is 71.

117. $\beta = 10 \log\left(\dfrac{I}{10^{-12}}\right)$

$\dfrac{\beta}{10} = \log\left(\dfrac{I}{10^{-12}}\right)$

$10^{\beta/10} = \dfrac{I}{10^{-12}}$

$I = 10^{\beta/10-12}$

(a) $\beta = 60$

  $I = 10^{60/10-12}$

  $= 10^{-6} \text{ watt/m}^2$

(b) $\beta = 135$

  $I = 10^{135/10-12}$

  $= 10^{1.5}$

  $= 10\sqrt{10} \text{ watts/m}^2$

(c) $\beta = 1$

  $I = 10^{1/10-12}$

  $= 10^{\frac{1}{10}} \times 10^{-12}$

  $\approx 1.259 \times 10^{-2} \text{ watt/m}^2$

119. True. By the inverse properties, $\log_b b^{2x} = 2x$.

Problem Solving for Chapter 3

1. $y = a^x$

$y_1 = 0.5^x$

$y_2 = 1.2^x$

$y_3 = 2.0^x$

$y_4 = x$

The curves $y = 0.5^x$ and $y = 1.2^x$ cross the line $y = x$. From checking the graphs it appears that $y = x$ will cross $y = a^x$ for $0 \le a \le 1.44$.

3. The exponential function, $y = e^x$, increases at a faster rate than the polynomial $y = x^n$.

5. (a) $f(u + v) = a^{u+v} = a^u \cdot a^v = f(u) \cdot f(v)$

(b) $f(2x) = a^{2x} = \left(a^x\right)^2 = \left[f(x)\right]^2$

7. (a)

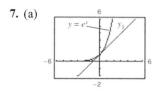

(b)

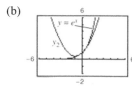

(c)

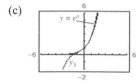

9. $f(x) = e^x - e^{-x}$

$y = e^x - e^{-x}$

$x = e^y - e^{-y}$

$x = \dfrac{e^{2y} - 1}{e^y}$

$xe^y = e^{2y} - 1$

$e^{2y} - xe^y - 1 = 0$

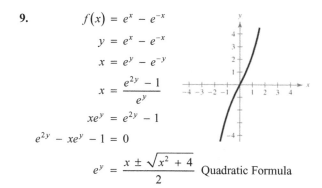

$e^y = \dfrac{x \pm \sqrt{x^2 + 4}}{2}$ Quadratic Formula

Choosing the positive quantity for e^y you have

$y = \ln\left(\dfrac{x + \sqrt{x^2 + 4}}{2}\right)$. So,

$f^{-1}(x) = \ln\left(\dfrac{x + \sqrt{x^2 + 4}}{2}\right)$.

11. Answer (c). $y = 6\left(1 - e^{-x^2/2}\right)$

The graph passes through $(0, 0)$ and neither (a) nor (b) pass through the origin. Also, the graph has y-axis symmetry and a horizontal asymptote at $y = 6$.

13. $y_1 = c_1\left(\dfrac{1}{2}\right)^{t/k_1}$ and $y_2 = c_2\left(\dfrac{1}{2}\right)^{t/k_2}$

$$c_1\left(\frac{1}{2}\right)^{t/k_1} = c_2\left(\frac{1}{2}\right)^{t/k_2}$$

$$\frac{c_1}{c_2} = \left(\frac{1}{2}\right)^{(t/k_2 - t/k_1)}$$

$$\ln\left(\frac{c_1}{c_2}\right) = \left(\frac{t}{k_2} - \frac{t}{k_1}\right)\ln\left(\frac{1}{2}\right)$$

$$\ln c_1 - \ln c_2 = t\left(\frac{1}{k_2} - \frac{1}{k_1}\right)\ln\left(\frac{1}{2}\right)$$

$$t = \frac{\ln c_1 - \ln c_2}{\left[(1/k_2) - (1/k_1)\right]\ln(1/2)}$$

15. (a) $y_1 \approx 252.606(1.0310)^t$

(b) $y_2 \approx 400.88t^2 - 1464.6t + 291{,}782$

(c)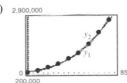

(d) The exponential model is a better fit for the data, but neither would be reliable to predict the population of the United States in 2015. The exponential model approaches infinity rapidly.

17.
$$(\ln x)^2 = \ln x^2$$

$$(\ln x)^2 - 2\ln x = 0$$

$$\ln x(\ln x - 2) = 0$$

$$\ln x = 0 \quad \text{or} \quad \ln x = 2$$

$$x = 1 \quad \text{or} \quad x = e^2$$

19. $y_4 = (x - 1) - \frac{1}{2}(x - 1)^2 + \frac{1}{3}(x - 1)^3 - \frac{1}{4}(x - 1)^4$

The pattern implies that

$$\ln x = (x - 1) - \frac{1}{2}(x - 1)^2 + \frac{1}{3}(x - 1)^3 - \frac{1}{4}(x - 1)^4 + \dots.$$

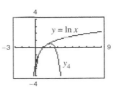

21. $y = 80.4 - 11\ln x$

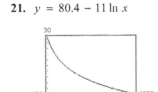

$$y(300) = 80.4 - 11\ln 300 \approx 17.7 \ \text{ft}^3/\text{min}$$

23. (a)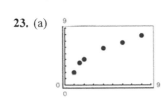

(b) The data could best be modeled by a logarithmic model.

(c) The shape of the curve looks much more logarithmic than linear or exponential.

(d) $y \approx 2.1518 + 2.7044\ln x$

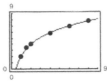

(e) The model is a good fit to the actual data.

25. (a)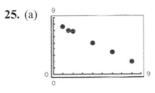

(b) The data could best be modeled by a linear model.

(c) The shape of the curve looks much more linear than exponential or logarithmic.

(d) $y \approx -0.7884x + 8.2566$

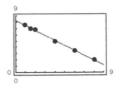

(e) The model is a good fit to the actual data.

Practice Test for Chapter 3

1. Solve for x: $x^{3/5} = 8$.

2. Solve for x: $3^{x-1} = \frac{1}{81}$.

3. Graph $f(x) = 2^{-x}$.

4. Graph $g(x) = e^x + 1$.

5. If $5000 is invested at 9% interest, find the amount after three years if the interest is compounded
   (a) monthly.
   (b) quarterly.
   (c) continuously.

6. Write the equation in logarithmic form: $7^{-2} = \frac{1}{49}$.

7. Solve for x: $x - 4 = \log_2 \frac{1}{64}$.

8. Given $\log_b 2 = 0.3562$ and $\log_b 5 = 0.8271$, evaluate $\log_b \sqrt[4]{8/25}$.

9. Write $5 \ln x - \frac{1}{2} \ln y + 6 \ln z$ as a single logarithm.

10. Using your calculator and the change of base formula, evaluate $\log_9 28$.

11. Use your calculator to solve for N: $\log_{10} N = 0.6646$

12. Graph $y = \log_4 x$.

13. Determine the domain of $f(x) = \log_3(x^2 - 9)$.

14. Graph $y = \ln(x - 2)$.

15. True or false: $\dfrac{\ln x}{\ln y} = \ln(x - y)$

16. Solve for x: $5^x = 41$

17. Solve for x: $x - x^2 = \log_5 \frac{1}{25}$

18. Solve for x: $\log_2 x + \log_2(x - 3) = 2$

19. Solve for x: $\dfrac{e^x + e^{-x}}{3} = 4$

20. Six thousand dollars is deposited into a fund at an annual interest rate of 13%. Find the time required for the investment to double if the interest is compounded continuously.

C H A P T E R   4
Trigonometry

CHAPTER 4
Trigonometry

Section 4.1 Radian and Degree Measure

1. coterminal

3. complementary; supplementary

5. linear; angular

7.

The angle shown is approximately 1 radian.

9.

The angle shown is approximately -3 radians.

11. (a) Because $0 < \dfrac{\pi}{4} < \dfrac{\pi}{2}, \dfrac{\pi}{4}$ lies in Quadrant I.

(b) Because $\pi < \dfrac{5\pi}{4} < \dfrac{3\pi}{2}, \dfrac{5\pi}{4}$ lies in Quadrant III.

13. (a) $\dfrac{\pi}{3}$

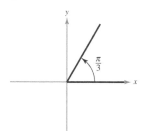

(b) $-\dfrac{2\pi}{3}$

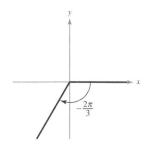

15. (a) $\dfrac{\pi}{6} + 2\pi = \dfrac{13\pi}{6} \quad \dfrac{\pi}{6} - 2\pi = -\dfrac{11\pi}{6}$

(b) $\dfrac{7\pi}{6} + 2\pi = \dfrac{19\pi}{6} \quad \dfrac{7\pi}{6} - 2\pi = -\dfrac{5\pi}{6}$

17. (a) Complement: $\dfrac{\pi}{2} - \dfrac{\pi}{3} = \dfrac{\pi}{6}$

Supplement: $\pi - \dfrac{\pi}{3} = \dfrac{2\pi}{3}$

(b) Complement: $\dfrac{\pi}{2} - \dfrac{\pi}{4} = \dfrac{\pi}{4}$

Supplement: $\pi - \dfrac{\pi}{4} = \dfrac{3\pi}{4}$

19. (a) Complement: $\dfrac{\pi}{2} - 1 \approx 0.57$

Supplement: $\pi - 1 \approx 2.14$

(b) Complement: Not possible, 2 is greater than $\dfrac{\pi}{2}$.

Supplement: $\pi - 2 \approx 1.14$

21.

The angle shown is approximately $210°$.

23.

The angle shown is approximately $-60°$.

25. (a) Because $90° < 130° < 180°, 130°$ lies in Quadrant II.

(b) Because $0° < 8.3° < 90°, 8.3°$ lies in Quadrant I.

27. (a) 270°

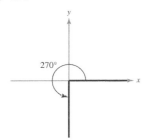

(b) 120°

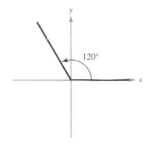

29. *Sample answers:*
(a) $45° + 360° = 405°$
$45° - 360° = -315°$
(b) $-36° + 360° = 324°$
$-36° - 360° = -396°$

31. (a) Complement: $90° - 18° = 72°$
Supplement: $180° - 18° = 162°$
(b) Complement: $90° - 85° = 5°$
Supplement: $180° - 85° = 95°$

33. (a) Complement: Not possible, $150°$ is greater than $90°$.
Supplement: $180° - 150° = 30°$
(b) Complement: $90° - 79° = 11°$
Supplement: $180° - 79° = 101°$

35. (a) $315° = 315°\left(\dfrac{\pi}{180°}\right) = \dfrac{7\pi}{4}$

(b) $-20° = -20\left(\dfrac{\pi}{180°}\right) = -\dfrac{\pi}{9}$

37. (a) $\dfrac{3\pi}{2} = \dfrac{3\pi}{2}\left(\dfrac{180°}{\pi}\right) = 270°$

(b) $\dfrac{7\pi}{6} = \dfrac{7\pi}{6}\left(\dfrac{180°}{\pi}\right) = 210°$

39. $45° = 45\left(\dfrac{\pi}{180°}\right) \approx 0.785$ radian

41. $345° = 345°\left(\dfrac{\pi}{180°}\right) \approx 6.021$ radians

43. $\dfrac{5\pi}{11} = \dfrac{5\pi}{11}\left(\dfrac{180°}{\pi}\right) \approx 81.818°$

45. $-4.2\pi = -4.2\pi\left(\dfrac{180°}{\pi}\right) = -756.000°$

47. (a) $54°45' = 54° + \left(\dfrac{45}{60}\right)^{\!\circ} = 54.75°$

(b) $-128°30' = -128° - \left(\dfrac{30}{60}\right)^{\!\circ} = -128.5°$

49. (a) $240.6° = 240° + 0.6(60)' = 240°36'$

(b) $-145.8° = -\left[145° + 0.8(60')\right] = -145°48'$

51. $r = 15$ inches, $\theta = 120°$
$s = r\theta$
$s = 15(120°)\left(\dfrac{\pi}{180°}\right) = 10\pi$ inches
≈ 31.42 inches

53. $r = 14$ feet, $s = 8$ feet
$s = r\theta$
$8 = 14\theta$
$\theta = \dfrac{8}{14} = \dfrac{4}{7}$ radian

55. $s = r\theta$
$28 = 7\theta$
$\theta = 4$ radians

57. $r = 12$ mm, $\theta = \dfrac{\pi}{4}$
$A = \dfrac{1}{2}r^2\theta = \dfrac{1}{2}(12)^2\left(\dfrac{\pi}{4}\right)$
$= 18\pi$ mm^2
≈ 56.55 mm^2

59. $\theta = 41°15'50'' - 32°47'39''$
$\approx 8.46972° \approx 0.14782$ radian
$s = r\theta \approx 4000(0.14782) \approx 591.3$ miles

61. $s = r\theta$
$2.5 = 6\theta$
$\theta = \dfrac{2.5}{6} = \dfrac{25}{60} = \dfrac{5}{12}$ radian

63. diameter $= 7\dfrac{1}{4} = \dfrac{29}{4}$ inches

       radius $= \dfrac{1}{2}$ diameter $= \dfrac{1}{2}\left(\dfrac{29}{4}\right) = \dfrac{29}{8}$ inches

    (a) Angular speed $= \dfrac{(5000)(2\pi) \text{ radians}}{1 \text{ minute}}$

                $= 10{,}000\pi$ radians per minute

                $\approx 31{,}415.927$ radians per minute

    (b) Linear speed $= \dfrac{\left(\dfrac{29}{8} \text{ in.}\right)\left(\dfrac{1 \text{ foot}}{12 \text{ in.}}\right)(5000)(2\pi)}{1 \text{ minute}}$

               $= \dfrac{18{,}125\pi}{6}$ feet per minute

               ≈ 9490.23 feet per minute

65. (a) $(200)(2\pi) \le$ Angular speed $\le (500)(2\pi)$ radians per minute

       Interval: $\left[400\pi, 1000\pi\right]$ radians per minute

    (b) $(6)(200)(2\pi) \le$ Linear speed $\le (6)(500)(2\pi)$ centimeters per minute

       Interval: $\left[2400\pi, 6000\pi\right]$ centimeters per minute

67. diameter $= 25$ inches

       radius $= \dfrac{1}{2}$ diameter $= \dfrac{1}{2}(25) = 12.5$ inches

    (a) 12.5 in. $\times \dfrac{1 \text{ foot}}{12 \text{ in.}} \times \dfrac{1 \text{ mile}}{5280 \text{ feet}} \times \dfrac{480 \text{ rev}}{\text{min}} \times \dfrac{60 \text{ min}}{1 \text{ hr}} \times \dfrac{2\pi \text{ radians}}{\text{rev}}$

       ≈ 35.70 miles per hour

    (b) $\dfrac{35.70 \text{ miles per hour}}{480 \text{ rev per minute}} = \dfrac{55 \text{ miles per hour}}{x \text{ rev per minute}}$

              $35.70x = 26{,}400$

                  $x \approx 739.50$ revolutions per minute

69. $A = \dfrac{1}{2}r^2\theta$

     $= \dfrac{1}{2}(15)^2(140°)\left(\dfrac{\pi}{180°}\right)$

     $= 87.5\pi$ square meters

     ≈ 274.89 square meters

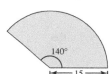

71. False. An angle measure of 4π radians corresponds to two complete revolutions from the initial side to the terminal side of an angle.

73. False. The terminal side of $-1260°$ lies on the negative x-axis.

75. 1 radian $= \left(\dfrac{180}{\pi}\right)^{\circ} \approx 57.3°,$

     so one radian is much larger than one degree.

77. Since $s = r\theta$, then the rate of change of θ is 0 and so does $\dfrac{ds}{dt} = \theta\dfrac{dr}{dt}.$

     That is, the arc length changes at a rate proportional to the rate of change of the radius and the proportionality constant is θ.

Section 4.2   Trigonometric Functions: The Unit Circle

1. unit circle

3. period

5. $x = \dfrac{12}{13}, \ y = \dfrac{5}{13}$

$\sin t = y = \dfrac{5}{13}$ $\csc t = \dfrac{1}{y} = \dfrac{13}{5}$

$\cos t = x = \dfrac{12}{13}$ $\sec t = \dfrac{1}{x} = \dfrac{13}{12}$

$\tan t = \dfrac{y}{x} = \dfrac{5}{12}$ $\cot t = \dfrac{x}{y} = \dfrac{12}{5}$

7. $x = -\dfrac{4}{5}, \ y = \dfrac{3}{5}$

$\sin t = y = -\dfrac{3}{5}$ $\csc t = \dfrac{1}{y} = -\dfrac{5}{3}$

$\cos t = x = -\dfrac{4}{5}$ $\sec t = \dfrac{1}{x} = -\dfrac{5}{4}$

$\tan t = \dfrac{y}{x} = \dfrac{3}{4}$ $\cot t = \dfrac{x}{y} = \dfrac{4}{3}$

9. $t = \dfrac{\pi}{2}$ corresponds to the point $(x, y) = (0, 1)$.

11. $t = \dfrac{5\pi}{6}$ corresponds to the point $(x, y) = \left(-\dfrac{\sqrt{3}}{2}, \dfrac{1}{2}\right)$.

13. $t = \dfrac{\pi}{4}$ corresponds to the point $(x, y) = \left(\dfrac{\sqrt{2}}{2}, \dfrac{\sqrt{2}}{2}\right)$.

$\sin \dfrac{\pi}{4} = y = \dfrac{\sqrt{2}}{2}$

$\cos \dfrac{\pi}{4} = x = \dfrac{\sqrt{2}}{2}$

$\tan \dfrac{\pi}{4} = \dfrac{y}{x} = 1$

15. $t = -\dfrac{\pi}{6}$ corresponds to $\left(\dfrac{\sqrt{3}}{2}, -\dfrac{1}{2}\right)$.

$\sin -\dfrac{\pi}{6} = y = -\dfrac{1}{2}$

$\cos -\dfrac{\pi}{6} = x = \dfrac{\sqrt{3}}{2}$

$\tan -\dfrac{\pi}{6} = \dfrac{y}{x} = -\dfrac{1}{\sqrt{3}} = -\dfrac{\sqrt{3}}{3}$

17. $t = -\dfrac{7\pi}{4}$ corresponds to the point

$(x, y) = \left(\dfrac{\sqrt{2}}{2}, \dfrac{\sqrt{2}}{2}\right)$

$\sin\left(-\dfrac{7\pi}{4}\right) = y = \dfrac{\sqrt{2}}{2}$

$\cos\left(-\dfrac{7\pi}{4}\right) = x = \dfrac{\sqrt{2}}{2}$

$\tan\left(-\dfrac{7\pi}{4}\right) = \dfrac{y}{x} = 1$

19. $t = \dfrac{11\pi}{6}$ corresponds to the point $(x, y) = \left(\dfrac{\sqrt{3}}{2}, -\dfrac{1}{2}\right)$.

$\sin \dfrac{11\pi}{6} = y = -\dfrac{1}{2}$

$\cos \dfrac{11\pi}{6} = x = \dfrac{\sqrt{3}}{2}$

$\tan \dfrac{11\pi}{6} = \dfrac{y}{x} = -\dfrac{1}{\sqrt{3}} = -\dfrac{\sqrt{3}}{3}$

21. $t = -\dfrac{3\pi}{2}$ corresponds to the point $(x, y) = (0, 1)$.

$\sin\left(-\dfrac{3\pi}{2}\right) = y = 1$

$\cos\left(-\dfrac{3\pi}{2}\right) = x = 0$

$\tan\left(-\dfrac{3\pi}{2}\right) = \dfrac{y}{x}$ is undefined.

23. $t = \dfrac{2\pi}{3}$ corresponds to the point $(x, y) = \left(-\dfrac{1}{2}, \dfrac{\sqrt{3}}{2}\right)$.

$$\sin \frac{2\pi}{3} = y = \frac{\sqrt{3}}{2} \qquad\qquad \csc \frac{2\pi}{3} = \frac{1}{y} = \frac{2\sqrt{3}}{3}$$

$$\cos \frac{2\pi}{3} = x = -\frac{1}{2} \qquad\qquad \sec \frac{2\pi}{3} = \frac{1}{x} = -2$$

$$\tan \frac{2\pi}{3} = \frac{y}{x} = \frac{\dfrac{\sqrt{3}}{2}}{-\dfrac{1}{2}} = -\sqrt{3} \qquad\qquad \cot \frac{2\pi}{3} = \frac{x}{y} = \frac{-\dfrac{1}{2}}{\dfrac{\sqrt{3}}{2}} = -\frac{\sqrt{3}}{3}$$

25. $t = \dfrac{4\pi}{3}$ corresponds to the point $(x, y) = \left(-\dfrac{1}{2}, -\dfrac{\sqrt{3}}{2}\right)$.

$$\sin \frac{4\pi}{3} = y = -\frac{\sqrt{3}}{2} \qquad\qquad \csc \frac{4\pi}{3} = \frac{1}{y} = -\frac{2\sqrt{3}}{3}$$

$$\cos \frac{4\pi}{3} = x = -\frac{1}{2} \qquad\qquad \sec \frac{4\pi}{3} = \frac{1}{x} = -2$$

$$\tan \frac{4\pi}{3} = \frac{y}{x} = \sqrt{3} \qquad\qquad \cot \frac{4\pi}{3} = \frac{x}{y} = \frac{\sqrt{3}}{3}$$

27. $t = -\dfrac{5\pi}{3}$ corresponds to the point $\left(-\dfrac{1}{2}, \dfrac{\sqrt{3}}{2}\right)$.

$$\sin\left(-\frac{5\pi}{3}\right) = y = \frac{\sqrt{3}}{2} \qquad\qquad \csc\left(-\frac{5\pi}{3}\right) = \frac{1}{y} = \frac{2}{\sqrt{3}}$$

$$\cos\left(-\frac{5\pi}{3}\right) = x = -\frac{1}{2} \qquad\qquad \sec\left(-\frac{5\pi}{3}\right) = \frac{1}{x} = -2$$

$$\tan\left(-\frac{5\pi}{3}\right) = \frac{y}{x} = -\sqrt{3} \qquad\qquad \cot\left(-\frac{5\pi}{3}\right) = \frac{x}{y} = -\frac{1}{\sqrt{3}}$$

29. $t = -\dfrac{\pi}{2}$ corresponds to the point $(x, y) = (0, -1)$.

$$\sin\left(-\frac{\pi}{2}\right) = y = -1 \qquad\qquad \csc\left(-\frac{\pi}{2}\right) = \frac{1}{y} = -1$$

$$\cos\left(-\frac{\pi}{2}\right) = x = 0 \qquad\qquad \sec\left(-\frac{\pi}{2}\right) = \frac{1}{x} \text{ is undefined.}$$

$$\tan\left(-\frac{\pi}{2}\right) = \frac{y}{x} \text{ is undefined.} \qquad \cot\left(-\frac{\pi}{2}\right) = \frac{x}{y} = 0$$

31. $\sin 4\pi = \sin 0 = 0$

33. $\cos \dfrac{7\pi}{3} = \cos \dfrac{\pi}{3} = \dfrac{1}{2}$

35. $\sin \dfrac{19\pi}{6} = \sin \dfrac{7\pi}{6} = -\dfrac{1}{2}$

37. $\sin t = \frac{1}{2}$

(a) $\sin(-t) = -\sin t = -\frac{1}{2}$

(b) $\csc(-t) = -\csc t = -2$

39. $\cos(-t) = -\dfrac{1}{5}$

(a) $\cos t = \cos(-t) = -\dfrac{1}{5}$

(b) $\sec(-t) = \dfrac{1}{\cos(-t)} = -5$

41. $\sin t = \frac{4}{5}$

   (a) $\sin(\pi - t) = \sin t = \frac{4}{5}$

   (b) $\sin(t + \pi) = -\sin t = -\frac{4}{5}$

43. $\tan \dfrac{\pi}{3} \approx 1.7321$

45. $\csc 0.8 = \dfrac{1}{\sin 0.8} \approx 1.3940$

47. $\sec 1.8 = \dfrac{1}{\sec(1.8)} \approx -4.4014$

49. $y(t) = \frac{1}{4}\cos 6t$

   (a) $y(0) = \frac{1}{4}\cos 0 = 0.25$ foot

   (b) $y\!\left(\frac{1}{4}\right) = \frac{1}{4}\cos\frac{3}{2} \approx 0.02$ foot

   (c) $y\!\left(\frac{1}{2}\right) = \frac{1}{4}\cos 3 \approx -0.25$ foot

51. False. $\sin(-t) = -\sin t$ means the function is odd, not that the sine of a negative angle is a negative number.

For example: $\sin\!\left(-\dfrac{3\pi}{2}\right) = -\sin\!\left(\dfrac{3\pi}{2}\right) = -(-1) = 1$.

Even though the angle is negative, the sine value is positive.

53. False. The real number 0 corresponds to the point $(1, 0)$ on the unit circle.

55. (a) The points have y-axis symmetry.

   (b) $\sin t_1 = \sin(\pi - t_1)$ because they have the same y-value.

   (c) $\cos(\pi - t_1) = -\cos t_1$ because the x-values have the opposite signs.

57. $\cos 2t$:

$\cos 1.5 = \cos\bigl(2(0.75)\bigr) \approx 0.0707$

$2\cos t$:

$2\cos 0.75 \approx 1.4634$

So, $\cos 2t \neq 2\cos t$.

59. (a)

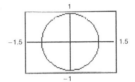

Circle of radius 1 centered at $(0, 0)$

   (b) The t-values represent the central angle in radians. The x- and y-values represent the location in the coordinate plane.

   (c) $-1 \le x \le 1, -1 \le y \le 1$

61. Let $h(t) = f(t)g(t) = \sin t \cos t$.

Then, $h(-t) = \sin(-t)\cos(-t)$

$= -\sin t \cos t$

$= -h(t).$

So, $h(t)$ is odd.

Section 4.3   Right Triangle Trigonometry

1. (i) $\dfrac{\text{hypotenuse}}{\text{adjacent}} = \sec\theta$ (e)

   (ii) $\dfrac{\text{adjacent}}{\text{opposite}} = \cot\theta$ (f)

   (iii) $\dfrac{\text{hypotenuse}}{\text{opposite}} = \csc\theta$ (d)

   (iv) $\dfrac{\text{adjacent}}{\text{hypotenuse}} = \cos\theta$ (b)

   (v) $\dfrac{\text{opposite}}{\text{hypotenuse}} = \sin\theta$ (a)

   (vi) $\dfrac{\text{opposite}}{\text{adjacent}} = \tan\theta$ (c)

3. Complementary

5. $\text{hyp} = \sqrt{6^2 + 8^2} = \sqrt{36 + 64} = \sqrt{100} = 10$

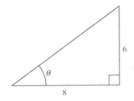

$\sin\theta = \dfrac{\text{opp}}{\text{hyp}} = \dfrac{6}{10} = \dfrac{3}{5}$ $\csc\theta = \dfrac{\text{hyp}}{\text{opp}} = \dfrac{10}{6} = \dfrac{5}{3}$

$\cos\theta = \dfrac{\text{adj}}{\text{hyp}} = \dfrac{8}{10} = \dfrac{4}{5}$ $\sec\theta = \dfrac{\text{hyp}}{\text{adj}} = \dfrac{10}{8} = \dfrac{5}{4}$

$\tan\theta = \dfrac{\text{opp}}{\text{adj}} = \dfrac{6}{8} = \dfrac{3}{4}$ $\cot\theta = \dfrac{\text{adj}}{\text{opp}} = \dfrac{8}{6} = \dfrac{4}{3}$

7. $\text{adj} = \sqrt{41^2 - 9^2} = \sqrt{1681 - 81} = \sqrt{1600} = 40$

$\sin \theta = \dfrac{\text{opp}}{\text{hyp}} = \dfrac{9}{41}$ $\qquad$ $\csc \theta = \dfrac{\text{hyp}}{\text{opp}} = \dfrac{41}{9}$

$\cos \theta = \dfrac{\text{adj}}{\text{hyp}} = \dfrac{40}{41}$ $\qquad$ $\sec \theta = \dfrac{\text{hyp}}{\text{adj}} = \dfrac{41}{40}$

$\tan \theta = \dfrac{\text{opp}}{\text{adj}} = \dfrac{9}{40}$ $\qquad$ $\cot \theta = \dfrac{\text{adj}}{\text{opp}} = \dfrac{40}{9}$

9.

$\text{hyp} = \sqrt{15^2 + 8^2} = \sqrt{289} = 17$

$\sin \theta = \dfrac{\text{opp}}{\text{hyp}} = \dfrac{8}{17}$ $\qquad$ $\csc \theta = \dfrac{\text{hyp}}{\text{opp}} = \dfrac{17}{8}$

$\cos \theta = \dfrac{\text{adj}}{\text{hyp}} = \dfrac{15}{17}$ $\qquad$ $\sec \theta = \dfrac{\text{hyp}}{\text{adj}} = \dfrac{17}{15}$

$\tan \theta = \dfrac{\text{opp}}{\text{adj}} = \dfrac{8}{15}$ $\qquad$ $\cot \theta = \dfrac{\text{adj}}{\text{opp}} = \dfrac{15}{8}$

$\text{hyp} = \sqrt{7.5^2 + 4^2} = \dfrac{17}{2}$

$\sin \theta = \dfrac{\text{opp}}{\text{hyp}} = \dfrac{4}{(17/2)} = \dfrac{8}{17}$ $\qquad$ $\csc \theta = \dfrac{\text{hyp}}{\text{opp}} = \dfrac{(17/2)}{4} = \dfrac{17}{8}$

$\cos \theta = \dfrac{\text{adj}}{\text{hyp}} = \dfrac{7.5}{(17/2)} = \dfrac{15}{17}$ $\qquad$ $\sec \theta = \dfrac{\text{hyp}}{\text{adj}} = \dfrac{(17/2)}{7.5} = \dfrac{17}{15}$

$\tan \theta = \dfrac{\text{opp}}{\text{adj}} = \dfrac{4}{7.5} = \dfrac{8}{15}$ $\qquad$ $\cot \theta = \dfrac{\text{adj}}{\text{opp}} = \dfrac{7.5}{4} = \dfrac{15}{8}$

The function values are the same because the triangles are similar, and corresponding sides are proportional.

11. $\text{adj} = \sqrt{3^2 - 1^2} = \sqrt{8} = 2\sqrt{2}$

$\sin \theta = \dfrac{\text{opp}}{\text{hyp}} = \dfrac{1}{3}$ $\qquad$ $\csc \theta = \dfrac{\text{hyp}}{\text{opp}} = 3$

$\cos \theta = \dfrac{\text{adj}}{\text{hyp}} = \dfrac{2\sqrt{2}}{3}$ $\qquad$ $\sec \theta = \dfrac{\text{hyp}}{\text{adj}} = \dfrac{3}{2\sqrt{2}} = \dfrac{3\sqrt{2}}{4}$

$\tan \theta = \dfrac{\text{opp}}{\text{adj}} = \dfrac{1}{2\sqrt{2}} = \dfrac{\sqrt{2}}{4}$ $\qquad$ $\cot \theta = \dfrac{\text{adj}}{\text{opp}} = 2\sqrt{2}$

$\text{adj} = \sqrt{6^2 - 2^2} = \sqrt{32} = 4\sqrt{2}$

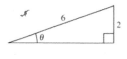

$\sin \theta = \dfrac{\text{opp}}{\text{hyp}} = \dfrac{2}{6} = \dfrac{1}{3}$ $\qquad$ $\csc \theta = \dfrac{\text{hyp}}{\text{opp}} = \dfrac{6}{2} = 3$

$\cos \theta = \dfrac{\text{adj}}{\text{hyp}} = \dfrac{4\sqrt{2}}{6} = \dfrac{2\sqrt{2}}{3}$ $\qquad$ $\sec \theta = \dfrac{\text{hyp}}{\text{adj}} = \dfrac{6}{4\sqrt{2}} = \dfrac{3}{2\sqrt{2}} = \dfrac{3\sqrt{2}}{4}$

$\tan \theta = \dfrac{\text{opp}}{\text{adj}} = \dfrac{5\sqrt{2}}{4} = \dfrac{1}{2\sqrt{2}} = \dfrac{\sqrt{2}}{4}$ $\qquad$ $\cot \theta = \dfrac{\text{adj}}{\text{opp}} = \dfrac{4\sqrt{2}}{2} = 2\sqrt{2}$

The function values are the same since the triangles are similar and the corresponding sides are proportional.

13. Given: $\tan \theta = \dfrac{3}{4} = \dfrac{\text{opp}}{\text{adj}}$

$3^2 + 4^2 = (\text{hyp})^2$

$\text{hyp} = 5$

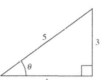

$\sin \theta = \dfrac{\text{opp}}{\text{hyp}} = \dfrac{3}{5}$

$\cos \theta = \dfrac{\text{adj}}{\text{hyp}} = \dfrac{4}{5}$

$\csc \theta = \dfrac{\text{hyp}}{\text{opp}} = \dfrac{5}{3}$

$\sec \theta = \dfrac{\text{hyp}}{\text{adj}} = \dfrac{5}{4}$

$\cot \theta = \dfrac{\text{adj}}{\text{opp}} = \dfrac{4}{3}$

15. Given: $\sec \theta = \dfrac{3}{2} = \dfrac{\text{hyp}}{\text{adj}}$

$(\text{opp})^2 + 2^2 = 3^2$

$\text{opp} = \sqrt{5}$

$\sin \theta = \dfrac{\text{opp}}{\text{hyp}} = \dfrac{\sqrt{5}}{3}$

$\cos \theta = \dfrac{\text{adj}}{\text{hyp}} = \dfrac{2}{3}$

$\tan \theta = \dfrac{\text{opp}}{\text{adj}} = \dfrac{\sqrt{5}}{2}$

$\csc \theta = \dfrac{\text{hyp}}{\text{opp}} = \dfrac{3\sqrt{5}}{5}$

$\cot \theta = \dfrac{\text{adj}}{\text{opp}} = \dfrac{2\sqrt{5}}{5}$

17. Given: $\sin \theta = \dfrac{1}{5} = \dfrac{\text{opp}}{\text{hyp}}$

$1^2 + (\text{adj})^2 = 5^2$

$\text{adj} = \sqrt{24} = 2\sqrt{6}$

$\cos \theta = \dfrac{\text{adj}}{\text{hyp}} = \dfrac{2\sqrt{6}}{5}$

$\tan \theta = \dfrac{\text{opp}}{\text{adj}} = \dfrac{\sqrt{6}}{12}$

$\csc \theta = \dfrac{\text{hyp}}{\text{opp}} = 5$

$\sec \theta = \dfrac{\text{hyp}}{\text{adj}} = \dfrac{5\sqrt{6}}{12}$

$\cot \theta = \dfrac{\text{adj}}{\text{opp}} = 2\sqrt{6}$

19. Given: $\cot \theta = 3 = \dfrac{3}{1} = \dfrac{\text{adj}}{\text{opp}}$

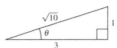

$1^2 + 3^2 = (\text{hyp})^2$

$\text{hyp} = \sqrt{10}$

$\sin \theta = \dfrac{\text{opp}}{\text{hyp}} = \dfrac{\sqrt{10}}{10}$

$\cos \theta = \dfrac{\text{adj}}{\text{hyp}} = \dfrac{3\sqrt{10}}{10}$

$\tan \theta = \dfrac{\text{opp}}{\text{adj}} = \dfrac{1}{3}$

$\csc \theta = \dfrac{\text{hyp}}{\text{opp}} = \sqrt{10}$

$\sec \theta = \dfrac{\text{hyp}}{\text{adj}} = \dfrac{\sqrt{10}}{3}$

21.

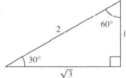

$30° = 30°\left(\dfrac{\pi}{180°}\right) = \dfrac{\pi}{6}$ radian

$\sin 30° = \dfrac{\text{opp}}{\text{hyp}} = \dfrac{1}{2}$

23.

degree	radian	value
$\sec 45°$	$\dfrac{\pi}{4}$	$\sqrt{2}$

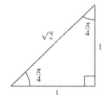

$\sec \dfrac{\pi}{4} = \dfrac{\sqrt{2}}{1} = \sqrt{2}$

25.

$\cot \theta = \dfrac{\sqrt{3}}{3} = \dfrac{1}{\sqrt{3}} = \dfrac{\text{adj}}{\text{opp}}$

$\theta = 60° = \dfrac{\pi}{3}$ radian

27.

$\dfrac{\pi}{6} = \dfrac{\pi}{6}\left(\dfrac{180°}{\pi}\right) = 30°$

$\csc \dfrac{\pi}{6} = \dfrac{\text{hyp}}{\text{opp}} = 2$

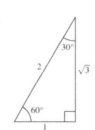

29. $\cot \theta = 1 = \dfrac{1}{1} = \dfrac{\text{adj}}{\text{opp}}$

$\theta = 45° = 45°\left(\dfrac{\pi}{180°}\right) = \dfrac{\pi}{4}$

31. (a) $\sin 10° \approx 0.1736$

(b) $\cos 80° \approx 0.1736$

Note: $\cos 80° = \sin(90° - 80°) = \sin 10°$

33. (a) $\sin 16.35° \approx 0.2815$

(b) $\csc 16.35° = \dfrac{1}{\sin 16.35°} \approx 3.5523$

35. (a) $\cos 4°50'15'' = \cos\left(4 + \dfrac{50}{60} + \dfrac{15}{3600}\right)° \approx 0.9964$

(b) $\sec 4°50'15'' = \dfrac{1}{\cos 4°50'15''} \approx 1.0036$

37. (a) $\cot 11°15' = \dfrac{1}{\tan 11.25°} \approx 5.0273$

(b) $\tan 11°15' = \tan 11.25° \approx 0.1989$

39. (a) $\csc 32°40'3'' = \dfrac{1}{\sin 32.6675°} \approx 1.8527$

(b) $\tan 44°28'16'' \approx \tan 44.4711° \approx 0.9817$

41. $\sin 60° = \dfrac{\sqrt{3}}{2}, \cos 60° = \dfrac{1}{2}$

(a) $\sin 30° = \cos 60° = \dfrac{1}{2}$

(b) $\cos 30° = \sin 60° = \dfrac{\sqrt{3}}{2}$

(c) $\tan 60° = \dfrac{\sin 60°}{\cos 60°} = \sqrt{3}$

(d) $\cot 60° = \dfrac{\cos 60°}{\sin 60°} = \dfrac{1}{\sqrt{3}} = \dfrac{\sqrt{3}}{3}$

43. $\cos \theta = \dfrac{1}{3}$

(a) $\sin^2 \theta + \cos^2 \theta = 1$

$\sin^2 \theta + \left(\dfrac{1}{3}\right)^2 = 1$

$\sin^2 \theta = \dfrac{8}{9}$

$\sin \theta = \dfrac{2\sqrt{2}}{3}$

(b) $\tan \theta = \dfrac{\sin \theta}{\cos \theta} = \dfrac{\frac{2\sqrt{2}}{3}}{\frac{1}{3}} = 2\sqrt{2}$

(c) $\sec \theta = \dfrac{1}{\cos \theta} = 3$

(d) $\csc(90° - \theta) = \sec \theta = 3$

45. $\cot \alpha = 5$

(a) $\tan \alpha = \dfrac{1}{\cot \alpha} = \dfrac{1}{5}$

(b) $\csc^2 \alpha = 1 + \cot^2 \alpha$

$\csc^2 \alpha = 1 + 5^2$

$\csc^2 \alpha = 26$

$\csc \alpha = \sqrt{26}$

(c) $\cot(90° - \alpha) = \tan \alpha = \dfrac{1}{5}$

(d) $\sec^2 \alpha = 1 + \tan^2 \alpha$

$\sec^2 \alpha = 1 + \left(\dfrac{1}{5}\right)^2$

$\sec^2 \alpha = \dfrac{26}{25}$

$\sec \alpha = \dfrac{\sqrt{26}}{5}$

$\cos \alpha = \dfrac{1}{\sec \alpha} = \dfrac{5\sqrt{26}}{26}$

47. $\tan \theta \cot \theta = \tan \theta\left(\dfrac{1}{\tan \theta}\right) = 1$

49. $\tan \alpha \cos \alpha = \left(\dfrac{\sin \alpha}{\cos \alpha}\right)\cos \alpha = \sin \alpha$

51. $(1 + \sin \theta)(1 - \sin \theta) = 1 - \sin^2 \theta = \cos^2 \theta$

53. $(\sec \theta + \tan \theta)(\sec \theta - \tan \theta) = \sec^2 \theta - \tan^2 \theta$

$$= (1 + \tan^2 \theta) - \tan^2 \theta$$

$$= 1$$

55. $\dfrac{\sin \theta}{\cos \theta} + \dfrac{\cos \theta}{\sin \theta} = \dfrac{\sin^2 \theta + \cos^2 \theta}{\sin \theta \cos \theta}$

$$= \dfrac{1}{\sin \theta \cos \theta}$$

$$= \dfrac{1}{\sin \theta} \cdot \dfrac{1}{\cos \theta}$$

$$= \csc \theta \sec \theta$$

57. (a) $\sin \theta = \dfrac{1}{2} \Rightarrow \theta = 30° = \dfrac{\pi}{6}$

(b) $\csc \theta = 2 \Rightarrow \theta = 30° = \dfrac{\pi}{6}$

59. (a) $\sec \theta = 2 \Rightarrow \theta = 60° = \dfrac{\pi}{3}$

(b) $\cot \theta = 1 \Rightarrow \theta = 45° = \dfrac{\pi}{4}$

61. (a) $\csc \theta = \dfrac{2\sqrt{3}}{3} \Rightarrow \theta = 60° = \dfrac{\pi}{3}$

(b) $\sin \theta = \dfrac{\sqrt{2}}{2} \Rightarrow \theta = 45° = \dfrac{\pi}{4}$

63. $\cos 60° = \dfrac{x}{18}$

$$x = 18 \cos 60° = 18\left(\dfrac{1}{2}\right) = 9$$

$$\sin 60° = \dfrac{y}{18}$$

$$y = 18 \sin 60° = 18\dfrac{\sqrt{3}}{2} = 9\sqrt{3}$$

65. $\tan 60° = \dfrac{32}{x}$

$$\sqrt{3} = \dfrac{32}{x}$$

$$\sqrt{3}x = 32$$

$$x = \dfrac{32}{\sqrt{3}} = \dfrac{32\sqrt{3}}{3}$$

$$\sin 60° = \dfrac{32}{r}$$

$$r = \dfrac{32}{\sin 60°}$$

$$r = \dfrac{32}{\dfrac{\sqrt{3}}{2}} = \dfrac{64\sqrt{3}}{3}$$

67.

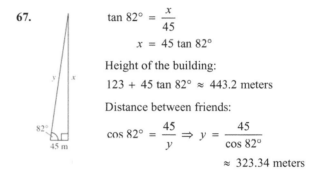

$$\tan 82° = \dfrac{x}{45}$$

$$x = 45 \tan 82°$$

Height of the building:

$$123 + 45 \tan 82° \approx 443.2 \text{ meters}$$

Distance between friends:

$$\cos 82° = \dfrac{45}{y} \Rightarrow y = \dfrac{45}{\cos 82°}$$

$$\approx 323.34 \text{ meters}$$

69.

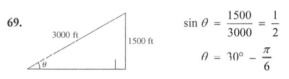

$$\sin \theta = \dfrac{1500}{3000} = \dfrac{1}{2}$$

$$\theta = 30° = \dfrac{\pi}{6}$$

71. (a) $\sin 43° = \dfrac{150}{x}$

$$x = \dfrac{150}{\sin 43°} \approx 219.9 \text{ ft}$$

(b) $\tan 43° = \dfrac{150}{y}$

$$y = \dfrac{150}{\tan 43°} \approx 160.9 \text{ ft}$$

73.

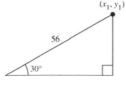

$$\sin 30° = \frac{y_1}{56}$$

$$y_1 = (\sin 30°)(56) = \left(\frac{1}{2}\right)(56) = 28$$

$$\cos 30° = \frac{x_1}{56}$$

$$x_1 = \cos 30°(56) = \frac{\sqrt{3}}{2}(56) = 28\sqrt{3}$$

$$(x_1, y_1) = \left(28\sqrt{3}, 28\right)$$

$$\sin 60° = \frac{y_2}{56}$$

$$y_2 = \sin 60°(56) = \left(\frac{\sqrt{3}}{2}\right)(56) = 28\sqrt{3}$$

$$\cos 60° = \frac{x_2}{56}$$

$$x_2 = (\cos 60°)(56) = \left(\frac{1}{2}\right)(56) = 28$$

$$(x_2, y_2) = \left(28, 28\sqrt{3}\right)$$

75. $x \approx 9.397,\ y \approx 3.420$

$$\sin 20° = \frac{y}{10} \approx 0.34$$

$$\cos 20° = \frac{x}{10} \approx 0.94$$

$$\tan 20° = \frac{y}{x} \approx 0.36$$

$$\cot 20° = \frac{x}{y} \approx 2.75$$

$$\sec 20° = \frac{10}{x} \approx 1.06$$

$$\csc 20° = \frac{10}{y} \approx 2.92$$

77. (a)

θ	0	0.3	0.6	0.9	1.2	1.5
$\sin\theta$	0	0.2955	0.5646	0.7833	0.9320	0.9975
$\cos\theta$	1	0.9553	0.8253	0.6216	0.3624	0.0707

(b) On $[0, 1.5]$, $\sin\theta$ is an increasing function.

(c) On $[0, 1.5]$, $\cos\theta$ is a decreasing function.

(d) As the angle increases the length of the side opposite the angle increases relative to the length of the hypotenuse and the length of the side adjacent to the angle decreases relative to the length of the hypotenuse. Thus the sine increases and the cosine decreases.

79. (a)

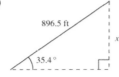

$$\sin 35.4° = \frac{x}{896.5}$$
$$x = 896.5 \sin 35.4° \approx 519.33 \text{ feet}$$

(b) Because the top of the incline is 1693.5 feet above sea level and the vertical rise of the inclined plane is 519.33 feet, the elevation of the lower end of the inclined plan is about
1693.5 − 519.33 = 1174.17 feet.

(c) Ascent time: $d = rt$
$$896.5 = 300t$$
$$3 \approx t$$

It takes about 3 minutes for the cars to get from the bottom to the top.

Vertical rate: $d = rt$
$$519.33 = r(3)$$
$$r = 173.11 \text{ ft/min}$$

81. $\sin 60° \csc 60° = 1$

True,

$$\csc x = \frac{1}{\sin x} \Rightarrow \sin 60° \csc 60° = \sin 60°\left(\frac{1}{\sin 60°}\right)$$
$$= 1$$

83. $\sin 45° + \sin 45° = 1$

False, $\dfrac{\sqrt{2}}{2} + \dfrac{\sqrt{2}}{2} = \sqrt{2} \neq 1$

85. $\tan\left[\left(5°\right)^2\right] = \tan^2 5°$

False.

$$\tan\left[\left(5°\right)^2\right] = \tan 25° \approx 0.466$$
$$\tan^2 5° = \left(\tan 5°\right)^2 \approx 0.008$$

87. (a)

θ	0.1	0.2	0.3	0.4	0.5
$\sin \theta$	0.0998	0.1987	0.2955	0.3894	0.4794

(b) In the interval $(0, 0.5]$, $\theta > \sin \theta$.

(c) As $\theta \to 0$, $\sin \theta \to 0$, and $\dfrac{\theta}{\sin \theta} \to 1$.

Section 4.4 Trigonometric Functions of Any Angle

1. $\dfrac{y}{r}$

3. $\dfrac{y}{x}$

5. $\cos \theta$

7. zero; defined

9. (a) $(x, y) = (4, 3)$

$r = \sqrt{16 + 9} = 5$

$$\sin \theta = \frac{y}{r} = \frac{3}{5} \qquad \csc \theta = \frac{r}{y} = \frac{5}{3}$$
$$\cos \theta = \frac{x}{r} = \frac{4}{5} \qquad \sec \theta = \frac{r}{x} = \frac{5}{4}$$
$$\tan \theta = \frac{y}{x} = \frac{3}{4} \qquad \cot \theta = \frac{x}{y} = \frac{4}{3}$$

(b) $(x, y) = (-8, 15)$

$r = \sqrt{64 + 225} = 17$

$$\sin \theta = \frac{y}{r} = \frac{15}{17} \qquad \csc \theta = \frac{r}{y} = \frac{17}{15}$$
$$\cos \theta = \frac{x}{r} = -\frac{8}{17} \qquad \sec \theta = \frac{r}{x} = -\frac{17}{8}$$
$$\tan \theta = \frac{y}{x} = -\frac{15}{8} \qquad \cot \theta = \frac{x}{y} = -\frac{8}{15}$$

11. (a) $(x, y) = \left(-\sqrt{3}, -1\right)$

$r = \sqrt{3 + 1} = 2$

$\sin \theta = \dfrac{y}{r} = -\dfrac{1}{2}$ $\csc \theta = \dfrac{r}{y} = -2$

$\cos \theta = \dfrac{x}{r} = -\dfrac{\sqrt{3}}{2}$ $\sec \theta = \dfrac{r}{x} = -\dfrac{2\sqrt{3}}{3}$

$\tan \theta = \dfrac{y}{x} = \dfrac{\sqrt{3}}{3}$ $\cot \theta = \dfrac{x}{y} = \sqrt{3}$

(b) $(x, y) = (4, -1)$

$r = \sqrt{16 + 1} = \sqrt{17}$

$\sin \theta = \dfrac{y}{r} = -\dfrac{1}{\sqrt{17}} = -\dfrac{\sqrt{17}}{17}$ $\csc \theta = \dfrac{r}{y} = -\sqrt{17}$

$\cos \theta = \dfrac{x}{r} = \dfrac{4}{\sqrt{17}} = \dfrac{4\sqrt{17}}{17}$ $\sec \theta = \dfrac{r}{x} = \dfrac{\sqrt{17}}{4}$

$\tan \theta = \dfrac{y}{x} = -\dfrac{1}{4}$ $\cot \theta = \dfrac{x}{y} = -4$

13. $(x, y) = (5, 12)$

$r = \sqrt{25 + 144} = 13$

$\sin \theta = \dfrac{y}{r} = \dfrac{12}{13}$ $\csc \theta = \dfrac{r}{y} = \dfrac{13}{12}$

$\cos \theta = \dfrac{x}{r} = \dfrac{5}{13}$ $\sec \theta = \dfrac{r}{x} = \dfrac{13}{5}$

$\tan \theta = \dfrac{y}{x} = \dfrac{12}{5}$ $\cot \theta = \dfrac{x}{y} = \dfrac{5}{12}$

15. $x = -5, \; y = -2$

$r = \sqrt{(-5)^2 + (-2)^2} = \sqrt{29}$

$\sin \theta = \dfrac{y}{r} = \dfrac{-2}{\sqrt{29}} = -\dfrac{2\sqrt{29}}{29}$

$\cos \theta = \dfrac{x}{r} = \dfrac{-5}{\sqrt{29}} = -\dfrac{5\sqrt{29}}{29}$

$\tan \theta = \dfrac{y}{x} = \dfrac{-2}{-5} = \dfrac{2}{5}$

$\csc \theta = \dfrac{r}{y} = \dfrac{\sqrt{29}}{-2} = -\dfrac{\sqrt{29}}{2}$

$\sec \theta = \dfrac{r}{x} = \dfrac{\sqrt{29}}{-5} = -\dfrac{\sqrt{29}}{5}$

$\cot \theta = \dfrac{x}{y} = \dfrac{-5}{-2} = \dfrac{5}{2}$

17. $(x, y) = (-5.4, 7.2)$

$r = \sqrt{29.16 + 51.84} = 9$

$\sin \theta = \dfrac{y}{r} = \dfrac{7.2}{9} = \dfrac{4}{5}$ $\csc \theta = \dfrac{r}{y} = \dfrac{9}{7.2} = \dfrac{5}{4}$

$\cos \theta = \dfrac{x}{r} = -\dfrac{5.4}{9} = -\dfrac{3}{5}$ $\sec \theta = \dfrac{r}{x} = -\dfrac{9}{5.4} = -\dfrac{5}{3}$

$\tan \theta = \dfrac{y}{x} = -\dfrac{7.2}{5.4} = -\dfrac{4}{3}$ $\tan \theta = \dfrac{x}{y} = -\dfrac{5.4}{7.2} = -\dfrac{3}{4}$

19. $\sin \theta > 0 \Rightarrow \theta$ lies in Quadrant I or in Quadrant II.

$\cos \theta > 0 \Rightarrow \theta$ lies in Quadrant I or in Quadrant IV.

$\sin \theta > 0$ and $\cos \theta > 0 \Rightarrow \theta$ lies in Quadrant I.

21. $\sin \theta > 0 \Rightarrow \theta$ lies in Quadrant I or in Quadrant II.

$\cos \theta < 0 \Rightarrow \theta$ lies in Quadrant II or in Quadrant III.

$\sin \theta > 0$ and $\cos \theta < 0 \Rightarrow \theta$ lies in Quadrant II.

23. $\tan \theta < 0$ and $\sin \theta > 0 \Rightarrow \theta$ is in Quadrant II

$\Rightarrow x < 0$ and $y > 0$.

$\tan \theta = \dfrac{y}{x} = \dfrac{15}{-8} \Rightarrow r = 17$

$\sin \theta = \dfrac{y}{r} = \dfrac{15}{17}$ $\csc \theta = \dfrac{r}{y} = \dfrac{17}{15}$

$\cos \theta = \dfrac{x}{r} = -\dfrac{8}{17}$ $\sec \theta = \dfrac{r}{x} = -\dfrac{17}{8}$

$\tan \theta = \dfrac{y}{x} = -\dfrac{15}{8}$ $\cot \theta = \dfrac{x}{y} = -\dfrac{8}{15}$

25. $\sin \theta = \dfrac{y}{r} = \dfrac{3}{5} \Rightarrow x^2 = 25 - 9 = 16$

θ in Quadrant II $\Rightarrow x = -4$

$\sin \theta = \dfrac{y}{r} = \dfrac{3}{5}$ $\csc \theta = \dfrac{r}{y} = \dfrac{5}{3}$

$\cos \theta = \dfrac{x}{r} = -\dfrac{4}{5}$ $\sec \theta = \dfrac{r}{x} = -\dfrac{5}{4}$

$\tan \theta = \dfrac{y}{x} = -\dfrac{3}{4}$ $\cot \theta = \dfrac{x}{y} = -\dfrac{4}{3}$

27. $\cot \theta = \dfrac{x}{y} = -\dfrac{3}{1} = \dfrac{3}{-1}$

$\cos \theta > 0 \Rightarrow \theta$ is in Quadrant IV $\Rightarrow x$ is positive;

$x = 3, y = -1, r = \sqrt{10}$

$\sin \theta = \dfrac{y}{r} = -\dfrac{\sqrt{10}}{10}$ $\csc \theta = \dfrac{r}{y} = -\sqrt{10}$

$\cos \theta = \dfrac{x}{r} = \dfrac{3\sqrt{10}}{10}$ $\sec \theta = \dfrac{r}{x} = \dfrac{\sqrt{10}}{3}$

$\tan \theta = \dfrac{y}{x} = -\dfrac{1}{3}$ $\cot \theta = \dfrac{x}{y} = -3$

29. $\sec \theta = \dfrac{r}{x} = \dfrac{2}{-1} \Rightarrow y^2 = 4 - 1 = 3$

$\sin \theta < 0 \Rightarrow \theta$ is in Quadrant III $\Rightarrow y = -\sqrt{3}$

$\sin \theta = \dfrac{y}{r} = -\dfrac{\sqrt{3}}{2}$ $\csc \theta = \dfrac{r}{y} = -\dfrac{2}{\sqrt{3}} = -\dfrac{2\sqrt{3}}{3}$

$\cos \theta = \dfrac{x}{r} = -\dfrac{1}{2}$ $\sec \theta = \dfrac{r}{x} = -2$

$\tan \theta = \dfrac{y}{x} = \sqrt{3}$ $\cot \theta = \dfrac{x}{y} = \dfrac{1}{\sqrt{3}} = \dfrac{\sqrt{3}}{3}$

31. $\cot \theta$ is undefined,

$\dfrac{\pi}{2} \le \theta \le \dfrac{3\pi}{2} \Rightarrow y = 0 \Rightarrow \theta = \pi$

$\sin \theta = 0$ $\csc \theta$ is undefined.

$\cos \theta = -1$ $\sec \theta = -1$

$\tan \theta = 0$ $\cot \theta$ is undefined.

33. To find a point on the terminal side of θ, use any point on the line $y = -x$ that lies in Quadrant II. $(-1, 1)$ is one such point.

$x = -1, y = 1, r = \sqrt{2}$

$\sin \theta = \dfrac{1}{\sqrt{2}} = \dfrac{\sqrt{2}}{2}$ $\csc \theta = \sqrt{2}$

$\cos \theta = -\dfrac{1}{\sqrt{2}} = -\dfrac{\sqrt{2}}{2}$ $\sec \theta = -\sqrt{2}$

$\tan \theta = -1$ $\cot \theta = -1$

35. To find a point on the terminal side of θ, use any point on the line $y = 2x$ that lies in Quadrant III. $(-1, -2)$ is one such point.

$x = -1, y = -2, y = \sqrt{5}$

$\sin \theta = -\dfrac{2}{\sqrt{5}} = -\dfrac{2\sqrt{5}}{5}$ $\csc \theta = \dfrac{\sqrt{5}}{-2} = -\dfrac{\sqrt{5}}{2}$

$\cos \theta = -\dfrac{1}{\sqrt{5}} = -\dfrac{\sqrt{5}}{5}$ $\sec \theta = \dfrac{\sqrt{5}}{-1} = -\sqrt{5}$

$\tan \theta = \dfrac{-2}{-1} = 2$ $\cot \theta = \dfrac{-1}{-2} = \dfrac{1}{2}$

37. $(x, y) = (-1, 0), r = 1$

$\sin \pi = \dfrac{y}{r} = \dfrac{0}{1} = 0$

39. $(x, y) = (0, -1), r = 1$

$\sec \dfrac{3\pi}{2} = \dfrac{r}{x} = \dfrac{1}{0} \Rightarrow$ undefined

41. $(x, y) = (0, 1), r = 1$

$\sin \dfrac{\pi}{2} = \dfrac{y}{r} = \dfrac{1}{1} = 1$

43. $(x, y) = (-1, 0), r = 1$

$\csc \pi = \dfrac{r}{y} = \dfrac{1}{0} \Rightarrow$ undefined

45. $\theta = 160°$

$\theta' = 180° - 160° = 20°$

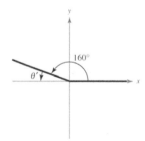

47. $\theta = -125°$

$360° - 125° = 235°$ (coterminal angle)

$\theta' = 235° - 180° = 55°$

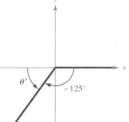

49. $\theta = \dfrac{2\pi}{3}$

$\theta' = \pi - \dfrac{2\pi}{3} = \dfrac{\pi}{3}$

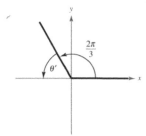

51. $\theta = 4.8$

$\theta' = 2\pi - 4.8\pi \approx 1.4832$

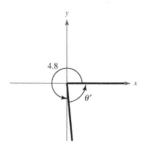

53. $\theta = 225°, \theta' = 45°,$ Quadrant III

$\sin 225° = -\sin 45° = -\dfrac{\sqrt{2}}{2}$

$\cos 225° = -\cos 45° = -\dfrac{\sqrt{2}}{2}$

$\tan 225° = \tan 45° = 1$

55. $\theta = 750°, \theta' = 30°,$ Quadrant I

$\sin 750° = \sin 30° = \dfrac{1}{2}$

$\cos 750° = \cos 30° = \dfrac{\sqrt{3}}{2}$

$\tan 750° = \tan 30° = \dfrac{\sqrt{3}}{3}$

57. $\theta = -840°$ is coterminal with $240°$.

$\theta' = 240° - 180° = 60°$ in Quadrant III.

$\sin(-840°) = -\sin 60° = -\dfrac{\sqrt{3}}{2}$

$\cos(-840°) = -\cos 60° = -\dfrac{1}{2}$

$\tan(-840°) = \tan 60° = \sqrt{3}$

59. $\theta = \dfrac{2\pi}{3}, \theta' = \dfrac{\pi}{3}$ in Quadrant II

$\sin \dfrac{2\pi}{3} = \sin \dfrac{\pi}{3} = \dfrac{\sqrt{3}}{2}$

$\cos \dfrac{2\pi}{3} = -\cos \dfrac{\pi}{3} = -\dfrac{1}{2}$

$\tan \dfrac{2\pi}{3} = -\tan \dfrac{\pi}{3} = -\sqrt{3}$

61. $\theta = \dfrac{5\pi}{4}, \theta' = \dfrac{\pi}{4}$ in Quadrant III

$\sin \dfrac{5\pi}{4} = -\sin \dfrac{\pi}{4} = -\dfrac{\sqrt{2}}{2}$

$\cos \dfrac{5\pi}{4} = -\cos \dfrac{\pi}{4} = -\dfrac{\sqrt{2}}{2}$

$\tan \dfrac{5\pi}{4} = \tan \dfrac{\pi}{4} = 1$

63. $\theta = -\dfrac{\pi}{6}, \theta' = \dfrac{\pi}{6},$ Quadrant IV

$\sin\left(-\dfrac{\pi}{6}\right) = -\sin \dfrac{\pi}{6} = -\dfrac{1}{2}$

$\cos\left(-\dfrac{\pi}{6}\right) = \cos \dfrac{\pi}{6} = \dfrac{\sqrt{3}}{2}$

$\tan\left(-\dfrac{\pi}{6}\right) = -\tan \dfrac{\pi}{6} = -\dfrac{\sqrt{3}}{3}$

65. $\theta = \dfrac{11\pi}{4}, \theta' = \dfrac{\pi}{4},$ Quadrant II

$\sin \dfrac{11\pi}{4} = \sin \dfrac{\pi}{4} = \dfrac{\sqrt{2}}{2}$

$\cos \dfrac{11\pi}{4} = -\cos \dfrac{\pi}{4} = -\dfrac{\sqrt{2}}{2}$

$\tan \dfrac{11\pi}{4} = -\tan \dfrac{\pi}{4} = -1$

67. $\theta = \dfrac{9\pi}{4}, \theta' = \dfrac{\pi}{4}$ in Quadrant I

$\sin \dfrac{9\pi}{4} = \sin \dfrac{\pi}{4} = \dfrac{\sqrt{2}}{2}$

$\cos \dfrac{9\pi}{4} = \cos \dfrac{\pi}{4} = \dfrac{\sqrt{2}}{2}$

$\tan \dfrac{9\pi}{4} = \tan \dfrac{\pi}{4} = 1$

69.
$$\sin \theta = -\frac{3}{5}$$

$$\sin^2 \theta + \cos^2 \theta = 1$$

$$\cos^2 \theta = 1 - \sin^2 \theta$$

$$\cos^2 \theta = 1 - \left(-\frac{3}{5}\right)^2$$

$$\cos^2 \theta = 1 - \frac{9}{25}$$

$$\cos^2 \theta = \frac{16}{25}$$

$\cos \theta > 0$ in Quadrant IV.

$$\cos \theta = \frac{4}{5}$$

71. $\tan \theta = \dfrac{3}{2}$

$$\sec^2 \theta = 1 + \tan^2 \theta$$

$$\sec^2 \theta = 1 + \left(\frac{3}{2}\right)^2$$

$$\sec^2 \theta = 1 + \frac{9}{4}$$

$$\sec^2 \theta = \frac{13}{4}$$

$\sec \theta < 0$ in Quadrant III.

$$\sec \theta = -\frac{\sqrt{13}}{2}$$

73. $\cos \theta = \dfrac{5}{8}$

$$\cos \theta = \frac{1}{\sec \theta} \Rightarrow \sec \theta = \frac{1}{\cos \theta}$$

$$\sec \theta = \frac{1}{\frac{5}{8}} = \frac{8}{5}$$

75. $\sin 10° \approx 0.1736$

77. $\cos(-110°) \approx -0.3420$

79. $\tan 304° \approx -1.4826$

81. $\sec 72° = \dfrac{1}{\cos 72°} \approx 3.2361$

83. $\tan 4.5 \approx 4.6373$

85. $\tan\left(\dfrac{\pi}{9}\right) \approx 0.3640$

87. $\sin(-0.65) \approx -0.6052$

89. $\cot\left(-\dfrac{11\pi}{8}\right) = \dfrac{1}{\tan(-11\pi/8)} \approx -0.4142$

91. (a) $\sin \theta = \dfrac{1}{2} \Rightarrow$ reference angle is $30°$ or $\dfrac{\pi}{6}$ and θ is in Quadrant I or Quadrant II.

Values in degrees: $30°, 150°$

Values in radian: $\dfrac{\pi}{6}, \dfrac{5\pi}{6}$

(b) $\sin \theta = \dfrac{1}{2} \Rightarrow$ reference angle is $30°$ or $\dfrac{\pi}{6}$ and θ is in Quadrant III or Quadrant IV.

Values in degrees: $210°, 330°$

Values in radians: $\dfrac{7\pi}{6}, \dfrac{11\pi}{6}$

93. (a) $\csc \theta = \dfrac{2\sqrt{3}}{3} \Rightarrow$ reference angle is $60°$ or $\dfrac{\pi}{3}$ and θ is in Quadrant I or Quadrant II.

Values in degrees: $60°, 120°$

Values in radians: $\dfrac{\pi}{3}, \dfrac{2\pi}{3}$

(b) $\cot \theta = -1 \Rightarrow$ reference angle is $45°$ or $\dfrac{\pi}{4}$ and θ is in Quadrant II or Quadrant IV.

Values in degrees: $135°, 315°$

Values in radians: $\dfrac{3\pi}{4}, \dfrac{7\pi}{4}$

95. (a) $\tan \theta = 1 \Rightarrow$ reference angle is $45°$ or $\dfrac{\pi}{4}$ and θ is in Quadrant I or Quadrant III.

Values in degrees: $45°, 225°$

Values in radians: $\dfrac{\pi}{4}, \dfrac{5\pi}{4}$

(b) $\cot \theta = -\sqrt{3} \Rightarrow$ reference angle is $30°$ or $\dfrac{\pi}{6}$ and θ is in Quadrant II or Quadrant IV.

Values in degrees: $150°, 330°$

Values in radians: $\dfrac{5\pi}{6}, \dfrac{11\pi}{6}$

97. $\sin \theta = \dfrac{6}{d} \Rightarrow d = \dfrac{6}{\sin \theta}$

    (a) $\theta = 30°$

$$d = \frac{6}{\sin 30°} = \frac{6}{1/2} = 12 \text{ miles}$$

    (b) $\theta = 90°$

$$d = \frac{6}{\sin 90°} = \frac{6}{1} = 6 \text{ miles}$$

    (c) $\theta = 120°$

$$d = \frac{6}{\sin 120°} = \frac{6}{\sqrt{3}/2} \approx 6.9 \text{ miles}$$

99. (a) New York City:

$$N \approx 22.1 \sin(0.52t - 2.22) + 55.01$$

    Fairbanks: $F \approx 36.6 \sin(0.50t - 1.83) + 25.61$

    (b)

Month	New York City	Fairbanks
February	35°	−1°
March	41°	14°
May	63°	48°
June	72°	59°
August	76°	56°
September	69°	42°
November	47°	7°

    (c) The periods are about the same for both models, approximately 12 months.

101. $y(t) = 2e^{-t} \cos 6t$

    (a) $t = 0$

$$y(0) = 2e^{-0} \cos 0 = 2 \text{ centimeters}$$

    (b) $t = \frac{1}{4}$

$$y\left(\tfrac{1}{4}\right) = 2e^{-1/4} \cos\left(6 \cdot \tfrac{1}{4}\right) \approx 0.11 \text{ centimeter}$$

    (c) $t = \frac{1}{2}$

$$y\left(\tfrac{1}{2}\right) = 2e^{-1/2} \cos\left(6 \cdot \tfrac{1}{2}\right) \approx -1.2 \text{ centimeters}$$

103. False. In each of the four quadrants, the sign of the secant function and the cosine function will be the same since they are reciprocals of each other.

105. $h(t) = f(t)g(t)$

$$h(-t) = f(-t)g(-t) = -f(t)g(t) = -h(t)$$

    Therefore, $h(t)$ is odd.

107. (a) $\sin t = y, \cos t = x$

    (b) r is the hypotenuse of the triangle which is equal to the radius of the circle. So, $r = 1$.

    (c) $\sin \theta = y, \cos \theta = x$

    (d) $\sin t = \sin \theta$ and $\cos t = \cos \theta$

Section 4.5 Graphs of Sine and Cosine Functions

1. cycle

3. phase shift

5. $y = 2 \sin 5x$

    Period: $\dfrac{2\pi}{5}$

    Amplitude: $|2| = 2$

7. $y = \dfrac{3}{4} \cos \dfrac{x}{2}$

    Period: $\dfrac{2\pi}{1/2} = 4\pi$

    Amplitude: $\left|\dfrac{3}{4}\right| = \dfrac{3}{4}$

9. $y = \dfrac{1}{2} \sin \dfrac{\pi x}{3}$

    Period: $\dfrac{2\pi}{\pi/3} = 6$

    Amplitude: $\left|\dfrac{1}{2}\right| = \dfrac{1}{2}$

11. $y = -4 \sin x$

    Period: $\dfrac{2\pi}{1} = 2\pi$

    Amplitude: $|-4| = 4$

13. $y = 3 \sin 10x$

    Period: $\dfrac{2\pi}{10} = \dfrac{\pi}{5}$

    Amplitude: $|3| = 3$

15. $y = \dfrac{5}{3}\cos\dfrac{4x}{5}$

Period: $\dfrac{2\pi}{4/5} = \dfrac{10\pi}{4} = \dfrac{5\pi}{2}$

Amplitude: $\left|\dfrac{5}{3}\right| = \dfrac{5}{3}$

17. $y = \dfrac{1}{4}\sin 2\pi x$

Period: $\dfrac{2\pi}{2\pi} = 1$

Amplitude: $\left|\dfrac{1}{4}\right| = \dfrac{1}{4}$

19. $f(x) = \sin x$

$g(x) = \sin(x - \pi)$

g is a horizontal shift to the right π units of the graph of f (a phase shift).

21. $f(x) = \cos 2x$

$g(x) = -\cos 2x$

g is a reflection in the x-axis of the graph of f.

23. $f(x) = \cos x$

$g(x) = \cos 2x$

The period of f is twice that of g.

25. $f(x) = \sin 2x$

$f(x) = 3 + \sin 2x$

g is a vertical shift three units upward of the graph of f.

27. The graph of g has twice the amplitude as the graph of f. The period is the same.

29. The graph of g is a horizontal shift π units to the right of the graph of f.

31. $f(x) = -2\sin x$

Period: $\dfrac{2\pi}{b} = \dfrac{2\pi}{1} = 2\pi$

Amplitude: 2

Symmetry: origin

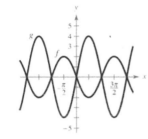

Key points: Intercept	Minimum	Intercept	Maximum	Intercept
$(0, 0)$	$\left(\dfrac{\pi}{2}, -2\right)$	$(\pi, 0)$	$\left(\dfrac{3\pi}{2}, 0\right)$	$(2\pi, 0)$

Because $g(x) = 4\sin x = (-2)f(x)$, generate key points for the graph of $g(x)$ by multiplying the y-coordinate of each key point of $f(x)$ by -2.

33. $f(x) = \cos x$

Period: $\dfrac{2\pi}{b} = \dfrac{2\pi}{1} = 2\pi$

Amplitude: $|1| = 1$

Symmetry: y-axis

Key points: Maximum	Intercept	Minimum	Intercept	Maximum
$(0, 1)$	$\left(\dfrac{\pi}{2}, 0\right)$	$(\pi, -1)$	$\left(\dfrac{3\pi}{2}, 0\right)$	$(2\pi, 1)$

Because $g(x) = 2 + \cos x = f(x) + 2$, the graph of $g(x)$ is the graph of $f(x)$, but translated upward by two units. Generate key points of $g(x)$ by adding 2 to the y-coordinate of each key point of $f(x)$.

35. $f(x) = -\dfrac{1}{2} \sin \dfrac{x}{2}$

Period: $\dfrac{2\pi}{b} = \dfrac{2\pi}{1/2} = 4\pi$

Amplitude: $\dfrac{1}{2}$

Symmetry: origin

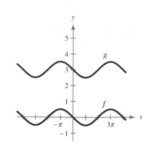

Key points: Intercept   Minimum   Intercept   Maximum   Intercept

$(0, 0)$ $\left(\pi, -\dfrac{1}{2}\right)$ $(2\pi, 0)$ $\left(3\pi, \dfrac{1}{2}\right)$ $(4\pi, 0)$

Because $g(x) = 3 - \dfrac{1}{2} \sin \dfrac{x}{2} = 3 - f(x)$, the graph of $g(x)$ is the graph of $f(x)$, but translated upward by three units.

Generate key points for the graph of $g(x)$ by adding 3 to the y-coordinate of each key point of $f(x)$.

37. $f(x) = 2 \cos x$

Period: $\dfrac{2\pi}{b} = \dfrac{2\pi}{1} = 2\pi$

Amplitude: 2

Symmetry: y-axis

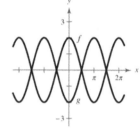

Key points: Maximum   Intercept   Minimum   Intercept   Maximum

$(0, 2)$ $\left(\dfrac{\pi}{2}, 0\right)$ $(\pi, -2)$ $\left(\dfrac{3\pi}{2}, 0\right)$ $(2\pi, 2)$

Because $g(x) = 2 \cos(x + \pi) = f(x + \pi)$, the graph of $g(x)$ is the graph of $f(x)$, but with a phase shift (horizontal translation) of $-\pi$. Generate key points for the graph of $g(x)$ by shifting each key point of $f(x)$ π units to the left.

39. $y = 5 \sin x$

Period: 2π

Amplitude: 5

Key points:

$(0, 0), \left(\dfrac{\pi}{2}, 5\right), (\pi, 0),$

$\left(\dfrac{3\pi}{2}, -5\right), (2\pi, 0)$

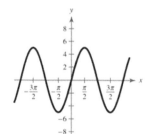

41. $y = \dfrac{1}{3} \cos x$

Period: 2π

Amplitude: $\dfrac{1}{3}$

Key points:

$\left(0, \dfrac{1}{3}\right), \left(\dfrac{\pi}{2}, 0\right), \left(\pi, -\dfrac{1}{3}\right),$

$\left(\dfrac{3\pi}{2}, 0\right), \left(2\pi, \dfrac{1}{3}\right)$

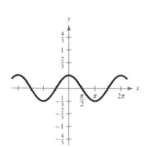

43. $y = \cos \dfrac{y}{2}$

Period $\dfrac{2\pi}{1/2} = 4\pi$

Amplitude: 1

Key points:

$(0, 1), (\pi, 0), (2\pi, -1),$

$(3\pi, 0), (4\pi, 1)$

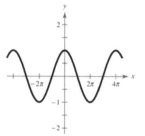

45. $y = \cos 2\pi x$

Period: $\dfrac{2\pi}{2\pi} = 1$

Amplitude: 1

Key points:

$(0, 1), \left(\dfrac{1}{4}, 0\right), \left(\dfrac{1}{2}, -1\right), \left(\dfrac{3}{4}, 0\right)$

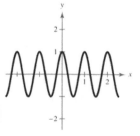

47. $y = -\sin \dfrac{2\pi x}{3}$

Period: $\dfrac{2\pi}{2\pi/3} = 3$

Amplitude: 1

Key points:

$(0, 0), \left(\dfrac{3}{4}, -1\right), \left(\dfrac{3}{2}, 0\right),$

$\left(\dfrac{9}{4}, 1\right), (3, 0)$

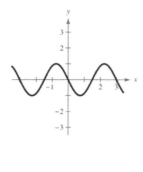

49. $y = 3\cos(x + \pi)$

Period: 2π

Amplitude: 3

Shift: Set $x + \pi = 0$ and $x + \pi = 2\pi$

$\qquad\qquad x = -\pi \qquad\qquad x = \pi$

Key points: $(-\pi, 3), \left(-\dfrac{\pi}{2}, 0\right), (0, -3), \left(\dfrac{\pi}{2}, 0\right), (\pi, 3)$

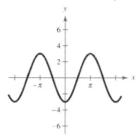

51. $y = \sin\left(x - \dfrac{\pi}{2}\right)$

Period: 2π

Amplitude: 1

Shift: Set $x - \dfrac{\pi}{2} = 0$ and $x - \dfrac{\pi}{2} = 2\pi$

$\qquad\qquad x = \dfrac{\pi}{2} \qquad\qquad x = \dfrac{5\pi}{2}$

Key points: $\left(\dfrac{\pi}{2}, 0\right), (\pi, 1), \left(\dfrac{3\pi}{2}, 0\right), (2\pi, -1), \left(\dfrac{5\pi}{2}, 0\right)$

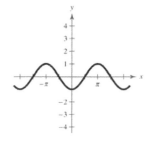

53. $y = 2 - \sin \dfrac{2\pi x}{3}$

Period: $\dfrac{2\pi}{2\pi/3} = 3$

Amplitude: 1

Key points:

$(0, 2), \left(\dfrac{3}{4}, 1\right), \left(\dfrac{3}{2}, 2\right),$

$\left(\dfrac{9}{4}, 3\right), (3, 2)$

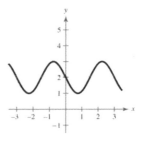

55. $y = 2 + \dfrac{1}{10}\cos 60\pi x$

Period: $\dfrac{2\pi}{60\pi} = \dfrac{1}{30}$

Amplitude: $\dfrac{1}{10}$

Vertical shift two units upward

Key points:

$(0, 2.1), \left(\dfrac{1}{120}, 2\right)\left(\dfrac{1}{60}, 1.9\right),$

$\left(\dfrac{1}{40}, 2\right), \left(\dfrac{1}{30}, 2.1\right)$

57. $y = 3\cos(x + \pi) - 3$

Period: 2π

Amplitude: 3

Shift: Set $x + \pi = 0$ and $x + \pi = 2\pi$

$\qquad\qquad x = -\pi \qquad\qquad\qquad x = \pi$

Key points: $(-\pi, 0), \left(-\dfrac{\pi}{2}, -3\right), (0, -6), \left(\dfrac{\pi}{2}, -3\right), (\pi, 0)$

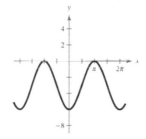

59. $y = \dfrac{2}{3}\cos\left(\dfrac{x}{2} - \dfrac{\pi}{4}\right)$

Period: $\dfrac{2\pi}{1/2} = 4\pi$

Amplitude: $\dfrac{2}{3}$

Shift: $\dfrac{x}{2} - \dfrac{\pi}{4} = 0$ and $\dfrac{\pi}{2} - \dfrac{\pi}{4} = 2\pi$

$$x = \dfrac{\pi}{2} \qquad\qquad x = \dfrac{9\pi}{2}$$

Key points:

$$\left(\dfrac{\pi}{2}, \dfrac{2}{3}\right), \left(\dfrac{3\pi}{2}, 0\right), \left(\dfrac{5\pi}{2}, \dfrac{-2}{3}\right), \left(\dfrac{7\pi}{2}, 0\right), \left(\dfrac{9\pi}{2}, \dfrac{2}{3}\right)$$

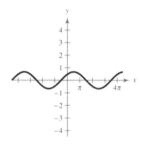

61. $g(x) = \sin(4x - \pi)$

(a) $g(x)$ is obtained by a horizontal shrink of four and a phase shift of $\dfrac{\pi}{4}$; and one cycle of $g(x)$ corresponds to the interval $\left[\dfrac{\pi}{4}, \dfrac{3\pi}{4}\right]$.

(b)

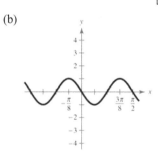

(c) $g(x) = f(4x - \pi)$ where $f(x) = \sin x$.

63. $g(x) = \cos(x - \pi) + 2$

(a) $g(x)$ is obtained by shifting $f(x)$ two units upward and a phase shift of π; and one cycle of $g(x)$ corresponds to the interval $[\pi, 3\pi]$.

(b)

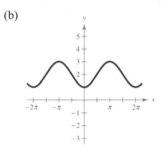

(c) $g(x) = f(x - \pi) + 2$ where $f(x) = \cos x$

65. $g(x) = 2\sin(4x - \pi) - 3$

(a) $g(x)$ is obtained by a horizontal shrink of four, a phase shift of $\dfrac{\pi}{4}$, shifting $f(x)$ three units downward, and has an amplitude of two. One cycle of $g(x)$ corresponds to the interval $\left[\dfrac{\pi}{4}, \dfrac{3\pi}{4}\right]$.

(b)

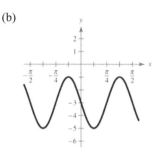

(c) $g(x) = 2f(4x - \pi) - 3$ where $f(x) = \sin x$

67. $y = -2\sin(4x + \pi)$

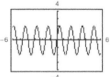

69. $y = \cos\left(2\pi x - \dfrac{\pi}{2}\right) + 1$

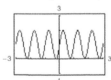

71. $y = -0.1 \sin\left(\dfrac{\pi x}{10} + \pi\right)$

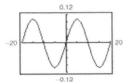

73. $f(x) = a \cos x + d$

Amplitude: $\frac{1}{2}\big[3 - (-1)\big] = 2 \Rightarrow a = 2$

$3 = 2 \cos 0 + d$

$d = 3 - 2 = 1$

$a = 2, d = 1$

75. $f(x) = a \cos x + d$

Amplitude: $\frac{1}{2}[8 - 0] = 4$

Reflected in the x-axis: $a = -4$

$0 = -4 \cos 0 + d$

$d = 4$

$a = -4, d = 4$

77. $y = a \sin(bx - c)$

Amplitude: $|a| = |3|$

Since the graph is reflected in the x-axis, we have $a = -3$.

Period: $\dfrac{2\pi}{b} = \pi \Rightarrow b = 2$

Phase shift: $c = 0$

$a = -3, b = 2, c = 0$

79. $y = a \sin(bx - c)$

Amplitude: $a = 2$

Period: $2\pi \Rightarrow b = 1$

Phase shift: $bx - c = 0$ when $x = -\dfrac{\pi}{4}$

$(1)\left(-\dfrac{\pi}{4}\right) - c = 0 \Rightarrow c = -\dfrac{\pi}{4}$

$a = 2, b = 1, c = -\dfrac{\pi}{4}$

81. $y_1 = \sin x$

$y_2 = -\dfrac{1}{2}$

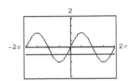

In the interval $[-2\pi, 2\pi]$,

$y_1 = y_2$ when $x = -\dfrac{5\pi}{6}, -\dfrac{\pi}{6}, \dfrac{7\pi}{6}, \dfrac{11\pi}{6}$.

Answers for 83–85 are sample answers.

83. $f(x) = 2 \sin(2x - \pi) + 1$

85. $f(x) = \cos(2x + 2\pi) - \dfrac{3}{2}$

87. $v = 1.75 \sin \dfrac{\pi t}{2}$

(a) Period $= \dfrac{2\pi}{\pi/2} = 4$ seconds

(b) $\dfrac{1 \text{ cycle}}{4 \text{ seconds}} \cdot \dfrac{60 \text{ seconds}}{1 \text{ minute}} = 15$ cycles per minute

(c)

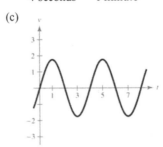

89. (a) $y = a\cos(bt - c) + d$

Amplitude: $a = \dfrac{1}{2}[\text{max temp} - \text{min temp}] = \dfrac{1}{2}[78.6 - 13.8] = 32.4$

Period: $p = 2[\text{month of max temp} - \text{month of min temp}] = 2[7 - 1] = 12$

$$b = \frac{2\pi}{p} = \frac{2\pi}{12} = \frac{\pi}{6}$$

Because the maximum temperature occurs in the seventh month,

$\dfrac{c}{b} = 7$ so $c \approx 3.67$.

The average temperature is $\dfrac{1}{2}(78.6 + 13.8) = 46.2°$, so $d = 46.2$.

So, $I(t) = 32.4\cos\left(\dfrac{\pi}{6}t - 3.67\right) + 46.2$.

(b)

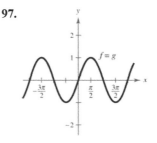

The model fits the data well.

(c)

The model fits the data well.

(d) The d value in each model represents the average temperature.

Las Vegas: $80.6°$; International Falls: $46.2°$

(e) The period of each model is 12. This is what you would expect because the time period is one year (twelve months).

(f) International Falls has the greater temperature variability. The amplitude determines the variability. The greater the amplitude, the greater the temperature varies.

91. $y = 0.001 \sin 880\pi t$

(a) Period: $\dfrac{2\pi}{880\pi} = \dfrac{1}{440}$ seconds

(b) $f = \dfrac{1}{p} = 440$ cycles per second

93. (a) Period $= \dfrac{2\pi}{\left(\dfrac{\pi}{10}\right)} = 20$ seconds

The wheel takes 20 seconds to revolve once.

(b) Amplitude: 50 feet

The radius of the wheel is 50 feet.

(c)

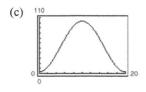

95. False. The graph of $\sin(x + 2\pi)$ is the graph of $\sin(x)$ translated to the *left* by one period, and the graphs are indeed identical.

97.

Because the graphs are the same, the conjecture is that

$$\sin(x) = \cos\left(x - \frac{\pi}{2}\right).$$

99.

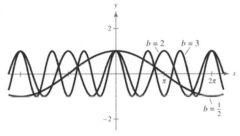

As the value of b increases, the period decreases.

$b = \dfrac{1}{2} \to \dfrac{1}{2}$ cycle

$b = 2 \to 2$ cycles

$b = 3 \to 3$ cycles

101. (a) $\sin \dfrac{1}{2} \approx \dfrac{1}{2} - \dfrac{(1/2)^3}{3!} + \dfrac{(1/2)^5}{5!} \approx 0.4794$

$\sin \dfrac{1}{2} \approx 0.4794$ (by calculator)

(b) $\sin 1 \approx 1 - \dfrac{1}{3!} + \dfrac{1}{5!} \approx 0.8417$

$\sin 1 \approx 0.8415$ (by calculator)

(c) $\sin \dfrac{\pi}{6} \approx 1 - \dfrac{(\pi/6)^3}{3!} + \dfrac{(\pi/6)^5}{5!} \approx 0.5000$

$\sin \dfrac{\pi}{6} = 0.5$ (by calculator)

(d) $\cos(-0.5) \approx 1 - \dfrac{(-0.5)^2}{2!} + \dfrac{(-0.5)^4}{4!} \approx 0.8776$

$\cos(-0.5) \approx 0.8776$ (by calculator)

(e) $\cos 1 \approx 1 - \dfrac{1}{2!} + \dfrac{1}{4!} \approx 0.5417$

$\cos 1 \approx 0.5403$ (by calculator)

(f) $\cos \dfrac{\pi}{4} \approx 1 - \dfrac{(\pi/4)^2}{2!} + \dfrac{(\pi/4)^2}{4!} = 0.7074$

$\cos \dfrac{\pi}{4} \approx 0.7071$ (by calculator)

The error in the approximation is not the same in each case. The error appears to increase as x moves farther away from 0.

Section 4.6   Graphs of Other Trigonometric Functions

1. odd; origin

3. reciprocal

5. π

7. $(-\infty, -1] \cup [1, \infty)$

9. $y = \sec 2x$

Period: $\dfrac{2\pi}{2} = \pi$

Matches graph (e).

10. $y = \tan \dfrac{x}{2}$

Period: $\dfrac{\pi}{b} = \dfrac{\pi}{1/2} = 2\pi$

Asymptotes: $x = -\pi, x = \pi$

Matches graph (c).

11. $y = \dfrac{1}{2} \cot \pi x$

Period: $\dfrac{\pi}{\pi} = 1$

Matches graph (a).

12. $y = -\csc x$

Period: 2π

Matches graph (d).

13. $y = \dfrac{1}{2} \sec \dfrac{\pi x}{2}$

Period: $\dfrac{2\pi}{b} = \dfrac{2\pi}{\pi/2} = 4$

Asymptotes: $x = -1, x = 1$

Matches graph (f).

14. $y = -2 \sec \dfrac{\pi x}{2}$

Period: $\dfrac{2\pi}{b} = \dfrac{2\pi}{\pi/2} = 4$

Asymptotes: $x = -1$, $x = 1$

Reflected in x-axis

Matches graph (b).

15. $y = \dfrac{1}{3} \tan x$

Period: π

Two consecutive asymptotes:

$x = -\dfrac{\pi}{2}$ and $x = \dfrac{\pi}{2}$

x	$-\dfrac{\pi}{4}$	0	$\dfrac{\pi}{4}$
y	$-\dfrac{1}{3}$	0	$\dfrac{1}{3}$

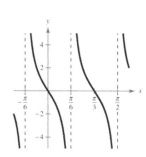

17. $y = -2 \tan 3x$

Period: $\dfrac{\pi}{3}$

Two consecutive asymptotes:

$x = -\dfrac{\pi}{6}$, $x = \dfrac{\pi}{6}$

x	$-\dfrac{\pi}{3}$	0	$\dfrac{\pi}{3}$
y	0	0	0

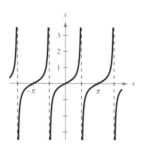

19. $y = -\dfrac{1}{2} \sec x$

Period: 2π

Two consecutive asymptotes:

$x = -\dfrac{\pi}{2}$, $x = \dfrac{\pi}{2}$

x	$-\dfrac{\pi}{3}$	0	$\dfrac{\pi}{3}$
y	-1	$-\dfrac{1}{2}$	-1

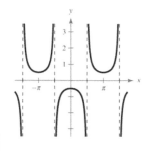

21. $y = \csc \pi x$

Period: $\dfrac{2\pi}{\pi} = 2$

Two consecutive asymptotes:

$x = 0$, $x = 1$

x	$\dfrac{1}{6}$	$\dfrac{1}{2}$	$\dfrac{5}{6}$
y	2	1	2

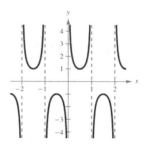

23. $y = \dfrac{1}{2} \sec \pi x$

Period: 2

Two consecutive asymptotes:

$x = -\dfrac{1}{2}$, $x = \dfrac{1}{2}$

x	-1	0	1
y	$-\dfrac{1}{2}$	$\dfrac{1}{2}$	$-\dfrac{1}{2}$

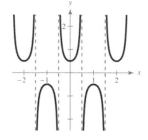

25. $y = \csc \dfrac{x}{2}$

Period: $\dfrac{2\pi}{1/2} = 4\pi$

Two consecutive asymptotes:

$x = 0$, $x = 2\pi$

x	$\dfrac{\pi}{3}$	π	$\dfrac{5\pi}{3}$
y	2	1	2

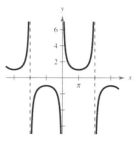

27. $y = 3 \cot 2x$

Period: $\dfrac{\pi}{2}$

Two consecutive asymptotes:

$x = -\dfrac{\pi}{2}$, $x = \dfrac{\pi}{2}$

x	$-\dfrac{\pi}{6}$	$-\dfrac{\pi}{8}$	$\dfrac{\pi}{8}$	$\dfrac{\pi}{6}$
y	$-3\sqrt{3}$	-3	3	$3\sqrt{3}$

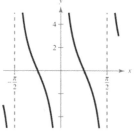

29. $y = 2 \sec 3x$

Period: $\dfrac{2\pi}{3}$

Two consecutive asymptotes:

$x = -\dfrac{\pi}{6}, x = \dfrac{\pi}{6}$

x	$-\dfrac{\pi}{3}$	0	$\dfrac{\pi}{3}$
y	-2	2	-2

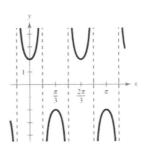

31. $y = \tan \dfrac{\pi x}{4}$

Period: $\dfrac{\pi}{\pi/4} = 4$

Two consecutive asymptotes:

$\dfrac{\pi x}{4} = -\dfrac{\pi}{2} \Rightarrow x = -2$

$\dfrac{\pi x}{4} = \dfrac{\pi}{2} \Rightarrow x = 2$

x	-1	0	1
y	-1	0	1

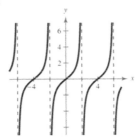

33. $y = 2 \csc(x - \pi)$

Period: 2π

Two consecutive asymptotes:

$x = -\pi, x = \pi$

x	$-\dfrac{\pi}{2}$	$\dfrac{\pi}{2}$	$\dfrac{3\pi}{2}$
y	2	-2	-2

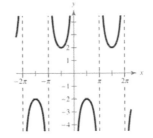

35. $y = 2 \sec(x + \pi)$

Period: 2π

Two consecutive asymptotes:

$x = -\dfrac{\pi}{2}, x = \dfrac{\pi}{2}$

x	$-\dfrac{\pi}{3}$	0	$\dfrac{\pi}{3}$
y	-4	-2	-4

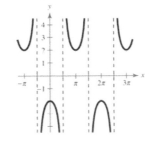

37. $y = \dfrac{1}{4} \csc\left(x + \dfrac{\pi}{4}\right)$

Period: 2π

Two consecutive asymptotes:

$x = -\dfrac{\pi}{4}, x = \dfrac{3\pi}{4}$

x	$-\dfrac{\pi}{12}$	$\dfrac{\pi}{4}$	$\dfrac{7\pi}{12}$
y	$\dfrac{1}{2}$	$\dfrac{1}{4}$	$\dfrac{1}{2}$

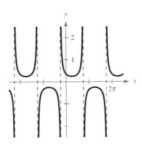

39. $y = \tan \dfrac{x}{3}$

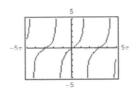

41. $y = -2 \sec 4x = \dfrac{-2}{\cos 4x}$

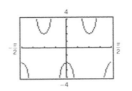

43. $y = \tan\left(x - \dfrac{\pi}{4}\right)$

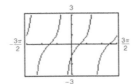

45. $y = -\csc(4x - \pi)$

$y = \dfrac{-1}{\sin(4x - \pi)}$

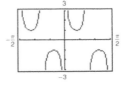

47. $y = 0.1 \tan\left(\dfrac{\pi x}{4} + \dfrac{\pi}{4}\right)$

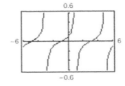

49. $\tan x = 1$

$$x = -\frac{7\pi}{4}, -\frac{3\pi}{4}, \frac{\pi}{4}, \frac{5\pi}{4}$$

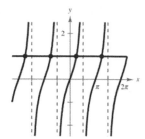

51. $\cot x = -\frac{\sqrt{3}}{3}$

$$x = -\frac{4\pi}{3}, -\frac{\pi}{3}, \frac{2\pi}{3}, \frac{5\pi}{3}$$

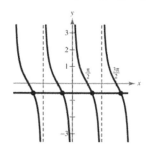

53. $\sec x = -2$

$$x = \frac{2\pi}{3}, \frac{4\pi}{3}, -\frac{2\pi}{3}, -\frac{4\pi}{3}$$

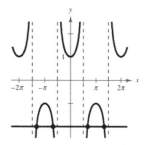

55. $\csc x = \sqrt{2}$

$$x = -\frac{7\pi}{4}, -\frac{5\pi}{4}, \frac{\pi}{4}, \frac{3\pi}{4}$$

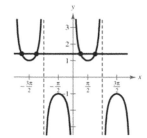

57. $f(x) = \sec x = \dfrac{1}{\cos x}$

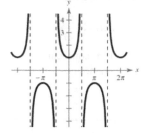

$f(-x) = \sec(-x)$

$\qquad = \dfrac{1}{\cos(-x)}$

$\qquad = \dfrac{1}{\cos x}$

$\qquad = f(x)$

So, $f(x) = \sec x$ is an even function and the graph has y-axis symmetry.

59. $g(x) = \cot x = \dfrac{1}{\tan x}$

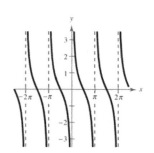

$g(-x) = \cot(-x)$

$\qquad = \dfrac{1}{\tan(-x)}$

$\qquad = -\dfrac{1}{\tan x}$

$\qquad = -g(x)$

So, $g(x) = \cot x$ is an odd function and the graph has origin symmetry.

61. $f(x) = x + \tan x$

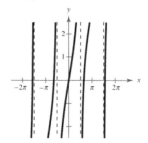

$f(-x) = (-x) + \tan(-x)$

$\qquad = -x - \tan x$

$\qquad = -(x + \tan x)$

$\qquad = -f(x)$

So, $f(x) = x + \tan x$ is an odd function and the graph has origin symmetry.

63. $g(x) = x \csc x = \dfrac{x}{\sin x}$

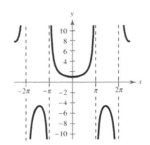

$g(-x) = (-x) \csc(-x)$

$= \dfrac{-x}{\sin(-x)}$

$= \dfrac{-x}{-\sin x}$

$= \dfrac{x}{\sin x}$

$= x \csc x$

$= g(x)$

So, $g(x) = x \csc x$ is an even function and the graph has y-axis symmetry.

65. $f(x) = |x \cos x|$

Matches graph (d).

As $x \to 0, f(x) \to 0$.

66. $f(x) = x \sin x$

Matches graph (a)

As $x \to 0, f(x) \to 0$.

67. $g(x) = |x| \sin x$

Matches graph (b).

As $x \to 0, g(x) \to 0$.

68. $g(x) = |x| \cos x$

Matches graph (c).

As $x \to 0, g(x) \to 0$.

69. $f(x) = \sin x + \cos\left(x + \dfrac{\pi}{2}\right)$

$g(x) = 0$

$f(x) = g(x)$

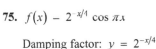

71. $f(x) = \sin^2 x$

$g(x) = \frac{1}{2}(1 - \cos 2x)$

$f(x) = g(x)$

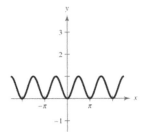

73. $g(x) = e^{-x^2/2} \sin x$

Damping factor: $e^{-x^2/2}$

As $x \to \infty, g(x) \to 0$.

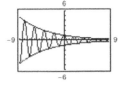

75. $f(x) = 2^{-x/4} \cos \pi x$

Damping factor: $y = 2^{-x/4}$

As $x \to \infty, f(x) \to 0$.

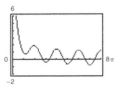

77. $y = \dfrac{6}{x} + \cos x, x > 0$

As $x \to 0, y \to \infty$.

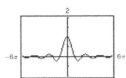

79. $g(x) = \dfrac{\sin x}{x}$

As $x \to 0, g(x) \to 1$.

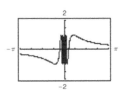

81. $f(x) = \sin \dfrac{1}{x}$

As $x \to 0, f(x)$ oscillates between -1 and 1.

83. (a) Period of $\cos \dfrac{\pi t}{6} = \dfrac{2\pi}{\pi/6} = 12$

Period of $\sin \dfrac{\pi t}{6} = \dfrac{2\pi}{\pi/6} = 12$

The period of $H(t)$ is 12 months.

The period of $L(t)$ is 12 months.

(b) From the graph, it appears that the greatest difference between high and low temperatures occurs in the summer. The smallest difference occurs in the winter.

(c) The highest high and low temperatures appear to occur about half of a month after the time when the sun is northernmost in the sky.

85. $\tan x = \dfrac{7}{d}$

$d = \dfrac{7}{\tan x} = 7 \cot x$

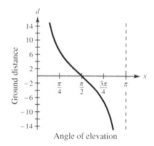

Angle of elevation

87. True.

$y = \sec x = \dfrac{1}{\cos x}$

If the reciprocal of $y = \sin x$ is translated $\pi/2$ units to the left, then

$y = \dfrac{1}{\sin\left(x + \dfrac{\pi}{2}\right)} = \dfrac{1}{\cos x} = \sec x.$

89. $f(x) = \csc x$

(a) $x \to 0^{+},\ f(x) \to \infty$

(b) $x \to 0^{-},\ f(x) \to -\infty$

(c) $x \to \pi^{+},\ f(x) \to -\infty$

(d) $x \to \pi^{-},\ f(x) \to \infty$

91. $f(x) = \sec x$

(a) $x \to \dfrac{\pi}{2}^{+},\ f(x) \to -\infty$

(b) $x \to \dfrac{\pi}{2}^{-},\ f(x) \to \infty$

(c) $x \to -\dfrac{\pi}{2}^{+},\ f(x) \to \infty$

(d) $x \to -\dfrac{\pi}{2}^{-},\ f(x) \to -\infty$

93. $f(x) = x - \cos x$

(a)

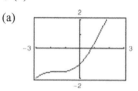

The zero between 0 and 1 occurs at $x \approx 0.7391$.

(b) $x_n = \cos(x_{n-1})$

$x_0 = 1$

$x_1 = \cos 1 \approx 0.5403$

$x_2 = \cos 0.5403 \approx 0.8576$

$x_3 = \cos 0.8576 \approx 0.6543$

$x_4 = \cos 0.6543 \approx 0.7935$

$x_5 = \cos 0.7935 \approx 0.7014$

$x_6 = \cos 0.7014 \approx 0.7640$

$x_7 = \cos 0.7640 \approx 0.7221$

$x_8 = \cos 0.7221 \approx 0.7504$

$x_9 = \cos 0.7504 \approx 0.7314$

$\vdots$

This sequence appears to be approaching the zero of f: $x \approx 0.7391$.

Section 4.7   Inverse Trigonometric Functions

Function	Alternative Notation	Domain	Range
1. $y = \arcsin x$	$y = \sin^{-1} x$	$-1 \le x \le 1$	$-\dfrac{\pi}{2} \le y \le \dfrac{\pi}{2}$
3. $y = \arctan x$	$y = \tan^{-1} x$	$-\infty < x < \infty$	$-\dfrac{\pi}{2} < y < \dfrac{\pi}{2}$

5. $y = \arcsin \dfrac{1}{2} \Rightarrow \sin y = \dfrac{1}{2}$ for $-\dfrac{\pi}{2} \le y \le \dfrac{\pi}{2} \Rightarrow y = \dfrac{\pi}{6}$

7. $y = \arccos \dfrac{1}{2} \Rightarrow \cos y = \dfrac{1}{2}$ for $0 \le y \le \pi \Rightarrow y = \dfrac{\pi}{3}$

9. $y = \arctan \dfrac{\sqrt{3}}{3} \Rightarrow \tan y = \dfrac{\sqrt{3}}{3}$ for $-\dfrac{\pi}{2} < y < \dfrac{\pi}{2} \Rightarrow y = \dfrac{\pi}{6}$

11. $y = \cos^{-1}\left(-\dfrac{\sqrt{3}}{2}\right) \Rightarrow \cos y = -\dfrac{\sqrt{3}}{2}$ for $0 \le y \le \pi \Rightarrow y = \dfrac{5\pi}{6}$

13. $y = \arctan\left(-\sqrt{3}\right) \to \tan y = -\sqrt{3}$ for $-\dfrac{\pi}{2} < y < \dfrac{\pi}{2} \Rightarrow y - -\dfrac{\pi}{3}$

15. $y = \arccos\left(-\dfrac{1}{2}\right) \Rightarrow \cos y = -\dfrac{1}{2}$ for $0 \le y \le \pi \Rightarrow y = \dfrac{2\pi}{3}$

17. $y = \sin^{-1}-\dfrac{\sqrt{3}}{2} \Rightarrow \sin y = -\dfrac{\sqrt{3}}{2}$ for $-\dfrac{\pi}{2} \le y \le \dfrac{\pi}{2} \Rightarrow y = -\dfrac{\pi}{3}$

19. $f(x) = \cos x$

$g(x) = \arccos x$

$y = x$

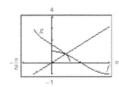

21. $\arccos 0.37 = \cos^{-1}(0.37) \approx 1.19$

23. $\arcsin(-0.75) = \sin^{-1}(-0.75) \approx -0.85$

25. $\arctan(-3) = \tan^{-1}(-3) \approx -1.25$

27. $\sin^{-1} 0.31 = \sin^{-1} 0.31 \approx 0.32$

29. $\arccos(-0.41) = \cos^{-1}(-0.41) \approx 1.99$

31. $\arctan 0.92 = \tan^{-1} 0.92 \approx 0.74$

33. $\arcsin \frac{7}{8} = \sin^{-1}\left(\frac{7}{8}\right) \approx 1.07$

35. $\tan^{-1}\left(\frac{19}{4}\right) \approx 1.36$

37. $\tan^{-1}\left(-\sqrt{372}\right) \approx -1.52$

39. $\arctan\left(-\sqrt{3}\right) = -\dfrac{\pi}{3}$

$\tan\left(-\dfrac{\pi}{6}\right) = -\dfrac{\sqrt{3}}{3}$

$\tan\left(\dfrac{\pi}{4}\right) = 1$

41. $\tan \theta = \dfrac{x}{4}$

$\theta = \arctan \dfrac{x}{4}$

43. $\sin \theta = \dfrac{x + 2}{5}$

$\theta = \arcsin\left(\dfrac{x + 2}{5}\right)$

45. $\cos \theta = \dfrac{x + 3}{2x}$

$\theta = \arccos \dfrac{x + 3}{2x}$

47. $\sin(\arcsin 0.3) = 0.3$

49. $\cos\left[\arccos(-0.1)\right] = -0.1$

51. $\arcsin(\sin 3\pi) = \arcsin(0) = 0$

Note: 3π is not in the range of the arcsine function.

53. Let $y = \arctan \dfrac{3}{4}$.

$\tan y = \dfrac{3}{4}, 0 < y < \dfrac{\pi}{2},$

$\sin\left(\arctan \dfrac{3}{4}\right) = \sin y = \dfrac{3}{5}$

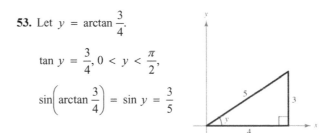

55. Let $y = \tan^{-1} 2$,

$\tan y = 2 = \dfrac{2}{1}, 0 < y < \dfrac{\pi}{2},$

$\cos\left(\tan^{-1} 2\right) = \cos y = \dfrac{1}{\sqrt{5}} = \dfrac{\sqrt{5}}{5}.$

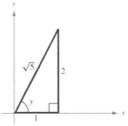

57. Let $y = \arcsin \dfrac{5}{13}$,

$$\sin y = \dfrac{5}{13}, 0 < y < \dfrac{\pi}{2},$$

$$\cos\left(\arcsin \dfrac{5}{13}\right) = \cos y = \dfrac{12}{13}.$$

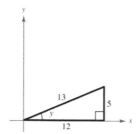

59. Let $y = \arctan\left(-\dfrac{3}{5}\right)$,

$$\tan y = -\dfrac{3}{5}, -\dfrac{\pi}{2} < y < 0,$$

$$\sec\left[\arctan\left(-\dfrac{3}{5}\right)\right] = \sec y = \dfrac{\sqrt{34}}{5}.$$

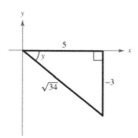

61. Let $y = \arccos\left(-\dfrac{2}{3}\right)$.

$$\cos y = -\dfrac{2}{3}, \dfrac{\pi}{2} < y < \pi,$$

$$\sin\left[\arccos\left(-\dfrac{2}{3}\right)\right] = \sin y = \dfrac{\sqrt{5}}{3}$$

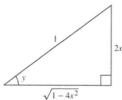

63. Let $u = \cos^{-1} \dfrac{\sqrt{3}}{2}$.

$$\cos u = \dfrac{\sqrt{3}}{2}, 0 < u < \dfrac{\pi}{2},$$

$$\csc\left[\cos^{-1} \dfrac{\sqrt{3}}{2}\right] = \csc u = 2.$$

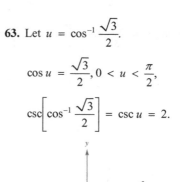

65. Let $y = \arctan x$.

$$\tan y = x = \dfrac{x}{1},$$

$$\cot(\arctan x) = \cot y = \dfrac{1}{x}$$

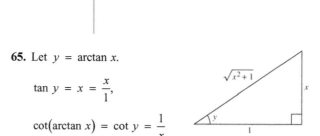

67. Let $y = \arcsin(2x)$.

$$\sin y = 2x = \dfrac{2x}{1},$$

$$\cos(\arcsin 2x) = \cos y = \sqrt{1 - 4x^2}$$

69. Let $y = \arccos x$.

$$\cos y = x = \dfrac{x}{1},$$

$$\sin(\arccos x) = \sin y = \sqrt{1 - x^2}$$

71. Let $y = \arccos\left(\dfrac{x}{3}\right)$.

$\cos y = \dfrac{x}{3}$,

$\tan\left(\arccos\dfrac{x}{3}\right) = \tan y = \dfrac{\sqrt{9 - x^2}}{x}$

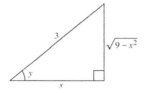

73. Let $y = \arctan\dfrac{x}{\sqrt{2}}$.

$\tan y = \dfrac{x}{\sqrt{2}}$,

$\csc\left(\arctan\dfrac{x}{\sqrt{2}}\right) = \csc y - \dfrac{\sqrt{x^2 + 2}}{x}$

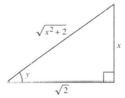

75. $f(x) = \sin(\arctan 2x)$, $g(x) = \dfrac{2x}{\sqrt{1 + 4x^2}}$

They are equal. Let $y = \arctan 2x$,

$\tan y = 2x = \dfrac{2x}{1}$,

and $\sin y = \dfrac{2x}{\sqrt{1 + 4x^2}}$.

$g(x) = \dfrac{2x}{\sqrt{1 + 4x^2}} = f(x)$

The graph has horizontal asymptotes at $y = \pm 1$.

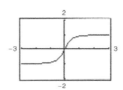

77. Let $y = \arctan\dfrac{9}{x}$.

$\tan y = \dfrac{9}{x}$ and $\sin y = \dfrac{9}{\sqrt{x^2 + 81}}$, $x > 0$

So,

$\arctan\dfrac{9}{x} = \arcsin\dfrac{9}{\sqrt{x^2 + 81}}$, $x > 0$.

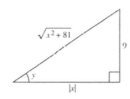

79. Let $y = \arccos\dfrac{3}{\sqrt{x^2 - 2x + 10}}$. Then,

$\cos y = \dfrac{3}{\sqrt{x^2 - 2x + 10}} = \dfrac{3}{\sqrt{(x - 1)^2 + 9}}$

and $\sin y = \dfrac{|x - 1|}{\sqrt{(x - 1)^2 + 9}}$.

So, $y = \arcsin\dfrac{|x - 1|}{\sqrt{x^2 - 2x + 10}}$.

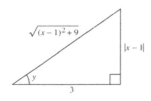

81. $g(x) = \arcsin(x - 1)$

Domain: $0 \le x \le 2$

Range: $-\dfrac{\pi}{2} \le y \le \dfrac{\pi}{2}$

This is the graph of $f(x) = \arcsin(x)$ shifted one unit to the right.

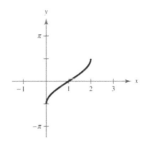

83. $y = 2\arccos x$

Domain: $-1 \le x \le 1$

Range: $0 \le y \le 2\pi$

This is the graph of $f(x) = \arccos x$ with a factor of 2.

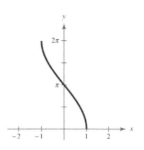

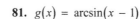

85. $f(x) = \arctan 2x$

Domain: all real numbers

Range: $-\dfrac{\pi}{2} < y < \dfrac{\pi}{2}$

This is the graph of
$g(x) = \arctan(x)$ with a
horizontal shrink of a
factor of 2.

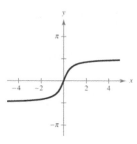

87. $h(v) = \arccos \dfrac{v}{2}$

Domain: $-2 \le v \le 2$

Range: $0 \le y \le \pi$

This is the graph of
$h(v) = \arccos v$ with
a horizontal stretch of
a factor of 2.

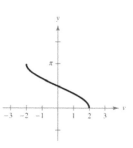

89. $f(x) = 2\arccos(2x)$

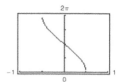

91. $f(x) = \arctan(2x - 3)$

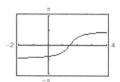

93. $f(x) = \pi - \sin^{-1}\left(\dfrac{2}{3}\right) \approx 2.412$

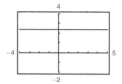

95. $f(t) = 3\cos 2t + 3\sin 2t = \sqrt{3^2 + 3^2}\,\sin\left(2t + \arctan\dfrac{3}{3}\right)$

$$= 3\sqrt{2}\,\sin(2t + \arctan 1)$$

$$= 3\sqrt{2}\,\sin\left(2t + \dfrac{\pi}{4}\right)$$

The graph implies that the identity is true.

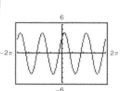

97. $\dfrac{\pi}{2}$

99. $\dfrac{\pi}{2}$

101. π

103. (a) $\sin \theta = \dfrac{5}{s}$

$\theta = \arcsin \dfrac{5}{s}$

(b) $s = 40$: $\theta = \arcsin \dfrac{5}{40} \approx 0.13$

$s = 20$: $\theta = \arcsin \dfrac{5}{20} \approx 0.25$

105. $\beta = \arctan \dfrac{3x}{x^2 + 4}$

(a)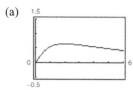

(b) β is maximum when $x = 2$ feet.

(c) The graph has a horizontal asymptote at $\beta = 0$.
As x increases, β decreases.

107.

(a) $\tan \theta = \dfrac{20}{41}$

$\theta = \arctan\left(\dfrac{20}{41}\right) \approx 26.0°$

(b) $\tan 26° = \dfrac{h}{50}$

$h = 50 \tan 26° \approx 24.4$ feet

109. (a) $\tan \theta = \dfrac{x}{20}$

$\theta = \arctan \dfrac{x}{20}$

(b) $x = 5:\ \theta = \arctan \dfrac{5}{20} \approx 14.0°$

$x = 12:\ \theta = \arctan \dfrac{12}{20} \approx 31.0°$

111. False.

$\dfrac{5\pi}{4}$ is not in the range of the arctangent function.

$\arctan 1 = \dfrac{\pi}{4}$

113. False. $\sin^{-1} x \neq \dfrac{1}{\sin x}$

The function $\sin^{-1} x$ is equivalent to arcsin x, which is the inverse sine function. The expression, $\dfrac{1}{\sin x}$ is the reciprocal of the sine function and is equivalent to csc x.

115. $y = \text{arccot } x$ if and only if $\cot y = x$.

Domain: $(-\infty, \infty)$

Range: $(0, \pi)$

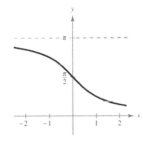

117. $y = \text{arccsc } x$ if and only if $\csc y = x$.

Domain: $(-\infty, -1] \cup [1, \infty)$

Range: $\left[-\dfrac{\pi}{2}, 0\right) \cup \left(0, \dfrac{\pi}{2}\right]$

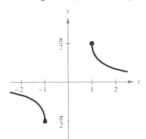

119. $y = \text{arcsec } \sqrt{2} \Rightarrow \sec y = \sqrt{2}$ and

$0 \le y < \dfrac{\pi}{2} \cup \dfrac{\pi}{2} < y \le \pi \Rightarrow y = \dfrac{\pi}{4}$

121. $y = \text{arccot}(-1) \Rightarrow \cot y = -1$ and

$0 < y < \pi \Rightarrow y = \dfrac{3\pi}{4}$

123. $y = \text{arccsc } 2 \Rightarrow \csc y = 2$ and

$-\dfrac{\pi}{2} \le y < 0 \cup 0 < y \le \dfrac{\pi}{2} \Rightarrow y = \dfrac{\pi}{6}$

125. $y = \text{arccsc}\left(\dfrac{2\sqrt{3}}{3}\right) \Rightarrow \csc y = \dfrac{2\sqrt{3}}{3}$ and

$-\dfrac{\pi}{2} \le y < 0 \cup 0 < y \le \dfrac{\pi}{2} \Rightarrow y = \dfrac{\pi}{3}$

127. $\text{arcsec } 2.54 = \arccos\left(\dfrac{1}{2.54}\right) \approx 1.17$

129. $\text{arccot } 5.25 = \arctan\left(\dfrac{1}{5.25}\right) \approx 0.19$

131. $\text{arccot}\left(\dfrac{5}{3}\right) = \arctan\left(\dfrac{3}{5}\right) \approx 0.54$

133. $\text{arccsc}\left(-\dfrac{25}{3}\right) = \arcsin\left(-\dfrac{3}{25}\right) \approx -0.12$

135. Area $= \arctan b - \arctan a$

(a) $a = 0, b = 1$

$$\text{Area} = \arctan 1 - \arctan 0 = \frac{\pi}{4} - 0 = \frac{\pi}{4}$$

(b) $a = -1, b = 1$

$$\text{Area} = \arctan 1 - \arctan(-1)$$

$$= \frac{\pi}{4} - \left(-\frac{\pi}{4}\right) = \frac{\pi}{2}$$

(c) $a = 0, b = 3$

$$\text{Area} = \arctan 3 - \arctan 0$$

$$\approx 1.25 - 0 = 1.25$$

(d) $a = -1, b = 3$

$$\text{Area} = \arctan 3 - \arctan(-1)$$

$$\approx 1.25 - \left(-\frac{\pi}{4}\right) \approx 2.03$$

137. $f(x) = \sin(x), f^{-1}(x) = \arcsin(x)$

(a) $f \circ f^{-1} = \sin(\arcsin x)$ $f^{-1} \circ f = \arcsin(\sin x)$

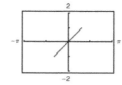   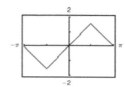

(b) The graphs coincide with the graph of $y = x$ only for certain values of x.

$f \circ f^{-1} = x$ over its entire domain, $-1 \le x \le 1$.

$f^{-1} \circ f = x$ over the region $-\frac{\pi}{2} \le x \le \frac{\pi}{2}$, corresponding to the region where $\sin x$ is one-to-one and has an inverse.

Section 4.8   Applications and Models

1. bearing

3. period

5. Given: $A = 30°, b = 3$

$$\tan A = \frac{a}{b} \Rightarrow a = b \tan A = 3 \tan 30° \approx 1.73$$

$$\cos A = \frac{b}{c} \Rightarrow c = \frac{b}{\cos A} = \frac{3}{\cos 30°} \approx 3.46$$

$$B = 90° - 30° = 60°$$

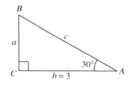

7. Given: $B = 71°, b = 24$

$$\tan B = \frac{b}{a} \Rightarrow a = \frac{b}{\tan B} = \frac{24}{\tan 71°} \approx 8.26$$

$$\sin B = \frac{b}{c} \Rightarrow c = \frac{b}{\sin B} = \frac{24}{\sin 71°} \approx 25.38$$

$$A = 90° - 71° = 19°$$

9. Given: $a = 3, b = 4$

$$a^2 + b^2 = c^2 \Rightarrow c^2 = (3)^2 + (4)^2 \Rightarrow c = 5$$

$$\tan A = \frac{a}{b} \Rightarrow A = \tan^{-1}\left(\frac{a}{b}\right) = \tan^{-1}\left(\frac{3}{4}\right) \approx 36.87°$$

$$B = 90° \quad 36.87° = 53.13°$$

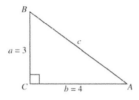

11. Given: $b = 16, c = 52$

$$a = \sqrt{52^2 - 16^2}$$

$$= \sqrt{2448} = 12\sqrt{17} \approx 49.48$$

$$\cos A = \frac{16}{52}$$

$$A = \arccos \frac{16}{52} \approx 72.80°$$

$$B = 90° - 72.08° \approx 17.92°$$

13. Given: $A = 12°15', c = 430.5$

$$B = 90° - 12°15' = 77°45'$$

$$\sin 12°15' = \frac{a}{430.5}$$

$$a = 430.5 \sin 12°15' \approx 91.34$$

$$\cos 12°15' = \frac{b}{430.5}$$

$$b = 430.5 \cos 12°15' \approx 420.70$$

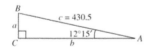

15. $\theta = 45°, b = 6$

$$\tan \theta = \frac{h}{(1/2)b} \Rightarrow h = \frac{1}{2}b \tan \theta$$

$$h = \frac{1}{2}(6) \tan 45° = 3.00 \text{ units}$$

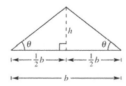

17. $\theta = 32°, b = 8$

$$\tan \theta = \frac{h}{(1/2)b} \Rightarrow h = \frac{1}{2}b \tan \theta$$

$$h = \frac{1}{2}(8) \tan 32° \approx 2.50 \text{ units}$$

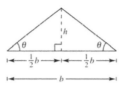

19. $\tan 25° = \dfrac{100}{x}$

$$x = \frac{100}{\tan 25°}$$

$$\approx 214.45 \text{ feet}$$

21. $\sin 80° = \dfrac{h}{20}$

$$20 \sin 80° = h$$

$$h \approx 19.7 \text{ feet}$$

23. Let the height of the church $= x$ and the height of the church and steeple $= y$. Then,

$$\tan 35° = \frac{x}{50} \text{ and } \tan 47°40' = \frac{y}{50}$$

$$x = 50 \tan 35° \text{ and } y = 50 \tan 47°40'$$

$$h = y - x = 50(\tan 47°40' - \tan 35°).$$

$$h \approx 19.9 \text{ feet}$$

25. $\cot 55 = \dfrac{d}{10} \Rightarrow d \approx 7 \text{ kilometers}$

$$\cot 28° = \frac{D}{10} \Rightarrow D \approx 18.8 \text{ kilometers}$$

Distance between towns:

$$D - d = 18.8 - 7 = 11.8 \text{ kilometers}$$

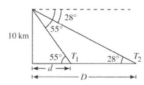

27. $\tan \theta = \frac{75}{50}$

$\theta = \arctan \frac{3}{2} \approx 56.3°$

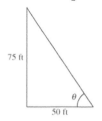

29. $1200 \text{ feet} + 150 \text{ feet} - 400 \text{ feet} = 950 \text{ feet}$

$5 \text{ miles} = 5 \text{ miles}\left(\dfrac{5280 \text{ feet}}{1 \text{ mile}}\right) = 26,400 \text{ feet}$

$\tan \theta = \dfrac{950}{26,400}$

$\theta = \arctan\left(\dfrac{950}{26,400}\right) \approx 2.06°$

Not drawn to scale

33. (a) $l^2 = (200)^2 + (150)^2$

$l = 250 \text{ feet}$

$\tan A = \dfrac{150}{200} \Rightarrow A = \arctan\left(\dfrac{150}{200}\right) \approx 36.87°$

$\tan B = \dfrac{200}{150} \Rightarrow B = \arctan\left(\dfrac{200}{150}\right) \approx 53.13°$

(b) $250 \text{ ft} \times \dfrac{\text{mile}}{5280 \text{ ft}} \times \dfrac{\text{hour}}{35 \text{ miles}} \times \dfrac{3600 \text{ sec}}{\text{hour}} \approx 4.87 \text{ seconds}$

35. The plane has traveled $1.5(600) = 900$ miles.

$\sin 38° = \dfrac{a}{900} \Rightarrow a \approx 554 \text{ miles north}$

$\cos 38° = \dfrac{b}{900} \Rightarrow b \approx 709 \text{ miles east}$

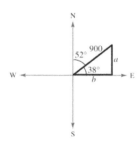

31. (a) $l^2 = (h + 17)^2 + 100^2$

$l = \sqrt{(h + 17)^2 + 10,000}$

$= \sqrt{h^2 + 34h + 10,289}$

(b) $\cos \theta = \dfrac{100}{l}$

$\theta = \arccos\left(\dfrac{100}{l}\right)$

(c) $\cos \theta = \dfrac{100}{l}$

$\cos 35° = \dfrac{100}{l}$

$l \approx 122.077$

$l^2 = 100^2 + (h + 17)^2$

$l^2 = h^2 + 34h + 10.289$

$0 = h^2 + 34h - 4613.794$

$h \approx 53.02 \text{ feet}$

37.

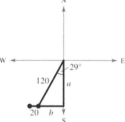

(a) $\cos 29° = \dfrac{a}{120} \Rightarrow a \approx 104.95 \text{ nautical miles south}$

$\sin 29° = \dfrac{b}{120} \Rightarrow b \approx 58.18 \text{ nautical miles west}$

(b) $\tan \theta = \dfrac{20 + b}{a} \approx \dfrac{78.18}{104.95} \Rightarrow \theta \approx 36.7°$

Bearing: S 36.7° W

Distance: $d \approx \sqrt{104.95^2 + 78.18^2}$

$\approx 130.9 \text{ nautical miles from port}$

39. $\tan \theta = \frac{45}{30} \Rightarrow \theta \approx 56.3°$

Bearing: N 56.31°

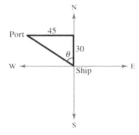

41. $\theta = 32°, \phi = 68°$

(a) $\alpha = 90° - 32° = 58°$

Bearing from
A to C: N 58° E

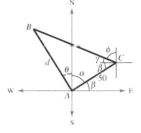

(b) $\quad \beta = \theta = 32°$

$\gamma = 90° - \phi = 22°$

$C = \beta + \gamma = 54°$

$\tan C = \frac{d}{50} \rightarrow \tan 54°$

$\qquad = \frac{d}{50} \Rightarrow d \approx 68.82$ meters

43. The diagonal of the base has a length of

$\sqrt{a^2 + a^2} = \sqrt{2}a$. Now, you have

$\tan \theta = \frac{a}{\sqrt{2}a} = \frac{1}{\sqrt{2}}$

$\theta = \arctan \frac{1}{\sqrt{2}}$

$\theta \approx 35.3°$.

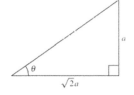

45. $\sin 36° = \frac{d}{25} \Rightarrow d \approx 14.69$

Length of side: $2d \approx 29.4$ inches

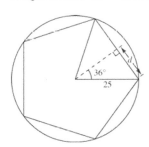

47. Use $d = a \sin \omega t$ because $d = 0$ when $t = 0$.

Period: $\frac{2\pi}{\omega} = 2 \Rightarrow \omega = \pi$

So, $d = 4 \sin(\pi t)$.

49. Use $d = a \cos \omega t$ because $d = 3$ when $t = 0$.

Period: $\frac{2\pi}{\omega} = 1.5 \Rightarrow \omega = \frac{4\pi}{3}$

So, $d = 3 \cos\left(\frac{4\pi}{3}t\right) = 3 \cos\left(\frac{4\pi t}{3}\right)$.

51. $\qquad d = a \sin \omega t$

Frequency $= \frac{\omega}{2\pi}$

$264 = \frac{\omega}{2\pi}$

$\omega = 2\pi(264) = 528\pi$

53. $d = 9 \cos \frac{6\pi}{5}t$

(a) Maximum displacement $=$ amplitude $= 9$

(b) Frequency $= \frac{\omega}{2\pi} = \frac{\frac{6\pi}{5}}{2\pi}$

$\qquad = \frac{3}{5}$ cycle per unit of time

(c) $d = 9 \cos \frac{6\pi}{5}(5) = 9$

(d) $9 \cos \frac{6\pi}{5}t = 0$

$\cos \frac{6\pi}{5}t = 0$

$\frac{6\pi}{5}t = \arccos 0$

$\frac{6\pi}{5}t = \frac{\pi}{2}$

$t = \frac{5}{12}$

55. $d = \frac{1}{4} \sin 6\pi t$

(a) Maximum displacement $=$ amplitude $= \frac{1}{4}$

(b) Frequency $= \frac{\omega}{2\pi} = \frac{6\pi}{2\pi}$

$\qquad = 3$ cycles per unit of time

(c) $d = \frac{1}{4} \sin 30\pi \approx 0$

(d) $\frac{1}{4} \sin 6\pi t = 0$

$\sin 6\pi t = 0$

$6\pi t = \arcsin 0$

$6\pi t = \pi$

$t = \frac{1}{6}$

57. $y = \dfrac{1}{4} \cos 16t, \; t > 0$

(a)

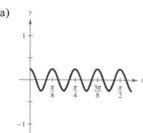

(b) Period: $\dfrac{2\pi}{16} = \dfrac{\pi}{8}$

(c) $\dfrac{1}{4} \cos 16t = 0$ when $16t = \dfrac{\pi}{2} \Rightarrow t = \dfrac{\pi}{32}$

59. (a)

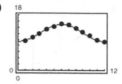

(b) Period $= \dfrac{2\pi}{n} = \dfrac{2\pi}{\pi/6} = 12$

The period is what you expect as the model examines the number of hours of daylight over one year (12 months).

(c) Amplitude $= |2.77| = 2.77$

The amplitude represents the maximum displacement from the average number of hours of daylight.

61. False. The tower isn't vertical and so the triangle formed is not a right triangle.

Review Exercises for Chapter 4

1. $\theta = \dfrac{15\pi}{4}$

(a)

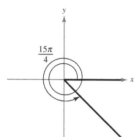

(b) Quadrant IV

(c) $\dfrac{15\pi}{4} - 2\pi = \dfrac{7\pi}{4}$

$\dfrac{7\pi}{4} - 2\pi = -\dfrac{\pi}{4}$

3. $\theta = -110°$

(a)

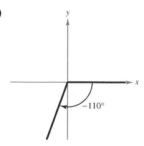

(b) Quadrant III

(c) Coterminal angles:

$-110° + 360° = 250°$

$-110° - 360° = -470°$

5. $450° = 450° \cdot \dfrac{\pi \text{ rad}}{180°} = \dfrac{5\pi}{2} \approx 7.854 \text{ radians}$

7. $-33°45' = -33.75° = -33.75° \cdot \dfrac{\pi \text{ rad}}{180°}$

$= -\dfrac{3\pi}{16} \text{ radian} \approx -0.589 \text{ radian}$

9. $\dfrac{3\pi}{10} = \dfrac{3\pi}{10} \cdot \dfrac{180°}{\pi \text{ rad}} = 54.000°$

11. $-3.5 \text{ rad} = -3.5 \text{ rad} \cdot \dfrac{180°}{\pi \text{ rad}} \approx -200.535°$

13. $198.4° = 198° + 0.4(60)' = 198°24'$

15. $138° = \dfrac{138\pi}{180} = \dfrac{23\pi}{30} \text{ radians}$

$s = r\theta = 20\left(\dfrac{23\pi}{30}\right) \approx 48.17 \text{ inches}$

17. $120° = \dfrac{120\pi}{180} = \dfrac{2\pi}{3} \text{ radians}$

$A = \dfrac{1}{2}r^2\theta = \dfrac{1}{2}(18)^2\left(\dfrac{2\pi}{3}\right) \approx 339.29 \text{ square inches}$

19. $t = \dfrac{2\pi}{3}$ corresponds to the point $\left(-\dfrac{1}{2}, \dfrac{\sqrt{3}}{2}\right)$.

21. $t = \dfrac{7\pi}{6}$ corresponds to the point

$$(x, y) = \left(-\dfrac{\sqrt{3}}{2}, -\dfrac{1}{2}\right).$$

23. $t = \dfrac{3\pi}{4}$ corresponds to the point $(x, y) = \left(-\dfrac{\sqrt{2}}{2}, \dfrac{\sqrt{2}}{2}\right).$

$\sin \dfrac{3\pi}{4} = y = \dfrac{\sqrt{2}}{2}$ $\csc \dfrac{3\pi}{4} = \dfrac{1}{y} = \sqrt{2}$

$\cos \dfrac{3\pi}{4} = x = -\dfrac{\sqrt{2}}{2}$ $\sec \dfrac{3\pi}{4} = \dfrac{1}{x} = -\sqrt{2}$

$\tan \dfrac{3\pi}{4} = \dfrac{y}{x} = -1$ $\cot \dfrac{3\pi}{4} = \dfrac{x}{y} = -1$

25. $\sin \dfrac{11\pi}{4} = \sin \dfrac{3\pi}{4} = \dfrac{\sqrt{2}}{2}$

27. $\sin\left(-\dfrac{17\pi}{6}\right) = \sin\left(-\dfrac{5\pi}{6}\right) = -\dfrac{1}{2}$

29. $\tan 33 \approx -75.3130$

31. $\sec\left(\dfrac{12\pi}{5}\right) = \dfrac{1}{\cos\left(\dfrac{12\pi}{5}\right)} \approx 3.2361$

33. opp $= 4$, adj $= 5$, hyp $= \sqrt{4^2 + 5^2} = \sqrt{41}$

$\sin \theta = \dfrac{\text{opp}}{\text{hyp}} = \dfrac{4}{\sqrt{41}} = \dfrac{4\sqrt{41}}{41}$ $\csc \theta = \dfrac{\text{hyp}}{\text{opp}} = \dfrac{\sqrt{41}}{4}$

$\cos \theta = \dfrac{\text{adj}}{\text{hyp}} = \dfrac{5}{\sqrt{41}} = \dfrac{5\sqrt{41}}{41}$ $\sec \theta = \dfrac{\text{hyp}}{\text{adj}} = \dfrac{\sqrt{41}}{5}$

$\tan \theta = \dfrac{\text{opp}}{\text{adj}} = \dfrac{4}{5}$ $\cot \theta = \dfrac{\text{adj}}{\text{opp}} = \dfrac{5}{4}$

35. $\tan 33° \approx 0.6494$

37. $\cot 15°14' = \dfrac{1}{\tan\left(15 + \dfrac{14}{60}\right)}$

≈ 3.6722

39. $\sin \theta = \dfrac{1}{3}$

(a) $\csc \theta = \dfrac{1}{\sin \theta} = 3$

(b) $\sin^2 \theta + \cos^2 \theta = 1$

$\left(\dfrac{1}{3}\right)^2 + \cos^2 \theta = 1$

$\cos^2 \theta - 1 - \dfrac{1}{9}$

$\cos^2 \theta = \dfrac{8}{9}$

$\cos \theta = \sqrt{\dfrac{8}{9}}$

$\cos \theta = \dfrac{2\sqrt{2}}{3}$

(c) $\sec \theta = \dfrac{1}{\cos \theta} = \dfrac{3}{2\sqrt{2}} = \dfrac{3\sqrt{2}}{4}$

(d) $\tan \theta = \dfrac{\sin \theta}{\cos \theta} = \dfrac{1/3}{\left(2\sqrt{2}\right)/3} = \dfrac{1}{2\sqrt{2}} = \dfrac{\sqrt{2}}{4}$

41. $\sin 1°10' = \dfrac{x}{3.5}$

$x = 3.5 \sin 1°10' \approx 0.07$ kilometer or 71.3 meters

Not drawn to scale

43. $x = 12, y = 16, r = \sqrt{144 + 256} = \sqrt{400} = 20$

$\sin \theta = \dfrac{y}{r} = \dfrac{4}{5}$ $\qquad$ $\csc \theta = \dfrac{r}{y} = \dfrac{5}{4}$

$\cos \theta = \dfrac{x}{r} = \dfrac{3}{5}$ $\qquad$ $\sec \theta = \dfrac{r}{x} = \dfrac{5}{3}$

$\tan \theta = \dfrac{y}{x} = \dfrac{4}{3}$ $\qquad$ $\cot \theta = \dfrac{x}{y} = \dfrac{3}{4}$

45. $x = 0.3, y = 0.4$

$r = \sqrt{(0.3)^2 + (0.4)^2} = 0.5$

$\sin \theta = \dfrac{y}{r} = \dfrac{0.4}{0.5} = \dfrac{4}{5} = 0.8$ $\qquad$ $\csc \theta = \dfrac{r}{y} = \dfrac{0.5}{0.4} = \dfrac{5}{4} = 1.25$

$\cos \theta = \dfrac{x}{r} = \dfrac{0.3}{0.5} = \dfrac{3}{5} = 0.6$ $\qquad$ $\sec \theta = \dfrac{r}{x} = \dfrac{0.5}{0.3} = \dfrac{5}{3} \approx 1.67$

$\tan \theta = \dfrac{y}{x} = \dfrac{0.4}{0.3} = \dfrac{4}{3} \approx 1.33$ $\qquad$ $\cot \theta = \dfrac{x}{y} = \dfrac{0.3}{0.4} = \dfrac{3}{4} = 0.75$

47. $\sec \theta = \dfrac{6}{5}, \tan \theta < 0 \Rightarrow \theta$ is in Quadrant IV.

$r = 6, x = 5, y = -\sqrt{36 - 25} = -\sqrt{11}$

$\sin \theta = \dfrac{y}{r} = -\dfrac{\sqrt{11}}{6}$

$\cos \theta = \dfrac{x}{r} = \dfrac{5}{6}$

$\tan \theta = \dfrac{y}{x} = -\dfrac{\sqrt{11}}{5}$

$\csc \theta = \dfrac{r}{y} = -\dfrac{6\sqrt{11}}{11}$

$\sec \theta = \dfrac{6}{5}$

$\cot \theta = -\dfrac{5\sqrt{11}}{11}$

49. $\cos \theta = \dfrac{x}{r} = \dfrac{-2}{5} \Rightarrow y^2 = 21$

$\sin \theta > 0 \Rightarrow \theta$ is in Quadrant II $\Rightarrow y = \sqrt{21}$

$\sin \theta = \dfrac{y}{r} = \dfrac{\sqrt{21}}{5}$

$\tan \theta = \dfrac{y}{x} = -\dfrac{\sqrt{21}}{2}$

$\csc \theta = \dfrac{r}{y} = \dfrac{5}{\sqrt{21}} = \dfrac{5\sqrt{21}}{21}$

$\sec \theta = \dfrac{r}{x} = \dfrac{5}{-2} = -\dfrac{5}{2}$

$\cot \theta = \dfrac{x}{y} = \dfrac{-2}{\sqrt{21}} = -\dfrac{2\sqrt{21}}{21}$

51. $\theta = 264°$

$\theta' = 264° - 180° = 84°$

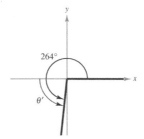

53. $\theta = -\dfrac{6\pi}{5}$

$-\dfrac{6\pi}{5} + 2\pi = \dfrac{4\pi}{5}$

$\theta' = \pi - \dfrac{4\pi}{5} = \dfrac{\pi}{5}$

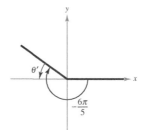

55. $\sin \dfrac{\pi}{3} = \dfrac{\sqrt{3}}{2}$

$\cos \dfrac{\pi}{3} = \dfrac{1}{2}$

$\tan \dfrac{\pi}{3} = \sqrt{3}$

57. $\sin 495° = \sin 45° = \dfrac{\sqrt{2}}{2}$

$\cos 495° = -\cos 45° = -\dfrac{\sqrt{2}}{2}$

$\tan 495° = -\tan 45° = -1$

59. $\sin 4 \approx -0.7568$

61. $\sin \dfrac{12\pi}{5} \approx 0.9511$

63. $y = \sin 6x$

Amplitude: 1

Period: $\dfrac{2\pi}{6} = \dfrac{\pi}{3}$

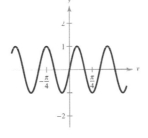

65. $y = 5 + \sin x$

Amplitude: 1

Period: 2π

Shift the graph of $y = \sin x$ 5 units upward

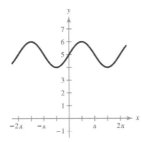

67. $g(t) = \frac{5}{2}\sin(t - \pi)$

Amplitude: $\frac{5}{2}$

Period: 2π

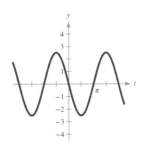

69. $y = a \sin bx$

(a) $a = 2,$

$\dfrac{2\pi}{b} = \dfrac{1}{264} \Rightarrow b = 528\pi$

$y = 2 \sin 528\pi x$

(b) $f = \dfrac{1}{1/264}$

$= 264$ cycles per second

71. $f(t) = \tan\!\left(t + \dfrac{\pi}{2}\right)$

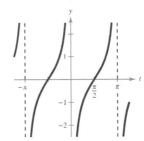

73. $f(x) = \dfrac{1}{2}\csc\dfrac{x}{2}$

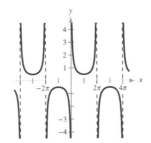

75. $f(x) = x \cos x$

Damping factor: x

As $x \to +\infty$, $f(x)$ oscillates.

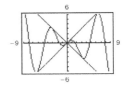

77. $\arcsin(-1) = -\dfrac{\pi}{2}$

79. $\text{arccot}\sqrt{3} = \dfrac{\pi}{6}$

81. $\tan^{-1}(-1.5) \approx -0.98$ radian

83. $\text{arccot}(10.5) = \arctan\!\left(\dfrac{1}{10.5}\right) \approx 0.09$

85. $f(x) = \arctan\!\left(\dfrac{x}{2}\right) = \tan^{-1}\!\left(\dfrac{x}{2}\right)$

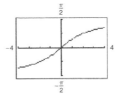

87. Let $u = \arctan\frac{3}{4}$ then $\tan u = \frac{3}{4}$.

$\cos\!\left(\arctan\frac{3}{4}\right) = \frac{4}{5}$

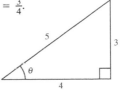

89. $\sec\left[\sin^{-1}\left(-\dfrac{1}{4}\right)\right]$

Let $y = \sin^{-1}\left(-\dfrac{1}{4}\right)$ then $\sin y = -\dfrac{1}{4}$ and

$\sec\left[\sin^{-1}\left(-\dfrac{1}{4}\right)\right] = \sec y = \dfrac{4\sqrt{15}}{15}.$

91. Let $y = \arccos\left(\dfrac{x}{2}\right)$. Then

$\cos y = \dfrac{x}{2}$ and $\tan y = \tan\left(\arccos\left(\dfrac{x}{2}\right)\right) = \dfrac{\sqrt{4-x^2}}{x}.$

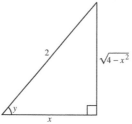

93. $\tan\theta = \dfrac{70}{30}$

$\theta = \arctan\left(\dfrac{70}{30}\right) \approx 66.8°$

95. $\sin 48° = \dfrac{d_1}{650} \Rightarrow d_1 \approx 483$
$\cos 25° = \dfrac{d_2}{810} \Rightarrow d_2 \approx 734$ $\Bigg\}$ $d_1 + d_2 \approx 1217$

$\cos 48° = \dfrac{d_3}{650} \Rightarrow d_3 \approx 435$
$\sin 25° = \dfrac{d_4}{810} \Rightarrow d_4 \approx 342$ $\Bigg\}$ $d_3 - d_4 \approx 93$

$\tan\theta \approx \dfrac{93}{1217} \Rightarrow \theta \approx 4.4°$

$\sec 4.4° \approx \dfrac{D}{1217} \Rightarrow D \approx 1217 \sec 4.4° \approx 1221$

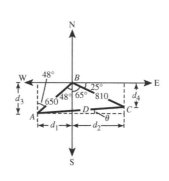

The distance is 1221 miles and the bearing is 85.6°.

97. False. For each θ there corresponds exactly one value of y.

99. $f(\theta) = \sec\theta$ is undefined at the zeros of

$g(\theta) = \cos\theta$ because $\sec\theta = \dfrac{1}{\cos\theta}.$

101. The ranges for the other four trigonometric functions are not bounded. For $y = \tan x$ and $y = \cot x$, the range is $(-\infty, \infty)$. For $y = \sec x$ and $y = \csc x$, the range is $(-\infty, -1] \cup [1, \infty)$.

Problem Solving for Chapter 4

1. (a) $8{:}57 - 6{:}45 = 2$ hours 12 minutes $= 132$ minutes

$$\frac{132}{48} = \frac{11}{4} \text{ revolutions}$$

$$\theta = \left(\frac{11}{4}\right)(2\pi) = \frac{11\pi}{2} \text{ radians or } 990°$$

(b) $s = r\theta = 47.25(5.5\pi) \approx 816.42$ feet

3. (a) $\sin 39° = \dfrac{3000}{d}$

$$d = \frac{3000}{\sin 39°} \approx 4767 \text{ feet}$$

(b) $\tan 39° = \dfrac{3000}{x}$

$$x = \frac{3000}{\tan 39°} \approx 3705 \text{ feet}$$

(c) $\tan 63° = \dfrac{w + 3705}{3000}$

$$3000 \tan 63° = w + 3705$$

$$w = 3000 \tan 63° - 3705 \approx 2183 \text{ feet}$$

5. (a) $h(x) = \cos^2 x$

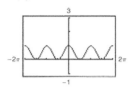

h is even.

(b) $h(x) = \sin^2 x$

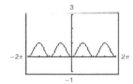

h is even.

7. If you alter the model so that $h = 1$ when $t = 0$, you can use either a sine or a cosine model.

$$a = \frac{1}{2}[\text{max} - \text{min}] = \frac{1}{2}[101 - 1] = 50$$

$$d = \frac{1}{2}[\text{max} + \text{min}] = \frac{1}{2}[101 + 1] = 51$$

$$b = 8\pi$$

Cosine model: $h = 51 - 50 \cos(8\pi t)$

Sine model: $h = 51 - 50 \sin\left(8\pi t + \dfrac{\pi}{2}\right)$

Notice that you needed the horizontal shift so that the sine value was one when $t = 0$.

Another model would be: $h = 51 + 50 \sin\left(8\pi t + \dfrac{3\pi}{2}\right)$

Here you wanted the sine value to be 1 when $t = 0$.

9. $P = 100 - 20 \cos\left(\dfrac{8\pi}{3}t\right)$

(a)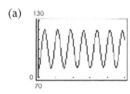

(b) Period $= \dfrac{2\pi}{8\pi/3} = \dfrac{6}{8} = \dfrac{3}{4}$ sec

This is the time between heartbeats.

(c) Amplitude: 20

The blood pressure ranges between $100 - 20 = 80$ and $100 + 20 = 120$.

(d) Pulse rate $= \dfrac{60 \text{ sec/min}}{\dfrac{3}{4} \text{ sec/beat}} = 80$ beats/min

(e) Period $= \dfrac{60}{64} = \dfrac{15}{16}$ sec

$$64 = \frac{60}{2\pi/b} \Rightarrow b = \frac{64}{60} \cdot 2\pi = \frac{32}{15}\pi$$

11. $f(x) = 2 \cos 2x + 3 \sin 3x$

$g(x) = 2 \cos 2x + 3 \sin 4x$

(a)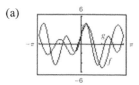

(b) The period of $f(x)$ is 2π.

The period of $g(x)$ is π.

(c) $h(x) = A \cos \alpha x + B \sin \beta x$ is periodic because the sine and cosine functions are periodic.

13.

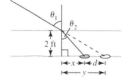

(a) $\dfrac{\sin \theta_1}{\sin \theta_2} = 1.333$

$\sin \theta_2 = \dfrac{\sin \theta_1}{1.333} = \dfrac{\sin 60°}{1.333} \approx 0.6497$

$\theta_2 = 40.5°$

(b) $\tan \theta_2 = \dfrac{x}{2} \Rightarrow x = 2 \tan 40.52° \approx 1.71$ feet

$\tan \theta_1 = \dfrac{y}{2} \Rightarrow y = 2 \tan 60° \approx 3.46$ feet

(c) $d = y - x = 3.46 - 1.71 = 1.75$ feet

(d) As you move closer to the rock, θ_1 decreases, which causes y to decrease, which in turn causes d to decrease.

Practice Test for Chapter 4

1. Express 350° in radian measure.

2. Express $(5\pi)/9$ in degree measure.

3. Convert $135°\ 14'\ 12''$ to decimal form.

4. Convert $-22.569°$ to $D°\ M'\ S''$ form.

5. If $\cos \theta = \frac{2}{3}$, use the trigonometric identities to find $\tan \theta$.

6. Find θ given $\sin \theta = 0.9063$

7. Solve for x in the figure below.

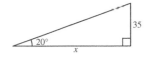

8. Find the reference angle θ' for $\theta = (6\pi)/5$.

9. Evaluate $\csc 3.92$.

10. Find $\sec \theta$ given that θ lies in Quadrant III and $\tan \theta = 6$.

11. Graph $y = 3 \sin \dfrac{x}{2}$.

12. Graph $y = -2 \cos(x - \pi)$.

13. Graph $y = \tan 2x$.

14. Graph $y = -\csc\left(x + \dfrac{\pi}{4}\right)$.

15. Graph $y = 2x + \sin x$, using a graphing calculator.

16. Graph $y = 3x \cos x$, using a graphing calculator.

17. Evaluate $\arcsin 1$.

18. Evaluate $\arctan(-3)$.

19. Evaluate $\sin\left(\arccos \dfrac{4}{\sqrt{35}}\right)$.

20. Write an algebraic expression for $\cos\left(\arcsin \dfrac{x}{4}\right)$.

For Exercises 21–23, solve the right triangle.

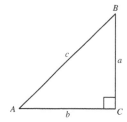

21. $A = 40°, c = 12$

22. $B = 6.84°, a = 21.3$

23. $a = 5, b = 9$

24. A 20-foot ladder leans against the side of a barn. Find the height of the top of the ladder if the angle of elevation of the ladder is 67°.

25. An observer in a lighthouse 250 feet above sea level spots a ship off the shore. If the angle of depression to the ship is 5°, how far out is the ship?

CHAPTER 5
Analytic Trigonometry

CHAPTER 5
Analytic Trigonometry

Section 5.1   Using Fundamental Identities

1. $\tan u$

3. $\cot u$

5. $\cot^2 u$

7. $\sin x = \dfrac{1}{2}, \cos x = \dfrac{\sqrt{3}}{2} \Rightarrow x$ is in Quadrant I.

$\tan x = \dfrac{\sin x}{\cos x} = \dfrac{1/2}{\sqrt{3}/2} = \dfrac{1}{\sqrt{3}} = \dfrac{\sqrt{3}}{3}$

$\cot x = \dfrac{1}{\tan x} = \dfrac{1}{1/\sqrt{3}} = \sqrt{3}$

$\sec x = \dfrac{1}{\cos x} = \dfrac{1}{\sqrt{3}/2} = \dfrac{2}{\sqrt{3}} = \dfrac{2\sqrt{3}}{3}$

$\csc x = \dfrac{1}{\sin x} = \dfrac{1}{1/2} = 2$

9. $\cos\left(\dfrac{\pi}{2} - x\right) = \dfrac{3}{5}, \cos x = \dfrac{4}{5} \Rightarrow x$ is in Quadrant I.

$\sin x = \sqrt{1 - \left(\dfrac{4}{5}\right)^2} = \dfrac{3}{5}$

$\tan x = \dfrac{\sin x}{\cos x} = \dfrac{3}{5} \cdot \dfrac{5}{4} = \dfrac{3}{4}$

$\csc x = \dfrac{1}{\sin x} = \dfrac{5}{3}$

$\sec x = \dfrac{1}{\cos x} = \dfrac{5}{4}$

$\cot x = \dfrac{1}{\tan x} = \dfrac{4}{3}$

11. $\sec x = 4, \sin x > 0 \Rightarrow x$ is in Quadrant I.

$\cos x = \dfrac{1}{\sec x} = \dfrac{1}{4}$

$\sin x = \sqrt{1 - \left(\dfrac{1}{4}\right)^2} = \dfrac{\sqrt{15}}{4}$

$\tan x = \dfrac{\sin x}{\cos x} = \dfrac{\sqrt{15}}{4} \cdot \dfrac{4}{1} = \sqrt{15}$

$\csc x = \dfrac{1}{\sin x} = \dfrac{4}{\sqrt{15}} = \dfrac{4\sqrt{15}}{15}$

$\cot x = \dfrac{1}{\tan x} = \dfrac{1}{\sqrt{15}} = \dfrac{\sqrt{15}}{15}$

13. $\sin \theta = -1, \cot \theta = 0 \Rightarrow \theta = \dfrac{3\pi}{2}$

$\cos \theta = \sqrt{1 - \sin^2 \theta} = 0$

$\sec \theta$ is undefined.

$\tan \theta$ is undefined.

$\csc \theta = -1$

15. $\sec x \cos x = \left(\dfrac{1}{\cancel{\cos x}}\right) \cancel{\cos x}$

$\qquad = 1$

Matches (c).

16. $\cot^2 x - \csc^2 x = \left(\csc^2 x - 1\right) - \csc^2 x$

$\qquad = -1$

Matches (b).

17. $\sec^4 x - \tan^4 x = \left(\sec^2 x + \tan^2 x\right)\left(\sec^2 x - \tan^2 x\right)$

$\qquad = \left(\sec^2 x + \tan^2 x\right)(1)$

$\qquad = \sec^2 x + \tan^2 x$

Matches (f).

18. $\cot x \sec x = \dfrac{\cos x}{\sin x} \cdot \dfrac{1}{\cos x} = \dfrac{1}{\sin x} = \csc x$

Matches (a).

19. $\dfrac{\sec^2 x - 1}{\sin^2 x} = \dfrac{\tan^2 x}{\sin^2 x} = \dfrac{\sin^2 x}{\cos^2 x} \cdot \dfrac{1}{\sin^2 x} = \sec^2 x$

Matches (e).

20. $\dfrac{\cos^2\left[(\pi/2) - x\right]}{\cos x} = \dfrac{\sin^2 x}{\cos x} = \dfrac{\sin x}{\cos x}\sin x = \tan x \sin x$

Matches (d).

21. $\tan^2 x - \tan^2 x \sin^2 x = \tan^2 x\left(1 - \sin^2 x\right)$

$\qquad = \tan^2 x \cos^2 x$

$\qquad = \dfrac{\sin^2 x}{\cos^2 x} \cdot \cos^2 x$

$\qquad = \sin^2 x$

23. $\dfrac{\sec^2 x - 1}{\sec x - 1} = \dfrac{(\sec x + 1)(\sec x - 1)}{\sec x - 1}$

$\qquad\qquad = \sec x + 1$

25. $1 - 2\cos^2 x + \cos^4 x = \left(1 - \cos^2 x\right)^2$

$\qquad\qquad\qquad\qquad\quad = \left(\sin^2 x\right)^2$

$\qquad\qquad\qquad\qquad\quad = \sin^4 x$

27. $\cot^3 x + \cot^2 x + \cot x + 1 = \cot^2 x(\cot x + 1) + (\cot x + 1)$

$\qquad\qquad\qquad\qquad\qquad\qquad - (\cot x + 1)\left(\cot^2 x + 1\right)$

$\qquad\qquad\qquad\qquad\qquad\qquad = (\cot x + 1)\csc^2 x$

29. $3\sin^2 x - 5\sin x - 2 = (3\sin x + 1)(\sin x - 2)$

31. $\cot^2 x + \csc x - 1 = \left(\csc^2 x - 1\right) + \csc x - 1$

$\qquad\qquad\qquad\qquad = \csc^2 x + \csc x - 2$

$\qquad\qquad\qquad\qquad = (\csc x - 1)(\csc x + 2)$

33. $(\sin x + \cos x)^2 = \sin^2 x + 2\sin x \cos x + \cos^2 x$

$\qquad\qquad\qquad\quad = \left(\sin^2 x + \cos^2 x\right) + 2\sin x \cos x$

$\qquad\qquad\qquad\quad = 1 + 2\sin x \cos x$

35. $\cot\theta \sec\theta = \dfrac{\cos\theta}{\sin\theta} \cdot \dfrac{1}{\cos\theta} = \dfrac{1}{\sin\theta} = \csc\theta$

37. $\sin\phi(\csc\phi - \sin\phi) = (\sin\phi)\dfrac{1}{\sin\phi} - \sin^2\phi$

$\qquad\qquad\qquad\qquad = 1 - \sin^2\phi = \cos^2\phi$

39. $\dfrac{1 - \sin^2 x}{\csc^2 x} = \dfrac{\cos^2 x}{1} = \cos^2 x \tan^2 x = \left(\cos^2 x\right)\dfrac{\sin^2 x}{\cos^2 x}$

$\qquad\qquad\qquad\qquad\qquad\qquad\qquad = \sin^2 x$

41. $\cos\left(\dfrac{\pi}{2} - x\right)\sec x = (\sin x)(\sec x)$

$\qquad\qquad\qquad\qquad = (\sin x)\left(\dfrac{1}{\cos x}\right)$

$\qquad\qquad\qquad\qquad = \dfrac{\sin x}{\cos x}$

$\qquad\qquad\qquad\qquad = \tan x$

43. $\sin\beta \tan\beta + \cos\beta = (\sin\beta)\dfrac{\sin\beta}{\cos\beta} + \cos\beta$

$\qquad\qquad\qquad\qquad\quad = \dfrac{\sin^2\beta}{\cos\beta} + \dfrac{\cos^2\beta}{\cos\beta}$

$\qquad\qquad\qquad\qquad\quad = \dfrac{\sin^2\beta + \cos^2\beta}{\cos\beta}$

$\qquad\qquad\qquad\qquad\quad = \dfrac{1}{\cos\beta}$

$\qquad\qquad\qquad\qquad\quad = \sec\beta$

45. $\dfrac{1}{1 + \cos x} + \dfrac{1}{1 - \cos x} = \dfrac{1 - \cos x + 1 + \cos x}{(1 + \cos x)(1 - \cos x)}$

$\qquad\qquad\qquad\qquad\qquad = \dfrac{2}{1 - \cos^2 x}$

$\qquad\qquad\qquad\qquad\qquad = \dfrac{2}{\sin^2 x}$

$\qquad\qquad\qquad\qquad\qquad = 2\csc^2 x$

47. $\tan x - \dfrac{\sec^2 x}{\tan x} = \dfrac{\tan^2 x - \sec^2 x}{\tan x}$

$\qquad\qquad\qquad = \dfrac{-1}{\tan x} = -\cot x$

49. $\dfrac{\sin^2 y}{1 - \cos y} = \dfrac{1 - \cos^2 y}{1 - \cos y}$

$\qquad\qquad = \dfrac{(1 + \cos y)(1 - \cos y)}{1 - \cos y} = 1 + \cos y$

51. $y_1 = \cos x \cot x + \sin x = \csc x$

$\cos x \cot x + \sin x = \cos x\left(\dfrac{\cos x}{\sin x}\right) + \sin x$

$\qquad\qquad\qquad\quad = \dfrac{\cos^2 x}{\sin x} + \dfrac{\sin^2 x}{\sin x}$

$\qquad\qquad\qquad\quad = \dfrac{\cos^2 x + \sin^2 x}{\sin x} = \dfrac{1}{\sin x} = \csc x$

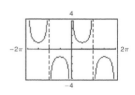

53. Let $x = 3\cos\theta$.

$$\sqrt{9 - x^2} = \sqrt{9 - (3\cos\theta)^2}$$
$$= \sqrt{9 - 9\cos^2\theta}$$
$$= \sqrt{9(1 - \cos^2\theta)}$$
$$= \sqrt{9\sin^2\theta} = 3\sin\theta$$

55. Let $x = 2\sec\theta$.

$$\sqrt{x^2 - 4} = \sqrt{(2\sec\theta)^2 - 4}$$
$$= \sqrt{4(\sec^2\theta - 1)}$$
$$= \sqrt{4\tan^2\theta}$$
$$= 2\tan\theta$$

57. Let $x = 3\sin\theta$.

$$\sqrt{9 - x^2} = 3$$
$$\sqrt{9 - (3\sin\theta)^2} = 3$$
$$\sqrt{9 - 9\sin^2\theta} = 3$$
$$\sqrt{9(1 - \sin^2\theta)} = 3$$
$$\sqrt{9\cos^2\theta} = 3$$
$$3\cos\theta = 3$$
$$\cos\theta = 1$$
$$\sin\theta = \sqrt{1 - \cos^2\theta} = \sqrt{1 - (1)^2} = 0$$

59. $\sin\theta = \sqrt{1 - \cos^2\theta}$

Let $y_1 = \sin x$ and $y_2 = \sqrt{1 - \cos^2 x}, 0 \le x \le 2\pi$.

$y_1 = y_2$ for $0 \le x \le \pi$.

So, $\sin\theta = \sqrt{1 - \cos^2\theta}$ for $0 \le \theta \le \pi$.

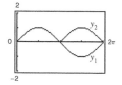

61. $\ln|\sin x| + \ln|\cot x| = \ln|\sin x \cot x|$

$$= \ln\left|\sin x \cdot \frac{\cos x}{\sin x}\right|$$
$$= \ln|\cos x|$$

63. $\ln|\cot t| + \ln(1 + \tan^2 t) = \ln\left[|\cot t|(1 + \tan^2 t)\right]$

$$= \ln|\cot t \sec^2 t|$$
$$= \ln\left|\frac{\cot t}{\sin t} \cdot \frac{1}{\cos^2 t}\right|$$
$$= \ln\left|\frac{1}{\sin t \cos t}\right|$$
$$= \ln|\csc t \sec t|$$

65. $\mu W \cos\theta = W \sin\theta$

$$\mu = \frac{W \sin\theta}{W \cos\theta} = \tan\theta$$

67. True. For example, $\sin(-x) = -\sin x$ means that the graph of $\sin x$ is symmetric about the origin.

69. As $x \to \dfrac{\pi^-}{2}$, $\tan x \to \infty$ and $\cot x \to 0$.

71. $\dfrac{\sin k\theta}{\cos k\theta} = \tan\theta$ *is not* an identity.

$$\frac{\sin k\theta}{\cos k\theta} = \tan k\theta$$

73. Let $u = a\tan\theta$, then

$$\sqrt{a^2 + u^2} = \sqrt{a^2 + (a\tan\theta)^2}$$
$$= \sqrt{a^2 + a^2\tan^2\theta}$$
$$= \sqrt{a^2(1 + \tan^2\theta)}$$
$$= \sqrt{a^2\sec^2\theta}$$
$$= a\sec\theta.$$

75. Because $\sin^2 \theta + \cos^2 \theta = 1$, then $\cos^2 \theta = 1 - \sin^2 \theta$.

$$\cos \theta = \pm\sqrt{1 - \sin \theta}$$

$$\tan \theta = \frac{\sin \theta}{\cos \theta} = \frac{\sin \theta}{\pm\sqrt{1 - \sin^2 \theta}}$$

$$\cot \theta = \frac{\cos \theta}{\sin \theta} = \frac{\pm\sqrt{1 - \sin^2 \theta}}{\sin \theta}$$

$$\sec \theta = \frac{1}{\cos \theta} = \frac{1}{\pm\sqrt{1 - \sin^2 \theta}}$$

$$\csc \theta = \frac{1}{\sin \theta}$$

Section 5.2   Verifying Trigonometric Identities

1. identity

3. $\tan u$

5. $\cos^2 u$

7. $-\csc u$

9. $\tan t \cot t = \dfrac{\sin t}{\cos t} \cdot \dfrac{\cos t}{\sin t} = 1$

11. $\cot^2 y\left(\sec^2 y - 1\right) = \cot^2 y \tan^2 y = 1$

13. $\left(1 + \sin \alpha\right)\left(1 - \sin \alpha\right) = 1 - \sin^2 \alpha = \cos^2 \alpha$

15. $\cos^2 \beta - \sin^2 \beta = \left(1 - \sin^2 \beta\right) - \sin^2 \beta$

$$= 1 - 2 \sin^2 \beta$$

17. $\dfrac{\tan^2 \theta}{\sec \theta} = \dfrac{\left(\sin \theta / \cos \theta\right)\tan \theta}{1/\cos \theta} = \sin \theta \tan \theta$

19. $\dfrac{\cot^2 t}{\csc t} = \dfrac{\cos^2 t / \sin^2 t}{1/\sin t} = \dfrac{\cos^2 t}{\sin t} = \dfrac{1 - \sin^2 t}{\sin t}$

21. $\sin^{1/2} x \cos x - \sin^{5/2} x \cos x = \sin^{1/2} x \cos x\left(1 - \sin^2 x\right) = \sin^{1/2} x \cos x \cdot \cos^2 x = \cos^3 x\sqrt{\sin x}$

23. $\dfrac{\cot x}{\sec x} = \dfrac{\cos x / \sin x}{1/\cos x} = \dfrac{\cos^2 x}{\sin x} = \dfrac{1 - \sin^2 x}{\sin x} = \dfrac{1}{\sin x} - \dfrac{\sin^2 x}{\sin x} = \csc x - \sin x$

25. $\sec x - \cos x = \dfrac{1}{\cos x} - \cos x$

$$= \dfrac{1 - \cos^2 x}{\cos x}$$

$$= \dfrac{\sin^2 x}{\cos x}$$

$$= \sin x \cdot \dfrac{\sin x}{\cos x}$$

$$= \sin x \tan x$$

27. $\dfrac{1}{\tan x} + \dfrac{1}{\cot x} = \dfrac{\cot x + \tan x}{\tan x \cot x}$

$$= \dfrac{\cot x + \tan x}{1}$$

$$= \tan x + \cot x$$

29. $\dfrac{1 + \sin \theta}{\cos \theta} + \dfrac{\cos \theta}{1 + \sin \theta} = \dfrac{\left(1 + \sin \theta\right)^2 + \cos^2 \theta}{\cos \theta\left(1 + \sin \theta\right)}$

$$= \dfrac{1 + 2 \sin \theta + \sin^2 \theta + \cos^2 \theta}{\cos \theta\left(1 + \sin \theta\right)}$$

$$= \dfrac{2 + 2 \sin \theta}{\cos \theta\left(1 + \sin \theta\right)}$$

$$= \dfrac{2\left(1 + \sin \theta\right)}{\cos \theta\left(1 + \sin \theta\right)}$$

$$= \dfrac{2}{\cos \theta}$$

$$= 2 \sec \theta$$

31. $\dfrac{1}{\cos x + 1} + \dfrac{1}{\cos x - 1} = \dfrac{\cos x - 1 + \cos x + 1}{(\cos x + 1)(\cos x - 1)}$

$$= \dfrac{2\cos x}{\cos^2 x - 1}$$

$$= \dfrac{2\cos x}{-\sin^2 x}$$

$$= -2 \cdot \dfrac{1}{\sin x} \cdot \dfrac{\cos x}{\sin x}$$

$$= -2\csc x \cot x$$

33. $\tan\left(\dfrac{\pi}{2} - \theta\right)\tan\theta = \cot\theta\tan\theta$

$$= \left(\dfrac{1}{\tan\theta}\right)\tan\theta$$

$$= 1$$

35. $\dfrac{\tan x \cot x}{\cos x} = \dfrac{1}{\cos x} = \sec x$

37. $(1 + \sin y)\left[1 + \sin(-y)\right] = (1 + \sin y)(1 - \sin y)$

$$= 1 - \sin^2 y$$

$$= \cos^2 y$$

39. $\dfrac{\tan x + \cot y}{\tan x \cot y} = \dfrac{\dfrac{1}{\cot x} + \dfrac{1}{\tan y}}{\dfrac{1}{\cot x} \cdot \dfrac{1}{\tan y}} \cdot \dfrac{\cot x \tan y}{\cot x \tan y}$

$$= \tan y + \cot x$$

41. $\sqrt{\dfrac{1 + \sin\theta}{1 - \sin\theta}} = \sqrt{\dfrac{1 + \sin\theta}{1 - \sin\theta} \cdot \dfrac{1 + \sin\theta}{1 + \sin\theta}}$

$$= \sqrt{\dfrac{(1 + \sin\theta)^2}{1 - \sin^2\theta}}$$

$$= \sqrt{\dfrac{(1 + \sin\theta)^2}{\cos^2\theta}}$$

$$= \dfrac{1 + \sin\theta}{|\cos\theta|}$$

43. $\cos^2\beta + \cos^2\left(\dfrac{\pi}{2} - \beta\right) = \cos^2\beta + \sin^2\beta = 1$

45. $\sin t \csc\left(\dfrac{\pi}{2} - t\right) = \sin t \sec t = \sin t\left(\dfrac{1}{\cos t}\right)$

$$= \dfrac{\sin t}{\cos t} = \tan t$$

47. Let $\theta = \sin^{-1} x \Rightarrow \sin\theta = x = \dfrac{x}{1}$.

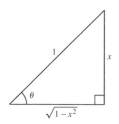

From the diagram,

$$\tan\left(\sin^{-1} x\right) = \tan\theta = \dfrac{x}{\sqrt{1 - x^2}}.$$

49. Let $\theta = \sin^{-1}\dfrac{x - 1}{4} \Rightarrow \sin\theta = \dfrac{x - 1}{4}$.

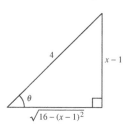

From the diagram,

$$\tan\left(\sin^{-1}\dfrac{x - 1}{4}\right) = \tan\theta = \dfrac{x - 1}{\sqrt{16 - (x - 1)^2}}.$$

51. The first line claims that $\cot(-x) = \cot x$, which is not true. The correct substitution is $\cot(-x) = -\cot x$.

53. (a)

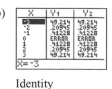

Identity

(b)

X	Y1	Y2
-3	49.214	49.214
-2	.20945	.20945
-1	.41228	.41228
0	ERROR	ERROR
1	.41228	.41228
2	.20945	.20945
3	49.214	49.214

X= -3

Identity

(c) $\left(1 + \cot^2 x\right)\left(\cos^2 x\right) = \csc^2 x \cos^2 x = \dfrac{1}{\sin^2 x} \cdot \cos^2 x = \cot^2 x$

55. (a)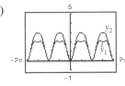

(b)

Not an identity

Not an identity

(c) $2 + \cos^2 x - 3\cos^4 x = \left(1 - \cos^2 x\right)\left(2 + 3\cos^2 x\right) = \sin^2 x\left(2 + 3\cos^2 x\right) \neq \sin^2 x\left(3 + 2\cos^2 x\right)$

57. (a)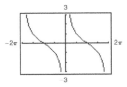

Identity

(b)

Identity

(c) $\dfrac{1 + \cos x}{\sin x} = \dfrac{(1 + \cos x)(1 - \cos x)}{\sin x(1 - \cos x)}$

$\qquad = \dfrac{1 - \cos^2 x}{\sin x(1 - \cos x)}$

$\qquad = \dfrac{\sin^2 x}{\sin x(1 - \cos x)}$

$\qquad = \dfrac{\sin x}{1 - \cos x}$

59. $\tan^3 x \sec^2 x - \tan^3 x = \tan^3 x\left(\sec^2 x - 1\right)$

$\qquad\qquad\qquad\qquad = \tan^3 x \tan^2 x$

$\qquad\qquad\qquad\qquad = \tan^5 x$

61. $\left(\sin^2 x - \sin^4 x\right)\cos x = \sin^2 x\left(1 - \sin^2 x\right)\cos x$

$\qquad\qquad\qquad\qquad = \sin^2 x \cos^2 x \cos x$

$\qquad\qquad\qquad\qquad = \sin^2 x \cos^3 x$

63. $\sin^2 25° + \sin^2 65° = \sin^2 25° + \cos^2\left(90° - 65°\right)$

$\qquad\qquad\qquad\quad = \sin^2 25° + \cos^2 25°$

$\qquad\qquad\qquad\quad = 1$

65. $\cos x - \csc x \cot x = \cos x - \dfrac{1}{\sin x}\dfrac{\cos x}{\sin x}$

$\qquad\qquad\qquad\quad = \cos x\left(1 - \dfrac{1}{\sin^2 x}\right)$

$\qquad\qquad\qquad\quad = \cos x\left(1 - \csc^2 x\right)$

$\qquad\qquad\qquad\quad = -\cos x\left(\csc^2 x - 1\right)$

$\qquad\qquad\qquad\quad = -\cos x \cot^2 x$

67. True. You can use many different techniques to verify a trigonometric identity.

69. False. Because $\sin x^2 = \sin(x \cdot x)$ and $\sin^2 x = (\sin x)(\sin x)$, $\sin x^2 \neq \sin^2 x$.

71. Because $\sin^2 \theta = 1 - \cos^2 \theta$, then $\sin \theta = \pm\sqrt{1 - \cos^2 \theta}$; $\sin \theta \neq \sqrt{1 - \cos^2 \theta}$ if θ lies in Quadrant III or IV.

One such angle is $\theta = \dfrac{7\pi}{4}$.

73.
$$1 - \cos \theta = \sin \theta$$
$$\left(1 - \cos \theta\right)^2 = \left(\sin \theta\right)^2$$
$$1 - 2\cos \theta + \cos^2 \theta = \sin^2 \theta$$
$$1 - 2\cos \theta + \cos^2 \theta = 1 - \cos^2 \theta$$
$$2\cos^2 \theta - 2\cos \theta = 0$$
$$2\cos \theta\left(\cos \theta - 1\right) = 0$$

The equation is not an identity because it is only true when $\cos \theta = 0$ or $\cos \theta = 1$. So, one angle for which the equation is not true is $-\dfrac{\pi}{2}$.

Section 5.3 Solving Trigonometric Equations

1. isolate

3. quadratic

5. $\tan x - \sqrt{3} = 0$

(a) $x = \dfrac{\pi}{3}$

$$\tan \frac{\pi}{3} - \sqrt{3} = \sqrt{3} - \sqrt{3} = 0$$

(b) $x = \dfrac{4\pi}{3}$

$$\tan \frac{4\pi}{3} - \sqrt{3} = \sqrt{3} - \sqrt{3} = 0$$

7. $3 \tan^2 2x - 1 = 0$

(a) $x = \dfrac{\pi}{12}$

$$3\left[\tan 2\left(\frac{\pi}{12}\right)\right]^2 - 1 = 3 \tan^2 \frac{\pi}{6} - 1$$
$$= 3\left(\frac{1}{\sqrt{3}}\right)^2 - 1$$
$$= 0$$

(b) $x = \dfrac{5\pi}{12}$

$$3\left[\tan 2\left(\frac{5\pi}{12}\right)\right]^2 - 1 = 3 \tan^2 \frac{5\pi}{6} - 1$$
$$= 3\left(-\frac{1}{\sqrt{3}}\right)^2 - 1$$
$$= 0$$

9. $2 \sin^2 x - \sin x - 1 = 0$

(a) $x = \dfrac{\pi}{2}$

$$2 \sin^2 \frac{\pi}{2} - \sin \frac{\pi}{2} - 1 = 2(1)^2 - 1 - 1$$
$$= 0$$

(b) $x = \dfrac{7\pi}{6}$

$$2 \sin^2 \frac{7\pi}{6} - \sin \frac{7\pi}{6} - 1 = 2\left(-\frac{1}{2}\right)^2 - \left(-\frac{1}{2}\right) - 1$$
$$= \frac{1}{2} + \frac{1}{2} - 1$$
$$= 0$$

11. $\sqrt{3} \csc x - 2 = 0$

$$\sqrt{3} \csc x = 2$$

$$\csc x = \frac{2}{\sqrt{3}}$$

$$x = \frac{\pi}{3} + 2n\pi$$

$$\text{or } x = \frac{2\pi}{3} + 2n\pi$$

13. $\cos x + 1 = -\cos x$

$$2 \cos x + 1 = 0$$

$$\cos x = -\frac{1}{2}$$

$$x = \frac{2\pi}{3} + 2n\pi \text{ or } x = \frac{4\pi}{3} + 2n\pi$$

15. $3 \sec^2 x - 4 = 0$

$$\sec^2 x = \frac{4}{3}$$

$$\sec x = \pm \frac{2}{\sqrt{3}}$$

$$x = \frac{\pi}{6} + n\pi$$

$$\text{or } x = \frac{5\pi}{6} + n\pi$$

17. $4 \cos^2 x - 1 = 0$

$$\cos^2 x = \frac{1}{4}$$

$$\cos^2 x = \pm \frac{1}{2}$$

$$x = \frac{\pi}{3} + n\pi \quad \text{or} \quad x = \frac{2\pi}{3} + n\pi$$

19. $2 \sin^2 2x = 1$

$$\sin 2x = \pm \frac{1}{\sqrt{2}} = \pm \frac{\sqrt{2}}{2}$$

$$2x = \frac{\pi}{4} + 2n\pi, \, 2x = \frac{3\pi}{4} + 2n\pi,$$

$$2x = \frac{5\pi}{4} + 2n\pi, \, 2x = \frac{7\pi}{4} + 2n\pi$$

So, $x = \dfrac{\pi}{8} + n\pi, \dfrac{3\pi}{8} + n\pi, \dfrac{5\pi}{8} + n\pi, \dfrac{7\pi}{8} + n\pi.$

You can combine these as follows:

$$x = \frac{\pi}{8} + \frac{n\pi}{2}, x = \frac{3\pi}{8} + \frac{n\pi}{2}$$

21. $\tan 3x(\tan x - 1) = 0$

$\tan 3x = 0$ or $\tan x - 1 = 0$

$3x = n\pi$ $\tan x = 1$

$x = \dfrac{n\pi}{3}$ $x = \dfrac{\pi}{4} + n\pi$

23. $\sin x(\sin x + 1) = 0$

$\sin x = 0$ or $\sin x = -1$

$x = n\pi$ $x = \dfrac{3\pi}{2} + 2n\pi$

25. $\cos^3 x = \cos x$

$\cos^3 x - \cos x = 0$

$\cos x(\cos^2 x - 1) = 0$

$\cos x = 0$ or $\cos^2 x - 1 = 0$

$x = \dfrac{\pi}{2}, \dfrac{3\pi}{2}$ $\cos x = \pm 1$

             $x = 0, \pi$

27. $3\tan^3 x - \tan x = 0$

$\tan x(3\tan^2 x - 1) = 0$

$\tan x = 0$ or $3\tan^2 x - 1 = 0$

$x = 0, \pi$ $\tan x = \pm\dfrac{\sqrt{3}}{3}$

         $x = \dfrac{\pi}{6}, \dfrac{5\pi}{6}, \dfrac{7\pi}{6}, \dfrac{11\pi}{6}$

29. $\sec^2 x - \sec x - 2 = 0$

$(\sec x - 2)(\sec x + 1) = 0$

$\sec x - 2 = 0$ or $\sec x + 1 = 0$

$\sec x = 2$ $\sec x = -1$

$x = \dfrac{\pi}{3}, \dfrac{5\pi}{3}$ $x = \pi$

31. $2\sin x + \csc x = 0$

$2\sin x + \dfrac{1}{\sin x} = 0$

$2\sin^2 x + 1 = 0$

$\sin^2 x = -\dfrac{1}{2} \Rightarrow$ No solution

33. $2\cos^2 x + \cos x - 1 = 0$

$(2\cos x - 1)(\cos x + 1) = 0$

$2\cos x - 1 = 0$ or $\cos x + 1 = 0$

$\cos x = \dfrac{1}{2}$ $\cos x = -1$

         $x = \pi$

$x = \dfrac{\pi}{3}, \dfrac{5\pi}{3}$

35. $2\sec^2 x + \tan^2 x - 3 = 0$

$2(\tan^2 x + 1) + \tan^2 x - 3 = 0$

$3\tan^2 x - 1 = 0$

$\tan x = \pm\dfrac{\sqrt{3}}{3}$

$x = \dfrac{\pi}{6}, \dfrac{5\pi}{6}, \dfrac{7\pi}{6}, \dfrac{11\pi}{6}$

37. $\csc x + \cot x = 1$

$(\csc x + \cot x)^2 = 1^2$

$\csc^2 x + 2\csc x \cot x + \cot^2 x = 1$

$\cot^2 x + 1 + 2\csc x \cot x + \cot^2 x = 1$

$2\cot^2 x + 2\csc x \cot x = 0$

$2\cot x(\cot x + \csc x) = 0$

$2\cot x = 0$ or $\cot x + \csc x = 0$

$x = \dfrac{\pi}{2}, \dfrac{3\pi}{2}$ $\dfrac{\cos x}{\sin x} = -\dfrac{1}{\sin x}$

$\left(\dfrac{3\pi}{2} \text{ is extraneous.}\right)$ $\cos x = -1$

                 $x = \pi$

             $(\pi \text{ is extraneous.})$

$x = \pi/2$ is the only solution.

39. $2\cos 2x - 1 = 0$

$\cos 2x = \dfrac{1}{2}$

$2x = \dfrac{\pi}{3} + 2n\pi$ or $2x = \dfrac{5\pi}{3} + 2n\pi$

$x = \dfrac{\pi}{6} + n\pi$ $x = \dfrac{5\pi}{6} + n\pi$

41. $\tan 3x - 1 = 0$

$\tan 3x = 1$

$3x = \dfrac{\pi}{4} + n\pi$

$x = \dfrac{\pi}{12} + \dfrac{n\pi}{3}$

43. $2\cos \dfrac{x}{2} = \sqrt{2} = 0$

$\cos \dfrac{x}{2} = \dfrac{\sqrt{2}}{2}$

$\dfrac{x}{2} = \dfrac{\pi}{4} + 2n\pi$ or $\dfrac{x}{2} = \dfrac{7\pi}{4} + 2n\pi$

$x = \dfrac{\pi}{2} + 4n\pi$ $x = \dfrac{7\pi}{2} + 4n\pi$

45. $y = \sin \dfrac{\pi x}{2} + 1$

$\sin\left(\dfrac{\pi x}{2}\right) + 1 = 0$

$\sin\left(\dfrac{\pi x}{2}\right) = -1$

$\dfrac{\pi x}{2} = \dfrac{3\pi}{2} + 2n\pi$

$x = 3 + 4n$

For $-2 < x < 4$, the intercepts are -1 and 3.

47. $y = \tan^2\left(\dfrac{\pi x}{6}\right) - 3$

$\tan^2\left(\dfrac{\pi x}{6}\right) - 3 = 0$

$\tan^2\left(\dfrac{\pi x}{6}\right) = 3$

$\tan\left(\dfrac{\pi x}{6}\right) = \pm\sqrt{3}$

$\dfrac{\pi x}{6} = \pm\dfrac{\pi}{3} + n\pi$

$x = \pm 2 + 6n$

For $-3 < x < 3$, the intercepts are -2 and 2.

49. $2 \sin x + \cos x = 0$

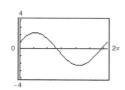

$x \approx 2.678$ and $x \approx 5.820$

51. $\dfrac{1 + \sin x}{\cos x} + \dfrac{\cos x}{1 + \sin x} - 4 = 0$

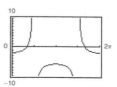

$x = \dfrac{\pi}{3} \approx 1.047$ and $x = \dfrac{5\pi}{3} \approx 5.236$

53. $x \tan x - 1 = 0$

$x \approx 0.860$ and $x \approx 3.426$

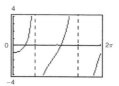

55. $\sec^2 x + 0.5 \tan x - 1 = 0$

$x = 0, x \approx 2.678,$

$x = \pi \approx 3.142$

$x \approx 5.820$

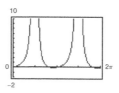

57. $2 \tan^2 x + 7 \tan x - 15 = 0$

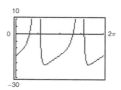

$x \approx 0.983, x \approx 1.768, x \approx 4.124$ and $x \approx 4.910$

59. $12 \sin^2 x - 13 \sin x + 3 = 0$

$$\sin x = \dfrac{-(-13) \pm \sqrt{(-13)^2 - 4(12)(3)}}{2(12)} = \dfrac{13 \pm 5}{24}$$

$\sin x = \dfrac{1}{3}$ or $\sin x = \dfrac{3}{4}$

$x \approx 0.3398, 2.8018 \qquad x \approx 0.8481, 2.2935$

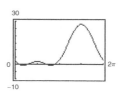

The x-intercepts occur at $x \approx 0.3398$,
$x \approx 0.8481, x \approx 2.2935,$ and $x \approx 2.8018$.

61. $\tan^2 x + 3 \tan x + 1 = 0$

$$\tan x = \frac{-3 \pm \sqrt{3^2 - 4(1)(1)}}{2(1)} = \frac{-3 \pm \sqrt{5}}{2}$$

$\tan x = \dfrac{-3 - \sqrt{5}}{2}$ or $\tan x = \dfrac{-3 + \sqrt{5}}{2}$

$\quad x \approx 1.9357, 5.0773 \qquad\qquad x \approx 2.7767, 5.9183$

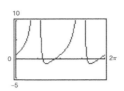

The *x*-intercepts occur at $x \approx 1.9357$, $x \approx 2.7767$, $x \approx 5.0773$, and $x \approx 5.9183$.

63. $\tan^2 x + \tan x - 12 = 0$

$(\tan x + 4)(\tan x - 3) = 0$

$\tan x + 4 = 0$ \qquad\qquad\qquad or $\tan x - 3 = 0$

$\quad \tan x = -4$ \qquad\qquad\qquad\qquad $\tan x = 3$

$\quad x = \arctan(-4) + \pi, \arctan(-4) + 2\pi$ \qquad $x = \arctan 3, \arctan 3 + \pi$

65. \qquad $\sec^2 x - 6 \tan x = -4$

$1 + \tan^2 x - 6 \tan x + 4 = 0$

$\quad \tan^2 x - 6 \tan x + 5 = 0$

$\quad (\tan x - 1)(\tan x - 5) = 0$

$\tan x - 1 = 0 \qquad \tan x - 5 = 0$

$\quad \tan x = 1 \qquad\quad \tan x = 5$

$\qquad x = \dfrac{\pi}{4}, \dfrac{5\pi}{4} \qquad\quad x = \arctan 5, \arctan 5 + \pi$

67. \qquad $2 \sin^2 x + 5 \cos x = 4$

$2(1 - \cos^2 x) + 5 \cos x - 4 = 0$

$\quad -2 \cos^2 x + 5 \cos x - 2 = 0$

$\quad -(2 \cos x - 1)(\cos x - 2) = 0$

$2 \cos x - 1 = 0 \qquad$ or $\cos x - 2 = 0$

$\qquad \cos x = \dfrac{1}{2} \qquad\qquad \cos x = 2$

$\qquad x = \dfrac{\pi}{3}, \dfrac{5\pi}{3} \qquad$ No solution

69. $\cot^2 x - 9 = 0$

$\quad \cot^2 x = 9$

$\qquad \dfrac{1}{9} = \tan^2 x$

$\qquad \pm\dfrac{1}{3} = \tan x$

$\qquad x = \arctan \tfrac{1}{3}, \arctan \tfrac{1}{3} + \pi, \arctan\left(-\tfrac{1}{3}\right) + \pi, \arctan\left(-\tfrac{1}{3}\right) + 2\pi$

71. $\sec^2 x - 4 \sec x = 0$

$\sec x(\sec x - 4) = 0$

$\sec x = 0 \qquad \sec x - 4 = 0$

No solution $\qquad \sec x = 4$

$$\frac{1}{4} = \cos x$$

$$x = \arccos \frac{1}{4}, -\arccos \frac{1}{4} + 2\pi$$

73. $\csc^2 x + 3 \csc x - 4 = 0$

$(\csc x + 4)(\csc x - 1) = 0$

$\csc x + 4 = 0 \qquad\qquad \text{or} \qquad\qquad \csc x - 1 = 0$

$\csc x = -4 \qquad\qquad\qquad\qquad\qquad \csc x = 1$

$-\dfrac{1}{4} = \sin x \qquad\qquad\qquad\qquad\qquad 1 = \sin x$

$x = \arcsin\left(\dfrac{1}{4}\right) + \pi, \arcsin\left(-\dfrac{1}{4}\right) + 2\pi \qquad\qquad x = \dfrac{\pi}{2}$

75. $3 \tan^2 x + 5 \tan x - 4 = 0, \left[-\dfrac{\pi}{2}, \dfrac{\pi}{2}\right]$

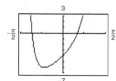

$x \approx -1.154, 0.534$

77. $4 \cos^2 x - 2 \sin x + 1 = 0, \left[-\dfrac{\pi}{2}, \dfrac{\pi}{2}\right]$

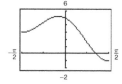

$x \approx 1.110$

79. (a) $f(x) = \sin^2 x + \cos x$

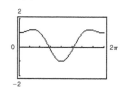

Maximum: $(1.0472, 1.25)$

Maximum: $(5.2360, 1.25)$

Minimum: $(0, 1)$

Minimum: $(3.1416, -1)$

(b) $2 \sin x \cos x - \sin x = 0$

$\sin x(2 \cos x - 1) = 0$

$\sin x = 0 \quad \text{or} \quad 2 \cos x - 1 = 0$

$x = 0, \pi \qquad\qquad\qquad \cos x = \dfrac{1}{2}$

$\approx 0, 3.1416 \qquad\qquad x = \dfrac{\pi}{3}, \dfrac{5\pi}{3}$

$\approx 1.0472, 5.2360$

81. (a) $f(x) = \sin x + \cos x$

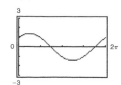

Maximum: $(0.7854, 1.4142)$

Minimum: $(3.9270, -1.4142)$

(b) $\cos x - \sin x = 0$

$\cos x = \sin x$

$1 = \dfrac{\sin x}{\cos x}$

$\tan x = 1$

$x = \dfrac{\pi}{4}, \dfrac{5\pi}{4}$

$\approx 0.7854, 3.9270$

83. (a) $f(x) = \sin x \cos x$

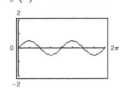

Maximum: $(0.7854, 0.5)$

Maximum: $(3.9270, 0.5)$

Minimum: $(2.3562, -0.5)$

Minimum: $(5.4978, -0.5)$

(b) $-\sin^2 x + \cos^2 x = 0$

$-\sin^2 x + 1 - \sin^2 x = 0$

$-2 \sin^2 x + 1 = 0$

$\sin^2 x = \dfrac{1}{2}$

$\sin x = \pm\sqrt{\dfrac{1}{2}} = \pm\dfrac{\sqrt{2}}{2}$

$x = \dfrac{\pi}{4}, \dfrac{3\pi}{4}, \dfrac{5\pi}{4}, \dfrac{7\pi}{4}$

$\approx 0.7854, 2.3562, 3.9270, 5.4978$

85. The graphs of $y_1 = 2 \sin x$ and $y_2 = 3x + 1$ appear to have one point of intersection. This implies there is one solution to the equation $2 \sin x = 3x + 1$.

87. $f(x) = \dfrac{\sin x}{x}$

(a) Domain: all real numbers except $x = 0$.

(b) The graph has y-axis symmetry.

(c) As $x \to 0$, $f(x) \to 1$.

(d) $\dfrac{\sin x}{x} = 0$ has four solutions in the interval $[-8, 8]$.

$\sin x\left(\dfrac{1}{x}\right) = 0$

$\sin x = 0$

$x = -2\pi, -\pi, \pi, 2\pi$

89. $y = \dfrac{1}{12}(\cos 8t - 3 \sin 8t)$

$\dfrac{1}{12}(\cos 8t - 3 \sin 8t) = 0$

$\cos 8t = 3 \sin 8t$

$\dfrac{1}{3} = \tan 8t$

$8t \approx 0.32175 + n\pi$

$t \approx 0.04 + \dfrac{n\pi}{8}$

In the interval $0 \le t \le 1, t \approx 0.04, 0.43,$ and 0.83.

91. Graph $y_1 = 58.3 + 32 \cos\left(\dfrac{\pi t}{6}\right)$

$y_2 = 75$.

Left point of intersection: $(1.95, 75)$

Right point of intersection: $(10.05, 75)$

So, sales exceed 7500 in January, November, and December.

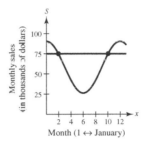

93. (a) and (c)

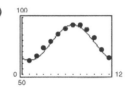

The model is a good fit.

(b) $H = a \cos(bt - c) + d$

$a = \dfrac{1}{2}[\text{high} - \text{low}] = \dfrac{1}{2}[93.6 - 62.3] = 15.65$

$p = 2[\text{high time} - \text{low time}] = 2[7 - 1] = 12$

$b = \dfrac{2\pi}{p} = \dfrac{2\pi}{12} = \dfrac{\pi}{6}$

$\dfrac{c}{b} = 7 \Rightarrow c = 7\left(\dfrac{\pi}{6}\right) = \dfrac{7\pi}{6}$

$d = \dfrac{1}{2}[\text{high} + \text{low}] = \dfrac{1}{2}[93.6 + 62.3] = 77.95$

$H = 15.65 \cos\left(\dfrac{\pi}{6}t - \dfrac{7\pi}{6}\right) + 77.95$

(d) The constant term, d, gives the average maximum temperature.

The average maximum temperature in Houston is $77.95°F$.

(e) The average maximum temperature is above $86°F$ from June to September. The average maximum temperature is below $86°F$ from October to May.

95. $A = 2x \cos x, 0 < x < \dfrac{\pi}{2}$

(a)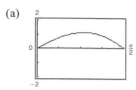

The maximum area of $A \approx 1.12$ occurs when $x \approx 0.86$.

(b) $A \geq 1$ for $0.6 < x < 1.1$

97. $f(x) = \tan \dfrac{\pi x}{4}$

Because $\tan \pi/4 = 1$, $x = 1$ is the smallest nonnegative fixed point.

99. True. The period of $2 \sin 4t - 1$ is $\dfrac{\pi}{2}$ and the period of $2 \sin t - 1$ is 2π.

In the interval $[0, 2\pi)$ the first equation has four cycles whereas the second equation has only one cycle, so the first equation has four times the x-intercepts (solutions) as the second equation.

101. $\cot x \cos^2 x = 2 \cot x$

$\cos^2 x = 2$

$\cos x = \pm\sqrt{2}$

No solution

Because you solved this problem by first dividing by $\cot x$, you do not get the same solution as Example 3.

When solving equations, you do not want to divide each side by a variable expression that will cancel out because you may accidentally remove one of the solutions.

103. (a)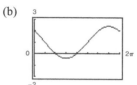

The graphs intersect when $x = \dfrac{\pi}{2}$ and $x = \pi$.

(b)

The x-intercepts are $\left(\dfrac{\pi}{2}, 0\right)$ and $(\pi, 0)$.

Both methods produce the same x-values.
Answers will vary on which method is preferred.

Section 5.4   Sum and Difference Formulas

1. $\sin u \cos v - \cos u \sin v$

3. $\dfrac{\tan u + \tan v}{1 - \tan u \tan v}$

5. $\cos u \cos v + \sin u \sin v$

7. (a) $\cos\left(\dfrac{\pi}{4} + \dfrac{\pi}{3}\right) = \cos \dfrac{\pi}{4} \cos \dfrac{\pi}{3} - \sin \dfrac{\pi}{4} \sin \dfrac{\pi}{3}$

$= \dfrac{\sqrt{2}}{2} \cdot \dfrac{1}{2} - \dfrac{\sqrt{2}}{2} \cdot \dfrac{\sqrt{3}}{2}$

$= \dfrac{\sqrt{2} - \sqrt{6}}{4}$

(b) $\cos \dfrac{\pi}{4} + \cos \dfrac{\pi}{3} = \dfrac{\sqrt{2}}{2} + \dfrac{1}{2} = \dfrac{\sqrt{2} + 1}{2}$

9. (a) $\sin(135° - 30°) = \sin 135° \cos 30° - \cos 135° \sin 30°$

$= \left(\dfrac{\sqrt{2}}{2}\right)\left(\dfrac{\sqrt{3}}{2}\right) - \left(-\dfrac{\sqrt{2}}{2}\right)\left(\dfrac{1}{2}\right) = \dfrac{\sqrt{6} + \sqrt{2}}{4}$

(b) $\sin 135° - \cos 30° = \dfrac{\sqrt{2}}{2} - \dfrac{\sqrt{3}}{2} = \dfrac{\sqrt{2} - \sqrt{3}}{2}$

11. $\sin\dfrac{11\pi}{12} = \sin\left(\dfrac{3\pi}{4} + \dfrac{\pi}{6}\right)$

$\qquad\qquad = \sin\dfrac{3\pi}{4}\cos\dfrac{\pi}{6} + \cos\dfrac{3\pi}{4}\sin\dfrac{\pi}{6}$

$\qquad\qquad = \dfrac{\sqrt{2}}{2}\cdot\dfrac{\sqrt{3}}{2} + \left(-\dfrac{\sqrt{2}}{2}\right)\dfrac{1}{2}$

$\qquad\qquad = \dfrac{\sqrt{2}}{4}\left(\sqrt{3} - 1\right)$

$\cos\dfrac{11\pi}{12} = \cos\left(\dfrac{3\pi}{4} + \dfrac{\pi}{6}\right)$

$\qquad\qquad = \cos\dfrac{3\pi}{4}\cos\dfrac{\pi}{6} - \sin\dfrac{3\pi}{4}\sin\dfrac{\pi}{6}$

$\qquad\qquad = -\dfrac{\sqrt{2}}{2}\cdot\dfrac{\sqrt{3}}{2} - \dfrac{\sqrt{2}}{2}\cdot\dfrac{1}{2} = -\dfrac{\sqrt{2}}{4}\left(\sqrt{3} + 1\right)$

$\tan\dfrac{11\pi}{4} = \tan\left(\dfrac{3\pi}{4} + \dfrac{\pi}{6}\right)$

$\qquad = \dfrac{\tan\dfrac{3\pi}{4} + \tan\dfrac{\pi}{6}}{1 - \tan\dfrac{3\pi}{4}\tan\dfrac{\pi}{6}}$

$\qquad = \dfrac{-1 + \dfrac{\sqrt{3}}{3}}{1 - (-1)\dfrac{\sqrt{3}}{3}}$

$\qquad = \dfrac{-3 + \sqrt{3}}{3 + \sqrt{3}}\cdot\dfrac{3 - \sqrt{3}}{3 - \sqrt{3}}$

$\qquad = \dfrac{-12 + 6\sqrt{3}}{6} = -2 + \sqrt{3}$

13. $\sin\dfrac{17\pi}{12} = \sin\left(\dfrac{9\pi}{4} - \dfrac{5\pi}{6}\right)$

$\qquad\qquad = \sin\dfrac{9\pi}{4}\cos\dfrac{5\pi}{6} - \cos\dfrac{9\pi}{4}\sin\dfrac{5\pi}{6}$

$\qquad\qquad = \dfrac{\sqrt{2}}{2}\left(-\dfrac{\sqrt{3}}{2}\right) - \left(\dfrac{\sqrt{2}}{2}\right)\left(\dfrac{1}{2}\right)$

$\qquad\qquad = -\dfrac{\sqrt{2}}{4}\left(\sqrt{3} + 1\right)$

$\cos\dfrac{17\pi}{12} = \cos\left(\dfrac{9\pi}{4} - \dfrac{5\pi}{6}\right)$

$\qquad\qquad = \cos\dfrac{9\pi}{4}\cos\dfrac{5\pi}{6} + \sin\dfrac{9\pi}{4}\sin\dfrac{5\pi}{6}$

$\qquad\qquad = \dfrac{\sqrt{2}}{2}\left(-\dfrac{\sqrt{3}}{2}\right) + \dfrac{\sqrt{2}}{2}\left(\dfrac{1}{2}\right)$

$\qquad\qquad = \dfrac{\sqrt{2}}{4}\left(1 - \sqrt{3}\right)$

$\tan\dfrac{17\pi}{12} = \tan\left(\dfrac{9\pi}{4} - \dfrac{5\pi}{6}\right)$

$\qquad = \dfrac{\tan(9\pi/4) - \tan(5\pi/6)}{1 + \tan(9\pi/4)\tan(5\pi/6)}$

$\qquad = \dfrac{1 - \left(-\sqrt{3}/3\right)}{1 + \left(-\sqrt{3}/3\right)}$

$\qquad = \dfrac{3 + \sqrt{3}}{3 - \sqrt{3}}\cdot\dfrac{3 + \sqrt{3}}{3 + \sqrt{3}}$

$\qquad = \dfrac{12 + 6\sqrt{3}}{6} = 2 + \sqrt{3}$

15. $\sin 105° = \sin(60° + 45°)$

$\qquad\qquad = \sin 60°\cos 45° + \cos 60°\sin 45°$

$\qquad\qquad = \dfrac{\sqrt{3}}{2}\cdot\dfrac{\sqrt{2}}{2} + \dfrac{1}{2}\cdot\dfrac{\sqrt{2}}{2}$

$\qquad\qquad = \dfrac{\sqrt{2}}{4}\left(\sqrt{3} + 1\right)$

$\cos 105° = \cos(60° + 45°)$

$\qquad\qquad = \cos 60°\cos 45° - \sin 60°\sin 45°$

$\qquad\qquad = \dfrac{1}{2}\cdot\dfrac{\sqrt{2}}{2} - \dfrac{\sqrt{3}}{2}\cdot\dfrac{\sqrt{2}}{2}$

$\qquad\qquad = \dfrac{\sqrt{2}}{4}\left(1 - \sqrt{3}\right)$

$\tan 105° = \tan(60° + 45°)$

$\qquad = \dfrac{\tan 60° + \tan 45°}{1 - \tan 60°\tan 45°}$

$\qquad = \dfrac{\sqrt{3} + 1}{1 - \sqrt{3}} = \dfrac{\sqrt{3} + 1}{1 - \sqrt{3}}\cdot\dfrac{1 + \sqrt{3}}{1 + \sqrt{3}}$

$\qquad = \dfrac{4 + 2\sqrt{3}}{-2} = -2 - \sqrt{3}$

17. $\sin 195° = \sin(225° - 30°)$

$\qquad = \sin 225° \cos 30° - \cos 225° \sin 30°$

$\qquad = -\sin 45° \cos 30° + \cos 45° \sin 30°$

$\qquad = -\dfrac{\sqrt{2}}{2} \cdot \dfrac{\sqrt{3}}{2} + \dfrac{\sqrt{2}}{2} \cdot \dfrac{1}{2}$

$\qquad = \dfrac{\sqrt{2}}{4}\left(1 - \sqrt{3}\right)$

$\cos 195° = \cos(225° - 30°)$

$\qquad = \cos 225° \cos 30° + \sin 225° \sin 30°$

$\qquad = -\cos 45° \cos 30° - \sin 45° \sin 30°$

$\qquad = -\dfrac{\sqrt{2}}{2} \cdot \dfrac{\sqrt{3}}{2} - \dfrac{\sqrt{2}}{2} \cdot \dfrac{1}{2}$

$\qquad = -\dfrac{\sqrt{2}}{4}\left(\sqrt{3} + 1\right)$

$\tan 195° = \tan(225° - 30°)$

$\qquad = \dfrac{\tan 225° - \tan 30°}{1 + \tan 225° \tan 30°}$

$\qquad = \dfrac{\tan 45° - \tan 30°}{1 + \tan 45° \tan 30°}$

$\qquad = \dfrac{1 - \left(\dfrac{\sqrt{3}}{3}\right)}{1 + \left(\dfrac{\sqrt{3}}{3}\right)} = \dfrac{3 - \sqrt{3}}{3 + \sqrt{3}} \cdot \dfrac{3 - \sqrt{3}}{3 - \sqrt{3}}$

$\qquad = \dfrac{12 - 6\sqrt{3}}{6} = 2 - \sqrt{3}$

19. $\dfrac{13\pi}{12} = \dfrac{3\pi}{4} + \dfrac{\pi}{3}$

$\sin \dfrac{13\pi}{12} = \sin\left(\dfrac{3\pi}{4} + \dfrac{\pi}{3}\right)$

$\qquad = \sin \dfrac{3\pi}{4} \cos \dfrac{\pi}{3} + \cos \dfrac{3\pi}{4} \sin \dfrac{\pi}{3}$

$\qquad = \dfrac{\sqrt{2}}{2} \cdot \dfrac{1}{2} + \left(-\dfrac{\sqrt{2}}{2}\right)\left(\dfrac{\sqrt{3}}{2}\right)$

$\qquad = \dfrac{\sqrt{2}}{4}\left(1 - \sqrt{3}\right)$

$\cos \dfrac{13\pi}{12} = \cos\left(\dfrac{3\pi}{4} + \dfrac{\pi}{3}\right)$

$\qquad = \cos \dfrac{3\pi}{4} \cos \dfrac{\pi}{3} - \sin \dfrac{3\pi}{4} \sin \dfrac{\pi}{3}$

$\qquad = -\dfrac{\sqrt{2}}{2} \cdot \dfrac{1}{2} - \dfrac{\sqrt{2}}{2} \cdot \dfrac{\sqrt{3}}{2} = -\dfrac{\sqrt{2}}{4}\left(1 + \sqrt{3}\right)$

$\tan \dfrac{13\pi}{12} = \tan\left(\dfrac{3\pi}{4} + \dfrac{\pi}{3}\right)$

$\qquad = \dfrac{\tan\left(\dfrac{3\pi}{4}\right) + \tan\left(\dfrac{\pi}{3}\right)}{1 - \tan\left(\dfrac{3\pi}{4}\right) \tan\left(\dfrac{\pi}{3}\right)}$

$\qquad = \dfrac{-1 + \sqrt{3}}{1 - (-1)\left(\sqrt{3}\right)}$

$\qquad = -\dfrac{1 - \sqrt{3}}{1 + \sqrt{3}} \cdot \dfrac{1 - \sqrt{3}}{1 - \sqrt{3}}$

$\qquad = -\dfrac{4 - 2\sqrt{3}}{-2}$

$\qquad = 2 - \sqrt{3}$

21. $-\dfrac{13\pi}{12} = -\left(\dfrac{3\pi}{4} + \dfrac{\pi}{3}\right)$

$$\sin\left[-\left(\dfrac{3\pi}{4} + \dfrac{\pi}{3}\right)\right] = -\sin\left(\dfrac{3\pi}{4} + \dfrac{\pi}{3}\right) = -\left[\sin\dfrac{3\pi}{4}\cos\dfrac{\pi}{3} + \cos\dfrac{3\pi}{4}\sin\dfrac{\pi}{3}\right]$$

$$= -\left[\dfrac{\sqrt{2}}{2}\left(\dfrac{1}{2}\right) + \left(-\dfrac{\sqrt{2}}{2}\right)\left(\dfrac{\sqrt{3}}{2}\right)\right] = -\dfrac{\sqrt{2}}{4}\left(1 - \sqrt{3}\right) = \dfrac{\sqrt{2}}{4}\left(\sqrt{3} - 1\right)$$

$$\cos\left[-\left(\dfrac{3\pi}{4} + \dfrac{\pi}{3}\right)\right] = \cos\left(\dfrac{3\pi}{4} + \dfrac{\pi}{3}\right) = \cos\dfrac{3\pi}{4}\cos\dfrac{\pi}{3} - \sin\dfrac{3\pi}{4}\sin\dfrac{\pi}{3}$$

$$= -\dfrac{\sqrt{2}}{2}\left(\dfrac{1}{2}\right) - \dfrac{\sqrt{2}}{2}\left(\dfrac{\sqrt{3}}{2}\right) = -\dfrac{\sqrt{2}}{4}\left(\sqrt{3} + 1\right)$$

$$\tan\left[-\left(\dfrac{3\pi}{4} + \dfrac{\pi}{3}\right)\right] = -\tan\left(\dfrac{3\pi}{4} + \dfrac{\pi}{3}\right) = -\dfrac{\tan\dfrac{3\pi}{4} + \tan\dfrac{\pi}{3}}{1 - \tan\dfrac{3\pi}{4}\tan\dfrac{\pi}{3}} = -\dfrac{-1 + \sqrt{3}}{1 - \left(-\sqrt{3}\right)}$$

$$= \dfrac{1 - \sqrt{3}}{1 + \sqrt{3}} \cdot \dfrac{1 - \sqrt{3}}{1 - \sqrt{3}} = \dfrac{4 - 2\sqrt{3}}{-2} = -2 + \sqrt{3}$$

23. $285° = 225° + 60°$

$$\sin 285° = \sin\left(225° + 60°\right) = \sin 225°\cos 60° + \cos 225°\sin 60°$$

$$= -\dfrac{\sqrt{2}}{2}\left(\dfrac{1}{2}\right) - \dfrac{\sqrt{2}}{2}\left(\dfrac{\sqrt{3}}{2}\right) = -\dfrac{\sqrt{2}}{4}\left(\sqrt{3} + 1\right)$$

$$\cos 285° = \cos\left(225° + 60°\right) = \cos 225°\cos 60° - \sin 225°\sin 60°$$

$$= -\dfrac{\sqrt{2}}{2}\left(\dfrac{1}{2}\right) - \left(-\dfrac{\sqrt{2}}{2}\right)\left(\dfrac{\sqrt{3}}{2}\right) = \dfrac{\sqrt{2}}{4}\left(\sqrt{3} - 1\right)$$

$$\tan 285° = \tan\left(225° + 60°\right) = \dfrac{\tan 225° + \tan 60°}{1 - \tan 225°\tan 60°}$$

$$= \dfrac{1 + \sqrt{3}}{1 - \sqrt{3}} \cdot \dfrac{1 + \sqrt{3}}{1 + \sqrt{3}} = \dfrac{4 + 2\sqrt{3}}{-2} = -2 - \sqrt{3} = -\left(2 + \sqrt{3}\right)$$

25. $-165° = -\left(120° + 45°\right)$

$$\sin\left(-165°\right) = \sin\left[-\left(120° + 45°\right)\right] = -\sin\left(120° + 45°\right) = -\left[\sin 120°\cos 45° + \cos 120°\sin 45°\right]$$

$$= -\left[\dfrac{\sqrt{3}}{2} \cdot \dfrac{\sqrt{2}}{2} - \dfrac{1}{2} \cdot \dfrac{\sqrt{2}}{2}\right] = -\dfrac{\sqrt{2}}{4}\left(\sqrt{3} - 1\right)$$

$$\cos\left(-165°\right) = \cos\left[-\left(120° + 45°\right)\right] = \cos\left(120° + 45°\right) = \cos 120°\cos 45° - \sin 120°\sin 45°$$

$$= -\dfrac{1}{2} \cdot \dfrac{\sqrt{2}}{2} - \dfrac{\sqrt{3}}{2} \cdot \dfrac{\sqrt{2}}{2} = -\dfrac{\sqrt{2}}{4}\left(1 + \sqrt{3}\right)$$

$$\tan\left(-165°\right) = \tan\left[-\left(120° + 45°\right)\right] = -\tan\left(120° + \tan 45°\right) = -\dfrac{\tan 120° + \tan 45°}{1 - \tan 120°\tan 45°}$$

$$= -\dfrac{-\sqrt{3} + 1}{1 - \left(-\sqrt{3}\right)(1)} = -\dfrac{1 - \sqrt{3}}{1 + \sqrt{3}} \cdot \dfrac{1 - \sqrt{3}}{1 - \sqrt{3}} = -\dfrac{4 - 2\sqrt{3}}{-2} = 2 - \sqrt{3}$$

27. $\sin 3\cos 1.2 - \cos 3\sin 1.2 = \sin\left(3 - 1.2\right) = \sin 1.8$

29. $\sin 60°\cos 15° + \cos 60°\sin 15° = \sin\left(60° + 15°\right)$
$$= \sin 75°$$

31. $\dfrac{\tan 45° - \tan 30°}{1 + \tan 45° \tan 30°} = \tan(45° - 30°)$

$= \tan 15°$

33. $\cos 3x \cos 2y + \sin 3x \sin 2y = \cos(3x - 2y)$

35. $\sin \dfrac{\pi}{12} \cos \dfrac{\pi}{4} + \cos \dfrac{\pi}{12} \sin \dfrac{\pi}{4} = \sin\left(\dfrac{\pi}{12} + \dfrac{\pi}{4}\right)$

$= \sin \dfrac{\pi}{3}$

$= \dfrac{\sqrt{3}}{2}$

37. $\sin 120° \cos 60° - \cos 120° \sin 60° = \sin(120° - 60°)$

$= \sin 60°$

$= \dfrac{\sqrt{3}}{2}$

39. $\dfrac{\tan(5\pi/6) - \tan(\pi/6)}{1 + \tan(5\pi/6) \tan(\pi/6)} = \tan\left(\dfrac{5\pi}{6} - \dfrac{\pi}{6}\right)$

$= \tan \dfrac{2\pi}{3}$

$= -\sqrt{3}$

For Exercises 41–45, you have:

$\sin u = \dfrac{5}{13}, u$ in Quadrant II $\Rightarrow \cos u = -\dfrac{12}{13}, \tan u = -\dfrac{5}{12}$

$\cos v = -\dfrac{3}{5}, v$ in Quadrant II $\Rightarrow \sin v = \dfrac{4}{5}, \tan v = -\dfrac{4}{3}$

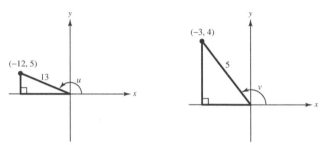

Figures for Exercises 41–45

41. $\sin(u + v) = \sin u \cos v + \cos u \sin v$

$= \left(\dfrac{5}{13}\right)\left(-\dfrac{3}{5}\right) + \left(-\dfrac{12}{13}\right)\left(\dfrac{4}{5}\right)$

$= -\dfrac{63}{65}$

43. $\tan(u + v) = \dfrac{\tan u + \tan v}{1 - \tan u \tan v} = \dfrac{-\dfrac{5}{12} + \left(-\dfrac{4}{3}\right)}{1 - \left(-\dfrac{5}{12}\right)\left(-\dfrac{4}{3}\right)}$

$= \dfrac{-\dfrac{21}{12}}{1 - \dfrac{5}{9}} = \left(-\dfrac{7}{4}\right)\left(\dfrac{9}{4}\right) = -\dfrac{63}{16}$

45. $\sec(v - u) = \dfrac{1}{\cos(v - u)} = \dfrac{1}{\cos v \cos u + \sin v \sin u}$

$= \dfrac{1}{\left(-\dfrac{3}{5}\right)\left(-\dfrac{12}{13}\right) + \left(\dfrac{4}{5}\right)\left(\dfrac{5}{13}\right)} = \dfrac{1}{\left(\dfrac{36}{65}\right) + \left(\dfrac{20}{65}\right)}$

$= \dfrac{1}{\dfrac{56}{65}} = \dfrac{65}{56}$

For Exercises 47–51, you have:

$$\sin u = -\tfrac{7}{25},\ u \text{ in Quadrant III} \Rightarrow \cos u = -\tfrac{24}{25},\ \tan u = \tfrac{7}{24}$$

$$\cos v = -\tfrac{4}{5},\ v \text{ in Quadrant III} \Rightarrow \sin v = -\tfrac{3}{5},\ \tan v = \tfrac{3}{4}$$

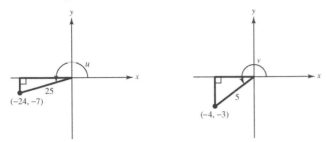

Figures for Exercises 47–51

47. $\cos(u + v) = \cos u \cos v - \sin u \sin v$

$$= \left(-\tfrac{24}{25}\right)\left(-\tfrac{4}{5}\right) - \left(-\tfrac{7}{25}\right)\left(-\tfrac{3}{5}\right)$$

$$= \tfrac{3}{5}$$

49. $\tan(u - v) = \dfrac{\tan u - \tan v}{1 + \tan u \tan v}$

$$= \dfrac{\dfrac{7}{24} - \dfrac{3}{4}}{1 + \left(\dfrac{7}{24}\right)\left(\dfrac{3}{4}\right)} = \dfrac{-\dfrac{11}{24}}{\dfrac{39}{32}} = -\dfrac{44}{117}$$

51. $\csc(u - v) = \dfrac{1}{\sin(u - v)} = \dfrac{1}{\sin u \cos v - \cos u \sin v}$

$$= \dfrac{1}{\left(-\dfrac{7}{25}\right)\left(-\dfrac{4}{5}\right) - \left(-\dfrac{24}{25}\right)\left(-\dfrac{3}{5}\right)}$$

$$= \dfrac{1}{-\dfrac{44}{125}}$$

$$= -\dfrac{125}{44}$$

53. $\sin(\arcsin x + \arccos x) - \sin(\arcsin x)\cos(\arccos x) + \sin(\arccos x)\cos(\arcsin x)$

$$= x \cdot x + \sqrt{1 - x^2} \cdot \sqrt{1 - x^2}$$

$$= x^2 + 1 - x^2$$

$$= 1$$

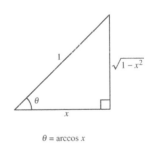

$\theta = \arcsin x$ $\theta = \arccos x$

55. $\cos(\arccos x + \arcsin x) = \cos(\arccos x)\cos(\arcsin x) - \sin(\arccos x)\sin(\arcsin x)$

$$= x \cdot \sqrt{1 - x^2} - \sqrt{1 - x^2} \cdot x$$

$$= 0$$

(Use the triangles in Exercise 53.)

57. $\sin\left(\dfrac{\pi}{2} - x\right) = \sin \dfrac{\pi}{2} \cos x - \cos \dfrac{\pi}{2} \sin x$

$$= (1)(\cos x) - (0)(\sin x)$$

$$= \cos x$$

59. $\sin\left(\dfrac{\pi}{6} + x\right) = \sin \dfrac{\pi}{6} \cos x + \cos \dfrac{\pi}{6} \sin x$

$$= \dfrac{1}{2}\left(\cos x + \sqrt{3} \sin x\right)$$

61. $\cos(\pi - \theta) + \sin\left(\dfrac{\pi}{2} + \theta\right) = \cos\pi\cos\theta + \sin\pi\sin\theta + \sin\dfrac{\pi}{2}\cos\theta + \cos\dfrac{\pi}{2}\sin\theta$

$$= (-1)(\cos\theta) + (0)(\sin\theta) + (1)(\cos\theta) + (\sin\theta)(0)$$

$$= -\cos\theta + \cos\theta$$

$$= 0$$

63. $\cos(x + y)\cos(x - y) = (\cos x\cos y - \sin x\sin y)(\cos x\cos y + \sin x\sin y)$

$$= \cos^2 x\cos^2 y - \sin^2 x\sin^2 y$$

$$= \cos^2 x\left(1 - \sin^2 y\right) - \sin^2 x\sin^2 y$$

$$= \cos^2 x - \cos^2 x\sin^2 y - \sin^2 x\sin^2 y$$

$$= \cos^2 x - \sin^2 y\left(\cos^2 x + \sin^2 x\right)$$

$$= \cos^2 x - \sin^2 y$$

65. $\cos\left(\dfrac{3\pi}{2} - x\right) = \cos\dfrac{3\pi}{2}\cos x + \sin\dfrac{3\pi}{2}\sin x$

$$= (0)(\cos x) + (-1)(\sin x)$$

$$= -\sin x$$

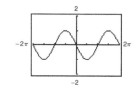

69.

$$\sin(x + \pi) - \sin x + 1 = 0$$

$$\sin x\cos\pi + \cos x\sin\pi - \sin x + 1 = 0$$

$$(\sin x)(-1) + (\cos x)(0) - \sin x + 1 = 0$$

$$-2\sin x + 1 = 0$$

$$\sin x = \dfrac{1}{2}$$

$$x = \dfrac{\pi}{6}, \dfrac{5\pi}{6}$$

67. $\sin\left(\dfrac{3\pi}{2} + \theta\right) = \sin\dfrac{3\pi}{2}\cos\theta + \cos\dfrac{3\pi}{2}\sin\theta$

$$= (-1)(\cos\theta) + (0)(\sin\theta)$$

$$= -\cos\theta$$

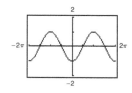

71.

$$\cos\left(x + \dfrac{\pi}{4}\right) - \cos\left(x - \dfrac{\pi}{4}\right) = 1$$

$$\cos x\cos\dfrac{\pi}{4} - \sin x\sin\dfrac{\pi}{4} - \left(\cos x\cos\dfrac{\pi}{4} + \sin x\sin\dfrac{\pi}{4}\right) = 1$$

$$-2\sin x\left(\dfrac{\sqrt{2}}{2}\right) = 1$$

$$-\sqrt{2}\sin x = 1$$

$$\sin x = -\dfrac{1}{\sqrt{2}}$$

$$\sin x = -\dfrac{\sqrt{2}}{2}$$

$$x = \dfrac{5\pi}{4}, \dfrac{7\pi}{4}$$

73.
$$\tan(x + \pi) + 2\sin(x + \pi) = 0$$

$$\frac{\tan x + \tan \pi}{1 - \tan x \tan \pi} + 2(\sin x \cos \pi + \cos x \sin \pi) = 0$$

$$\frac{\tan x + 0}{1 - \tan x(0)} + 2\big[\sin x(-1) + \cos x(0)\big] = 0$$

$$\frac{\tan x}{1} - 2\sin x = 0$$

$$\frac{\sin x}{\cos x} = 2\sin x$$

$$\sin x = 2\sin x \cos x$$

$$\sin x(1 - 2\cos x) = 0$$

$$\sin x = 0 \quad \text{or} \quad \cos x = \frac{1}{2}$$

$$x = 0, \pi \qquad x = \frac{\pi}{3}, \frac{5\pi}{3}$$

75. $\cos\left(x + \dfrac{\pi}{4}\right) + \cos\left(x - \dfrac{\pi}{4}\right) = 1$

Graph $y_1 = \cos\left(x + \dfrac{\pi}{4}\right) + \cos\left(x - \dfrac{\pi}{4}\right)$ and $y_2 = 1$.

$x = \dfrac{\pi}{4}, \dfrac{7\pi}{4}$

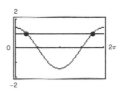

77. $\sin\left(x + \dfrac{\pi}{2}\right) + \cos^2 x = 0$

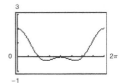

$x = \dfrac{\pi}{2}, \pi, \dfrac{3\pi}{2}$

79. $y = \dfrac{1}{3}\sin 2t + \dfrac{1}{4}\cos 2t$

  (a) $a = \dfrac{1}{3}, b = \dfrac{1}{4}, B = 2$

    $C = \arctan \dfrac{b}{a} = \arctan \dfrac{3}{4} \approx 0.6435$

    $y \approx \sqrt{\left(\dfrac{1}{3}\right)^2 + \left(\dfrac{1}{4}\right)^2}\, \sin(2t + 0.6435) = \dfrac{5}{12}\sin(2t + 0.6435)$

  (b) Amplitude: $\dfrac{5}{12}$ feet

  (c) Frequency: $\dfrac{1}{\text{period}} = \dfrac{B}{2\pi} = \dfrac{2}{2\pi} = \dfrac{1}{\pi}$ cycle per second

81. True.

$$\sin(u + v) = \sin u \cos v + \cos u \sin v$$

$$\sin(u - v) = \sin u \cos v - \cos u \sin v$$

So, $\sin(u \pm v) = \sin u \cos v \pm \cos u \sin v.$

83. False.

$$\tan\left(x - \frac{\pi}{4}\right) = \frac{\tan x - \tan(\pi/4)}{1 + \tan x \tan(\pi/4)}$$

$$= \frac{\tan x - 1}{1 + \tan x}$$

85. (a) The domains of f and g are the same, all real numbers h, except $h = 0$.

(b)

h	0.5	0.2	0.1	0.05	0.02	0.01
$f(h)$	0.267	0.410	0.456	0.478	0.491	0.496
$g(h)$	0.267	0.410	0.456	0.478	0.491	0.496

(c)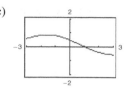

(d) As $h \to 0$, $f \to 0.5$ and $g \to 0.5$.

87. $\cos(n\pi + \theta) = \cos n\pi \cos \theta - \sin n\pi \sin \theta$

$\qquad = (-1)^n (\cos \theta) - (0)(\sin \theta)$

$\qquad = (-1)^n (\cos \theta)$, where n is an integer.

89. $C = \arctan \dfrac{b}{a} \Rightarrow \sin C = \dfrac{b}{\sqrt{a^2 + b^2}}, \cos C = \dfrac{a}{\sqrt{a^2 + b^2}}$

$\sqrt{a^2 + b^2} \sin(B\theta + C) = \sqrt{a^2 + b^2}\left(\sin B\theta \cdot \dfrac{a}{\sqrt{a^2 + b^2}} + \dfrac{b}{\sqrt{a^2 + b^2}} \cdot \cos B\theta \right) = a \sin B\theta + b \cos B\theta$

91. $\sin \theta + \cos \theta$

$a = 1, b = 1, B = 1$

(a) $C = \arctan \dfrac{b}{a} = \arctan 1 = \dfrac{\pi}{4}$

$\quad \sin \theta + \cos \theta = \sqrt{a^2 + b^2} \sin(B\theta + C)$

$\qquad = \sqrt{2} \sin\left(\theta + \dfrac{\pi}{4} \right)$

(b) $C = \arctan \dfrac{a}{b} = \arctan 1 = \dfrac{\pi}{4}$

$\quad \sin \theta + \cos \theta = \sqrt{a^2 + b^2} \cos(B\theta - C)$

$\qquad = \sqrt{2} \cos\left(\theta - \dfrac{\pi}{4} \right)$

93. $12 \sin 3\theta + 5 \cos 3\theta$

$a = 12, b = 5, B = 3$

(a) $C = \arctan \dfrac{b}{a} = \arctan \dfrac{5}{12} \approx 0.3948$

$\quad 12 \sin 3\theta + 5 \cos 3\theta = \sqrt{a^2 + b^2} \sin(B\theta + C)$

$\qquad \approx 13 \sin(3\theta + 0.3948)$

(b) $C = \arctan \dfrac{a}{b} = \arctan \dfrac{12}{5} \approx 1.1760$

$\quad 12 \sin 3\theta + 5 \cos 3\theta = \sqrt{a^2 + b^2} \cos(B\theta - C)$

$\qquad \approx 13 \cos(3\theta - 1.1760)$

95. $C = \arctan \dfrac{b}{a} = \dfrac{\pi}{4} \Rightarrow a = b, a > 0, b > 0$

$\sqrt{a^2 + b^2} = 2 \Rightarrow a = b = \sqrt{2}$

$B = 1$

$2 \sin\left(\theta + \dfrac{\pi}{4} \right) = \sqrt{2} \sin \theta + \sqrt{2} \cos \theta$

97. $m_1 = \tan \alpha$ and $m_2 = \tan \beta$

$\beta + \delta = 90° \Rightarrow \delta = 90° - \beta$

$\alpha + \theta + \delta = 90° \Rightarrow \alpha + \theta + (90° - \beta) = 90° \Rightarrow \theta = \beta - \alpha$

So, $\theta = \arctan m_2 - \arctan m_1$.

For $y = x$ and $y = \sqrt{3}x$ you have $m_1 = 1$ and $m_2 = \sqrt{3}$.

$\theta = \arctan\sqrt{3} - \arctan 1 = 60° - 45° = 15°$

99. $y_1 = \cos(x + 2)$, $y_2 = \cos x + \cos 2$

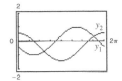

No, $y_1 \neq y_2$ because their graphs are different.

101. (a) To prove the identity for $\sin(u + v)$ you first need to prove the identity for $\cos(u - v)$.

Assume $0 < v < u < 2\pi$ and locate u, v, and $u - v$ on the unit circle.

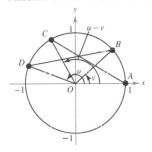

The coordinates of the points on the circle are:

$A = (1, 0)$, $B = (\cos v, \sin v)$, $C = (\cos(u - v), \sin(u - v))$, and $D = (\cos u, \sin u)$.

Because $\angle DOB = \angle COA$, chords AC and BD are equal. By the Distance Formula:

$$\sqrt{[\cos(u - v) - 1]^2 + [\sin(u - v) - 0]^2} = \sqrt{(\cos u - \cos v)^2 + (\sin u - \sin v)^2}$$

$$\cos^2(u - v) - 2\cos(u - v) + 1 + \sin^2(u - v) = \cos^2 u - 2\cos u \cos v + \cos^2 v + \sin^2 u - 2\sin u \sin v + \sin^2 v$$

$$[\cos^2(u - v) + \sin^2(u - v)] + 1 - 2\cos(u - v) = (\cos^2 u + \sin^2 u) + (\cos^2 v + \sin^2 v) - 2\cos u \cos v - 2\sin u \sin v$$

$$2 - 2\cos(u - v) = 2 - 2\cos u \cos v - 2\sin u \sin v$$

$$-2\cos(u - v) = -2(\cos u \cos v + \sin u \sin v)$$

$$\cos(u - v) = \cos u \cos v + \sin u \sin v$$

Now, to prove the identity for $\sin(u + v)$, use cofunction identities.

$$\sin(u + v) = \cos\left[\frac{\pi}{2} - (u + v)\right] = \cos\left[\left(\frac{\pi}{2} - u\right) - v\right]$$

$$= \cos\left(\frac{\pi}{2} - u\right)\cos v + \sin\left(\frac{\pi}{2} - u\right)\sin v$$

$$= \sin u \cos v + \cos u \sin v$$

(b) First, prove $\cos(u - v) = \cos u \cos v + \sin u \sin v$ using the figure containing points

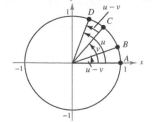

$A(1, 0)$

$B(\cos(u - v), \sin(u - v))$

$C(\cos v, \sin v)$

$D(\cos u, \sin u)$

on the unit circle.

Because chords AB and CD are each subtended by angle $u - v$, their lengths are equal. Equating

$\left[d(A, B)\right]^2 = \left[d(C, D)\right]^2$ you have $\left(\cos(u - v) - 1\right)^2 + \sin^2(u - v) = \left(\cos u - \cos v\right)^2 + \left(\sin u - \sin v\right)^2$.

Simplifying and solving for $\cos(u - v)$, you have $\cos(u - v) = \cos u \cos v + \sin u \sin v$.

Using $\sin \theta = \cos\left(\dfrac{\pi}{2} - \theta\right)$,

$$\sin(u - v) = \cos\left[\frac{\pi}{2} - (u - v)\right] = \cos\left[\left(\frac{\pi}{2} - u\right) - (-v)\right] = \cos\left(\frac{\pi}{2} - u\right)\cos(-v) + \sin\left(\frac{\pi}{2} - u\right)\sin(-v)$$

$$= \sin u \cos v - \cos u \sin v$$

Section 5.5   Multiple-Angle and Product-to-Sum Formulas

1. $2 \sin u \cos u$

3. $\tan^2 u$

5. $\dfrac{1}{2}\left[\sin(u + v) + \sin(u - v)\right]$

7.
$$\sin 2x - \sin x = 0$$
$$2 \sin x \cos x - \sin x = 0$$
$$\sin x(2 \cos x - 1) = 0$$

$\sin x = 0$ or $2 \cos x - 1 = 0$

$x = 0, \pi$ $\cos x = \dfrac{1}{2}$

$\qquad\qquad\qquad x = \dfrac{\pi}{3}, \dfrac{5\pi}{3}$

$x = 0, \dfrac{\pi}{3}, \pi, \dfrac{5\pi}{3}$

9.
$$\cos 2x - \cos x = 0$$
$$\cos 2x = \cos x$$
$$\cos^2 x - \sin^2 x = \cos x$$
$$\cos^2 x - \left(1 - \cos^2 x\right) - \cos x = 0$$
$$2 \cos^2 x - \cos x - 1 = 0$$
$$\left(2 \cos x + 1\right)\left(\cos x - 1\right) = 0$$

$2 \cos x + 1 = 0$ or $\cos x - 1 = 0$

$\cos x = -\dfrac{1}{2}$ $\cos x = 1$

$x = \dfrac{2\pi}{3}, \dfrac{4\pi}{3}$ $x = 0$

11.
$$\sin 4x = -2 \sin 2x$$
$$\sin 4x + 2 \sin 2x = 0$$
$$2 \sin 2x \cos 2x + 2 \sin 2x = 0$$
$$2 \sin 2x(\cos 2x + 1) = 0$$

$2 \sin 2x = 0$ or $\cos 2x + 1 = 0$

$\sin 2x = 0$ $\cos 2x = -1$

$2x = n\pi$ $2x = \pi + 2n\pi$

$x = \dfrac{n}{2}\pi$ $x = \dfrac{\pi}{2} + n\pi$

$x = 0, \dfrac{\pi}{2}, \pi, \dfrac{3\pi}{2}$ $x = \dfrac{\pi}{2}, \dfrac{3\pi}{2}$

13. $\tan 2x - \cot x = 0$

$$\frac{2 \tan x}{1 - \tan^2 x} = \cot x$$

$$2 \tan x = \cot x\left(1 - \tan^2 x\right)$$

$$2 \tan x = \cot x - \cot x \tan^2 x$$

$$2 \tan x = \cot x - \tan x$$

$$3 \tan x = \cot x$$

$$3 \tan x - \cot x = 0$$

$$3 \tan x - \frac{1}{\tan x} = 0$$

$$\frac{3 \tan^2 x - 1}{\tan x} = 0$$

$$\frac{1}{\tan x}\left(3 \tan^2 x - 1\right) = 0$$

$$\cot x\left(3 \tan^2 x - 1\right) = 0$$

$\cot x = 0$ or $3 \tan^2 x - 1 = 0$

$\quad x = \dfrac{\pi}{2}, \dfrac{3\pi}{2} \qquad\qquad \tan^2 x = \dfrac{1}{3}$

$$\tan x = \pm\frac{\sqrt{3}}{3}$$

$$x = \frac{\pi}{6}, \frac{5\pi}{6}, \frac{7\pi}{6}, \frac{11\pi}{6}$$

$$x = \frac{\pi}{6}, \frac{\pi}{2}, \frac{5\pi}{6}, \frac{7\pi}{6}, \frac{3\pi}{2}, \frac{11\pi}{6}$$

15. $6 \sin x \cos x = 3(2 \sin x \cos x)$

$\qquad\qquad = 3 \sin 2x$

17. $6 \cos^2 x - 3 = 3\left(2 \cos^2 x - 1\right)$

$\qquad\qquad\qquad = 3 \cos 2x$

19. $4 - 8 \sin^2 x = 4\left(1 - 2 \sin^2 x\right)$

$\qquad\qquad\quad = 4 \cos 2x$

21. $\sin u = -\dfrac{3}{5}, \dfrac{3\pi}{2} < u < 2\pi$

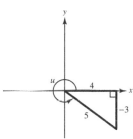

$$\sin 2u = 2 \sin u \cos u = 2\left(-\frac{3}{5}\right)\left(\frac{4}{5}\right) = -\frac{24}{25}$$

$$\cos 2u = \cos^2 u - \sin^2 u = \frac{16}{25} - \frac{9}{25} = \frac{7}{25}$$

$$\tan 2u = \frac{2 \tan u}{1 - \tan^2 u} = \frac{2\left(-\dfrac{3}{4}\right)}{1 - \dfrac{9}{16}} = -\frac{3}{2}\left(\frac{16}{7}\right) = -\frac{24}{7}$$

23. $\tan u = \dfrac{3}{5}, 0 < u < \dfrac{\pi}{2}$

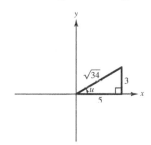

$$\sin 2u = 2 \sin u \cos u = 2\left(\frac{3}{\sqrt{34}}\right)\left(\frac{5}{\sqrt{34}}\right) = \frac{15}{17}$$

$$\cos 2u = \cos^2 u - \sin^2 u = \frac{25}{34} - \frac{9}{34} = \frac{8}{17}$$

$$\tan 2u = \frac{2 \tan u}{1 - \tan^2 u} = \frac{2\left(\dfrac{3}{5}\right)}{1 - \dfrac{9}{25}} = \frac{6}{5}\left(\frac{25}{16}\right) = \frac{15}{8}$$

25. $\cos 4x = \cos(2x + 2x)$

$\qquad\quad = \cos 2x \cos 2x - \sin 2x \sin 2x$

$\qquad\quad = \cos^2 2x - \sin^2 2x$

$\qquad\quad = \cos^2 2x - \left(1 - \cos^2 2x\right)$

$\qquad\quad = 2 \cos^2 2x - 1$

$\qquad\quad = 2\left(\cos 2x\right)^2 - 1$

$\qquad\quad = 2\left(2 \cos^2 x - 1\right)^2 - 1$

$\qquad\quad = 2\left(4 \cos^4 x - 4 \cos x + 1\right) - 1$

$\qquad\quad = 8 \cos^4 x - 8 \cos x + 1$

27. $\cos^4 x = \left(\cos^2 x\right)\left(\cos^2 x\right) = \left(\dfrac{1 + \cos 2x}{2}\right)\left(\dfrac{1 + \cos 2x}{2}\right) = \dfrac{1 + 2\cos 2x + \cos^2 2x}{4}$

$$= \dfrac{1 + 2\cos 2x + \dfrac{1 + \cos 4x}{2}}{4}$$

$$= \dfrac{2 + 4\cos 2x + 1 + \cos 4x}{8}$$

$$= \dfrac{3 + 4\cos 2x + \cos 4x}{8}$$

$$= \dfrac{1}{8}(3 + 4\cos 2x + \cos 4x)$$

29. $\tan^4 2x = \left(\tan^2 2x\right)^2$

$$= \left(\dfrac{1 - \cos 4x}{1 + \cos 4x}\right)^2$$

$$= \dfrac{1 - 2\cos 4x + \cos^2 4x}{1 + 2\cos 4x + \cos^2 4x}$$

$$= \dfrac{1 - 2\cos 4x + \dfrac{1 + \cos 8x}{2}}{1 + 2\cos 4x + \dfrac{1 + \cos 8x}{2}}$$

$$= \dfrac{\dfrac{1}{2}(2 - 4\cos 4x + 1 + \cos 8x)}{\dfrac{1}{2}(2 + 4\cos 4x + 1 + \cos 8x)}$$

$$= \dfrac{3 - 4\cos 4x + \cos 8x}{3 + 4\cos 4x + \cos 8x}$$

31. $\sin^2 2x \cos^2 2x = \left(\dfrac{1 - \cos 4x}{2}\right)\left(\dfrac{1 + \cos 4x}{2}\right)$

$$= \dfrac{1}{4}\left(1 - \cos^2 4x\right)$$

$$= \dfrac{1}{4}\left(1 - \dfrac{1 + \cos 8x}{2}\right)$$

$$= \dfrac{1}{4} - \dfrac{1}{8} - \dfrac{1}{8}\cos 8x$$

$$= \dfrac{1}{8} - \dfrac{1}{8}\cos 8x$$

$$= \dfrac{1}{8}(1 - \cos 8x)$$

33. $\sin 75° = \sin\left(\dfrac{1}{2} \cdot 150°\right) = \sqrt{\dfrac{1 - \cos 150°}{2}} = \sqrt{\dfrac{1 + \left(\sqrt{3}/2\right)}{2}}$

$$= \dfrac{1}{2}\sqrt{2 + \sqrt{3}}$$

$\cos 75° = \cos\left(\dfrac{1}{2} \cdot 150°\right) = \sqrt{\dfrac{1 + \cos 150°}{2}} = \sqrt{\dfrac{1 - \left(\sqrt{3}/2\right)}{2}}$

$$= \dfrac{1}{2}\sqrt{2 - \sqrt{3}}$$

$\tan 75° = \tan\left(\dfrac{1}{2} \cdot 150°\right) = \dfrac{\sin 150°}{1 + \cos 150°} = \dfrac{1/2}{1 - \left(\sqrt{3}/2\right)}$

$$= \dfrac{1}{2 - \sqrt{3}} \cdot \dfrac{2 + \sqrt{3}}{2 + \sqrt{3}} = \dfrac{2 + \sqrt{3}}{4 - 3} = 2 + \sqrt{3}$$

35. $\sin\dfrac{\pi}{8} = \sin\left[\dfrac{1}{2}\left(\dfrac{\pi}{4}\right)\right] = \sqrt{\dfrac{1-\cos\dfrac{\pi}{4}}{2}} = \dfrac{1}{2}\sqrt{2-\sqrt{2}}$

$\cos\dfrac{\pi}{8} = \cos\left[\dfrac{1}{2}\left(\dfrac{\pi}{4}\right)\right] = \sqrt{\dfrac{1+\cos\dfrac{\pi}{4}}{2}} = \dfrac{1}{2}\sqrt{2+\sqrt{2}}$

$\tan\dfrac{\pi}{8} = \tan\left[\dfrac{1}{2}\left(\dfrac{\pi}{4}\right)\right] = \dfrac{\sin\dfrac{\pi}{4}}{1+\cos\dfrac{\pi}{4}} = \dfrac{\dfrac{\sqrt{2}}{2}}{1+\dfrac{\sqrt{2}}{2}} = \sqrt{2}-1$

37. $\cos u = \dfrac{7}{25},\ 0 < u < \dfrac{\pi}{2}$

(a) Because u is in Quadrant I, $\dfrac{u}{2}$ is also in Quadrant I.

(b) $\sin\dfrac{u}{2} = \sqrt{\dfrac{1-\cos u}{2}} = \sqrt{\dfrac{1-\dfrac{7}{25}}{2}} = \sqrt{\dfrac{9}{25}} = \dfrac{3}{5}$

$\cos\dfrac{u}{2} = \sqrt{\dfrac{1+\cos u}{2}} = \sqrt{\dfrac{1+\dfrac{7}{25}}{2}} = \sqrt{\dfrac{16}{25}} = \dfrac{4}{5}$

$\tan\dfrac{u}{2} = \dfrac{1-\cos u}{\sin u} = \dfrac{1-\dfrac{7}{25}}{\dfrac{24}{25}} = \dfrac{3}{4}$

39. $\tan u = -\dfrac{5}{12},\ \dfrac{3\pi}{2} < u < 2\pi$

(a) Because u is in Quadrant IV, $\dfrac{u}{2}$ is in Quadrant II.

(b) $\sin\dfrac{u}{2} = \sqrt{\dfrac{1-\cos u}{2}} = \sqrt{\dfrac{1-\dfrac{12}{13}}{2}} = \sqrt{\dfrac{1}{26}} = \dfrac{\sqrt{26}}{26}$

$\cos\dfrac{u}{2} = -\sqrt{\dfrac{1+\cos u}{2}} = -\sqrt{\dfrac{1+\dfrac{12}{13}}{2}} = -\sqrt{\dfrac{25}{26}} = -\dfrac{5\sqrt{26}}{26}$

$\tan\dfrac{u}{2} = \dfrac{1-\cos u}{\sin u} = \dfrac{1-\dfrac{12}{13}}{\left(-\dfrac{5}{13}\right)} = -\dfrac{1}{5}$

41. $\sqrt{\dfrac{1-\cos 6x}{2}} = \left|\sin 3x\right|$

43. $-\sqrt{\dfrac{1-\cos 8x}{1+\cos 8x}} = -\dfrac{\sqrt{\dfrac{1-\cos 8x}{2}}}{\sqrt{\dfrac{1+\cos 8x}{2}}} = -\left|\dfrac{\sin 4x}{\cos 4x}\right| = -\left|\tan 4x\right|$

45. $\sin \dfrac{x}{2} + \cos x = 0$

$$\pm\sqrt{\dfrac{1 - \cos x}{2}} = -\cos x$$

$$\dfrac{1 - \cos x}{2} = \cos^2 x$$

$$0 = 2\cos^2 x + \cos x - 1$$

$$= (2\cos x - 1)(\cos x + 1)$$

$$\cos x = \dfrac{1}{2} \quad \text{or} \quad \cos x = -1$$

$$x = \dfrac{\pi}{3}, \dfrac{5\pi}{3} \qquad x = \pi$$

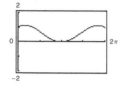

By checking these values in the original equation,
$x = \pi/3$ and $x = 5\pi/3$ are extraneous, and $x = \pi$
is the only solution.

47. $\cos \dfrac{x}{2} - \sin x = 0$

$$\pm\sqrt{\dfrac{1 + \cos x}{2}} = \sin x$$

$$\dfrac{1 + \cos x}{2} = \sin^2 x$$

$$1 + \cos x = 2\sin^2 x$$

$$1 + \cos x = 2 - 2\cos^2 x$$

$$2\cos^2 x + \cos x - 1 = 0$$

$$(2\cos x - 1)(\cos x + 1) = 0$$

$$2\cos x - 1 = 0 \quad \text{or} \quad \cos x + 1 = 0$$

$$\cos x = \dfrac{1}{2} \qquad\qquad \cos x = -1$$

$$x = \dfrac{\pi}{3}, \dfrac{5\pi}{3} \qquad\qquad x = \pi$$

$$x = \dfrac{\pi}{3}, \pi, \dfrac{5\pi}{3}$$

$\pi/3$, π, and $5\pi/3$ are all solutions to the equation.

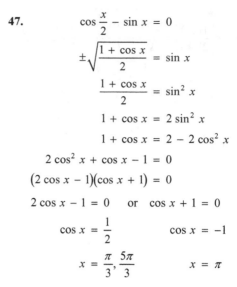

49. $\sin 5\theta \sin 3\theta = \dfrac{1}{2}\big[\cos(5\theta - 3\theta) - \cos(5\theta + 3\theta)\big] = \dfrac{1}{2}(\cos 2\theta - \cos 8\theta)$

51. $\cos 2\theta \cos 4\theta = \dfrac{1}{2}\big[\cos(2\theta - 4\theta) + \cos(2\theta + 4\theta)\big] = \dfrac{1}{2}\big[\cos(-2\theta) + \cos 6\theta\big]$

53. $\sin 5\theta - \sin 3\theta = 2\cos\left(\dfrac{5\theta + 3\theta}{2}\right)\sin\left(\dfrac{5\theta - 3\theta}{2}\right)$

$$= 2\cos 4\theta \sin\theta$$

55. $\cos 6x + \cos 2x = 2\cos\left(\dfrac{6x + 2x}{2}\right)\cos\left(\dfrac{6x - 2x}{2}\right)$

$$= 2\cos 4x \cos 2x$$

57. $\sin 75° + \sin 15° = 2\sin\left(\dfrac{75° + 15°}{2}\right)\cos\left(\dfrac{75° - 15°}{2}\right) = 2\sin 45° \cos 30° = 2\left(\dfrac{\sqrt{2}}{2}\right)\left(\dfrac{\sqrt{3}}{2}\right) = \dfrac{\sqrt{6}}{2}$

59. $\cos\dfrac{3\pi}{4} - \cos\dfrac{\pi}{4} = -2\sin\left(\dfrac{\dfrac{3\pi}{4} + \dfrac{\pi}{4}}{2}\right)\sin\left(\dfrac{\dfrac{3\pi}{4} - \dfrac{\pi}{4}}{2}\right) = -2\sin\dfrac{\pi}{2}\sin\dfrac{\pi}{4}$

$$\cos\dfrac{3\pi}{4} - \cos\dfrac{\pi}{4} = -\dfrac{\sqrt{2}}{2} - \dfrac{\sqrt{2}}{2} = -\sqrt{2}$$

61.
$$\sin 6x + \sin 2x = 0$$

$$2 \sin\left(\frac{6x + 2x}{2}\right) \cos\left(\frac{6x - 2x}{2}\right) = 0$$

$$2(\sin 4x) \cos 2x = 0$$

$$\sin 4x = 0 \quad \text{or} \quad \cos 2x = 0$$

$$4x = n\pi \qquad\qquad 2x = \frac{\pi}{2} + n\pi$$

$$x = \frac{n\pi}{4} \qquad\qquad x = \frac{\pi}{4} + \frac{n\pi}{2}$$

In the interval $[0, 2\pi)$

$$x = 0, \frac{\pi}{4}, \frac{\pi}{2}, \frac{3\pi}{4}, \pi, \frac{5\pi}{4}, \frac{3\pi}{2}, \frac{7\pi}{4}.$$

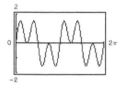

63.
$$\frac{\cos 2x}{\sin 3x - \sin x} - 1 = 0$$

$$\frac{\cos 2x}{\sin 3x - \sin x} = 1$$

$$\frac{\cos 2x}{2 \cos 2x \sin x} = 1$$

$$2 \sin x = 1$$

$$\sin x = \frac{1}{2}$$

$$x = \frac{\pi}{6}, \frac{5\pi}{6}$$

65. $\csc 2\theta = \dfrac{1}{\sin 2\theta}$

$$= \frac{1}{2 \sin \theta \cos \theta}$$

$$= \frac{1}{\sin \theta} \cdot \frac{1}{2 \cos \theta}$$

$$= \frac{\csc \theta}{2 \cos \theta}$$

67. $1 + \cos 10y = 1 + \cos^2 5y - \sin^2 5y$

$$= 1 + \cos^2 5y - \left(1 - \cos^2 5y\right)$$

$$= 2 \cos^2 5y$$

69. $(\sin x + \cos x)^2 = \sin^2 x + 2 \sin x \cos x + \cos^2 x$

$$= \left(\sin^2 x + \cos^2 x\right) + 2 \sin x \cos x$$

$$= 1 + \sin 2x$$

71. $\dfrac{\sin x \pm \sin y}{\cos x + \cos y} = \dfrac{2 \sin\left(\dfrac{x \pm y}{2}\right) \cos\left(\dfrac{x \mp y}{2}\right)}{2 \cos\left(\dfrac{x + y}{2}\right) \cos\left(\dfrac{x - y}{2}\right)}$

$$= \tan\left(\frac{x \pm y}{2}\right)$$

73. (a) $\quad \sin\left(\dfrac{\theta}{2}\right) = \pm\sqrt{\dfrac{1 - \cos \theta}{2}} = \dfrac{1}{M}$

$$\left(\pm\sqrt{\frac{1 - \cos \theta}{2}}\right)^2 = \left(\frac{1}{M}\right)^2$$

$$\frac{1 - \cos \theta}{2} = \frac{1}{M^2}$$

$$M^2(1 - \cos \theta) = 2$$

$$1 - \cos \theta = \frac{2}{M^2}$$

$$-\cos \theta = \frac{2}{M^2} - 1$$

$$\cos \theta = 1 - \frac{2}{M^2}$$

$$\cos \theta = \frac{M^2 - 2}{M^2}$$

(b) When $M = 1$, $\cos \theta = \dfrac{1 - 2}{1} = -1$. So, $\theta = \pi$.

(c) When $M = 4.5$, $\cos \theta = \dfrac{(4.5)^2 - 2}{(4.5)^2}$

$$\cos \theta \approx 0.901235.$$

So, $\theta \approx 0.4482$ radian.

(d) When $M = 1$, $\dfrac{\text{speed of object}}{\text{speed of sound}} = M$

$$\frac{\text{speed of object}}{760 \text{ mph}} = 1$$

$$\text{speed of object} = 760 \text{ mph}.$$

When $M = 4.5$, $\dfrac{\text{speed of object}}{\text{speed of sound}} = M$

$$\frac{\text{speed of object}}{760 \text{ mph}} = 4.5$$

$$\text{speed of object} = 3420 \text{ mph}.$$

75. $\dfrac{x}{2} = 2r \sin^2 \dfrac{\theta}{2} = 2r\left(\dfrac{1 - \cos \theta}{2}\right) = r(1 - \cos \theta)$

So, $x = 2r(1 - \cos \theta)$.

77. False. For $u < 0$,

$$\sin 2u = -\sin(-2u)$$

$$= -2 \sin(-u) \cos(-u)$$

$$= -2(-\sin u) \cos u$$

$$= 2 \sin u \cos u.$$

Review Exercises for Chapter 5

1. $\dfrac{\sin x}{\cos x} = \tan x$

3. $\dfrac{1}{\tan x} = \cot x$

5. $\tan \theta = \dfrac{2}{3}, \ \sec \theta = \dfrac{\sqrt{13}}{3}$

θ is in Quadrant I.

$\cos \theta = \dfrac{1}{\sec \theta} = \dfrac{3}{\sqrt{13}} = \dfrac{3\sqrt{13}}{13}$

$\sin \theta = \sqrt{1 - \cos^2 \theta} = \sqrt{1 - \dfrac{9}{13}} = \sqrt{\dfrac{4}{13}} = \dfrac{2\sqrt{13}}{13}$

$\csc \theta = \dfrac{1}{\sin \theta} = \dfrac{\sqrt{13}}{2}$

$\cot \theta = \dfrac{1}{\tan \theta} = \dfrac{3}{2}$

7. $\dfrac{1}{\cot^2 x + 1} = \dfrac{1}{\csc^2 x} = \sin^2 x$

9. $\tan^2 x \left(\csc^2 x - 1 \right) = \tan^2 x \left(\cot^2 x \right)$

$\qquad\qquad\qquad = \tan^2 x \left(\dfrac{1}{\tan^2 x} \right)$

$\qquad\qquad\qquad = 1$

11. $\dfrac{\cot\left(\dfrac{\pi}{2} - u\right)}{\cos u} = \dfrac{\tan u}{\cos u} = \tan u \sec u$

13. $\cos^2 x + \cos^2 x \cot^2 x = \cos^2 x \left(1 + \cot^2 x \right)$

$\qquad\qquad\qquad\qquad = \cos^2 x \left(\csc^2 x \right)$

$\qquad\qquad\qquad\qquad = \cos^2 x \left(\dfrac{1}{\sin^2 x} \right)$

$\qquad\qquad\qquad\qquad = \dfrac{\cos^2 x}{\sin^2 x}$

$\qquad\qquad\qquad\qquad = \cot^2 x$

15. $\dfrac{1}{\csc \theta + 1} - \dfrac{1}{\csc \theta - 1} = \dfrac{(\csc \theta - 1) - (\csc \theta + 1)}{(\csc \theta + 1)(\csc \theta - 1)}$

$\qquad\qquad\qquad\qquad = \dfrac{-2}{\csc^2 \theta - 1}$

$\qquad\qquad\qquad\qquad = \dfrac{-2}{\cot^2 \theta}$

$\qquad\qquad\qquad\qquad = -2 \tan^2 \theta$

17. Let $x = 5 \sin \theta$, then

$\sqrt{25 - x^2} = \sqrt{25 - (5 \sin \theta)^2} = \sqrt{25 - 25 \sin^2 \theta} = \sqrt{25(1 - \sin^2 \theta)} = \sqrt{25 \cos^2 \theta} = 5 \cos \theta.$

19. $\cos x \left(\tan^2 x + 1 \right) = \cos x \sec^2 x$

$\qquad\qquad\qquad = \dfrac{1}{\sec x} \sec^2 x$

$\qquad\qquad\qquad = \sec x$

21. $\sec\left(\dfrac{\pi}{2} - \theta\right) = \csc \theta$

23. $\dfrac{1}{\tan \theta \csc \theta} = \dfrac{1}{\dfrac{\sin \theta}{\cos \theta} \cdot \dfrac{1}{\sin \theta}} = \cos \theta$

25. $\sin^5 x \cos^2 x = \sin^4 x \cos^2 x \sin x$

$\qquad\qquad\quad = \left(1 - \cos^2 x \right)^2 \cos^2 x \sin x$

$\qquad\qquad\quad = \left(1 - 2 \cos^2 x + \cos^4 x \right) \cos^2 x \sin x$

$\qquad\qquad\quad = \left(\cos^2 x - 2 \cos^4 x + \cos^6 x \right) \sin x$

27. $\sin x = \sqrt{3} - \sin x$

$\sin x = \dfrac{\sqrt{3}}{2}$

$x = \dfrac{\pi}{3} + 2\pi n, \ \dfrac{2\pi}{3} + 2\pi n$

29. $3\sqrt{3} \tan u = 3$

$\tan u = \dfrac{1}{\sqrt{3}}$

$u = \dfrac{\pi}{6} + n\pi$

31. $3 \csc^2 x = 4$

$$\csc^2 x = \frac{4}{3}$$

$$\sin x = \pm\frac{\sqrt{3}}{2}$$

$$x = \frac{\pi}{3} + 2\pi n, \frac{2\pi}{3} + 2\pi n, \frac{4\pi}{3} + 2\pi n, \frac{5\pi}{3} + 2\pi n$$

These can be combined as:

$$x = \frac{\pi}{3} + n\pi \quad \text{or} \quad x = \frac{2\pi}{3} + n\pi$$

33. $2\cos^2 x - \cos x = 1$

$$2\cos^2 x - \cos x - 1 = 0$$

$$(2\cos x + 1)(\cos x - 1) = 0$$

$$2\cos x + 1 = 0 \qquad \cos x - 1 = 0$$

$$\cos x = -\frac{1}{2} \qquad \cos x = 1$$

$$x = \frac{2\pi}{3}, \frac{4\pi}{3} \qquad x = 0$$

35. $\cos^2 x + \sin x = 1$

$$1 - \sin^2 x + \sin x - 1 = 0$$

$$-\sin x(\sin x - 1) = 0$$

$$\sin x = 0 \qquad \sin x - 1 = 0$$

$$x = 0, \pi \qquad \sin x = 1$$

$$x = \frac{\pi}{2}$$

37. $2\sin 2x - \sqrt{2} = 0$

$$\sin 2x = \frac{\sqrt{2}}{2}$$

$$2x = \frac{\pi}{4} + 2\pi n, \frac{3\pi}{4} + 2\pi n$$

$$x = \frac{\pi}{8} + \pi n, \frac{3\pi}{8} + \pi n$$

$$x = \frac{\pi}{8}, \frac{3\pi}{8}, \frac{9\pi}{8}, \frac{11\pi}{8}$$

45. $\tan^2 \theta + \tan \theta - 6 = 0$

$$(\tan \theta + 3)(\tan \theta - 2) = 0$$

$$\tan \theta + 3 = 0 \qquad \text{or} \qquad \tan \theta - 2 = 0$$

$$\tan \theta = -3 \qquad\qquad \tan \theta = 2$$

$$\theta = \arctan(-3) + \pi, \arctan(-3) + 2\pi \qquad \theta = \arctan 2, \arctan 2 + \pi$$

39. $3\tan^2\left(\frac{x}{3}\right) - 1 = 0$

$$\tan^2\left(\frac{x}{3}\right) = \frac{1}{3}$$

$$\tan \frac{x}{3} = \pm\sqrt{\frac{1}{3}}$$

$$\tan \frac{x}{3} = \pm\frac{\sqrt{3}}{3}$$

$$\frac{x}{3} = \frac{\pi}{6}, \frac{5\pi}{6}, \frac{7\pi}{6}$$

$$x = \frac{\pi}{2}, \frac{5\pi}{2}, \frac{7\pi}{2}$$

$\frac{5\pi}{2}$ and $\frac{7\pi}{2}$ are greater than 2π, so they are not

solutions. The solution is $x = \frac{\pi}{2}$.

41. $\cos 4x(\cos x - 1) = 0$

$$\cos 4x = 0 \qquad\qquad \cos x - 1 = 0$$

$$4x = \frac{\pi}{2} + 2\pi n, \frac{3\pi}{2} + 2\pi n \qquad \cos x = 1$$

$$x = \frac{\pi}{8} + \frac{\pi}{2}n, \frac{3\pi}{8} + \frac{\pi}{2}n \qquad x = 0$$

$$x = 0, \frac{\pi}{8}, \frac{3\pi}{8}, \frac{5\pi}{8}, \frac{7\pi}{8}, \frac{9\pi}{8}, \frac{11\pi}{8}, \frac{13\pi}{8}, \frac{15\pi}{8}$$

43. $\tan^2 x - 2\tan x = 0$

$$\tan x(\tan x - 2) = 0$$

$$\tan x = 0 \qquad \text{or} \quad \tan x - 2 = 0$$

$$x = 0, \pi \qquad\qquad \tan x = 2$$

$$x = \arctan 2, \arctan 2 + \pi$$

$$x = 0, \pi, \arctan 2, \arctan 2 + \pi$$

47. $\sin 285° = \sin(315° - 30°)$

$\qquad = \sin 315° \cos 30° - \cos 315° \sin 30°$

$\qquad = \left(-\dfrac{\sqrt{2}}{2}\right)\left(\dfrac{\sqrt{3}}{2}\right) - \left(\dfrac{\sqrt{2}}{2}\right)\left(\dfrac{1}{2}\right)$

$\qquad = -\dfrac{\sqrt{2}}{4}\left(\sqrt{3} + 1\right)$

$\cos 285° = \cos(315° - 30°)$

$\qquad = \cos 315° \cos 30° + \sin 315° \sin 30°$

$\qquad = \left(\dfrac{\sqrt{2}}{2}\right)\left(\dfrac{\sqrt{3}}{2}\right) + \left(-\dfrac{\sqrt{2}}{2}\right)\left(\dfrac{1}{2}\right)$

$\qquad = \dfrac{\sqrt{2}}{4}\left(\sqrt{3} - 1\right)$

$\tan 285° = \tan(315° - 30°) = \dfrac{\tan 315° - \tan 30°}{1 + \tan 315° \tan 30°}$

$\qquad = \dfrac{(-1) - \left(\dfrac{\sqrt{3}}{3}\right)}{1 + (-1)\left(\dfrac{\sqrt{3}}{3}\right)} = -2 - \sqrt{3}$

49. $\sin \dfrac{25\pi}{12} = \sin\left(\dfrac{11\pi}{6} + \dfrac{\pi}{4}\right) = \sin \dfrac{11\pi}{6} \cos \dfrac{\pi}{4} + \cos \dfrac{11\pi}{6} \sin \dfrac{\pi}{4}$

$\qquad = \left(-\dfrac{1}{2}\right)\left(\dfrac{\sqrt{2}}{2}\right) + \left(\dfrac{\sqrt{3}}{2}\right)\left(\dfrac{\sqrt{2}}{2}\right) = \dfrac{\sqrt{2}}{4}\left(\sqrt{3} - 1\right)$

$\cos \dfrac{25\pi}{12} = \cos\left(\dfrac{11\pi}{6} + \dfrac{\pi}{4}\right) = \cos \dfrac{11\pi}{6} \cos \dfrac{\pi}{4} - \sin \dfrac{11\pi}{6} \sin \dfrac{\pi}{4}$

$\qquad = \left(\dfrac{\sqrt{3}}{2}\right)\left(\dfrac{\sqrt{2}}{2}\right) - \left(-\dfrac{1}{2}\right)\left(\dfrac{\sqrt{2}}{2}\right) = \dfrac{\sqrt{2}}{4}\left(\sqrt{3} + 1\right)$

$\tan \dfrac{25\pi}{12} = \tan\left(\dfrac{11\pi}{6} + \dfrac{\pi}{4}\right) = \dfrac{\tan \dfrac{11\pi}{6} + \tan \dfrac{\pi}{4}}{1 - \tan \dfrac{11\pi}{6} \tan \dfrac{\pi}{4}}$

$\qquad = \dfrac{\left(-\dfrac{\sqrt{3}}{3}\right) + 1}{1 - \left(-\dfrac{\sqrt{3}}{3}\right)(1)} = 2 - \sqrt{3}$

51. $\sin 60° \cos 45° - \cos 60° \sin 45° = \sin(60° - 45°)$

$\qquad\qquad\qquad\qquad\qquad\qquad\quad = \sin 15°$

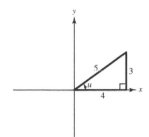
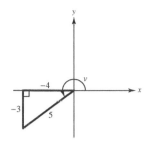

Figures for Exercises 53–57

53. $\sin(u + v) = \sin u \cos v + \cos u \sin v = \frac{3}{5}\left(-\frac{4}{5}\right) + \frac{4}{5}\left(-\frac{3}{5}\right) - -\frac{24}{25}$

55. $\cos(u - v) = \cos u \cos v + \sin u \sin v = \frac{4}{5}\left(-\frac{4}{5}\right) + \frac{3}{5}\left(-\frac{3}{5}\right) = -1$

57. $\cos\left(x + \frac{\pi}{2}\right) = \cos x \cos \frac{\pi}{2} - \sin x \sin \frac{\pi}{2} = \cos x(0) - \sin x(1) = -\sin x$

59. $\tan(\pi - x) = \dfrac{\tan \pi - \tan x}{1 - \tan \pi \tan x} = -\tan x$

61. $\sin\left(x + \dfrac{\pi}{4}\right) - \sin\left(x - \dfrac{\pi}{4}\right) = 1$

$$2 \cos x \sin \frac{\pi}{4} = 1$$

$$\cos x = \frac{\sqrt{2}}{2}$$

$$x = \frac{\pi}{4}, \frac{7\pi}{4}$$

63. $\sin u = -\dfrac{4}{5}, \ \pi < u < \dfrac{3\pi}{2}$

$\cos u = -\sqrt{1 - \sin^2 u} = \dfrac{-3}{5}$

$\tan u = \dfrac{\sin u}{\cos u} = \dfrac{4}{3}$

$\sin 2u = 2 \sin u \cos u = 2\left(-\dfrac{4}{5}\right)\left(-\dfrac{3}{5}\right) = \dfrac{24}{25}$

$\cos 2u = \cos^2 u - \sin^2 u - \left(-\dfrac{3}{5}\right)^2 - \left(\dfrac{4}{5}\right)^2 = -\dfrac{7}{25}$

$\tan 2u = \dfrac{2 \tan u}{1 - \tan^2 u} = \dfrac{2\left(\dfrac{4}{3}\right)}{1 - \left(\dfrac{4}{3}\right)^2} = -\dfrac{24}{7}$

65. $\sin 4x - 2 \sin 2x \cos 2x$

$$= 2\left[2 \sin x \cos x\left(\cos^2 x - \sin^2 x\right)\right]$$

$$= 4 \sin x \cos x\left(2 \cos^2 x - 1\right)$$

$$= 8 \cos^3 x \sin x - 4 \cos x \sin x$$

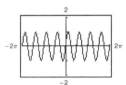

67. $\tan^2 2x = \dfrac{\sin^2 2x}{\cos^2 2x} = \dfrac{\dfrac{1 - \cos 4x}{2}}{\dfrac{1 + \cos 4x}{2}} = \dfrac{1 - \cos 4x}{1 + \cos 4x}$

69. $\sin(-75°) = -\sqrt{\dfrac{1 - \cos 150°}{2}} = -\sqrt{\dfrac{1 - \left(-\dfrac{\sqrt{3}}{2}\right)}{2}} = -\dfrac{\sqrt{2 + \sqrt{3}}}{2} = -\dfrac{1}{2}\sqrt{2 + \sqrt{3}}$

$\cos(-75°) = -\sqrt{\dfrac{1 + \cos 150°}{2}} = \sqrt{\dfrac{1 + \left(-\dfrac{\sqrt{3}}{2}\right)}{2}} = \dfrac{\sqrt{2 - \sqrt{3}}}{2} = \dfrac{1}{2}\sqrt{2 - \sqrt{3}}$

$\tan(-75°) = -\left(\dfrac{1 - \cos 150°}{\sin 150°}\right) = -\left(\dfrac{1 - \left(-\dfrac{\sqrt{3}}{2}\right)}{\dfrac{1}{2}}\right) = -\left(2 + \sqrt{3}\right) = -2 - \sqrt{3}$

71. $\tan u = \dfrac{4}{3},\ \pi < u < \dfrac{3\pi}{2}$

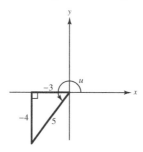

(a) Because u is in Quadrant III, $\dfrac{u}{2}$ is in Quadrant II.

(b) $\sin \dfrac{u}{2} = \sqrt{\dfrac{1 - \cos u}{2}} = \sqrt{\dfrac{1 - \left(-\dfrac{3}{5}\right)}{2}} = \sqrt{\dfrac{4}{5}}$

$\quad = \dfrac{2\sqrt{5}}{5}$

$\cos \dfrac{u}{2} = -\sqrt{\dfrac{1 + \cos u}{2}} = -\sqrt{\dfrac{1 + \left(-\dfrac{3}{5}\right)}{2}} = -\sqrt{\dfrac{1}{5}}$

$\quad = -\dfrac{\sqrt{5}}{5}$

$\tan \dfrac{u}{2} = \dfrac{1 - \cos u}{\sin u} = \dfrac{1 - \left(-\dfrac{3}{5}\right)}{\left(-\dfrac{4}{5}\right)} = -2$

73. $-\sqrt{\dfrac{1 + \cos 10x}{2}} = -\left|\cos \dfrac{10x}{2}\right| = -\left|\cos 5x\right|$

75. $\cos 4\theta \sin 6\theta = \dfrac{1}{2}\left[\sin(4\theta + 6\theta) - \sin(4\theta - 6\theta)\right] = \dfrac{1}{2}\left(\sin 10\theta - \sin(-2\theta)\right)$

77. $\cos 6\theta + \cos 5\theta = 2 \cos\left(\dfrac{6\theta + 5\theta}{2}\right)\cos\left(\dfrac{6\theta - 5\theta}{2}\right) = 2 \cos \dfrac{11\theta}{2} \cos \dfrac{\theta}{2}$

79. $r = \dfrac{1}{32}v_0^2 \sin 2\theta$

range $= 100$ feet

$v_0 = 80$ feet per second

$r = \dfrac{1}{32}(80)^2 \sin 2\theta = 100$

$\sin 2\theta = 0.5$

$2\theta = 30°$

$\theta = 15°$ or $\dfrac{\pi}{12}$

81. False. If $\dfrac{\pi}{2} < \theta < \pi$, then $\dfrac{\pi}{4} < \dfrac{\theta}{2} < \dfrac{\pi}{2}$ and $\dfrac{\theta}{2}$ is in

Quadrant I.

$\cos \dfrac{\theta}{2} > 0$

83. True. $4 \sin(-x)\cos(-x) = 4(-\sin x)\cos x$

$= -4 \sin x \cos x$

$= -2(2 \sin x \cos x)$

$= -2 \sin 2x$

85. No. For an equation to be an identity, the equation must be true for all real numbers. $\sin \theta = \frac{1}{2}$ has an infinite number of solutions but is not an identity.

Problem Solving for Chapter 5

1. $\sin \theta = \pm\sqrt{1 - \cos^2 \theta}$

$\tan \theta = \dfrac{\sin \theta}{\cos \theta} = \pm\dfrac{\sqrt{1 - \cos^2 \theta}}{\cos \theta}$

$\csc \theta = \dfrac{1}{\sin \theta} = \pm\dfrac{1}{\sqrt{1 - \cos^2 \theta}}$

$\sec \theta = \dfrac{1}{\cos \theta}$

$\cot \theta = \dfrac{1}{\tan \theta} = \pm\dfrac{\cos \theta}{\sqrt{1 - \cos^2 \theta}}$

You also have the following relationships:

$\sin \theta = \cos\left(\dfrac{\pi}{2} - \theta\right)$

$\tan \theta = \dfrac{\cos\left[(\pi/2) - \theta\right]}{\cos \theta}$

$\csc \theta = \dfrac{1}{\cos\left[(\pi/2) - \theta\right]}$

$\sec \theta = \dfrac{1}{\cos \theta}$

$\cot \theta = \dfrac{\cos \theta}{\cos\left[(\pi/2) - \theta\right]}$

3. $\sin\left[\dfrac{(12n + 1)\pi}{6}\right] = \sin\left[\dfrac{1}{6}(12n\pi + \pi)\right]$

$= \sin\left(2n\pi + \dfrac{\pi}{6}\right)$

$= \sin \dfrac{\pi}{6} = \dfrac{1}{2}$

So, $\sin\left[\dfrac{(12n + 1)\pi}{6}\right] = \dfrac{1}{2}$ for all integers n.

5. From the figure, it appears that $u + v = w$. Assume that u, v, and w are all in Quadrant I.

From the figure:

$$\tan u = \frac{s}{3s} = \frac{1}{3}$$

$$\tan v = \frac{s}{2s} = \frac{1}{2}$$

$$\tan w = \frac{s}{s} = 1$$

$$\tan(u + v) = \frac{\tan u + \tan v}{1 - \tan u \tan v} = \frac{1/3 + 1/2}{1 - (1/3)(1/2)} = \frac{5/6}{1 - (1/6)} = 1 = \tan w.$$

So, $\tan(u + v) = \tan w$. Because u, v, and w are all in Quadrant I, you have

$$\arctan\left[\tan(u + v)\right] = \arctan\left[\tan w\right] u + v = w.$$

7. (a)

$$\sin \frac{\theta}{2} = \frac{\frac{1}{2}b}{10} \qquad \text{and} \qquad \cos \frac{\theta}{2} = \frac{h}{10}$$

$$b = 20 \sin \frac{\theta}{2} \qquad \qquad h = 10 \cos \frac{\theta}{2}$$

$$A = \frac{1}{2}bh$$

$$= \frac{1}{2}\left(20 \sin \frac{\theta}{2}\right)\left(10 \cos \frac{\theta}{2}\right)$$

$$= 100 \sin \frac{\theta}{2} \cos \frac{\theta}{2}$$

(b) $A = 50\left(2 \sin \frac{\theta}{2} \cos \frac{\theta}{2}\right)$

$$= 50 \sin\left(2\left(\frac{\theta}{2}\right)\right)$$

$$= 50 \sin \theta$$

Because $\sin \frac{\pi}{2} = 1$ is a maximum, $\theta = \frac{\pi}{2}$. So, the area is a maximum at $A = 50 \sin \frac{\pi}{2} = 50$ square meters.

9. $F = \frac{0.6W \sin(\theta + 90°)}{\sin 12°}$

(a) $F = \frac{0.6W(\sin \theta \cos 90° + \cos \theta \sin 90°)}{\sin 12°}$

$$= \frac{0.6W\left[(\sin \theta)(0) + (\cos \theta)(1)\right]}{\sin 12°}$$

$$= \frac{0.6W \cos \theta}{\sin 12°}$$

(b) Let $y_1 = \frac{0.6(185) \cos x}{\sin 12°}$.

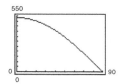

(c) The force is maximum (533.88 pounds) when $\theta = 0°$.

The force is minimum (0 pounds) when $\theta = 90°$.

11. $d = 35 - 28 \cos \dfrac{\pi}{6.2} t$ when $t = 0$ corresponds to 12:00 A.M.

(a) The high tides occur when $\cos \dfrac{\pi}{6.2} t = -1$. Solving yields $t = 6.2$ or $t = 18.6$.

These t-values correspond to 6:12 A.M. and 6:36 P.M.

The low tide occurs when $\cos \dfrac{\pi}{6.2} t = 1$. Solving yields $t = 0$ and $t = 12.4$ which corresponds to 12:00 A.M. and 12:24 P.M.

(b) The water depth is never 3.5 feet. At low tide, the depth is $d = 35 - 28 = 7$ feet.

(c)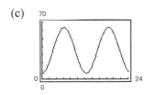

13. (a) $n = \dfrac{\sin\left(\dfrac{\theta}{2} + \dfrac{\alpha}{2}\right)}{\sin \dfrac{\theta}{2}}$

$= \dfrac{\sin\left(\dfrac{\theta}{2}\right)\cos\left(\dfrac{\alpha}{2}\right) + \cos\left(\dfrac{\theta}{2}\right)\sin\left(\dfrac{\alpha}{2}\right)}{\sin\left(\dfrac{\theta}{2}\right)}$

$= \cos\left(\dfrac{\alpha}{2}\right) + \cot\left(\dfrac{\theta}{2}\right)\sin\left(\dfrac{\alpha}{2}\right)$

For $\alpha = 60°$, $n = \cos 30° + \cot\left(\dfrac{\theta}{2}\right)\sin 30°$

$n = \dfrac{\sqrt{3}}{2} + \dfrac{1}{2}\cot\left(\dfrac{\theta}{2}\right)$.

(b) For glass, $n = 1.50$.

$1.50 = \dfrac{\sqrt{3}}{2} + \dfrac{1}{2}\cot\left(\dfrac{\theta}{2}\right)$

$2\left(1.50 - \dfrac{\sqrt{3}}{2}\right) = \cot\left(\dfrac{\theta}{2}\right)$

$\dfrac{1}{3 - \sqrt{3}} = \tan\left(\dfrac{\theta}{2}\right)$

$\theta = 2\tan^{-1}\left(\dfrac{1}{3 - \sqrt{3}}\right)$

$\theta \approx 76.5°$

15. (a) Let $y_1 = \sin x$ and $y_2 = 0.5$.

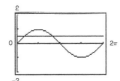

$\sin x \geq 0.5$ on the interval $\left[\dfrac{\pi}{6}, \dfrac{5\pi}{6}\right]$.

(b) Let $y_1 = \cos x$ and $y_2 = -0.5$.

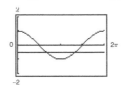

$\cos x \leq -0.5$ on the interval $\left[\dfrac{2\pi}{3}, \dfrac{4\pi}{3}\right]$.

(c) Let $y_1 = \tan x$ and $y_2 = \sin x$.

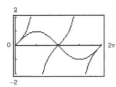

$\tan x < \sin x$ on the intervals $\left(\dfrac{\pi}{2}, \pi\right)$ and $\left(\dfrac{3\pi}{2}, 2\pi\right)$.

(d) Let $y_1 = \cos x$ and $y_2 = \sin x$.

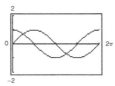

$\cos x \geq \sin x$ on the intervals $\left[0, \dfrac{\pi}{4}\right]$ and $\left[\dfrac{5\pi}{4}, 2\pi\right)$.

Practice Test for Chapter 5

1. Find the value of the other five trigonometric functions, given $\tan x = \frac{4}{11}$, $\sec x < 0$.

2. Simplify $\dfrac{\sec^2 x + \csc^2 x}{\csc^2 x\left(1 + \tan^2 x\right)}$.

3. Rewrite as a single logarithm and simplify $\ln|\tan \theta| - \ln|\cot \theta|$.

4. True or false:

$$\cos\left(\frac{\pi}{2} - x\right) = \frac{1}{\csc x}$$

5. Factor and simplify: $\sin^4 x + \left(\sin^2 x\right)\cos^2 x$

6. Multiply and simplify: $\left(\csc x + 1\right)\left(\csc x - 1\right)$

7. Rationalize the denominator and simplify:

$$\frac{\cos^2 x}{1 - \sin x}$$

8. Verify:

$$\frac{1 + \cos \theta}{\sin \theta} + \frac{\sin \theta}{1 + \cos \theta} = 2 \csc \theta$$

9. Verify:

$$\tan^4 x + 2 \tan^2 x + 1 = \sec^4 x$$

10. Use the sum or difference formulas to determine:

   (a) $\sin 105°$

   (b) $\tan 15°$

11. Simplify: $\left(\sin 42°\right)\cos 38° - \left(\cos 42°\right)\sin 38°$

12. Verify $\tan\left(\theta + \dfrac{\pi}{4}\right) = \dfrac{1 + \tan \theta}{1 - \tan \theta}$.

13. Write $\sin\left(\arcsin x - \arccos x\right)$ as an algebraic expression in x.

14. Use the double-angle formulas to determine:

   (a) $\cos 120°$

   (b) $\tan 300°$

15. Use the half-angle formulas to determine:

   (a) $\sin 22.5°$

   (b) $\tan \dfrac{\pi}{12}$

16. Given $\sin \theta = 4/5$, θ lies in Quadrant II, find $\cos(\theta/2)$.

17. Use the power-reducing identities to write $\left(\sin^2 x\right)\cos^2 x$ in terms of the first power of cosine.

18. Rewrite as a sum: $6(\sin 5\theta)\cos 2\theta$.

19. Rewrite as a product: $\sin(x + \pi) + \sin(x - \pi)$.

20. Verify $\dfrac{\sin 9x + \sin 5x}{\cos 9x - \cos 5x} = -\cot 2x$.

21. Verify:

$$(\cos u)\sin v = \tfrac{1}{2}\big[\sin(u + v) - \sin(u - v)\big].$$

22. Find all solutions in the interval $[0, 2\pi)$:

$$4\sin^2 x = 1$$

23. Find all solutions in the interval $[0, 2\pi)$:

$$\tan^2 \theta + \left(\sqrt{3} - 1\right)\tan \theta - \sqrt{3} = 0$$

24. Find all solutions in the interval $[0, 2\pi)$:

$$\sin 2x = \cos x$$

25. Use the quadratic formula to find all solutions in the interval $[0, 2\pi)$:

$$\tan^2 x - 6\tan x + 4 = 0$$

APPENDIX A
Review of Fundamental Concepts of Algebra

APPENDIX A
Review of Fundamental Concepts of Algebra

Appendix A.1   Real Numbers and Their Properties

1. irrational

3. absolute value

5. terms

7. $-9, -\frac{7}{2}, 5, \frac{2}{3}, \sqrt{2}, 0, 1, -4, 2, -11$

(a) Natural numbers: 5, 1, 2

(b) Whole numbers: 0, 5, 1, 2

(c) Integers: $-9, 5, 0, 1, -4, 2, -11$

(d) Rational numbers: $-9, -\frac{7}{2}, 5, \frac{2}{3}, 0, 1, -4, 2, -11$

(e) Irrational numbers: $\sqrt{2}$

9. $2.01, 0.666\ldots, -13, 0.010110111\ldots, 1, -6$

(a) Natural numbers: 1

(b) Whole numbers: 1

(c) Integers: $-13, 1, -6$

(d) Rational numbers: $2.01, 0.666\ldots, -13, 1, -6$

(e) Irrational numbers: $0.010110111\ldots$

11. (a)

(b)

(c)

(d)

13. $-4 > -8$

15. $\frac{5}{6} > \frac{2}{3}$

17. (a) The inequality $x \le 5$ denotes the set of all real numbers less than or equal to 5.

(b)

(c) The interval is unbounded.

19. (a) The interval $[4, \infty)$ denotes the set of all real numbers greater than or equal to 4.

(b)

(c) The interval is unbounded.

21. (a) The inequality $-2 < x < 2$ denotes the set of all real numbers greater than -2 and less than 2.

(b)

(c) The interval is bounded.

23. (a) The interval $[-5, 2)$ denotes the set of all real numbers greater than or equal to -5 and less than 2.

(b)

(c) The interval is bounded.

25. $y \ge 0; [0, \infty)$

27. $10 \le t \le 22; [10, 22]$

29. $W > 65; (65, \infty)$

31. $|-10| = -(-10) = 10$

33. $|3 - 8| = |-5| = -(-5) = 5$

35. $|-1| - |-2| = 1 - 2 = -1$

37. $\dfrac{-5}{|-5|} = \dfrac{-5}{-(-5)} = \dfrac{-5}{5} = -1$

39. If $x < -2$, then $x + 2$ is negative.

So, $\dfrac{|x + 2|}{x + 2} = \dfrac{-(x + 2)}{x + 2} = -1$.

41. $|-4| = |4|$ because $|-4| = 4$ and $|4| = 4$.

43. $-|-6| < |-6|$ because $|-6| = 6$ and $-|-6| = -(6) = -6$.

45. $d(126, 75) = |75 - 126| = 51$

47. $d\left(-\frac{5}{2}, 0\right) = \left|0 - \left(-\frac{5}{2}\right)\right| = \frac{5}{2}$

502

49. $d\left(\frac{16}{5}, \frac{112}{75}\right) = \left|\frac{112}{75} - \frac{16}{5}\right| = \frac{128}{75}$

53. $d(y, a) = |y - a|$ and $d(y, a) \le 2$, so $|y - a| \le 2$.

51. $d(x, 5) = |x - 5|$ and $d(x, 5) \le 3$, so $|x - 5| \le 3$.

Receipts, R	Expenditures, E	$|R - E|$
55. $1880.1	$2292.8	$|1880.1 - 2292.8| = \$412.7$ billion
57. $2524.0	$2982.5	$|2524.0 - 2982.5| = \$458.5$ billion

59. $7x + 4$

Terms: $7x, 4$

Coefficient: 7

61. $4x^3 + \frac{x}{2} - 5$

Terms: $4x^3, \frac{x}{2}, -5$

Coefficients: $4, \frac{1}{2}$

63. $4x - 6$

(a) $4(-1) - 6 = -4 - 6 = -10$

(b) $4(0) - 6 = 0 - 6 = -6$

65. $-x^2 + 5x - 4$

(a) $-(-1)^2 + 5(-1) - 4 = -1 - 5 - 4 = -10$

(b) $-(1)^2 + 5(1) - 4 = -1 + 5 - 4 = 0$

67. $\frac{1}{(h + 6)}(h + 6) = 1, h \ne -6$

Multiplicative Inverse Property

69. $2(x + 3) = 2 \cdot x + 2 \cdot 3$

Distributive Property

71. $x(3y) = (x \cdot 3)y$ Associative Property of Multiplication

$= (3x)y$ Commutative Property of Multiplication

73. $\frac{5}{8} - \frac{5}{12} + \frac{1}{6} = \frac{15}{24} - \frac{10}{24} + \frac{4}{24} = \frac{9}{24} = \frac{3}{8}$

75. $\frac{2x}{3} - \frac{x}{4} = \frac{8x}{12} - \frac{3x}{12} = \frac{5x}{12}$

77. (a) Because $A > 0, -A < 0$.

The expression is negative.

(b) Because $B < A, B - A < 0$.

The expression is negative.

(c) Because $C < 0, -C > 0$.

The expression is positive.

(d) Because $A > C, A - C > 0$.

The expression is positive.

79. False. Because 0 is nonnegative but not positive, not every nonnegative number is positive.

81. (a)

n	0.0001	0.01	1	100	10,000
$5/n$	50,000	500	5	0.05	0.0005

(b) (i) As n approaches 0, the value of $5/n$ increases without bound (approaches infinity).

(ii) As n increases without bound (approaches infinity), the value of $5/n$ approaches 0.

Appendix A.2   Exponents and Radicals

1. exponent; base

3. square root

5. like radicals

7. rationalizing

9. (a) $3 \cdot 3^3 = 3^4 = 81$

(b) $\frac{3^2}{3^4} = 3^{-2} = \frac{1}{3^2} = \frac{1}{9}$

11. (a) $\left(2^3 \cdot 3^2\right)^2 = 2^{3\cdot2} \cdot 3^{2\cdot2}$

$$= 2^6 \cdot 3^4 = 64 \cdot 81 = 5184$$

(b) $\left(-\dfrac{3}{5}\right)^3\left(\dfrac{5}{3}\right)^2 = (-1)^3\dfrac{3^3}{5^3} \cdot \dfrac{5^2}{3^2} = -1 \cdot 3^{3-2} \cdot 5^{2-3}$

$$= -3 \cdot 5^{-1} = -\dfrac{3}{5}$$

13. (a) $\dfrac{4 \cdot 3^{-2}}{2^{-2} \cdot 3^{-1}} = 4 \cdot 2^2 \cdot 3^{-2-(-1)} = 4 \cdot 4 \cdot 3^{-1} = \dfrac{16}{3}$

(b) $(-2)^0 = 1$

15. When $x = 2$,

$$-3x^3 = -3(2)^3 = -24.$$

17. When $x = 10$,

$$6x^0 = 6(10)^0 = 6(1) = 6.$$

19. When $x = -2$,

$$-3x^4 = -3(-2)^4 = -3(16) = -48.$$

21. (a) $(-5z)^3 = (-5)^3z^3 = -125z^3$

(b) $5x^4\left(x^2\right) = 5x^{4+2} = 5x^6$

23. (a) $6y^2\left(2y^0\right)^2 = 6y^2(2 \cdot 1)^2 = 6y^2(4) = 24y^2$

(b) $(-z)^3\left(3z^4\right) = (-1)^3\left(z^3\right)3z^4$

$$= -1 \cdot 3 \cdot z^{3+4} = -3z^7$$

25. (a) $\left(\dfrac{4}{y}\right)^3\left(\dfrac{3}{y}\right)^4 = \dfrac{4^3}{y^3} \cdot \dfrac{3^4}{y^4} = \dfrac{64 \cdot 81}{y^{3+4}} = \dfrac{5184}{y^7}$

(b) $\left(\dfrac{b^{-2}}{a^{-2}}\right)\left(\dfrac{b}{a}\right)^2 = \left(\dfrac{a^2}{b^2}\right)\left(\dfrac{b^2}{a^2}\right) = 1, a \neq 0, b \neq 0$

27. (a) $(x + 5)^0 = 1, x \neq -5$

(b) $\left(2x^2\right)^{-2} = \dfrac{1}{\left(2x^2\right)^2} = \dfrac{1}{4x^4}$

29. (a) $\left(\dfrac{x^{-3}y^4}{5}\right)^{-3} = \left(\dfrac{5x^3}{y^4}\right)^3 = \dfrac{125x^4}{y^{12}}$

(b) $\left(\dfrac{a^{-2}}{b^{-2}}\right)\left(\dfrac{b}{a}\right)^3 = \left(\dfrac{b^2}{a^2}\right)\left(\dfrac{b^3}{a^3}\right) = \dfrac{b^5}{a^5}$

31. $10{,}250.4 = 1.02504 \times 10^4$

33. $0.00003937 = 3.937 \times 10^{-5}$ inch

35. $-1.801 \times 10^5 = -180{,}100$

37. $9.46 \times 10^{12} = 9{,}460{,}000{,}000{,}000$ kilometers

39. (a) $\left(2.0 \times 10^9\right)\left(3.4 \times 10^{-4}\right) = 6.8 \times 10^5$

(b) $\left(1.2 \times 10^7\right)\left(5.0 \times 10^{-3}\right) = 6.0 \times 10^4$

41. (a) $\sqrt{9} = 3$

(b) $\sqrt[3]{\dfrac{27}{8}} = \dfrac{\sqrt[3]{27}}{\sqrt[3]{8}} = \dfrac{3}{2}$

43. (a) $\left(\sqrt[5]{2}\right)^5 = 2^{5/5} = 2^1 = 2$

(b) $\sqrt[5]{32x^5} = \sqrt[5]{(2x)^5} = 2x$

45. (a) $\sqrt{20} = \sqrt{4 \cdot 5}$

$$= \sqrt{4}\sqrt{5} = 2\sqrt{5}$$

(b) $\sqrt[3]{128} = \sqrt[3]{64 \cdot 2}$

$$= \sqrt[3]{64}\sqrt[3]{2} = 4\sqrt[3]{2}$$

47. (a) $\sqrt{72x^3} = \sqrt{36x^2 \cdot 2x}$

$$= 6x\sqrt{2x}$$

(b) $\sqrt{\dfrac{18^2}{z^3}} = \dfrac{\sqrt{18^2}}{\sqrt{z^2 \cdot z}} = \dfrac{18}{z\sqrt{z}} = \dfrac{18\sqrt{z}}{z^2}$

49. (a) $\sqrt[3]{16x^5} = \sqrt[3]{8x^3 \cdot 2x^2}$

$$= 2x\sqrt[3]{2x^2}$$

(b) $\sqrt{75x^2y^{-4}} = \sqrt{\dfrac{75x^2}{y^4}}$

$$= \dfrac{\sqrt{25x^2 \cdot 3}}{\sqrt{y^4}}$$

$$= \dfrac{5|x|\sqrt{3}}{y^2}$$

51. (a) $10\sqrt{32} - 6\sqrt{18} = 10\sqrt{16 \cdot 2} - 6\sqrt{9 \cdot 2}$

$$= 10\left(4\sqrt{2}\right) - 6\left(3\sqrt{2}\right)$$

$$= 40\sqrt{2} - 18\sqrt{2}$$

$$= 22\sqrt{2}$$

(b) $\sqrt[3]{16} + 3\sqrt[3]{54} = \sqrt[3]{2 \cdot 2^3} + 3\sqrt[3]{2 \cdot 3^3}$

$$= 2\sqrt[3]{2} + 3 \cdot \left(3\sqrt[3]{2}\right)$$

$$= 2\sqrt[3]{2} + 9\sqrt[3]{2}$$

$$= 11\sqrt[3]{2}$$

53. (a) $-3\sqrt{48x^2} + 7\sqrt{75x^2} = -3\sqrt{3 \cdot 4^2 \cdot x^2} + 7\sqrt{3 \cdot 5^2 \cdot x^2}$

$$= -3 \cdot \left(4|x|\sqrt{3}\right) + 7 \cdot \left(5|x|\sqrt{3}\right)$$

$$= -12|x|\sqrt{3} + 35|x|\sqrt{3} = 23|x|\sqrt{3}$$

(b) $7\sqrt{80x} - 2\sqrt{125x} = 7\sqrt{16 \cdot 5x} - 2\sqrt{25 \cdot 5x} = 7\left(4\sqrt{5x}\right) - 2\left(5\sqrt{5x}\right) = 28\sqrt{5x} - 10\sqrt{5x} - 18\sqrt{5x}$

55. $\dfrac{1}{\sqrt{3}} = \dfrac{1}{\sqrt{3}} \cdot \dfrac{\sqrt{3}}{\sqrt{3}} = \dfrac{\sqrt{3}}{3}$

57. $\dfrac{5}{\sqrt{14} - 2} = \dfrac{5}{\sqrt{14} - 2} \cdot \dfrac{\sqrt{14} + 2}{\sqrt{14} + 2} = \dfrac{5\left(\sqrt{14} + 2\right)}{\left(\sqrt{14}\right)^2 - (2)^2} = \dfrac{5\left(\sqrt{14} + 2\right)}{14 - 4} = \dfrac{5\left(\sqrt{14} + 2\right)}{10} = \dfrac{\sqrt{14} + 2}{2}$

59. $\dfrac{\sqrt{8}}{2} = \dfrac{\sqrt{4 \cdot 2}}{2} = \dfrac{2\sqrt{2}}{2} = \dfrac{\sqrt{2}}{1} \cdot \dfrac{\sqrt{2}}{\sqrt{2}} = \dfrac{2}{\sqrt{2}}$

61. $\dfrac{\sqrt{5} + \sqrt{3}}{3} = \dfrac{\sqrt{5} + \sqrt{3}}{3} \cdot \dfrac{\sqrt{5} - \sqrt{3}}{\sqrt{5} - \sqrt{3}} = \dfrac{5 - 3}{3\left(\sqrt{5} - \sqrt{3}\right)} = \dfrac{2}{3\left(\sqrt{5} - \sqrt{3}\right)}$

63. $\sqrt[3]{64} = 4$, Given $64^{1/3} = 4$, Answer

Radical Form	**Rational Exponent Form**
65. $\dfrac{3}{\sqrt[3]{x^2}}, x \neq 0$	$3x^{-2/3} = \dfrac{3}{x^{2/3}}$

67. $x\sqrt{3xy}$, Given $x \cdot 3^{1/2} x^{1/2} y^{1/2} = 3^{1/2} x^{3/2} y^{1/2}$, Answer

69. (a) $32^{-3/5} = \dfrac{1}{32^{3/5}} = \dfrac{1}{\left(\sqrt[5]{32}\right)^3} = \dfrac{1}{(2)^3} = \dfrac{1}{8}$

(b) $\left(\dfrac{16}{81}\right)^{-3/4} = \left(\dfrac{81}{16}\right)^{3/4} = \left(\sqrt[4]{\dfrac{81}{16}}\right)^3 = \left(\dfrac{3}{2}\right)^3 = \dfrac{27}{8}$

71. (a) $\dfrac{\left(2x^2\right)^{3/2}}{2^{1/2} x^4} = \dfrac{2^{3/2}\left(x^2\right)^{3/2}}{2^{1/2} x^4}$

$$= \dfrac{2^{3/2}|x|^3}{2^{1/2} x^4} = 2^{3/2 - 1/2}|x|^{3-4} = 2^1|x|^{-1} = \dfrac{2}{|x|}$$

(b) $\dfrac{x^{4/3} y^{2/3}}{(xy)^{1/3}} = \dfrac{x^{4/3} y^{2/3}}{x^{1/3} y^{1/3}} = x^{3/3} y^{1/3} = xy^{1/3}$

73. (a) $\sqrt[4]{3^2} = 3^{2/4} = 3^{1/2} = \sqrt{3}$

(b) $\sqrt[6]{(x + 1)^4} = (x + 1)^{4/6} = (x + 1)^{2/3} = \sqrt[3]{(x + 1)^2}$

75. (a) $\sqrt{\sqrt{32}} = \left(32^{1/2}\right)^{1/2}$

$$= 32^{1/4} = \sqrt[4]{32} = \sqrt[4]{16 \cdot 2} = 2\sqrt[4]{2}$$

(b) $\sqrt{\sqrt[4]{2x}} = \left((2x)^{1/4}\right)^{1/2} = (2x)^{1/8} = \sqrt[8]{2x}$

77. (a) $(x - 1)^{1/3}(x - 1)^{2/3} = (x - 1)^{3/3} = (x - 1)$

(b) $(x - 1)^{1/3}(x - 1)^{-4/3} = (x - 1)^{-3/3} = (x - 1)^{-1} = \dfrac{1}{x - 1}$

79. $t = 0.03\left[12^{5/2} - (12 - h)^{5/2}\right], 0 \le h \le 12$

(a)

h (in centimeters)	t (in seconds)
0	0
1	2.93
2	5.48
3	7.67
4	9.53
5	11.08
6	12.32
7	13.29
8	14.00
9	14.50
10	14.80
11	14.93
12	14.96

(b) As h approaches 12, t approaches
$0.03\left(12^{5/2}\right) = 8.64\sqrt{3} = 14.96$ seconds.

81. True. When dividing variables, you subtract exponents.

83. False. When a sum is raised to a power, you multiply the sum by itself using the Distributive Property.

$(a + b)^2 = a^2 + 2ab + b^2 \ne a^2 + b^2$

Appendix A.3   Polynomials and Factoring

1. n; a_n; a_0

3. like terms

5. factoring

7. perfect square binomial

9. (a) Standard form: $-\frac{1}{2}x^5 + 14x$

    (b) Degree: 5
        Leading coefficient: $-\frac{1}{2}$

    (c) Binomial

11. (a) Standard form: $-x^6 + 3$

    (b) Degree: 6
        Leading coefficient: -1

    (c) Binomial

13. (a) Standard form: 3

    (b) Degree: 0
        Leading coefficient: 3

    (c) Monomial

15. (a) Standard form: $-4x^5 + 6x^4 + 1$

    (b) Degree: 5
        Leading coefficient: -4

    (c) Trinomial

17. (a) Standard form: $4x^3y$

    (b) Degree: 4 (add the exponents on x and y)
        Leading coefficient: 4

    (c) Monomial

19. $(6x + 5) - (8x + 15) = 6x + 5 - 8x - 15$
$$= (6x - 8x) + (5 - 15)$$
$$= -2x - 10$$

21. $\left(15x^2 - 6\right) - \left(-8.3x^3 - 14.7x^2 - 17\right) = 15x^2 - 6 + 8.3x^3 + 14.7x^2 + 17$
$$= 8.3x^3 + \left(15x^2 + 14.7x^2\right) + (-6 + 17)$$
$$= 8.3x^3 + 29.7x^2 + 11$$

23. $3x(x^2 - 2x + 1) = 3x(x^2) + 3x(-2x) + 3x(1)$

$$= 3x^3 - 6x^2 + 3x$$

25. $-5z(3z - 1) = -5z(3z) + (-5z)(-1)$

$$= -15z^2 + 5z$$

27. $(x + 3)(x + 4) = x^2 + 4x + 3x + 12$ FOIL

$$= x^2 + 7x + 12$$

29. $(x^2 - x + 1)(x^2 + x + 1)$

Multiply: $x^2 - x + 1$

         $x^2 + x + 1$

          $\overline{x^4 - x^3 + x^2}$

             $x^3 - x^2 + x$

                $x^2 - x + 1$

$$\overline{x^4 - 0x^3 + x^2 + 0x + 1} = x^4 + x^2 + 1$$

31. $(x + 10)(x - 10) = x^2 - 10^2 = x^2 - 100$

33. $(2x + 3)^2 = (2x)^2 + 2(2x)(3) + 3^2$

$$= 4x^2 + 12x + 9$$

35. $(x + 1)^3 = x^3 + 3x^2(1) + 3x(1^2) + 1^3$

$$= x^3 + 3x^2 + 3x + 1$$

37. $[(m - 3) + n][(m - 3) - n] = (m - 3)^2 - (n)^2$

$$= m^2 - 6m + 9 - n^2$$

$$= m^2 - n^2 - 6m + 9$$

39. $[(x - 3) + y]^2 = (x - 3)^2 + 2y(x - 3) + y^2$

$$= x^2 - 6x + 9 + 2xy - 6y + y^2$$

$$= x^2 + 2xy + y^2 - 6x - 6y + 9$$

41. $2x^3 - 6x = 2x(x^2 - 3)$

43. $3x(x - 5) + 8(x - 5) = (x - 5)(3x + 8)$

45. $\frac{1}{2}x^3 + 2x^2 - 5x = \frac{1}{2}x^3 + \frac{4}{2}x^2 - \frac{10}{2}x$

$$= \frac{1}{2}x(x^2 + 4x - 10)$$

47. $\frac{2}{3}x(x - 3) - 4(x - 3) = \frac{2}{3}x(x - 3) - \frac{12}{3}(x - 3)$

$$= \frac{2}{3}(x - 3)(x - 6)$$

49. $x^2 - 81 = x^2 - 9^2 = (x + 9)(x - 9)$

51. $(x - 1)^2 - 4 = (x - 1)^2 - (2)^2$

$$= [(x - 1) + 2][(x - 1) - 2]$$

$$= (x + 1)(x - 3)$$

53. $x^2 - 4x + 4 = x^2 - 2(2)x + 2^2 = (x - 2)^2$

55. $9u^2 + 24uv + 16v^2 = (3u)^2 + 2(3u)(4v) + (4v)^2$

$$= (3u + 4v)^2$$

57. $z^2 + z + \frac{1}{4} = z^2 + 2(z)\left(\frac{1}{2}\right) + \left(\frac{1}{2}\right)^2 = \left(z + \frac{1}{2}\right)^2$

59. $x^3 - 8 = x^3 - 2^3 = (x - 2)(x^2 + 2x + 4)$

61. $27x^3 + 8 = (3x)^3 + 2^3 = (3x + 2)(9x^2 - 6x + 4)$

63. $x^2 + x - 2 = (x + 2)(x - 1)$

65. $20 - y - y^2 = -(y^2 + y - 20) = -(y + 5)(y - 4)$

67. $3x^2 - 5x + 2 = (3x - 2)(x - 1)$

69. $5x^2 + 26x + 5 = (5x + 1)(x + 5)$

71. $x^3 - x^2 + 2x - 2 = x^2(x - 1) + 2(x - 1)$

$$= (x - 1)(x^2 + 2)$$

73. $2x^3 - x^2 - 6x + 3 = x^2(2x - 1) - 3(2x - 1)$

$$= (2x - 1)(x^2 - 3)$$

75. $x^5 + 2x^3 + x^2 + 2 = x^3(x^2 + 2) + (x^2 + 2)$

$$= (x^2 + 2)(x^3 + 1)$$

$$= (x^2 + 2)(x + 1)(x^2 - x + 1)$$

77. $a \cdot c = (2)(9) - 18$. Rewrite the middle term,

$9x = 6x + 3x$, because $(6)(3) = 18$ and $6 + 3 = 9$.

$2x^2 + 9x + 9 = 2x^2 + 6x + 3x + 9$

$$= 2x(x + 3) + 3(x + 3)$$

$$= (x + 3)(2x + 3)$$

79. $a \cdot c = (6)(-15) = -90$. Rewrite the middle term,

$-x = -10x + 9x$, because $(-10)(9) = -90$ and

$-10 + 9 = -1$.

$$6x^2 - x - 15 = 6x^2 - 10x + 9x - 15$$
$$= 2x(3x - 5) + 3(3x - 5)$$
$$= (2x + 3)(3x - 5)$$

81. $6x^2 - 54 = 6(x^2 - 9) = 6(x + 3)(x - 3)$

83. $x^3 - x^2 = x^2(x - 1)$

85. $x^2 - 2x + 1 = (x - 1)^2$

87. $2x^2 + 4x - 2x^3 = -2x(-x - 2 + x^2)$
$$= -2x(x^2 - x - 2)$$
$$= -2x(x + 1)(x - 2)$$

89. $5 - x + 5x^2 - x^3 = 1(5 - x) + x^2(5 - x)$
$$= (5 - x)(1 + x^2)$$

91. $5(3 - 4x)^2 - 8(3 - 4x)(5x - 1) = (3 - 4x)[5(3 - 4x) - 8(5x - 1)]$
$$= (3 - 4x)[15 - 20x - 40x + 8]$$
$$= (3 - 4x)(23 - 60x)$$

93. $x^4(4)(2x + 1)^3(2x) + (2x + 1)^4(4x^3) = 2x^3(2x + 1)^3[4x^2 + 2(2x + 1)]$
$$= 2x^3(2x + 1)^3(4x^2 + 4x + 2)$$
$$= 4x^3(2x + 1)^3(2x^2 + 2x + 1)$$

95. (a) $V = \pi R^2 h - \pi r^2 h$
$$= \pi h(R^2 - r^2)$$
$$= \pi h(R + r)(R - r)$$

(b) Let w = thickness of the shell and let p = average radius of the shell.

So, $R = p + \dfrac{1}{2}w$ and $r = p - \dfrac{1}{2}w$

$V = \pi h(R + r)(R - r)$

$$= \pi h\left[\left(p + \frac{1}{2}w\right) + \left(p - \frac{1}{2}w\right)\right]\left[\left(p + \frac{1}{2}w\right) - \left(p - \frac{1}{2}w\right)\right]$$
$$= \pi h(2p)(w)$$
$$= 2\pi pwh$$
$$= 2\pi(\text{average radius})(\text{thickness of shell})\, h$$

97. False. $(4x^2 + 1)(3x + 1) = 12x^3 + 4x^2 + 3x + 1$

99. True. $a^2 - b^2 = (a + b)(a - b)$

101. Because $x^m x^n = x^{m+n}$, the degree of the product is $m + n$.

103. The unknown polynomial may be found by adding $-x^3 + 3x^2 + 2x - 1$ and $5x^2 + 8$:

$$\left(-x^3 + 3x^2 + 2x - 1\right) + \left(5x^2 + 8\right) = -x^3 + \left(3x^2 + 5x^2\right) + 2x + (-1 + 8)$$
$$= -x^3 + 8x^2 + 2x + 7$$

105. $x^2 + 3x + 2 = (x + 2)(x + 1)$

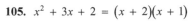
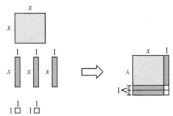

107. $x^{2n} - y^{2n} = \left(x^n\right)^2 - \left(y^n\right)^2 = \left(x^n + y^n\right)\left(x^n - y^n\right)$

This is not completely factored unless $n = 1$.

For $n = 2$: $\left(x^2 + y^2\right)\left(x^2 - y^2\right) = \left(x^2 + y^2\right)(x + y)(x - y)$

For $n = 3$: $\left(x^3 + y^3\right)\left(x^3 - y^3\right) = (x + y)\left(x^2 - xy + y^2\right)(x - y)\left(x^2 + xy + y^2\right)$

For $n = 4$: $\left(x^4 + y^4\right)\left(x^4 - y^4\right) = \left(x^4 + y^4\right)\left(x^2 + y^2\right)(x + y)(x - y)$

Appendix A.4   Rational Expressions

1. domain

3. complex

5. The domain of the polynomial $3x^2 - 4x + 7$ is the set of all real numbers.

7. The domain of $\dfrac{1}{3 - x}$ is the set of all real numbers x such that $x \neq 3$.

9. The domain of $\dfrac{x^2 - 1}{x^2 - 2x + 1} = \dfrac{(x + 1)(x - 1)}{(x - 1)(x - 1)}$ is the set of all real numbers x such that $x \neq 1$.

11. The domain of $\dfrac{x^2 - 2x - 3}{x^2 - 6x + 9} = \dfrac{(x - 3)(x + 1)}{(x - 3)(x - 3)}$ is the set of all real numbers x such that $x \neq 3$.

13. The domain of $\sqrt{4 - x}$ is the set of all real numbers x such that $x \leq 4$.

15. The domain of $\dfrac{1}{\sqrt{x - 3}}$ is the set of all real numbers x such that $x > 3$.

17. $\dfrac{15x^2}{10x} = \dfrac{5x(3x)}{5x(2)} = \dfrac{3x}{2}, x \neq 0$

19. $\dfrac{3xy}{xy + x} = \dfrac{x(3y)}{x(y + 1)} = \dfrac{3y}{y + 1}, x \neq 0$

21. $\dfrac{x - 5}{10 - 2x} = \dfrac{x - 5}{-2(x - 5)}$

$= -\dfrac{1}{2}, x \neq 5$

23. $\dfrac{y^2 - 16}{y + 4} = \dfrac{(y + 4)(y - 4)}{y + 4}$

$= y - 4, y \neq -4$

25. $\dfrac{x^3 + 5x^2 + 6x}{x^2 - 4} = \dfrac{x(x + 2)(x + 3)}{(x + 2)(x - 2)} = \dfrac{x(x + 3)}{x - 2}, x \neq -2$

27. $\dfrac{2 - x + 2x^2 - x^3}{x^2 - 4} = \dfrac{(2 - x) + x^2(2 - x)}{(x + 2)(x - 2)}$

$= \dfrac{(2 - x)\left(1 + x^2\right)}{(x + 2)(x - 2)}$

$= \dfrac{-(x - 2)\left(x^2 + 1\right)}{(x + 2)(x - 2)}$

$= -\dfrac{x^2 + 1}{x + 2}, x \neq 2$

29. $\dfrac{z^3 - 8}{z^2 + 2z + 4} = \dfrac{(z - 2)\left(z^2 + 2z + 4\right)}{z^2 + 2z + 4} = z - 2$

31. $\dfrac{5x^3}{2x^3 + 4} = \dfrac{5x^3}{2\left(x^3 + 2\right)}$

There are no common factors so this expression cannot be simplified. In this case, factors of terms were incorrectly cancelled.

33. $\dfrac{5}{x-1} \cdot \dfrac{x-1}{25(x-2)} = \dfrac{1}{5(x-2)}, \; x \neq 1$

35. $\dfrac{4y-16}{5y+15} \div \dfrac{4-y}{2y+6} = \dfrac{4y-16}{5y+15} \cdot \dfrac{2y+6}{4-y} = \dfrac{4(y-4)}{5(y+3)} \cdot \dfrac{2(y+3)}{(-1)(y-4)}$

$$= \dfrac{8}{-5} = -\dfrac{8}{5}, \; y \neq -3, 4$$

37. $\dfrac{x^2+xy-2y^2}{x^3+x^2y} \cdot \dfrac{x}{x^2+3xy+2y^2} = \dfrac{(x+2y)(x-y)}{x^2(x+y)} \cdot \dfrac{x}{(x+2y)(x+y)} = \dfrac{x-y}{x(x+y)^2}, \; x \neq -2y$

39. $\dfrac{x^2-14x+49}{x^2-49} \div \dfrac{3x-21}{x+7} = \dfrac{(x-7)(x-7)}{(x+7)(x-7)} \cdot \dfrac{x+7}{3(x-7)}$

$$= \dfrac{1}{3}, \; x \neq \pm 7$$

41. $\dfrac{3}{x-2} + \dfrac{5}{2-x} = \dfrac{3}{x-2} - \dfrac{5}{x-2} = -\dfrac{2}{x-2}$

43. $\dfrac{4}{2x+1} - \dfrac{x}{x+2} = \dfrac{4(x+2)}{(2x+1)(x+2)} - \dfrac{x(2x+1)}{(x+2)(2x+1)}$

$$= \dfrac{4x+8-2x^2-x}{(x+2)(2x+1)}$$

$$= \dfrac{-2x^2+3x+8}{(x+2)(2x+1)}$$

45. $-\dfrac{1}{x} + \dfrac{2}{x^2+1} + \dfrac{1}{x^3+x} = \dfrac{-(x^2+1)}{x(x^2+1)} + \dfrac{2x}{x(x^2+1)} + \dfrac{1}{x(x^2+1)}$

$$= \dfrac{-x^2-1+2x+1}{x(x^2+1)} = \dfrac{-x^2+2x}{x(x^2+1)} = \dfrac{-x(x-2)}{x(x^2+1)}$$

$$= -\dfrac{x-2}{x^2+1} = \dfrac{2-x}{x^2+1}, \; x \neq 0$$

47. $\dfrac{x+4}{x+2} - \dfrac{3x-8}{x+2} = \dfrac{(x+4)-(3x-8)}{x+2}$

$$= \dfrac{x+4-3x+8}{x+2} = \dfrac{-2x+12}{x+2} = \dfrac{-2(x-6)}{x+2}$$

The error was incorrect subtraction in the numerator.

49. $\dfrac{\left(\dfrac{x}{2}-1\right)}{(x-2)} = \dfrac{\left(\dfrac{x}{2}-\dfrac{2}{2}\right)}{\left(\dfrac{x-2}{1}\right)}$

$$= \dfrac{x-2}{2} \cdot \dfrac{1}{x-2}$$

$$= \dfrac{1}{2}, \; x \neq 2$$

51. $\dfrac{\left[\dfrac{x^2}{(x+1)^2}\right]}{\left[\dfrac{x}{(x+1)^3}\right]} = \dfrac{x^2}{(x+1)^2} \cdot \dfrac{(x+1)^3}{x}$

$$= x(x+1), \; x \neq -1, 0$$

53. $\dfrac{\left(\sqrt{x}-\dfrac{1}{2\sqrt{x}}\right)}{\sqrt{x}} = \dfrac{\left(\sqrt{x}-\dfrac{1}{2\sqrt{x}}\right)}{\sqrt{x}} \cdot \dfrac{2\sqrt{x}}{2\sqrt{x}}$

$$= \dfrac{2x-1}{2x}, \; x > 0$$

55. $x^5 - 2x^{-2} = x^{-2}(x^7-2) = \dfrac{x^7-2}{x^2}$

57. $x^2(x^2+1)^{-5} - (x^2+1)^{-4} = (x^2+1)^{-5}\left[x^2-(x^2+1)\right]$

$$= -\dfrac{1}{(x^2+1)^5}$$

59. $2x^2(x-1)^{1/2} - 5(x-1)^{-1/2} = (x-1)^{-1/2}\left[2x^2(x-1)^1 - 5\right] = \dfrac{2x^3-2x^2-5}{(x-1)^{1/2}}$

61. $\dfrac{3x^{1/3} - x^{-2/3}}{3x^{-2/3}} = \dfrac{3x^{1/3} - x^{-2/3}}{3x^{-2/3}} \cdot \dfrac{x^{2/3}}{x^{2/3}} = \dfrac{3x^1 - x^0}{3x^0} = \dfrac{3x - 1}{3}, \; x \neq 0$

63. $\dfrac{\left(\dfrac{1}{x+h} - \dfrac{1}{x}\right)}{h} = \dfrac{\left(\dfrac{1}{x+h} - \dfrac{1}{x}\right)}{h} \cdot \dfrac{x(x+h)}{x(x+h)} = \dfrac{x - (x+h)}{hx(x+h)} = \dfrac{-h}{hx(x+h)} = -\dfrac{1}{x(x+h)}, \; h \neq 0$

65. $\dfrac{\left(\dfrac{1}{x+h-4} - \dfrac{1}{x-4}\right)}{h} = \dfrac{\left(\dfrac{1}{x+h-4} - \dfrac{1}{x-4}\right)}{h} \cdot \dfrac{(x-4)(x+h-4)}{(x-4)(x+h-4)}$

$$= \dfrac{(x-4) - (x+h-4)}{h(x-4)(x+h-4)}$$

$$= \dfrac{-h}{h(x-4)(x+h-4)}$$

$$= -\dfrac{1}{(x-4)(x+h-4)}, \; h \neq 0$$

67. $\dfrac{\sqrt{x+2} - \sqrt{x}}{2} = \dfrac{\sqrt{x+2} - \sqrt{x}}{2} \cdot \dfrac{\sqrt{x+2} + \sqrt{x}}{\sqrt{x+2} + \sqrt{x}} = \dfrac{(x+2) - x}{2\left(\sqrt{x+2} + \sqrt{x}\right)} = \dfrac{2}{2\left(\sqrt{x+2} + \sqrt{x}\right)} = \dfrac{1}{\sqrt{x+2} + \sqrt{x}}$

69. $\dfrac{\sqrt{t+3} - \sqrt{3}}{t} = \dfrac{\sqrt{t+3} - \sqrt{3}}{t} \cdot \dfrac{\sqrt{t+3} + \sqrt{3}}{\sqrt{t+3} + \sqrt{3}}$

$$= \dfrac{(t+3) - 3}{t\left(\sqrt{t+3} + \sqrt{3}\right)}$$

$$= \dfrac{t}{t\left(\sqrt{t+3} + \sqrt{3}\right)}$$

$$= \dfrac{1}{\sqrt{t+3} + \sqrt{3}}$$

71. $\dfrac{\sqrt{x+h+1} - \sqrt{x+1}}{h} = \dfrac{\sqrt{x+h+1} - \sqrt{x+1}}{h} \cdot \dfrac{\sqrt{x+h+1} + \sqrt{x+1}}{\sqrt{x+h+1} + \sqrt{x+1}}$

$$= \dfrac{(x+h+1) - (x+1)}{h\left(\sqrt{x+h+1} + \sqrt{x+1}\right)}$$

$$= \dfrac{h}{h\left(\sqrt{x+h+1} + \sqrt{x+1}\right)}$$

$$= \dfrac{1}{\sqrt{x+h+1} + \sqrt{x+1}}, \; h \neq 0$$

73. $T = 10\left(\dfrac{4t^2 + 16t + 75}{t^2 + 4t + 10}\right)$

(a)

t	0	2	4	6	8	10	12	14	16	18	20	22
T	75°	55.9°	48.3°	45°	43.3°	42.3°	41.7°	41.3°	41.1°	40.9°	40.7°	40.6°

(b) T is approaching 40°.

75. Probability $= \dfrac{\text{Shaded area}}{\text{Total area}} = \dfrac{x(x/2)}{x(2x+1)} = \dfrac{x/2}{2x+1} \cdot \dfrac{2}{2} = \dfrac{x}{2(2x+1)}$

77. (a)

Year	Banking using model (in millions)	Paying Bills using model (in millions)
2005	46.9	17
2006	57.6	25.6
2007	63.5	27.3
2008	67.3	28.8
2009	69.9	30.8
2010	71.9	33.7

(b) The values given by the models are close to the actual data.

(c) $\dfrac{\text{Number of households paying bills online}}{\text{Number of households banking online}}$

$$= \frac{\dfrac{0.307t^2 - 6.54t + 24.6}{0.015t^2 - 0.28t + 1.0}}{\dfrac{-33.74t + 121.8}{-0.40t + 1.0}}$$

$$= \frac{0.307t^2 - 6.54t + 24.6}{0.015t^2 - 0.28t + 1.0} \cdot \frac{-0.40t + 1.0}{-33.74t + 121.8}$$

$$= \frac{(0.307t^2 - 6.54t + 24.6)(-0.40t + 1.0)}{(0.015t^2 - 0.28t + 1.0)(-33.74t + 121.8)}$$

(d) When $t = 5$,

$$\frac{\left[0.307(5)^2 - 6.54(5) + 24.6\right]\left[-0.40(5) + 1.0\right]}{\left[0.015(5)^2 - 0.28(5) + 1.0\right]\left[-33.74(5) + 121.8\right]} \approx 0.362$$

When $t = 6$,

$$\frac{\left[0.307(6)^2 - 6.54(6) + 24.6\right]\left[-0.40(6) + 1.0\right]}{\left[0.015(6)^2 - 0.28(6) + 1.0\right]\left[-33.74(6) + 121.8\right]} \approx 0.445$$

When $t = 7$,

$$\frac{\left[0.307(7)^2 - 6.54(7) + 24.6\right]\left[-0.40(7) + 1.0\right]}{\left[0.015(7)^2 - 0.28(7) + 1.0\right]\left[-33.74(7) + 121.8\right]} \approx 0.429$$

When $t = 8$,

$$\frac{\left[0.307(8)^2 - 6.54(8) + 24.6\right]\left[-0.40(8) + 1.0\right]}{\left[0.015(8)^2 - 0.28(8) + 1.0\right]\left[-33.74(8) + 121.8\right]} \approx 0.428$$

When $t = 9$,

$$\frac{\left[0.307(9)^2 - 6.54(9) + 24.6\right]\left[-0.40(9) + 1.0\right]}{\left[0.015(9)^2 - 0.28(9) + 1.0\right]\left[-33.74(9) + 121.8\right]} \approx 0.440$$

When $t = 10$,

$$\frac{\left[0.307(10)^2 - 6.54(10) + 24.6\right]\left[-0.40(10) + 1.0\right]}{\left[0.015(10)^2 - 0.28(10) + 1.0\right]\left[-33.74(10) + 121.8\right]} \approx 0.468$$

For each year, the ratio is about the same.

79. $R_T = \dfrac{1}{\dfrac{1}{R_1} + \dfrac{1}{R_2}}$

$= \dfrac{1}{\dfrac{R_2 + R_1}{R_1 R_2}}$

$= \dfrac{R_1 R_2}{R_1 + R_2}$

81. False. In order for the simplified expression to be equivalent to the original expression, the domain of the simplified expression needs to be restricted. If n is even, $x \neq \pm 1$. If n is odd, $x \neq 1$.

Appendix A.5   Solving Equations

1. equation

3. extraneous

5.
$$x + 11 = 15$$
$$x + 11 - 11 = 15 - 11$$
$$x = 4$$

7.
$$7 - 2x = 25$$
$$7 - 7 - 2x = 25 - 7$$
$$-2x = 18$$
$$\frac{-2x}{-2} = \frac{18}{-2}$$
$$x = -9$$

9.
$$4y + 2 - 5y = 7 - 6y$$
$$4y - 5y + 2 = 7 - 6y$$
$$-y + 2 = 7 - 6y$$
$$-y + 6y + 2 = 7 - 6y + 6y$$
$$5y + 2 = 7$$
$$5y + 2 - 2 = 7 - 2$$
$$5y = 5$$
$$\frac{5y}{5} = \frac{5}{5}$$
$$y = 1$$

11.
$$x - 3(2x + 3) = 8 - 5x$$
$$x - 6x - 9 = 8 - 5x$$
$$-5x - 9 = 8 - 5x$$
$$-5x + 5x - 9 = 8 - 5x + 5x$$
$$-9 \neq 8$$

No solution

13.
$$\frac{3x}{8} - \frac{4x}{3} = 4 \quad \text{or} \quad \frac{3x}{8} - \frac{4x}{3} - 4$$

$$\frac{9x}{24} - \frac{32x}{24} = 4 \qquad 24\left(\frac{3x}{8} - \frac{4x}{3}\right) = 24(4)$$

$$-\frac{23x}{24} = 4 \qquad\qquad 9x - 32x = 96$$

$$-\frac{23x}{24}\left(-\frac{24}{23}\right) = 4\left(-\frac{24}{23}\right) \qquad -23x = 96$$

$$x = -\frac{96}{23} \qquad\qquad x = -\frac{96}{23}$$

The second method is easier. The fractions are eliminated in the first step.

15.
$$\frac{5x - 4}{5x + 4} = \frac{2}{3}$$
$$3(5x - 4) = 2(5x + 4)$$
$$15x - 12 = 10x + 8$$
$$5x = 20$$
$$x = 4$$

17.
$$10 - \frac{13}{x} = 4 + \frac{5}{x}$$
$$\frac{10x - 13}{x} = \frac{4x + 5}{x}$$
$$10x - 13 = 4x + 5$$
$$6x = 18$$
$$x = 3$$

19.
$$\frac{x}{x + 4} + \frac{4}{x + 4} + 2 = 0$$
$$\frac{x + 4}{x + 4} + 2 = 0$$
$$1 + 2 = 0$$
$$3 \neq 0$$

Contradiction; no solution

21. $\dfrac{2}{(x-4)(x-2)} = \dfrac{1}{x-4} + \dfrac{2}{x-2}$ Multiply both sides by $(x-4)(x-2)$.

$$2 = 1(x-2) + 2(x-4)$$
$$2 = x - 2 + 2x - 8$$
$$2 = 3x - 10$$
$$12 = 3x$$
$$4 = x$$

A check reveals that $x = 4$ is an extraneous solution—it makes the denominator zero. There is no real solution.

23. $\dfrac{1}{x-3} + \dfrac{1}{x+3} = \dfrac{10}{x^2-9}$

$\dfrac{1}{x-3} + \dfrac{1}{x+3} = \dfrac{10}{(x+3)(x-3)}$ Multiply both sides by $(x+3)(x-3)$.

$$1(x+3) + 1(x-3) = 10$$
$$2x = 10$$
$$x = 5$$

25. $6x^2 + 3x = 0$

$3x(2x+1) = 0$

$3x = 0$ or $2x + 1 = 0$

$x = 0$ or $x = -\dfrac{1}{2}$

27. $x^2 - 2x - 8 = 0$

$(x-4)(x+2) = 0$

$x - 4 = 0$ or $x + 2 = 0$

$x = 4$ or $x = -2$

29. $x^2 + 10x + 25 = 0$

$(x+5)(x+5) = 0$

$x + 5 = 0$

$x = -5$

31. $x^2 + 4x = 12$

$x^2 + 4x - 12 = 0$

$(x+6)(x-2) = 0$

$x + 6 = 0$ or $x - 2 = 0$

$x = -6$ or $x = 2$

33. $\dfrac{3}{4}x^2 + 8x + 20 = 0$

$4\left(\dfrac{3}{4}x^2 + 8x + 20\right) = 4(0)$

$3x^2 + 32x + 80 = 0$

$(3x+20)(x+4) = 0$

$3x + 20 = 0$ or $x + 4 = 0$

$x = -\dfrac{20}{3}$ or $x = -4$

35. $x^2 = 49$

$x = \pm 7$

37. $3x^2 = 81$

$x^2 = 27$

$x = \pm 3\sqrt{3}$

39. $(x-12)^2 = 16$

$x - 12 = \pm 4$

$x = 12 \pm 4$

$x = 16$ or $x = 8$

41. $(2x-1)^2 = 18$

$2x - 1 = \pm\sqrt{18}$

$2x = 1 \pm 3\sqrt{2}$

$x = \dfrac{1 \pm 3\sqrt{2}}{2}$

43. $x^2 + 4x - 32 = 0$

$x^2 + 4x = 32$

$x^2 + 4x + 2^2 = 32 + 2^2$

$(x+2)^2 = 36$

$x + 2 = \pm 6$

$x = -2 \pm 6$

$x = 4$ or $x = -8$

45. $x^2 + 6x + 2 = 0$

$x^2 + 6x = -2$

$x^2 + 6x + 3^2 = -2 + 3^2$

$(x + 3)^2 = 7$

$x + 3 = \pm\sqrt{7}$

$x = -3 \pm \sqrt{7}$

47. $9x^2 - 18x = -3$

$x^2 - 2x = -\dfrac{1}{3}$

$x^2 - 2x + 1^2 = -\dfrac{1}{3} + 1^2$

$(x - 1)^2 = \dfrac{2}{3}$

$x - 1 = \pm\sqrt{\dfrac{2}{3}}$

$x = 1 \pm \sqrt{\dfrac{2}{3}}$

$x = 1 \pm \dfrac{\sqrt{6}}{3}$

49. $2x^2 + 5x - 8 = 0$

$2x^2 + 5x = 8$

$x^2 + \dfrac{5}{2}x = 4$

$x^2 + \dfrac{5}{2}x + \left(\dfrac{5}{4}\right)^2 = 4 + \left(\dfrac{5}{4}\right)^2$

$\left(x + \dfrac{5}{4}\right)^2 = \dfrac{89}{16}$

$x + \dfrac{5}{4} = \pm\dfrac{\sqrt{89}}{4}$

$x = -\dfrac{5}{4} \pm \dfrac{\sqrt{89}}{4}$

$x = \dfrac{-5 \pm \sqrt{89}}{4}$

51. $2x^2 + x - 1 = 0$

$x = \dfrac{-b \pm \sqrt{b^2 - 4ac}}{2a}$

$= \dfrac{-1 \pm \sqrt{1^2 - 4(2)(-1)}}{2(2)}$

$= \dfrac{-1 \pm 3}{4} = \dfrac{1}{2}, -1$

53. $2 + 2x - x^2 = 0$

$-x^2 + 2x + 2 = 0$

$x = \dfrac{-b \pm \sqrt{b^2 - 4ac}}{2a}$

$= \dfrac{-2 \pm \sqrt{2^2 - 4(-1)(2)}}{2(-1)}$

$= \dfrac{-2 \pm 2\sqrt{3}}{-2} = 1 \pm \sqrt{3}$

55. $2x^2 - 3x - 4 = 0$

$x = \dfrac{-b \pm \sqrt{b^2 - 4ac}}{2a}$

$= \dfrac{3 \pm \sqrt{(-3)^2 - 4(2)(-4)}}{2(2)}$

$= \dfrac{3 \pm \sqrt{41}}{4} = \dfrac{3}{4} \pm \dfrac{\sqrt{41}}{4}$

57. $9x^2 - 37 = 6x$

$9x^2 - 6x - 37 = 0$

$x = \dfrac{-b \pm \sqrt{b^2 - 4ac}}{2a}$

$= \dfrac{6 \pm \sqrt{(-6)^2 - 4(9)(-37)}}{2(9)}$

$= \dfrac{6 \pm 6\sqrt{38}}{18} = \dfrac{1}{3} \pm \dfrac{\sqrt{38}}{3}$

59. $28x - 49x^2 = 4$

$-49x^2 + 28x - 4 = 0$

$x = \dfrac{-b \pm \sqrt{b^2 - 4ac}}{2a}$

$= \dfrac{-28 \pm \sqrt{28^2 - 4(-49)(-4)}}{2(-49)}$

$= \dfrac{-28 + 0}{-98} = \dfrac{2}{7}$

61. $8t = 5 + 2t^2$

$-2t^2 + 8t - 5 = 0$

$t = \dfrac{-b \pm \sqrt{b^2 - 4ac}}{2a}$

$= \dfrac{-8 \pm \sqrt{8^2 - 4(-2)(-5)}}{2(-2)}$

$= \dfrac{-8 \pm 2\sqrt{6}}{-4} = 2 \pm \dfrac{\sqrt{6}}{2}$

63. $(y - 5)^2 = 2y$

$y^2 - 12y + 25 = 0$

$y = \dfrac{-b \pm \sqrt{b^2 - 4ac}}{2a}$

$= \dfrac{-(-12) \pm \sqrt{(-12)^2 - 4(1)(25)}}{2(1)}$

$= \dfrac{12 \pm 2\sqrt{11}}{2} = 6 \pm \sqrt{11}$

65. $x^2 - 2x - 1 = 0$ Complete the square.

$x^2 - 2x = 1$

$x^2 - 2x + 1^2 = 1 + 1^2$

$(x - 1)^2 = 2$

$x - 1 = \pm\sqrt{2}$

$x = 1 \pm \sqrt{2}$

67. $(x + 3)^2 = 81$ Extract square roots.

$x + 3 = \pm 9$

$x + 3 = 9$ or $x + 3 = -9$

$x = 6$ or $x = -12$

69. $x^2 - x - \frac{11}{4} = 0$ Complete the square.

$x^2 - x = \frac{11}{4}$

$x^2 - x + \left(\frac{1}{2}\right)^2 = \frac{11}{4} + \left(\frac{1}{2}\right)^2$

$\left(x - \frac{1}{2}\right)^2 = \frac{12}{4}$

$x - \frac{1}{2} = \pm\sqrt{\frac{12}{4}}$

$x = \frac{1}{2} \pm \sqrt{3}$

71. $(x + 1)^2 = x^2$ Extract square roots.

$x^2 = (x + 1)^2$

$x = \pm(x + 1)$

For $x = +(x + 1)$:

$0 \neq 1$ No solution

For $x = -(x + 1)$:

$2x = -1$

$x = -\frac{1}{2}$

73. $6x^4 - 14x^2 = 0$

$2x^2(3x^2 - 7) = 0$

$2x^2 = 0 \Rightarrow x = 0$

$3x^2 - 7 = 0 \Rightarrow x = \pm\dfrac{\sqrt{21}}{3}$

75. $5x^3 + 3 - x^2 + 45x = 0$

$5x(x^2 + 6x + 9) = 0$

$5x(x + 3)^2 = 0$

$5x = 0 \Rightarrow x = 0$

$x + 3 = 0 \Rightarrow x = -3$

77. $\sqrt{3x} - 12 = 0$

$\sqrt{3x} = 12$

$3x = 144$

$x = 48$

79. $\sqrt[3]{2x + 5} + 3 = 0$

$\sqrt[3]{2x + 5} = -3$

$2x + 5 = -27$

$2x = -32$

$x = -16$

81. $-\sqrt{26 - 11x} + 4 = x$

$4 - x = \sqrt{26 - 11x}$

$16 - 8x + x^2 = 26 - 11x$

$x^2 + 3x - 10 = 0$

$(x + 5)(x - 2) = 0$

$x + 5 = 0 \Rightarrow x = -5$

$x - 2 = 0 \Rightarrow x = 2$

83. $\sqrt{x} - \sqrt{x - 5} = 1$

$\sqrt{x} = 1 + \sqrt{x - 5}$

$\left(\sqrt{x}\right)^2 = \left(1 + \sqrt{x - 5}\right)^2$

$x = 1 + 2\sqrt{x - 5} + x - 5$

$4 = 2\sqrt{x - 5}$

$2 = \sqrt{x - 5}$

$4 = x - 5$

$9 = x$

85. $(x - 5)^{3/2} = 8$

$(x - 5)^3 = 8^2$

$x - 5 = \sqrt[3]{64}$

$x = 5 + 4 = 9$

87. $\left(x^2 - 5\right)^{3/2} = 27$

$\left(x^2 - 5\right)^3 = 27^2$

$x^2 - 5 = \sqrt[3]{27^2}$

$x^2 = 5 + 9$

$x^2 = 14$

$x = \pm\sqrt{14}$

89. $\left|2x - 5\right| = 11$

$2x - 5 = 11 \Rightarrow x = 8$

$-(2x - 5) = 11 \Rightarrow x = -3$

91. $\left|x^2 + 6x\right| = 3x + 18$

First equation:

$x^2 + 6x = 3x + 18$

$x^2 + 3x - 18 = 0$

$(x - 3)(x + 6) = 0$

$x - 3 = 0 \Rightarrow x = 3$

$x + 6 = 0 \Rightarrow x = -6$

Second equation:

$-\left(x^2 + 6x\right) = 3x + 18$

$0 = x^2 + 9x + 18$

$0 = (x + 3)(x + 6)$

$0 = x + 3 \Rightarrow x = -3$

$x = x + 6 \Rightarrow x = -6$

The solutions of the original equation are $x = \pm 3$ and $x = -6$.

93. $V = \dfrac{4}{3}\pi r^3$

$5.96 = \dfrac{4}{3}\pi r^3$

$17.88 = 4\pi r^3$

$\dfrac{17.88}{4\pi} = r^3$

$r = \sqrt[3]{\dfrac{4.47}{\pi}} \approx 1.12$ inches

95. Let $y = 18$:

$y = 0.432x - 10.44$

$18 = 0.432x - 10.44$

$28.44 = 0.432x$

$\dfrac{28.44}{0.432} = x$

$65.8 \approx x$

So, the height of the female is about 65.8 inches or 5 feet 6 inches.

97. False.

$\sqrt{2x + 1} = -2 + \sqrt{x + 1}$

$2x + 1 = 4 - 4\sqrt{x + 1} + (x + 1)$

$x - 4 = -4\sqrt{x + 1}$

$x^2 - 8x + 16 = 16(x + 1)$

$x^2 - 24x = 0$

$x(x - 24) = 0$

$x = 0 \quad 1 \neq -2 + 1, \ x - 24 \quad 5 \neq 2 + 5$

99. $\sqrt{x - 10} - \sqrt{x - 10} = 0$

$\sqrt{x - 10} = \sqrt{x - 10}$

False. The equation is an identity, so every real number is a solution.

101. Equivalent equations are derived from the substitution principle and simplification techniques. They have the same solution(s).

$2x + 3 = 8$ and $2x = 5$ are equivalent equations.

Appendix A.6   Linear Inequalities in One Variable

1. solution set

3. double

5. Interval: $[0, 9)$

    (a) Inequality: $0 \le x \le 9$

    (b) The interval is bounded.

7. Interval: $[-1, 5]$

    (a) Inequality: $-1 \le x \le 5$

    (b) The interval is bounded.

9. Interval: $(11, \infty)$

    (a) Inequality: $x > 11$

    (b) The interval is unbounded.

11. Interval: $(-\infty, -2)$

    (a) Inequality: $x < -2$

    (b) The interval is unbounded.

13. $4x < 12$

    $\frac{1}{4}(4x) < \frac{1}{4}(12)$

       $x < 3$

15. $-2x > -3$

    $-\frac{1}{2}(-2x) < \left(-\frac{1}{2}\right)(-3)$

        $x < \frac{3}{2}$

17. $x - 5 \geq 7$

     $x \geq 12$

19. $2x + 7 < 3 + 4x$

    $-2x < -4$

      $x > 2$

21. $2x - 1 \geq 1 - 5x$

     $7x \geq 2$

      $x \geq \frac{2}{7}$

23. $4 - 2x < 3(3 - x)$

    $4 - 2x < 9 - 3x$

       $x < 5$

25. $\frac{3}{4}x - 6 \leq x - 7$

    $-\frac{1}{4}x \leq -1$

       $x \geq 4$

27. $\frac{1}{2}(8x + 1) \geq 3x + \frac{5}{2}$

    $4x + \frac{1}{2} \geq 3x + \frac{5}{2}$

       $x \geq 2$

29. $3.6x + 11 \geq -3.4$

    $3.6x \geq 14.4$

      $x \geq -4$

31. $1 < 2x + 3 < 9$

    $-2 < 2x < 6$

    $-1 < x < 3$

33. $0 < 3(x + 7) \leq 20$

    $0 < x + 7 \leq \frac{20}{3}$

    $-7 < x \leq -\frac{1}{3}$

35. $-4 < \dfrac{2x - 3}{3} < 4$

    $-12 < 2x - 3 < 12$

    $-9 < 2x < 15$

    $-\dfrac{9}{2} < x < \dfrac{15}{2}$

37. $-1 < \dfrac{-x - 2}{3} \leq 1$

    $-3 < -x - 2 \leq 3$

    $-1 < -x \leq 5$

    $1 > x \geq -5$

    $-5 \leq x < 1$

39. $\frac{3}{4} > x + 1 > \frac{1}{4}$

    $-\frac{1}{4} > x > -\frac{3}{4}$

    $-\frac{3}{4} < x < -\frac{1}{4}$

41. $3.2 \leq 0.4x - 1 \leq 4.4$

    $4.2 \leq 0.4x \leq 5.4$

    $10.5 \leq x \leq 13.5$

43. $|x| < 5$

    $-5 < x < 5$

45. $\left|\dfrac{x}{2}\right| > 1$

    $\dfrac{x}{2} < -1$ or $\dfrac{x}{2} > 1$

    $x < -2$ $x > 2$

47. $|x - 5| < -1$

    No solution. The absolute value of a number cannot be less than a negative number.

49. $|x - 20| \leq 6$

    $-6 \leq x - 20 \leq 6$

    $14 \leq x \leq 26$

51. $|3 - 4x| \geq 9$

    $3 - 4x \leq -9$ or $3 - 4x \geq 9$

    $-4x \leq -12$ $-4x \geq 6$

       $x \geq 3$ $x \leq -\frac{3}{2}$

53. $\left|\dfrac{x-3}{2}\right| \geq 4$

$\dfrac{x-3}{2} \leq -4$ or $\dfrac{x-3}{2} \geq 4$

$x - 3 \leq -8 \qquad\quad x - 3 \geq 8$

$x \leq -5 \qquad\qquad\quad x \geq 11$

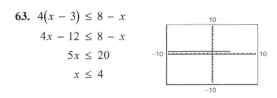

55. $|9 - 2x| - 2 < -1$

$|9 - 2x| < 1$

$-1 < 9 - 2x < 1$

$-10 < -2x < -8$

$5 > x > 4$

$4 < x < 5$

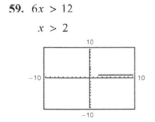

57. $2|x + 10| \geq 9$

$|x + 10| \geq \dfrac{9}{2}$

$x + 10 \leq -\dfrac{9}{2}$ or $x + 10 \geq \dfrac{9}{2}$

$x \leq -\dfrac{29}{2} \qquad\qquad x \geq -\dfrac{11}{2}$

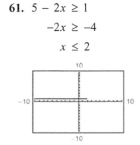

59. $6x > 12$

$x > 2$

61. $5 - 2x \geq 1$

$-2x \geq -4$

$x \leq 2$

63. $4(x - 3) \leq 8 - x$

$4x - 12 \leq 8 - x$

$5x \leq 20$

$x \leq 4$

65. $|x - 8| \leq 14$

$-14 \leq x - 8 \leq 14$

$-6 \leq x \leq 22$

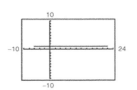

67. $2|x + 7| \geq 13$

$|x + 7| \geq \dfrac{13}{2}$

$x + 7 \leq -\dfrac{13}{2}$ or $x + 7 \geq \dfrac{13}{2}$

$x \leq -\dfrac{27}{2} \qquad\qquad x \geq -\dfrac{1}{2}$

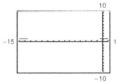

69. $y = 2x - 3$

(a) $\qquad y \geq 1$

$2x - 3 \geq 1$

$2x \geq 4$

$x \geq 2$

(b) $\qquad y \leq 0$

$2x - 3 \leq 0$

$2x \leq 3$

$x \leq \dfrac{3}{2}$

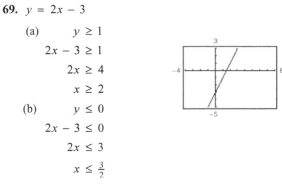

71. $y = -\dfrac{1}{2}x + 2$

(a) $\quad 0 \leq y \leq 3$

$0 \leq -\dfrac{1}{2}x + 2 \leq 3$

$-2 \leq -\dfrac{1}{2}x \leq 1$

$4 \geq x \geq -2$

(b) $\qquad y \geq 0$

$-\dfrac{1}{2}x + 2 \geq 0$

$-\dfrac{1}{2}x \geq -2$

$x \leq 4$

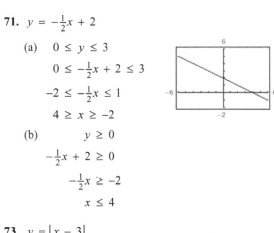

73. $y = |x - 3|$

(a) $\qquad y \leq 2$

$|x - 3| \leq 2$

$-2 \leq x - 3 \leq 2$

$1 \leq x \leq 5$

(b) $\qquad y \geq 4$

$|x - 3| \geq 4$

$x - 3 \leq -4$ or $x - 3 \geq 4$

$x \leq -1$ or $\qquad x \geq 7$

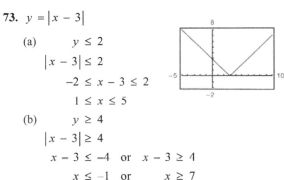

75. $x - 5 \geq 0$

$x \geq 5$

$[5, \infty)$

77. $x + 3 \geq 0$

$x \geq -3$

$[-3, \infty)$

79. $7 - 2x \geq 0$

$-2x \geq -7$

$x \leq \frac{7}{2}$

$\left(-\infty, \frac{7}{2}\right]$

81. All real numbers less than 8 units from 10.

83. The midpoint of the interval $[-3, 3]$ is 0. The interval represents all real numbers x no more than 3 units from 0.

$|x - 0| \leq 3$

$|x| \leq 3$

85. The graph shows all real numbers at least 3 units from 7.

$|x - 7| \geq 3$

87. All real numbers at least 10 units from 12

$|x - 12| \geq 10$

89. All real numbers more than 4 units from -3

$|x - (-3)| > 4$

$|x + 3| > 4$

91. $\$4.10 \leq E \leq \$4.25$

93. $r \leq 0.08$

95. $r = 220 - A = 220 - 20 = 200$ beats per minute

$0.50(200) \leq r \leq 0.85(200)$

$100 \leq r \leq 170$

The target heart rate is at least 100 beats per minute and at most 170 beats per minute.

97. $9.00 + 0.75x > 13.50$

$0.75x > 4.50$

$x > 6$

You must produce at least 6 units each hour in order to yield a greater hourly wage at the second job.

99. $1000\big(1 + r(2)\big) > 1062.50$

$1 + 2r > 1.0625$

$2r > 0.0625$

$r > 0.03125$

$r > 3.125\%$

101. $R > C$

$115.95x > 95x + 750$

$20.95x > 750$

$x \geq 35.7995$

$x \geq 36$ units

103. Let $x = $ number of dozen doughnuts sold per day.

Revenue: $R = 7.95x$

Cost: $C = 1.45x + 165$

$P = R - C$

$= 7.95x - (1.45x + 165)$

$= 6.50x - 165$

$400 \leq P \leq 1200$

$400 \leq 6.50x - 165 \leq 1200$

$565 \leq 6.50x \leq 1365$

$86.9 \leq x \leq 210$

The daily sales vary between 87 and 210 dozen doughnuts per day.

105. (a)

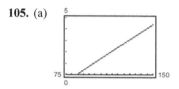

(b) From the graph you see that $y \geq 3$ when $x \geq 129$.

(c) Algebraically:

$3 \leq 0.067x - 5.638$

$8.638 \leq 0.067x$

$x \geq 129$

(d) IQ scores are not a good predictor of GPAs. Other factors include study habits, class attendance, and attitude.

107. (a) $S = 1.36t + 41.1$

$45 \leq 1.36t + 41.1 \leq 50$

$3.9 \leq 1.36t \leq 8.9$

$2.9 \leq t \leq 6.5$

Between the years 2002 and 2006 the average salary was between $45,000 and $50,000.

(b) $1.36t + 41.1 \geq 62$

$1.36t \geq 20.9$

$t \geq 15.4$

The average salary will exceed $62,000 sometime during the year 2015.

Appendix A.7   Errors and the Algebra of Calculus

1. numerator

3. $2x - (3y + 4) \neq 2x - 3y + 4$

Change all signs when distributing the minus sign.

$2x - (3y + 4) = 2x - 3y - 4$

5. $\dfrac{4}{16x - (2x + 1)} \neq \dfrac{4}{14x + 1}$

Change all signs when distributing the minus sign.

$\dfrac{4}{16x - (2x + 1)} = \dfrac{4}{16x - 2x - 1} = \dfrac{4}{14x - 1}$

7. $(5z)(6z) \neq 30z$

z occurs twice as a factor.

$(5z)(6z) = 30z^2$

9. $a\left(\dfrac{x}{y}\right) \neq \dfrac{ax}{ay}$

The fraction as a whole is multiplied by a, not the numerator and denominator separately.

$a\left(\dfrac{x}{y}\right) = \dfrac{a}{1} \cdot \dfrac{x}{y} = \dfrac{ax}{y}$

11. $\sqrt{x + 9} \neq \sqrt{x} + 3$

Do not apply the radical to the terms.

$\sqrt{x + 9}$ does not simplify.

13. $\dfrac{2x^2 + 1}{5x} \neq \dfrac{2x + 1}{5}$

Divide out common factors not common terms.

$\dfrac{2x^2 + 1}{5x}$ cannot be simplified.

15. $\dfrac{1}{a^{-1} + b^{-1}} \neq \left(\dfrac{1}{a + b}\right)^{-1}$

To get rid of negative exponents:

$\dfrac{1}{a^{-1} + b^{-1}} = \dfrac{1}{a^{-1} + b^{-1}} \cdot \dfrac{ab}{ab} = \dfrac{ab}{b + a}$

17. $\left(x^2 + 5x\right)^{1/2} \neq x(x + 5)^{1/2}$

Factor within grouping symbols before applying the exponent to each factor.

$\left(x^2 + 5x\right)^{1/2} = \left[x(x + 5)\right]^{1/2} = x^{1/2}(x + 5)^{1/2}$

19. $\dfrac{3}{x} + \dfrac{4}{y} = \dfrac{3}{x} \cdot \dfrac{y}{y} + \dfrac{4}{y} \cdot \dfrac{x}{x} = \dfrac{3y + 4x}{xy}$

To add fractions, they must have a common denominator.

21. To add fractions, first find a common denominator.

$\dfrac{x}{2y} + \dfrac{y}{3} = \dfrac{3x}{6y} + \dfrac{2y^2}{6y} = \dfrac{3x + 2y^2}{6y}$

23. $\dfrac{5x + 3}{4} = \dfrac{1}{4}(5x + 3)$

The required factor is $5x + 3$.

25. $\dfrac{2}{3}x^2 + \dfrac{1}{3}x + 5 = \dfrac{2}{3}x^2 + \dfrac{1}{3}x + \dfrac{15}{3} = \dfrac{1}{3}\left(2x^2 + x + 15\right)$

The required factor is $2x^2 + x + 15$.

27. $x^2\left(x^3 - 1\right)^4 = \dfrac{1}{3}\left(x^3 - 1\right)^4\left(3x^2\right)$

The required factor is $\dfrac{1}{3}$.

29. $2(y - 5)^{1/2} + y(y - 5)^{-1/2} = (y - 5)^{-1/2}(3y - 10)$

The required factor is $3y - 10$.

31. $\dfrac{4x + 6}{\left(x^2 + 3x + 7\right)^3} = \dfrac{2(2x + 3)}{\left(x^2 + 3x + 7\right)^3} = \dfrac{2}{1} \cdot \dfrac{(2x + 3)}{1} \cdot \dfrac{1}{\left(x^2 + 3x + 7\right)^3} = (2)\dfrac{1}{\left(x^2 + 3x + 7\right)^3}(2x + 3)$

The required factor is 2.

33. $\dfrac{3}{x} + \dfrac{5}{2x^2} - \dfrac{3}{2}x = \dfrac{6x}{2x^2} + \dfrac{5}{2x^2} - \dfrac{3x^3}{2x^2}$

$= \left(\dfrac{1}{2x^2}\right)\left(6x + 5 - 3x^3\right)$

The required factor is $\dfrac{1}{2x^2}$.

35. $\dfrac{25x^2}{36} + \dfrac{4y^2}{9} = \dfrac{x^2}{\dfrac{36}{25}} + \dfrac{y^2}{\dfrac{9}{4}}$

The required factors are $\dfrac{36}{25}$ and $\dfrac{9}{4}$.

37. $\dfrac{x^2}{\dfrac{3}{10}} - \dfrac{y^2}{\dfrac{4}{5}} = \dfrac{10x^2}{3} - \dfrac{5y^2}{4}$

The required factors are 3 and 4.

39. $x^{1/3} - 5x^{4/3} = x^{1/3}\left(1 - 5x^{3/3}\right) = x^{1/3}\left(1 - 5x\right)$

The required factor is $1 - 5x$.

41. $\left(1 - 3x\right)^{4/3} - 4x\left(1 - 3x\right)^{1/3} = \left(1 - 3x\right)^{1/3}\left[\left(1 - 3x\right)^{1} - 4x\right]$

$\qquad\qquad\qquad\qquad\qquad\qquad = \left(1 - 3x\right)^{1/3}\left(1 - 7x\right)$

The required factor is $1 - 7x$.

43. $\tfrac{1}{10}\left(2x + 1\right)^{5/2} - \tfrac{1}{6}\left(2x + 1\right)^{3/2} = \tfrac{3}{30}\left(2x + 1\right)^{3/2}\left(2x + 1\right)^{1} - \tfrac{5}{30}\left(2x + 1\right)^{3/2}$

$\qquad\qquad\qquad\qquad\qquad\qquad\quad = \tfrac{1}{30}\left(2x + 1\right)^{3/2}\left[3\left(2x + 1\right) - 5\right]$

$\qquad\qquad\qquad\qquad\qquad\qquad\quad = \tfrac{1}{30}\left(2x + 1\right)^{3/2}\left(6x - 2\right)$

$\qquad\qquad\qquad\qquad\qquad\qquad\quad = \tfrac{1}{30}\left(2x + 1\right)^{3/2}2\left(3x - 1\right)$

$\qquad\qquad\qquad\qquad\qquad\qquad\quad = \tfrac{1}{15}\left(2x + 1\right)^{3/2}\left(3x - 1\right)$

The required factor is $3x - 1$.

45. $\dfrac{7}{\left(x + 3\right)^5} = 7\left(x + 3\right)^{-5}$

49. $\dfrac{4}{3x} + \dfrac{4}{x^4} - \dfrac{7x}{\sqrt[3]{2x}} = 4\left(3x\right)^{-1} + 4x^{-4} - 7x\left(2x\right)^{-1/3}$

47. $\dfrac{2x^5}{\left(3x + 5\right)^4} = 2x^5\left(3x + 5\right)^{-4}$

51. $\dfrac{x^2 + 6x + 12}{3x} = \dfrac{x^2}{3x} + \dfrac{6x}{3x} + \dfrac{12}{3x} = \dfrac{x}{3} + 2 + \dfrac{4}{x}$

53. $\dfrac{4x^3 - 7x^2 + 1}{x^{1/3}} = \dfrac{4x^3}{x^{1/3}} - \dfrac{7x^2}{x^{1/3}} + \dfrac{1}{x^{1/3}} = 4x^{3-1/3} - 7x^{2-1/3} + \dfrac{1}{x^{1/3}} = 4x^{8/3} - 7x^{5/3} + \dfrac{1}{x^{1/3}}$

55. $\dfrac{3 - 5x^2 - x^4}{\sqrt{x}} = \dfrac{3}{\sqrt{x}} - \dfrac{5x^2}{\sqrt{x}} - \dfrac{x^4}{\sqrt{x}} = \dfrac{3}{\sqrt{x}} - 5x^{2-1/2} - x^{4-1/2} = \dfrac{3}{x^{1/2}} - 5x^{3/2} - x^{7/2}$

57. $\dfrac{-2\left(x^2 - 3\right)^{-3}\left(2x\right)\left(x + 1\right)^3 - 3\left(x + 1\right)^2\left(x^2 - 3\right)^{-2}}{\left[\left(x + 1\right)^3\right]^2} = \dfrac{\left(x^2 - 3\right)^{-3}\left(x + 1\right)^2\left[-4x\left(x + 1\right) - 3\left(x^2 - 3\right)\right]}{\left(x + 1\right)^6}$

$\qquad\qquad\qquad\qquad\qquad\qquad\qquad\qquad\qquad\qquad\quad = \dfrac{-4x^2 - 4x - 3x^2 + 9}{\left(x^2 - 3\right)^3\left(x + 1\right)^4}$

$\qquad\qquad\qquad\qquad\qquad\qquad\qquad\qquad\qquad\qquad\quad = \dfrac{-7x^2 - 4x + 9}{\left(x^2 - 3\right)^3\left(x + 1\right)^4}$

59. $\dfrac{\left(6x + 1\right)^3\left(27x^2 + 2\right) - \left(9x^3 + 2x\right)\left(3\right)\left(6x + 1\right)^2\left(6\right)}{\left[\left(6x + 1\right)^3\right]^2} = \dfrac{\left(6x + 1\right)^2\left[\left(6x + 1\right)\left(27x^2 + 2\right) - 18\left(9x^3 + 2x\right)\right]}{\left(6x + 1\right)^6}$

$\qquad\qquad\qquad\qquad\qquad\qquad\qquad\qquad\qquad\qquad\quad = \dfrac{162x^3 + 12x + 27x^2 + 2 - 162x^3 - 36x}{\left(6x + 1\right)^4}$

$\qquad\qquad\qquad\qquad\qquad\qquad\qquad\qquad\qquad\qquad\quad = \dfrac{27x^2 - 24x + 2}{\left(6x + 1\right)^4}$

61. $\dfrac{(x + 2)^{3/4}(x + 3)^{-2/3} - (x + 3)^{1/3}(x + 2)^{-1/4}}{\left[(x + 2)^{3/4}\right]^2} = \dfrac{(x + 2)^{-1/4}(x + 3)^{-2/3}\left[(x + 2) - (x + 3)\right]}{(x + 2)^{6/4}}$

$$= \dfrac{x + 2 - x - 3}{(x + 2)^{1/4}(x + 3)^{2/3}(x + 2)^{6/4}}$$

$$= -\dfrac{1}{(x + 3)^{2/3}(x + 2)^{7/4}}$$

63. $\dfrac{2(3x - 1)^{1/3} - (2x + 1)(1/3)(3x - 1)^{-2/3}(3)}{(3x - 1)^{2/3}} = \dfrac{(3x - 1)^{-2/3}\left[2(3x - 1) - (2x + 1)\right]}{(3x - 1)^{2/3}}$

$$= \dfrac{6x - 2 - 2x - 1}{(3x - 1)^{2/3}(3x - 1)^{2/3}}$$

$$= \dfrac{4x - 3}{(3x - 1)^{4/3}}$$

65. $\dfrac{1}{(x^2 + 4)^{1/2}} \cdot \dfrac{1}{2}(x^2 + 4)^{-1/2}(2x) = \dfrac{1}{(x^2 + 4)^{1/2}} \cdot \dfrac{1}{(x^2 + 4)^{1/2}} \cdot \dfrac{1}{2}(2x) = \dfrac{1}{(x^2 + 4)^1}(x) = \dfrac{x}{x^2 + 4}$

67. $(x^2 + 5)^{1/2}\left(\dfrac{3}{2}\right)(3x - 2)^{1/2}(3) + (3x - 2)^{3/2}\left(\dfrac{1}{2}\right)(x^2 + 5)^{-1/2}(2x) = \dfrac{9}{2}(x^2 + 5)^{1/2}(3x - 2)^{1/2} + x(x^2 + 5)^{-1/2}(3x - 2)^{3/2}$

$$= \dfrac{9}{2}(x^2 + 5)^{1/2}(3x - 2)^{1/2} + \dfrac{2}{2}x(x^2 + 5)^{-1/2}(3x - 2)^{3/2}$$

$$= \dfrac{1}{2}(x^2 + 5)^{-1/2}(3x - 2)^{1/2}\left[9(x^2 + 5)^1 + 2x(3x - 2)^1\right]$$

$$= \dfrac{1}{2}(x^2 + 5)^{-1/2}(3x - 2)^{1/2}(9x^2 + 45 + 6x^2 - 4x)$$

$$= \dfrac{(3x - 2)^{1/2}(15x^2 - 4x + 45)}{2(x^2 + 5)^{1/2}}$$

69. $t = \dfrac{\sqrt{x^2 + 4}}{2} + \dfrac{\sqrt{(4 - x)^2 + 4}}{6}$

(a)

x	t
0.5	1.70
1.0	1.72
1.5	1.78
2.0	1.89
2.5	2.02
3.0	2.18
3.5	2.36
4.0	2.57

(b) She should swim to a point about $\dfrac{1}{2}$ mile down the coast to minimize the time required to reach the finish line.

(c) $\dfrac{1}{2}x\left(x^2 + 4\right)^{-1/2} + \dfrac{1}{6}(x - 4)\left(x^2 - 8x + 20\right)^{-1/2} = \dfrac{3}{6}x\left(x^2 + 4\right)^{-1/2} + \dfrac{1}{6}(x - 4)\left(x^2 - 8x + 20\right)^{-1/2}$

$$= \dfrac{1}{6}\left[3x\left(x^2 + 4\right)^{-1/2} + (x - 4)\left(x^2 - 8x + 20\right)^{-1/2}\right]$$

$$= \dfrac{1}{6}\left[\dfrac{3x}{\left(x^2 + 4\right)^{1/2}} + \dfrac{x - 4}{\left(x^2 - 8x + 20\right)^{1/2}}\right]$$

$$= \dfrac{3x\sqrt{x^2 - 8x + 20} + (x - 4)\sqrt{x^2 + 4}}{6\sqrt{x^2 + 4}\sqrt{x^2 - 8x + 20}}$$

71. You cannot move term-by-term from the denominator to the numerator.

CHECKPOINTS
Chapter 1

Checkpoints for Section 1.1

1.

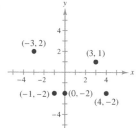

2. To sketch a scatter plot of the data, represent each pair of values by an ordered pair (t, N) and plot the resulting points.

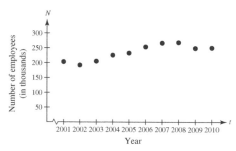

3. Let $(x_1, y_1) = (3, 1)$ and $(x_2, y_2) = (-3, 0)$.

Then apply the Distance Formula.

$$d = \sqrt{(x_2 - x_1)^2 + (y_2 - y_1)^2}$$
$$= \sqrt{(-3 - 3)^2 + (0 - 1)^2}$$
$$= \sqrt{(-6)^2 + (-1)^2}$$
$$= \sqrt{36 + 1}$$
$$= \sqrt{37}$$
$$\approx 6.08$$

So, the distance between the points is about 6.08 units.

4. The three points are plotted in the figure.

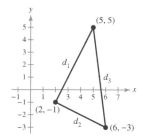

Using the Distance Formula, the lengths of the three sides are as follows.

$$d_1 = \sqrt{(5 - 2)^2 + (5 - (-1))^2}$$
$$= \sqrt{3^2 + 6^2}$$
$$= \sqrt{9 + 36}$$
$$= \sqrt{45}$$

$$d_2 = \sqrt{(6 - 2)^2 + (-3 - (-1))^2}$$
$$= \sqrt{4^2 + (-2)^2}$$
$$= \sqrt{16 + 4}$$
$$= \sqrt{20}$$

$$d_3 = \sqrt{(6 - 5)^2 + (-3 - 5)^2}$$
$$= \sqrt{(1)^2 + (-8)^2}$$
$$= \sqrt{1 + 64}$$
$$= \sqrt{65}$$

Because $(d_1)^2 + (d_2)^2 = 45 + 20 = 65$, you can conclude by the Pythagorean Theorem that the triangle must be a right triangle.

5. Let $(x_1, y_1) = (-2, 8)$ and $(x_2, y_2) = (-4, -0)$.

$$\text{Midpoint} = \left(\frac{x_1 + x_2}{2}, \frac{y_1 + y_2}{2}\right)$$

$$= \left(\frac{-2 + 4}{2}, \frac{8 + (-10)}{2}\right)$$

$$= \left(\frac{2}{2}, -\frac{2}{2}\right)$$

$$= 1, -1$$

The midpoint of the line segment is $(1, -1)$.

6. You can find the length of the pass by finding the distance between the points $(10, 10)$ and $(25, 32)$.

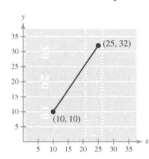

$$d = \sqrt{(x_2 - x_1)^2 + (y_2 - y_1)^2}$$

$$= \sqrt{(25 - 10)^2 + (32 - 10)^2}$$

$$= \sqrt{15^2 + 22^2}$$

$$= \sqrt{225 + 484}$$

$$= \sqrt{709}$$

$$\approx 26.6 \text{ years}$$

So, the pass is about 26.6 yard long.

7. Assuming that the annual revenue from Yahoo! Inc. followed a linear pattern, you can estimate the 2009 annual revenue by finding the midpoint of the line segment connecting the points $(2008, 7.2)$ and $(2010, 6.3)$.

$$\text{Midpoint} = \left(\frac{x_1 + x_2}{2}, \frac{y_1 + y_2}{2}\right)$$

$$= \left(\frac{2008 + 2010}{2}, \frac{7.2 + 6.3}{2}\right)$$

$$= (2009, 6.75)$$

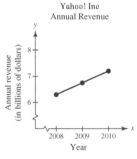

Yahoo! Inc
Annual Revenue

So, you can estimate the annual revenue for Yahoo! Inc. was $6.75 billion in 2009.

8. To shift the vertices two units to the left, subtract 2 from each of the x-coordinates. To shift the vertices four units down, subtract 4 from each of the y-coordinates.

Original point	**Translated Point**
$(1, 4)$	$(1 - 2, 4 - 4) = (-1, 0)$
$(1, 0)$	$(1 - 2, 0 - 4) = (-1, -4)$
$(3, 2)$	$(3 - 2, 2 - 4) = (1, -2)$
$(3, 6)$	$(3 - 2, 6 - 4) = (1, 2)$

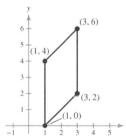
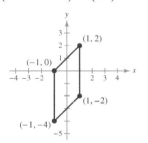

Checkpoints for Section 1.2

1. (a) $y = 14 - 6x$ Write original equation.

$-5 \overset{?}{=} 14 - 6(3)$ Substitute 3 for x and -5 for y.

$-5 \overset{?}{=} 14 - 18$

$-5 \neq -4$

(b) $y = 14 - 6x$ Write original equation.

$26 \overset{?}{=} 14 - 6(-2)$ Substitute -2 for x and 26 for y.

$26 \overset{?}{=} 14 + 12$

$26 \neq 26$ $(-2, 26)$ is a solution. ✓

2. (a) To graph $y = -3x + 2$, construct a table of values that consists of several solution points. Then plot the points and connect them.

x	$y = -3x + 2$	(x, y)
-2	$y = -3(-2) + 2 = 8$	$(-2, -8)$
-1	$y = -3(-1) + 2 = 5$	$(-1, 5)$
0	$y = -3(0) + 2 = 2$	$(0, 2)$
1	$y = -3(1) + 2 = -1$	$(1, -2)$
2	$y = -3(2) + 2 = -4$	$(2, -4)$

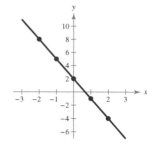

(b) To graph $y = 2x + 1$, construct a table of values that consists of several solution points. Then plot the points and connect them.

x	$y = 2x + 1$	(x, y)
-2	$y = 2(-2) + 1 = -3$	$(-2, -3)$
-1	$y = 2(-1) + 1 = -1$	$(-1, -1)$
0	$y = 2(0) + 1 = 1$	$(0, 1)$
1	$y = 2(1) + 1 = 3$	$(1, 3)$
2	$y = 2(2) + 1 = 5$	$(2, 5)$

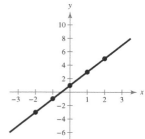

3. (a) To graph $y = x^2 + 3$, construct a table of values that consists of several solution points. Then plot the points and connect them with a smooth curve.

x	$y = x^2 + 3$	(x, y)
-2	$y = (-2)^2 + 3 = 7$	$(-2, 7)$
-1	$y = (-1)^2 + 3 = 4$	$(-1, 4)$
0	$y = (0)^2 + 3 = 3$	$(0, 3)$
1	$y = (1)^2 + 3 = 4$	$(1, 4)$
2	$y = 2(2) + 3 = 7$	$(2, 7)$

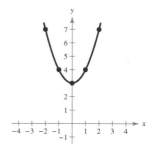

(b) To graph $y = 1 - x^2$, construct a table of values that consists of several solution points. Then plot the points and connect them with a smooth curve.

x	$y = 1 - x^2$	(x, y)
-2	$y = 1 - (-2)^2 = -3$	$(-2, -3)$
-1	$y = 1 - (-1)^2 = 0$	$(-1, 0)$
0	$y = 1 - (0)^2 = 1$	$(0, 1)$
1	$y = 1 - (1)^2 = 0$	$(1, 0)$
2	$y = 1 - (2)^2 = -3$	$(2, -3)$

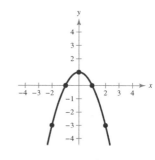

4. From the figure, you can see that the graph of the equation $y = -x^2 + 5x$ has x-intercepts (where y is 0) at $(0, 0)$ and $(5, 0)$ and a y-intercept (where x is 0) at $(0, 0)$. Since the graph passes through the origin or $(0, 0)$, that point can be considered as both an x-intercept and a y-intercept.

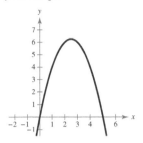

5. x-Axis:

$y^2 = 6 - x$ Write original equation.

$(-y)^2 = 6 - x$ Replace y with $-y$.

$y^2 = 6 - x$ Result is the original equation.

y-Axis:

$y^2 = 6 - x$ Write original equation.

$y^2 = 6 - (-x)$ Replace x with $-x$.

$y^2 = 6 + x$ Result is *not* an equivalent equation.

Origin:

$y^2 = 6 - x$ Write original equation.

$(-y)^2 = 6 - (-x)$ Replace y with $-y$ and x with $-x$.

$y^2 = 6 + x$ Result is *not* an equivalent equation.

Of the three tests for symmetry, the only one that is satisfied is the test for x-axis symmetry.

6. Of the three test of symmetry, the only one that is satisfied is the test for y-axis symmetry because $y = (-x)^2 - 4$ is equivalent to $y = x^2 - 4$. Using symmetry, you only need to find solution points to the right of the y-axis and then reflect them about the y-axis to obtain the graph.

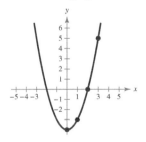

7. The equation $y = |x - 2|$ fails all three tests for symmetry and consequently its graph is not symmetric with respect to either axis or to the origin. So, construct a table of values. Then plot and connect the points.

x	$y = \lvert x - 2 \rvert$	(x, y)
-2	$y = \lvert(-2) - 2\rvert = 4$	$(-2, 4)$
-1	$y = \lvert(-1) - 2\rvert = 3$	$(-1, 3)$
0	$y = \lvert(0) - 2\rvert = 2$	$(0, 2)$
1	$y = \lvert(1) - 2\rvert = 1$	$(1, 1)$
2	$y = \lvert(2) - 2\rvert = 0$	$(3, 0)$
3	$y = \lvert(2) - 2\rvert = 0$	$(3, 1)$
4	$y = \lvert(2) - 2\rvert = 0$	$(4, 2)$

From the table, you can see that the x-intercept is $(2, 0)$ and the y-intercept is $(0, 2)$.

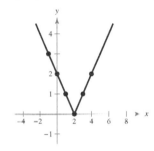

8. The radius of the circle is the distance between $(1, -2)$ and $(-3, -5)$.

$$r = \sqrt{(x - h)^2 + (y - k)^2}$$
$$= \sqrt{[1 - (-3)]^2 + [-2 - (-5)]^2}$$
$$= \sqrt{4^2 + 3^2}$$
$$= \sqrt{16 + 9}$$
$$= \sqrt{25}$$
$$= 5$$

Using $(h, k) = (-3, -5)$ and $r = 5$, the equation of the circle is

$$(x - h)^2 + (y - k)^2 = r^2$$
$$[x - (-3)]^2 + [y - (-5)]^2 = (5)^2$$
$$(x + 3)^2 + (y + 5)^2 = 25.$$

9. From the graph, you can estimate that a height of 75 inches corresponds to a weight of about 175 pounds.

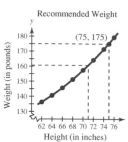

Recommended Weight

To confirm your estimate algebraically, substitute 75 for x in the model.

Let $x = 75$: $y = 0.073x^2 - 6.99x + 289.0$

$$= 0.073(75)^2 - 6.99(75) + 289.0$$

$$= 175.375$$

Algebraically, you can conclude that a height of 75 inches corresponds to a weight of 175.375 pounds. So, the graphical estimate of 175 is fairly good.

Checkpoints for Section 1.3

1. (a) Because $b = 2$, the y-intercept is $(0, 2)$. Because the slope is $m = -3$, the line falls three units for each unit the line moves to the right.

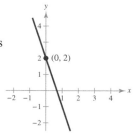

(b) By writing this equation in the form $y = (0)x - 3$, you can see that the y-intercept is $(0, -3)$ and the slope is $m = 0$. A zero slope implies that the line is horizontal.

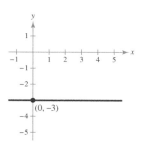

(c) By writing this equation in slope-intercept form

$$4x + y = 5$$

$$y = -4x + 5$$

you can see that the y-intercept is $(0, 5)$. Because the slope is $m = -4$, the line falls four units for each unit the line moves to the right.

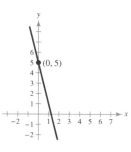

2. (a) The slope of the line passing through $(-5, -6)$ and $(2, 8)$ is $m = \dfrac{8 - (-6)}{2 - (-5)} = \dfrac{14}{7} = 2$.

(b) The slope of the line passing through $(4, 2)$ and $(2, 5)$ is $m = \dfrac{5 - 2}{2 - 4} = \dfrac{3}{-2} = -\dfrac{3}{2}$.

(c) The slope of the line passing through $(0, 0)$ and $(0, -6)$ is $m = \dfrac{-6 - 0}{0 - 0} = \dfrac{-6}{0}$. Because division by 0 is undefined, the slope is undefined and the line is vertical.

(d) The slope of the line passing through $(0, -1)$ and $(3, -1)$ is $m = \dfrac{-1 - (-1)}{3 - 0} = \dfrac{0}{3} = 0$.

3. (a) Use the point-slope form with $m = 2$ and $(x_1, y_1) = (3, -7)$.

$$y - y_1 = m(x - x_1)$$
$$y - (-7) = 2(x - 3)$$
$$y + 7 = 2x - 6$$
$$y = 2x - 13$$

The slope-intercept form of this equation is $y = 2x - 13$.

(b) Use the point-slope form with $m = \dfrac{-2}{3}$ and $(x_1, y_1) = (1, 1)$

$$y - y_1 = m(x - x_1)$$
$$y - 1 = \frac{-2}{3}(x - 1)$$
$$y - 1 = \frac{-2}{3}x + \frac{2}{3}$$
$$y = \frac{-2}{3}x + \frac{5}{3}$$

The slope-intercept form of this equation is $y = -\dfrac{2}{3}x + \dfrac{5}{3}$.

(c) Use the point-slope form with $m = 0$ and $(x_1, y_1) = (1, 1)$.

$$y - y_1 = m(x - x_1)$$
$$y - 1 = 0(x - 1)$$
$$y - 1 = 0$$
$$y - 1$$

The slope-intercept of the equation is the line $y = 1$.

4. By writing the equation of the given line in slope-intercept form

$$5x - 3y = 8$$
$$-3y = -5x + 8$$
$$y = \frac{5}{3}x - \frac{8}{3}$$

You can see that it has a slope of $m = \dfrac{5}{3}$.

(a) Any line parallel to the given line must also have a slope of $m = \dfrac{5}{3}$. So, the line through $(-4, 1)$ that is parallel to the given line has the following equation.

$$y - y_1 = m(x - x_1)$$
$$y - 1 = \frac{5}{3}(x - (-4))$$
$$y - 1 = \frac{5}{3}(x + 4)$$
$$y - 1 = \frac{5}{3}x + \frac{20}{3}$$
$$y = \frac{5}{3}x + \frac{23}{3}$$

(b) Any line perpendicular to the given line must also have a slope of $m = -\dfrac{3}{5}$ because $-\dfrac{3}{5}$ is the negative reciprocal of $\dfrac{5}{3}$. So, the line through $(-4, 1)$ that is perpendicular to the given line has the following equation.

$$y - y_1 = m(x - x_1)$$
$$y - 1 = -\frac{3}{5}(x - (-4))$$
$$y - 1 = -\frac{3}{5}(x + 4)$$
$$y - 1 = -\frac{3}{5}x - \frac{12}{5}$$
$$y = -\frac{3}{5}x - \frac{7}{5}$$

5. The horizontal length of the ramp is 32 feet or $12(32) = 384$ inches.

So, the slope of the ramp is

$$\text{Slope} = \frac{\text{vertical change}}{\text{horizontal change}} = \frac{36 \text{ in.}}{384 \text{ in.}} \approx 0.094.$$

Because $\dfrac{1}{12} \approx 0.083$, the slope of the ramp is steeper than recommended.

6. The y-intercept $(0, 1500)$ tells you that the value of the copier when it was purchased $(t = 0)$ was $1500. The slope of $m = -300$ tells you that the value of the copier decreases $300 each year since the copier was purchased.

7. Let V represent the value of the machine at the end of year t. The initial value of the machine can be represented by the data point $(0, 24{,}750)$ and the salvage value of the machine can be represented by the data point $(6, 0)$. The slope of the line is

$$m = \frac{0 - 24{,}750}{6 - 0}$$

$$m = -\$4125$$

The slope represents the annual depreciation in dollars per year. Using the point-slope form, you can write the equation of the line as follows

$$V - 24{,}750 = -4125(t - 0)$$

$$V - 24{,}750 = -4125t$$

$$V = -4125t + 24{,}750$$

The equation $V = -4125t + 24{,}750$ represents the book value of the machine each year.

8. Let $t = 9$ represent 2009. Then the two given values are represented by the data points $(9, 58.6)$ and $(10, 56.6)$.

The slope of the line through these points is

$$m = \frac{56.6 - 58.6}{10 - 9} = -2.0.$$

You can find the equation that relates the sales y and the year t to be,

$$y - 56.6 = -2.0(t - 10)$$

$$y - 56.6 = -2.0t + 20.0$$

$$y = -2.0t + 76.6$$

According to this equation, the sales in 2013 will be
$$y = -2.0(13) + 76.6$$

$$= -26 + 76.6$$

$$= \$50.6 \text{ billion.}$$

Checkpoints for Section 1.4

1. (a) This mapping *does not* describe y as a function of x. The input value of -1 is assigned or matched to two different y-values.

 (b) The table *does* describe y as a function of x. Each input value is matched with exactly one output value.

2. (a) Solving for y yields

$$x^2 + y^2 = 8 \qquad \text{Write original equation.}$$

$$y^2 = 8 - x^2 \qquad \text{Subtract } x^2 \text{ from each side.}$$

$$y = \pm\sqrt{8 - x^2}. \quad \text{Solve for } y.$$

The $\pm$ indicates that to a given value of x there corresponds two values of y. So y is not a function of x.

 (b) Solving for y yields,

$$y - 4x^2 = 36 \qquad \text{Write original equation.}$$

$$y = 36 + 4x^2 \qquad \text{Add } 4x^2 \text{ to each side.}$$

To each value of x there corresponds exactly one value of y. So, y is a function of x.

3. (a) Replacing x with 2 in $f(x) = 10 - 3x^2$ yields the following.

$$f(2) = 10 - 3(2)^2$$

$$= 10 - 12$$

$$= -2$$

 (b) Replacing x with -4 yields the following.

$$f(-4) = 10 - 3(-4)^2$$

$$= 10 - 48$$

$$= -38$$

 (c) Replacing x with $x - 1$ yields the following.

$$f(x - 1) = 10 - 3(x - 1)^2$$

$$= 10 - 3(x^2 - 2x + 1)$$

$$= 10 - 3x^2 + 6x - 3$$

$$= -3x^2 + 6x + 7$$

4. Because $x = -2$ is less than 0, use $f(x) = x^2 + 1$ to

obtain $f(-2) = (-2)^2 + 1 = 4 + 1 = 5$.

Because $x = 2$ is greater than or equal to 0, use
$f(x) = x - 1$ to obtain $f(2) = 2 - 1 = 1$.

For $x = 3$, use $f(x) = x - 1$ to obtain

$f(3) = 3 - 1 = 2$.

5. Set $f(x) = 0$ and solve for x.

$$f(x) = 0$$
$$x^2 - 16 = 0$$
$$(x + 4)(x - 4) = 0$$
$$x + 4 = 0 \Rightarrow x = -4$$
$$x - 4 = 0 \Rightarrow x = 4$$

So, $f(x) = 0$ when $x = -4$ or $x = 4$.

6.

$x^2 + 6x - 24 = 4x - x^2$	Set $f(x)$ equal to $g(x)$.
$2x^2 + 2x - 24 = 0$	Write in general form.
$2(x^2 + x - 12) = 0$	Factor out common factor.
$x^2 + x - 12 = 0$	Divide each side by 2.
$(x + 4)(x - 3) = 0$	Factor.
$x + 4 = 0 \Rightarrow x = -4$	Set 1st factor equal to 0.
$x - 3 = 0 \Rightarrow x = 3$	Set 2nd factor equal to 0.

So, $f(x) = g(x)$, when $x = -4$ or $x = 3$.

7. (a) The domain of f consists of all first coordinates in the set of ordered pairs.

Domain $= \{-2, -1, 0, 1, 2\}$

(b) Excluding x-values that yield zero in the denominator, the domain of g is the set of all real numbers x except $x = 3$.

(c) Because the function represents the circumference of a circle, the values of the radius r must be positive. So, the domain is the set of real numbers r such that $r > 0$.

(d) This function is defined only for x-values for which $x - 16 \geq 0$. You can conclude that $x \geq 16$. So, the domain is the interval $[16, \infty)$.

8. Use the formula for surface area of a cylinder,

$$s = 2\pi r^2 + 2\pi rh.$$

(a) $s(r) = 2\pi r^2 + 2\pi r(4r)$

$\quad = 2\pi r^2 + 8\pi r^2$

$\quad = 10\pi r^2$

(b) $s(h) = 2\pi\left(\dfrac{h}{4}\right)^2 + 2\pi\left(\dfrac{h}{4}\right)h$

$\quad = 2\pi\left(\dfrac{h^2}{16}\right) + \dfrac{\pi h^2}{2}$

$\quad = \dfrac{1}{8}\pi h^2 + \dfrac{1}{2}\pi h^2$

$\quad = \dfrac{5}{8}\pi h^2$

9. When $x = 60$, you can find the height of the baseball as follows

$f(x) = -0.004x^2 + 0.3x + 6$	Write original function.
$f(60) = -0.004(60)^2 + 0.3(60) + 6$	Substitute 60 for x.
$\quad = 9.6$	Simplify.

When $x = 60$, the height of the ball thrown from the second baseman is 9.6 feet. So, the first baseman cannot catch the baseball without jumping.

10. From 2003 through 2005, use $V(t) = 33.65t + 77.8$.

2003: $V(3) = 33.65(3) + 77.8 = 178.75$ thousand vehicles

2004: $V(4) = 33.65(4) + 77.8 = 212.40$ thousand vehicles

2005: $V(5) = 33.65(5) + 77.8 = 246.05$ thousand vehicles

From 2006 through 2009, use $V(t) = 70.75t - 126.6$.

2006: $V(6) = 70.75(6) - 126.6 = 297.90$ thousand vehicles

2007: $V(7) = 70.75(7) - 126.6 = 368.65$ thousand vehicles

2008: $V(8) = 70.75(8) - 126.6 = 439.40$ thousand vehicles

2009: $V(9) = 70.75(9) - 126.6 = 510.15$ thousand vehicles

11.
$$\frac{f(x+h) - f(x)}{h} = \frac{\left[(x+h)^2 + 2(x+h) - 3\right] - \left(x^2 + 2x - 3\right)}{h}$$
$$= \frac{x^2 + 2xh + h^2 + 2x + 2h - 3 - x^2 - 2x + 3}{h}$$
$$= \frac{2xh + h^2 + 2h}{h}$$
$$= \frac{2(2x + h + 2)}{h}$$
$$= 2x + h + 2, \quad h \neq 0$$

Checkpoints for Section 1.5

1. (a) The open dot at $(-3, -6)$ indicates that $x = -3$ is not in the domain of f. So, the domain of f is all real numbers, except $x \neq -3$, or $(-\infty, -3) \cup (-3, \infty)$.

(b) Because $(0, 3)$ is a point on the graph of f, it follows that $f(0) = 3$. Similarly, because the point $(3, -6)$ is a point on the graph of f, it follows that $f(3) = -6$.

(c) Because the graph of f does not extend above $f(0) = 3$, the range of f is the interval $(-\infty, 3]$.

2.

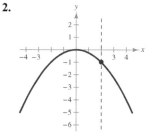

This *is* a graph of y as a function of x, because every vertical line intersects the graph at most once. That is, for a particular input x, there is at most one output y.

3. To find the zeros of a function, set the function equal to zero, and solve for the independent variable.

(a) $2x^2 + 13x - 24 = 0$ Set $f(x)$ equal to 0.

     $(2x - 3)(x + 8) = 0$ Factor.

         $2x - 3 = 0 \Rightarrow x = \dfrac{3}{2}$ Set 1st factor equal to 0.

         $x + 8 = 0 \Rightarrow x = -8$ Set 2nd factor equal to 0.

The zeros of f are $x = \dfrac{3}{2}$ and $x = -8$. The graph of f has $\left(\dfrac{3}{2}, 0\right)$ and $(-8, 0)$ as its x-intercepts.

(b) $\sqrt{t - 25} = 0$ Set $g(t)$ equal to 0.

     $\left(\sqrt{t - 25}\right)^2 = (0)^2$ Square each side.

         $t - 25 = 0$ Simplify.

            $t = 25$ Add 25 to each side.

The zero of g is $t = 25$. The graph of g has $(25, 0)$ as its t-intercept.

(c)
$$\frac{x^2 - 2}{x - 1} = 0 \qquad \text{Set } h(x) \text{ equal to zero.}$$

$$(x - 1)\left(\frac{x^2 - 2}{x - 1}\right) = (x - 1)(0) \qquad \text{Multiply each side by } x - 1.$$

$$x^2 - 2 = 0 \qquad \text{Simplify.}$$

$$x^2 = 2 \qquad \text{Add 2 to each side.}$$

$$x = \pm\sqrt{2} \qquad \text{Extract square roots.}$$

The zeros of h are $x = \pm\sqrt{2}$. The graph of h has $\left(\sqrt{2}, 0\right)$ and $\left(-\sqrt{2}, 0\right)$ as its x-intercepts.

4.

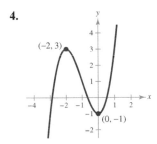

This function is increasing on the interval $(-\infty, -2)$, decreasing on the interval $(-2, 0)$, and increasing on the interval $(0, \infty)$.

5.

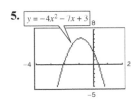

By using the zoom and the trace features or the maximum feature of a graphing utility, you can determine that the function has a relative maximum at the point $\left(-\frac{7}{8}, \frac{97}{16}\right)$ or $(-0.875, 6.0625)$.

6. (a) The average rate of change of f from $x_1 = -3$ to $x_2 = -2$ is

$$\frac{f(x_2) - f(x_1)}{x_2 - x_1} = \frac{f(-2) - f(-3)}{-2 - (-3)}$$

$$= \frac{0 - 3}{1} = -3.$$

(b) The average rate of change of f from $x_1 = -2$ to $x_2 = 0$ is

$$\frac{f(x_2) - f(x_1)}{x_2 - x_1} = \frac{f(0) - f(-2)}{0 - (-2)}$$

$$= \frac{0 - 0}{2} = 0.$$

7. (a) The average speed of the car from $t_1 = 0$ to $t_2 = 1$ second is

$$\frac{s(t_2) - s(t_1)}{t_2 - t_1} = \frac{20 - 0}{1 - 0} = 20 \text{ feet per second.}$$

(b) The average speed of the car from $t_1 = 1$ to $t_2 = 4$ seconds is

$$\frac{s(t_2) - s(t_1)}{t_2 - t_1} = \frac{160 - 20}{4 - 1}$$

$$= \frac{140}{3}$$

$$\approx 46.7 \text{ feet per second.}$$

8. (a) The function $f(x) = 5 - 3x$ is neither odd nor even because $f(-x) \neq -f(x)$ and $f(-x) \neq f(x)$ as follows.

$$f(-x) = 5 - 3(-x)$$

$$= 5 + 3x \neq -f(x) \qquad \text{not odd}$$

$$\neq f(x) \qquad \text{not even}$$

So, the graph of f is not symmetric to the origin nor the y-axis.

(b) The function $g(x) = x^4 - x^2 - 1$ is even because $g(-x) = g(x)$ as follows.

$$g(-x) = (-x)^4 - (-x)^2 - 1$$

$$= x^4 - x^2 - 1$$

$$= g(x)$$

So, the graph of g is symmetric to the y-axis.

(c) The function $h(x) = 2x^3 + 3x$ is odd because $h(-x) = -h(x),$

$$h(-x) = 2(-x)^3 + 3(-x)$$

$$= -2x^3 - 3x$$

$$= -\left(2x^3 + 3x\right)$$

$$= -h(x)$$

So, the graph of h is symmetric to the origin.

Checkpoints for Section 1.6

1. To find the equation of the line that passes through the points $(x_1, y_1) = (-2, 6)$ and $(x_2, y_2) = (4, -4)$, first find the slope of the line.

$$m = \frac{y_2 - y_1}{x_2 - x_1} = \frac{-9 - 6}{4 - (-2)} = \frac{-15}{6} = \frac{-5}{2}$$

Next, use the point-slope form of the equation of the line.

$y - y_1 = m(x - x_1)$ Point-slope form

$y - 6 = -\dfrac{5}{2}\big[x - (-2)\big]$ Substitute x_1, y_1 and m.

$y - 6 = -\dfrac{5}{2}(x + 2)$ Simplify.

$y - 6 = -\dfrac{5}{2}x - 5$ Simplify.

$y = -\dfrac{5}{2}x + 1$ Simplify.

$f(x) = -\dfrac{5}{2}x + 1$ Function notation

2. For $x = -\frac{3}{2}$, $f\left(-\frac{3}{2}\right) = \left[\!\left[-\frac{3}{2} + 2\right]\!\right]$

$= \left[\!\left[\frac{1}{2}\right]\!\right]$

$= 0$

Since the greatest integer $\leq \frac{1}{2}$ is 0, $f\left(-\frac{3}{2}\right) = 0$.

For $x = 1$, $f(1) = \left[\!\left[1 + 2\right]\!\right]$

$= \left[\!\left[3\right]\!\right]$

$= 3$

Since the greatest integer ≤ 3 is 3, $f(1) = 3$.

For $x = -\frac{5}{2}$, $f\left(-\frac{5}{2}\right) = \left[\!\left[-\frac{5}{2} + 2\right]\!\right]$

$= \left[\!\left[-\frac{1}{2}\right]\!\right]$

$= -1$

Since the greatest integer $\leq -\frac{1}{2}$ is -1, $f\left(-\frac{5}{2}\right) = -1$.

3. This piecewise-defined function consists of two linear functions. At $x = -4$ and to the left of $x = -4$, the graph is the line $y = -\frac{1}{2}x - 6$, and to the right of $x = -4$ the graph is the line $y = x + 5$. Notice that the point $(-4, -2)$ is a solid dot and $(-4, 1)$ is an open dot. This is because $f(-4) = -2$.

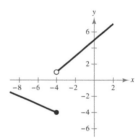

Checkpoints for Section 1.7

1. (a) Relative to the graph of $f(x) = x^3$, the graph of $h(x) = x^3 + 5$ is an upward shift of five units.

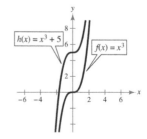

    (b) Relative to the graph of $f(x) = x^3$, the graph of $g(x) = (x - 3)^3 + 2$ involves a right shift of three units and an upward shift of two units.

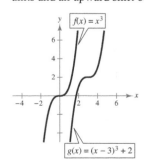

2. The graph of j is a horizontal shift of three units to the left *followed by* a reflection in the x-axis of the graph of $f(x) = x^4$. So, the equation for j is $j(x) = -(x + 3)^4$.

3. (a) **Algebraic Solution:**

   The graph of g is a reflection of the graph of f in the x-axis because

   $$g(x) = -\sqrt{x - 1}$$
   $$= -f(x).$$

   Graphical Solution:

   Graph f and g on the same set of coordinate axes. From the graph, you can see that the graph of g is a reflection of the graph of f in the x-axis.

   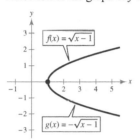

   (b) **Algebraic Solution:**

   The graph of h is a reflection of the graph of f in the y-axis because

   $$h(x) = \sqrt{-x - 1}$$
   $$= f(-x).$$

   Graphical Solution:

   Graph f and h on the same set of coordinate axes. From the graph, you can see that the graph h is a reflection of the graph of f, in the y-axis.

   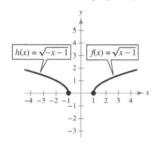

4. (a) Relative to the graph of $f(x) = x^2$, the graph of $g(x) = 4x^2 = 4f(x)$ is a vertical stretch (each y-value is multiplied by 4) of the graph of f.

   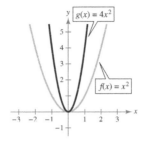

   (b) Relative to the graph of $f(x) = x^2$, the graph of $h(x) = \frac{1}{4}x^2 = \frac{1}{4}f(x)$ is a vertical shrink $\left(\text{each } y\text{-value is multiplied by } \frac{1}{4}\right)$ of the graph of f.

   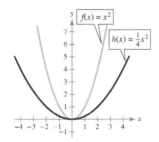

5. (a) Relative to the graph of $f(x) = x^2 + 3$, the graph of $g(x) = f(2x) = (2x)^2 + 3 = 4x^2 + 3$ is a horizontal shrink $(c > 1)$ of the graph of f.

   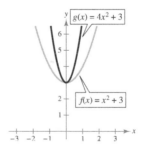

   (b) Relative to the graph of $f(x) = x^2 + 3$, the graph of $h(x) = f\left(\frac{1}{2}x\right) = \left(\frac{1}{2}x\right)^2 + 3 = \frac{1}{4}x^2 + 3$ is a horizontal stretch $(0 < c < 1)$ of the graph of f.

   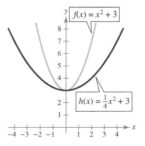

Checkpoints for Section 1.8

1. The sum of f and g is

$$(f + g)(x) = f(x) + g(x)$$
$$= (x^2) + (1 - x)$$
$$= x^2 - x + 1.$$

When $x = 2$, the value of this sum is

$$(f + g)(2) = (2)^2 - (2) + 1$$
$$= 3.$$

2. The difference of f and g is

$$(f - g)(x) = f(x) - g(x)$$
$$= (x^2) - (1 - x)$$
$$= x^2 + x - 1.$$

When $x = 3$, the value of the difference is

$$(f - g)(3) = (3)^2 + (3) - 1$$
$$= 11.$$

3. The product of f and g is

$$(f\,g) = f(x)g(x)$$
$$= (x^2)(1 - x)$$
$$= x^2 - x^3$$
$$= -x^3 + x^2.$$

When $x = 3$, the value of the product is

$$(f\,g)(3) = -(3)^3 - (3)^2$$
$$= -27 + 9$$
$$= -18.$$

4. The quotient of f and g is

$$\left(\frac{f}{g}\right)(x) = \frac{f(x)}{g(x)} = \frac{\sqrt{x - 3}}{\sqrt{16 - x^2}}.$$

The quotient of g and f is

$$\left(\frac{g}{f}\right)(x) = \frac{g(x)}{f(x)} = \frac{\sqrt{16 - x^2}}{\sqrt{x - 3}}.$$

The domain of f is $[3, \infty)$ and the domain of g is $[-4, 4]$. The intersection of these two domains is $[3, 4]$. So, the domain of f/g is $[3, 4)$ and the domain of g/f is $(3, 4]$.

5. (a) The composition of f with g is as follows.

$$(f \circ g)(x) = f(g(x))$$
$$= f(4x^2 + 1)$$
$$= 2(4x^2 + 1) + 5$$
$$= 8x^2 + 2 + 5$$
$$= 8x^2 + 7$$

(b) The composition of g with f is as follows.

$$(g \circ f)(x) = g(f(x))$$
$$= g(2x + 5)$$
$$= 4(2x + 5)^2 + 1$$
$$= 4(4x^2 + 20x + 25) + 1$$
$$= 16x^2 + 80x + 100 + 1$$
$$= 16x^2 + 80x + 101$$

(c) Use the result of part (a).

$$(f \circ g)\left(-\tfrac{1}{2}\right) = 8\left(-\tfrac{1}{2}\right)^2 + 7$$
$$= 8\left(\tfrac{1}{4}\right) + 7$$
$$= 2 + 7$$
$$= 9$$

6. The composition of f with g is as follows.

$$(f \circ g)(x) = f(g(x))$$
$$= f(x^2 + 4)$$
$$= \sqrt{x^2 + 4}$$

The domain of f is $[0, \infty)$ and the domain of g is the set of all real numbers. The range of g is $[4, \infty)$, which is in the range of f, $[0, \infty)$. Therefore the domain of $f \circ g$ is all real numbers.

7. Let the inner function to be $g(x) = 8 - x$ and the outer function to be $f(x) = \dfrac{\sqrt[3]{x}}{5}$.

$$h(x) = \frac{\sqrt[3]{8 - x}}{5}$$
$$= f(8 - x)$$
$$= f(g(x))$$

8. (a) $(N \circ T)(t) = N\big(T(t)\big)$

$$= 8(2t + 2)^2 - 14(2t + 2) + 200$$

$$= 8\big(4t^2 + 8t + 4\big) - 28t - 28 + 200$$

$$= 32t^2 + 64t + 32 - 28t - 28 + 200$$

$$= 32t^2 + 36t + 204$$

The composite function $(N \circ T)(t)$ represents the number of bacteria in the food as a function of the amount of time the food has been out of refrigeration.

(b) Let $(N \circ T)(t) = 1000$ and solve for t.

$$32t^2 + 36t + 204 = 1000$$

$$32t^2 + 36t - 796 = 0$$

$$4\big(8t^2 + 9t - 199\big) = 0$$

$$8t^2 + 9t - 199 = 0$$

Use the quadratic formula:

$$t = \frac{-9 \pm \sqrt{(9)^2 - 4(8)(-199)}}{2(8)}$$

$$- \frac{-9 \pm \sqrt{6449}}{16}$$

$t \approx 4.5$ and $t \approx -5.6$.

Using $t \approx 4.5$ hours, the bacteria count reaches approximately 1000 about 4.5 hours after the food is removed from the refrigerator.

Checkpoints for Section 1.9

1. The function f multiplies each input by $\frac{1}{5}$. To "undo" this function, you need to multiply each input by 5. So, the inverse function of $f(x) = \frac{1}{5}x$ is $f^{-1}(x) = 5x$.

To verify this, show that

$$f\big(f^{-1}(x)\big) = x \text{ and } f^{-1}\big(f(x)\big) = x.$$

$$f\big(f^{-1}(x)\big) = f(5x) = \tfrac{1}{5}(5x) = x$$

$$f^{-1}\big(f(x)\big) = f^{-1}\big(\tfrac{1}{5}x\big) = 5\big(\tfrac{1}{5}x\big) = x$$

So, the inverse function of $f(x) = \frac{1}{5}x$ is $f^{-1}(x) = 5x$.

2. By forming the composition of f and g, you have

$$f\big(g(x)\big) = f(7x + 4) = \frac{(7x + 4) - 4}{7} = \frac{7x}{7} = x.$$

So, it appears that g is the inverse function of f. To confirm this, form the composition of g and f.

$$g\big(f(x)\big) = g\left(\frac{x - 4}{7}\right) = 7\left(\frac{x - 4}{7}\right) + 4 = x - 4 + 4 = x$$

By forming the composition of f and h, you can see that h is *not* the inverse function of f, since the result is not the identity function x.

$$f\big(h(x)\big) = f\left(\frac{7}{x - 4}\right) = \frac{\left(\dfrac{7}{x - 4}\right) - 4}{7} = \frac{23 - 4x}{7(x - 4)} \neq x$$

So, g is the inverse function of f.

3. The graphs of $f(x) = 4x - 1$ and $f^{-1}(x) = \frac{1}{4}(x + 1)$ are shown. You can see that they are reflections of each other in the line $y = x$. This reflective property can also be verified using a few points and the fact that if the point (a, b) is on the graph of f then the point (b, a) is on the graph of f^{-1}.

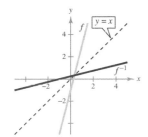

Graph of $f(x) = 4x - 1$	Graph of $f^{-1}(x) = \frac{1}{4}(x + 1)$
$(-1, -5)$	$(-5, -1)$
$(0, -1)$	$(-1, 0)$
$(1, 3)$	$(3, 1)$
$(2, 7)$	$(7, 2)$

4. The graphs of $f(x) = x^2 + 1$, $x \geq 0$ and $f^{-1}(x) = \sqrt{x - 1}$ are shown. You can see that they are reflections of each other in the line $y = x$. This reflective property can also be verified using a few points and the fact that if the point (a, b) is on the graph of f then the point (b, a) is on the graph of f^{-1}.

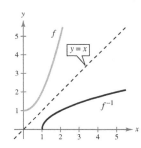

Graph of $f(x) = x^2 + 1$, $x \geq 0$	Graph of $f^{-1}(x) = \sqrt{x - 1}$
$(0, 1)$	$(1, 0)$
$(1, 2)$	$(2, 1)$
$(2, 5)$	$(5, 2)$
$(3, 10)$	$(10, 3)$

5. (a) The graph of $f(x) = \frac{1}{2}(3 - x)$ is shown.

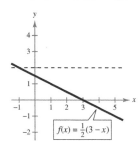

Because no horizontal line intersects the graph of f at more than one point, f is a one-to-one function and *does* have an inverse function.

(b) The graph of $f(x) = |x|$ is shown.

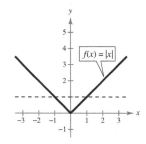

Because it is possible to find a horizontal line that intersects the graph of f at more than one point, f is *not* a one-to-one function and *does not* have an inverse function.

6. The graph of $f(x) = \dfrac{5 - 3x}{x + 2}$ is shown.

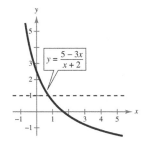

This graph passes the Horizontal Line Test. So, you know f is one-to-one and has an inverse function.

$$f(x) = \frac{5 - 3x}{x + 2} \qquad \text{Write original function.}$$

$$y = \frac{5 - 3x}{x + 2} \qquad \text{Replace } f(x) \text{ with } y.$$

$$x = \frac{5 - 3y}{y + 2} \qquad \text{Interchange } x \text{ and } y.$$

$$x(y + 2) = 5 - 3y \qquad \text{Multiply each side by } y + 2.$$

$$xy + 2x = 5 - 3y \qquad \text{Distribute Property}$$

$$xy + 3y = 5 - 2x \qquad \text{Collect like terms with } y.$$

$$y(x + 3) = 5 - 2x \qquad \text{Factor.}$$

$$y = \frac{5 - 2x}{x + 3} \qquad \text{Solve for } y.$$

$$f^{-1}(x) = \frac{5 - 2x}{x + 3} \qquad \text{Replace } y \text{ with } f^{-1}(x).$$

7. The graph of $f(x) = \sqrt[3]{10 + x}$ is shown.

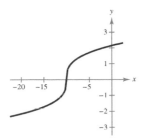

Because this graph passes the Horizontal Line Test, you know that f is one-to-one and has an inverse function.

$$f(x) = \sqrt[3]{10 + x}$$
$$y = \sqrt[3]{10 + x}$$
$$x = \sqrt[3]{10 + y}$$
$$x^3 = 10 + y$$
$$y = x^3 - 10$$
$$f^{-1}(x) = x^3 - 10$$

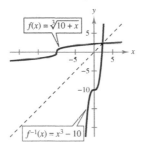

The graphs of f and f^{-1} are reflections of each other in the line $y = x$. So, the inverse of $f(x) = \sqrt[3]{10 + x}$

is $f^{-1}(x) = x^3 - 10$.

To verify, check that $f\big(f^{-1}(x)\big) = x$ and $f^{-1}\big(f(x)\big) = x$.

$$f\big(f^{-1}(x)\big) = f\big(x^3 - 10\big) \qquad\qquad f^{-1}\big(f(x)\big) = f^{-1}\big(\sqrt[3]{10 + x}\big)$$
$$= \sqrt[3]{10 + \big(x^3 - 10\big)} \qquad\qquad\qquad = \big(\sqrt[3]{10 + x}\big)^3 - 10$$
$$= \sqrt[3]{x^3} \qquad\qquad\qquad\qquad\qquad = 10 + x - 10$$
$$= x \qquad\qquad\qquad\qquad\qquad\qquad = x$$

Checkpoints for Section 1.10

1.

The graph shows Median sales price (in thousands of dollars) on the y-axis versus Year (3 ↔ 2003) on the t-axis.

Solution: The actual data are plotted, along with the graph of the linear model. From the graph, it appears that the model is a "good fit" for the actual data. You can see how well the model fits by comparing the actual values of y with the values of y given by the model. The values given by the model are labeled y^* in the table below.

t	3	4	5	6	7	8	9	10
y	179.4	185.4	191.0	196.7	202.6	208.7	214.9	221.4
y^*	179.2	185.1	191.1	197.1	203.0	209.0	214.9	220.9

2.

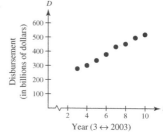

Solution   Let $t = 3$ represents 2003. The scatter plot for the data is shown. Using the *regression* feature of a graphing utility, you can determine that the equation of the least squares regression line is

$M = 36.85t + 161.2$

To check this model, compare the actual M values with the M values given by the model, which are labeled M^* in the table. The correlation coefficient for this model is $r \approx 0.996$, which implies that the model is a good fit.

t	3	4	5	6	7	8	9	10
M	277.8	301.5	336.9	380.4	434.8	455.1	498.2	521.1
M^*	271.8	308.6	345.5	382.3	419.2	456.0	492.9	529.7

3. *Verbal Model*: | Simple interest | $= \boxed{r}$ | Amount of investment |

Labels: Simple interest $= I$ (dollars)

          Amount of investment $= P$ (dollars)

          Interest rate $= r$ (percent in decimal form)

Equation: $I = rP$

To solve for r, substitute the given information into the equation $I = rP$, and then solve for r.

$I = rP$ Write direct variation model.

$187.50 = r(2500)$ Substitute 187.50 for t and 2500 for P.

$\dfrac{187.50}{2500} = r$ Divide each side by 2500.

$0.075 = r$ Simplify.

So, the mathematical model is $I = 0.075P$.

4. Letting s be the distance (in feet) the object falls and letting t be the time (in seconds) that the object falls, you have $s = Kt^2$.

Because $s = 144$ feet when $t = 3$ seconds, you can see that $K = \frac{144}{9}$ as follows.

$s = Kt^2$ Write direct variation model.

$144 = K(3)^2$ Substitute 144 for s and 3 for t.

$144 = 9K$ Simplify.

$\frac{144}{9} = K$ Divide each side by 9.

$16 = K$

So, the equation relating distance to time is $s = 16t^2$.

To find the distance the object falls in 6 seconds , let $t = 6$.

$s = 16t^2$ Write direct variation model.

$s = 16(6)^2$ Substitute 6 for t.

$s = 16(36)$ Simplify.

$s = 576$ Simplify.

So, the object falls 576 feet in 6 seconds.

5. Let p be the price and let x be the demand. Because x varies inversely as p, you have

$$x = \frac{k}{p}$$

Now because $x = 600$ then $p = 2.75$ you have

$$x = \frac{k}{p} \qquad \text{Write inverse variation model.}$$

$$600 = \frac{k}{2.75} \qquad \text{Substitute 600 for } x \text{ and 2.75 for } p.$$

$$(600)(2.75) = k \qquad \text{Multiply each side by 2.75.}$$

$$1650 = k. \qquad \text{Simplify.}$$

So, the equation relating price and demand is

$$x = \frac{1650}{p}.$$

When $p = 3.25$ the demand is

$$x = \frac{1650}{p} \qquad \text{Write inverse variation model.}$$

$$= \frac{1650}{3.25} \qquad \text{Substitute 3.25 for } p.$$

$$\approx 508 \text{ units.} \quad \text{Simplify.}$$

So, the demand for the product is 508 units when the price of the product is $3.25.

6. Let R be the resistance (in ohms), let L be the length (in inches), and let A be the cross-sectional area (in square inches).

Because R varies directly as L and inversely as A, you have

$$R = \frac{kL}{A}.$$

Now, because $R = 66.17$ ohms when

$L = 1000$ feet $= 12{,}000$ inches and

$$A = \pi \left(\frac{0.0126}{2} \right)^2 \approx 1.247 \times 10^{-4} \text{ square inches,}$$

you have

$$66.17 = \frac{k(12{,}000)}{1.247 \times 10^{-4}}$$

$$6.876 \times 10^{-7} \approx k$$

So, the equation relating resistance, length, and the cross-sectional area is $R = 6.876 \times 10^{-7}\, \dfrac{L}{A}.$

To find the length of copper wire that will produce a resistance of 33.5 ohms, let $R = 33.5$ and $A = 1.247 \times 10^{-4}$ and solve for L.

$$R = \left(6.876 \times 10^{-7}\right)\frac{L}{A}$$

$$33.5 = \left(6.876 \times 10^{-7}\right)\frac{L}{\left(1.247 \times 10^{-4}\right)}$$

$$(33.5)\left(1.247 \times 10^{-4}\right) = \left(6.876 \times 10^{-7}\right)L$$

$$\frac{(33.5)\left(1.247 \times 10^{-4}\right)}{\left(6.876 \times 10^{-7}\right)} = L$$

$$6075.4 \times L$$

So, the length of the wire is approximately 6075.4 inches or about 506.3 feet.

7. $E = $ kinetic energy, $m = $ mass, and $V = $ velocity.

Because E varies jointly with the object's mass, m and the square of the object's velocity, V you have

$$E = kmV^2$$

For $E = 6400$ joules, $m = 50$ kg, and $V = 16$m/sec, you have

$$E = kmV^2$$

$$6400 = k(50)(16)^2$$

$$6400 = k(12800)$$

$$\tfrac{1}{2} = k$$

So, the equation relating kinetic energy, mass, and velocity is $E = \tfrac{1}{2}mV$.

When $m = 70$ and $V = 20$, the kinetic energy is

$$E = \tfrac{1}{2}mV^2 = \tfrac{1}{2}(70)(20)^2 = \tfrac{1}{2}(70)(400)$$

$$= 14{,}000 \text{ joules.}$$

Chapter 2

Checkpoints for Section 2.1

1. (a) Compared with the graph of $y = x^2$, each output of $f(x) = \frac{1}{4}x^2$ "shrinks" by a factor of $\frac{1}{4}$, creating a broader parabola.

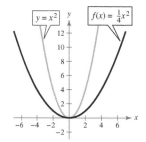

(b) Compared with the graph of $y = x^2$, each output of $f(x) = -\frac{1}{6}x^2$ is reflected in the x-axis and "shrinks" by a factor of $\frac{1}{6}$, creating a broader parabola.

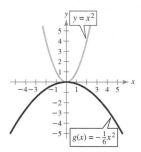

(c) Compared with $y = x^2$, each output of of $h(x) = \frac{5}{2}x^2$ "stretches" by a factor of $\frac{5}{2}$, creating a narrower parabola.

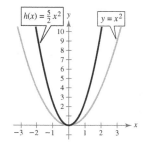

(d) Compared with $y = -4x^2$, each output of $k(x)$ is reflected in the x-axis and "stretches" by a factor of 4.

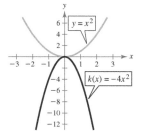

2. $f(x) = 3x^2 - 6x + 4$ Write original function.

$\quad = 3(x^2 - 2x) + 4$ Factor 3 out of x-terms.

$\quad = 3(x^2 - 2x + 1 - 1) + 4$ Add and subtract 1 within parenthesis.

$\quad = 3(x^2 - 2x + 1) - 3(1) + 4$ Regroup terms.

$\quad = 3(x^2 - 2x + 1) - 3 + 4$ Simplify.

$\quad = 3(x - 1)^2 + 1$ Write in standard form.

You can see that the graph of f is a parabola that opens upward and has its vertex at $(1, 1)$.

This corresponds to a right shift of one unit and an upward shift of one unit relative to the graph of $y = 3x^2$, which is a "stretch" of $y = x^2$.

The axis of the parabola is the vertical line through the vertex, $x = 1$.

3. $f(x) = x^2 - 4x + 3$ Write original function.

$\quad\quad = \left(x^2 - 4x + 4 - 4\right) + 3$ Add and subtract 4 within parenthesis.

$\quad\quad = \left(x^2 - 4x + 4\right) - 4 + 3$ Regroup terms.

$\quad\quad = \left(x^2 - 4x + 4\right) - 1$ Simplify.

$\quad\quad = \left(x^2 - 2\right)^2 - 1$ Write in standard form.

In standard form, you can see that f is a parabola that opens upward with vertex $(2, -1)$.

The x-intercepts of the graph are determined as follows.

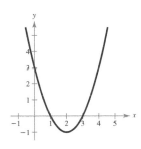

$x^2 - 4x + 3 = 0$

$(x - 3)(x - 1) = 0$

$\quad\quad x - 3 = 0 \Rightarrow x = 3$

$\quad\quad x - 1 = 0 \Rightarrow x = 1$

So, the x-intercepts are $(3, 0)$ and $(1, 0)$.

4. Because the vertex is $(h, k) = (-4, 11)$ the equation has the form

$\quad f(x) = a(x + 4)^2 + 11.$

Because the parabola passes through the point $(-6, 15)$ it follows that $f(-6) = 15$.

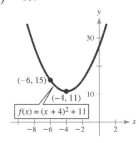

$f(x) = a(x + 4)^2 + 11$ Write standard form.

$\quad 15 = a(-6 + 4)^2 + 11$ Substitute -6 for x and 15 for $f(x)$.

$\quad 15 = a(-2)^2 + 11$ Simplify.

$\quad\quad 4 = 4a$ Subtract 11 from each side.

$\quad\quad 1 = a$ Divide each side by 4.

The equation in standard form is $f(x) = (x + 4)^2 + 11$.

5. For this quadratic function,

$\quad f(x) = ax^2 + bx + c = -0.007x^2 + x + 4$

which implies that $a = -0.007$ and $b = 1$.

Because $a < 0$, the function has a maximum at $x = -\dfrac{b}{2a}$. So, the baseball reaches its maximum height when it is

$x = -\dfrac{b}{2a} = -\dfrac{1}{2(-0.007)} = \dfrac{1}{0.014} \approx 71.4$ feet from home plate.

At this distance, the maximum height is $f(71.4) = -0.007(71.4)^2 + (71.4) + 4 \approx 39.7$ feet.

Checkpoints for Section 2.2

1. (a) The graph of $f(x) = (x + 5)^4$ is a left shift by five units of the graph of $y = x^4$.

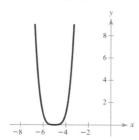

(b) The graph of $g(x) = x^4 - 7$ is a downward shift of seven units of the graph of $y = x^4$.

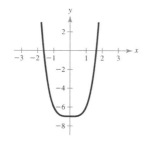

(c) The graph of $h(x) = 7 - x^4 = -x^4 + 7$ is a reflection in the x-axis then an upward shift of seven units of the graph of $y = x^4$.

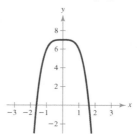

(d) The graph of $k(x) = \frac{1}{4}(x - 3)^4$ is a right shift by three units and a vertical "shrink" by a factor of $\frac{1}{4}$ of the graph of $y = x^4$.

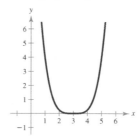

2. (a) Because the degree is odd and the leading coefficient is positive, the graph falls to the left and rises to the right.

(b) Because the degree is odd and the leading coefficient is negative, the graph rises to the left and falls to the right.

3. To find the real zeros of $f(x) = x^3 - 12x^2 + 36x$, set $f(x)$ equal to zero, and solve for x.

$$x^3 - 12x^2 + 36x = 0$$
$$x(x^2 - 12x + 36) = 0$$
$$x(x - 6)^2 = 0$$
$$x = 0$$
$$x - 6 = 0 \Rightarrow x = 6$$

So, the real zeros are $x = 0$ and $x = 6$. Because the function is a third-degree polynomial, the graph of f can have at most $3 - 1 = 2$ turning points. In this case, the graph of f has two turning points.

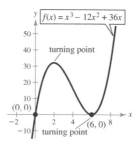

4. 1. *Apply the Leading Coefficient Test.*

Because the leading coefficient is positive and the degree is odd, you know that the graph eventually falls to the left and rises to the right.

2. *Find the Real Zeros of the Polynomial.*

By factoring $f(x) = 2x^3 - 6x^2$

$$= 2x^2(x - 3)$$

you can see that the real zeros of f are $x = 0$ (even multiplicity) and $x = 3$ (odd multiplicity). So, the x-intercepts occur at $(0, 0)$ and $(3, 0)$

3. *Plot a Few Additional Points.*

x	-1	1	2	4
$f(x)$	-8	-4	-8	32

4. *Draw the Graph.*

Draw a continuous curve through all of the points. Because $x = 0$ is of even multiplicity, you know that the graph touches the x-axis but does not cross it at $(0, 0)$. Because $x = 3$ is of odd multiplicity, you know that the graph should cross the x-axis at $(3, 0)$.

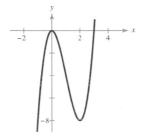

5. 1. *Apply the Leading Coefficient Test.*

Because the leading coefficient is negative and the degree is even, you know that the graph eventually falls to the left and falls to the right.

2. *Find the Real Zeros of the Polynomial.*

By factoring $f(x) = -\frac{1}{4}x^4 + \frac{3}{2}x^3 - \frac{9}{4}x^2$

$$= -\frac{1}{4}x^2(x^2 - 6x + 9)$$

$$= -\frac{1}{4}x^2(x - 3)^2$$

you can see that the real zeros of f are $x = 0$ (even multiplicity) and $x = 3$ (even multiplicity). So, the x-intercepts occur at $(0, 0)$ and $(3, 0)$.

3. *Plot a Few Additional Points.*

x	-1	1	2	4
$f(x)$	-4	-1	-1	-4

4. *Draw the graph.*

Draw a continuous curve through the points. As indicated by the multiplicities of the zeros, the graph touches but does not cross the x-axis at $(0, 0)$ and $(3, 0)$.

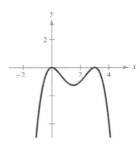

6. Begin by computing a few function values of $f(x) = x^3 - 3x^2 - 2$.

x	-1	0	1	2	3	4
$f(x)$	-6	-2	-4	-6	-2	14

Because $f(3)$ is negative and $f(4)$ is positive, you can apply the Intermediate Value Theorem to conclude that the function has a real zero between $x = 3$ and $x = 4$. To find this real zero more closely, divide the interval $[3, 4]$ into tenths and evaluate the function at each point.

x	3.1	3.2	3.3	3.4	3.5	3.6	3.7	3.8	3.9
$f(x)$	-1.039	0.048	1.267	2.624	4.125	5.776	7.583	9.552	11.689

So, f must have a real zero between 3.1 and 3.2.

To find a more accurate approximation, you can compute the function value between $f(3.1)$ and $f(3.2)$ and apply the Intermediate Value Theorem again.

Checkpoints for Section 2.3

1. To divide $3x^2 + 19x + 28$ by $x + 4$ using long division, you can set up the operation as shown.

$$
\require{enclose}
\begin{array}{r}
3x + 7 \\
x + 4 \enclose{longdiv}{3x^2 + 19x + 28} \\
\end{array}
$$

$$
\begin{array}{rl}
\underline{3x^2 + 12x} & \text{Multiply by: } 3x(x + 4). \\
7x + 28 & \text{Subtract.} \\
\underline{7x + 28} & \text{Multiply by: } 7(x + 4). \\
0 & \text{Subtract.}
\end{array}
$$

From this division, you can conclude that

$$3x^2 + 19x + 28 = (x + 4)(3x + 7).$$

2. To divide $x^3 - 2x^2 - 9$ by $x - 3$ using long division, you can set up the operation as shown. Because there is no x-term in the dividend, rewrite the dividend as $x^3 - 2x^2 + 0x - 9$ before you apply the Division Algorithm.

$$
\begin{array}{r}
x^2 + x + 3 \\
x - 3 \enclose{longdiv}{x^3 - 2x^2 + 0x - 9} \\
\end{array}
$$

$$
\begin{array}{rl}
\underline{x^3 - 3x^2} & \text{Multiply } x^2 \text{ by } x - 3. \\
x^2 + 0x - 9 & \text{Subtract.} \\
\underline{x^2 - 3x} & \text{Multiply } x \text{ by } x - 3. \\
3x - 9 & \text{Subtract.} \\
\underline{3x - 9} & \text{Multiply } 3 \text{ by } x - 3. \\
0 & \text{Subtract.}
\end{array}
$$

So, $x - 3$ divides evenly into $x^3 - 2x^2 - 9$, and you can write $\dfrac{x^3 - 2x^2 - 9}{x - 3} = x^2 + x + 3,\ x \neq 3.$

You can check this result by multiplying

$$(x - 3)(x^2 + x + 3) = x^3 - 3x^2 + x^2 - 3x + 3x - 9$$
$$= x^3 - 2x^2 - 9.$$

3. To divide $-x^3 + 9x + 6x^4 - x^2 - 3$ by $1 + 3x$ using long division, begin by rewriting the dividend and divisor in descending powers of x.

$$
\begin{array}{r}
2x^3 - x^2 \quad\quad + 3 \\
3x + 1 \enclose{longdiv}{6x^4 - x^3 - x^2 + 9x - 3} \\
\end{array}
$$

$$
\begin{array}{rl}
\underline{6x^4 + 2x^3} & \text{Multiply } 2x^3 \text{ by } 3x + 1. \\
-3x^3 - x^2 + 9x - 3 & \text{Subtract.} \\
\underline{-3x^3 - x^2} & \text{Multiply } -x^2 \text{ by } 3x + 1. \\
9x - 3 & \text{Subtract.} \\
\underline{9x + 3} & \text{Multiply } 3 \text{ by } 3x + 1. \\
-6 & \text{Subtract.}
\end{array}
$$

So, you have $\dfrac{6x^4 - x^3 - x^2 + 9x - 3}{3x + 1} = 2x^3 - x^2 + 3 - \dfrac{6}{3x + 1}.$

4. To divide $5x^3 + 8x^2 - x + 6$ by $x + 2$ using synthetic division, you can set up the array as show.

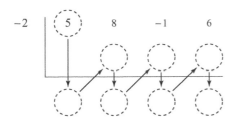

Then, use the synthetic division pattern by adding terms in columns and multiplying the results by -2.

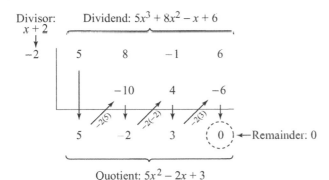

Quotient: $5x^2 - 2x + 3$

So, you have, $\dfrac{5x^3 + 8x^2 - x + 6}{x + 2} = 5x^2 - 2x + 3$.

5. (a) $f(-1)$

$$-1 \,\big|\, \begin{array}{cccc} 4 & 10 & -3 & -8 \\ & -4 & -6 & 9 \\ \hline 4 & 6 & -9 & 1 \end{array}$$

Because the remainder is $r = 1$, $f(-1) = 1$.

Check: $f(-1) = 4(-1)^3 + 10(-1)^2 - 3(-1) - 8$
$= 4(-1) + 10(1) + 3 - 8$
$= 1$

(b) $f(4)$

$$4 \,\big|\, \begin{array}{cccc} 4 & 10 & -3 & -8 \\ & 16 & 104 & 404 \\ \hline 4 & 26 & 101 & 396 \end{array}$$

Because the remainder is $r = 396$, $f(4) = 396$.

Check: $f(4) = 4(4)^3 + 10(4)^2 - 3(4) - 8$
$= 4(64) + 10(16) - 12 - 8$
$= 396$

(c) $f\left(\frac{1}{2}\right)$

$$\tfrac{1}{2} \,\big|\, \begin{array}{cccc} 4 & 10 & -3 & -8 \\ & 2 & 6 & \frac{3}{2} \\ \hline 4 & 12 & 3 & -\frac{13}{2} \end{array}$$

Because the remainder is $r = -\frac{13}{2}$, $f\left(\frac{1}{2}\right) = -\frac{13}{2}$.

Check: $f\left(\frac{1}{2}\right) = 4\left(\frac{1}{2}\right)^3 + 10\left(\frac{1}{2}\right)^2 - 3\left(\frac{1}{2}\right) - 8$
$= 4\left(\frac{1}{8}\right) + 10\left(\frac{1}{4}\right) - \frac{3}{2} - 8$
$= \frac{1}{2} + \frac{5}{2} - \frac{3}{2} - 8$
$= -\frac{13}{2}$

(d) $f(-3)$

$$-3 \,\big|\, \begin{array}{cccc} 4 & 10 & -3 & -8 \\ & -12 & 6 & -9 \\ \hline 4 & -2 & 3 & -17 \end{array}$$

Because the remainder is $r = -17$, $f(-3) = -17$.

Check: $f(-3) = 4(-3)^3 + 10(-3)^2 - 3(-3) - 8$
$= 4(-27) + 10(9) + 9 - 8$
$= -17$

6. Algebraic Solution:

Using synthetic division with the factor $(x + 3)$, you obtain the following.

$$
\begin{array}{r|rrrr}
-3 & 1 & 0 & -19 & -30 \\
   &   & -3 & 9 & 30 \\
\hline
   & 1 & -3 & -10 & 0
\end{array}
\quad \rightarrow \quad 0 \text{ remainder, so } f(-3) = 0 \text{ and } (x + 3) \text{ is a factor.}
$$

Because the resulting quadratic expression factors as $x^2 - 3x - 10 = (x - 5)(x + 2)$, the complete factorization of $f(x)$ is $f(x) = x^3 - 19x - 30 = (x + 3)(x - 5)(x + 2)$.

Graphical Solution:

From the graph of $f(x) = x^3 - 19x - 30$, you can see there are three x-intercepts. These occur at $x = -3$, $x = -2$, and $x = 5$. This implies that $(x + 3)$, $x + 2$, and $(x - 5)$ are factors of $f(x)$.

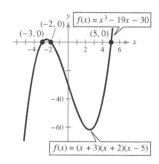

Checkpoints for Section 2.4

1. (a) $(7 + 3i) + (5 - 4i) = 7 + 3i + 5 - 4i$ Remove parentheses.

$\qquad\qquad\qquad\qquad = (7 + 5) + (3 - 4)i$ Group like terms.

$\qquad\qquad\qquad\qquad = 12 - i$ Write in standard form.

(b) $(3 + 4i) - (5 - 3i) = 3 + 4i - 5 + 3i$ Remove parentheses.

$\qquad\qquad\qquad\qquad = (3 - 5) + (4 + 3)i$ Group like terms.

$\qquad\qquad\qquad\qquad = -2 + 7i$ Write in standard form.

(c) $2i + (-3 - 4i) - (-3 - 3i) = 2i - 3 - 4i + 3 + 3i$ Remove parentheses.

$\qquad\qquad\qquad\qquad\qquad = (-3 + 3) + (2 - 4 + 3)i$ Group like terms.

$\qquad\qquad\qquad\qquad\qquad = i$ Write in standard form.

(d) $(5 - 3i) + (3 + 5i) - (8 + 2i) = 5 - 3i + 3 + 5i - 8 - 2i$ Remove parentheses.

$\qquad\qquad\qquad\qquad\qquad = (5 + 3 - 8) + (-3 + 5 - 2)i$ Group like terms.

$\qquad\qquad\qquad\qquad\qquad = 0 + 0i$ Simplify.

$\qquad\qquad\qquad\qquad\qquad = 0$ Write in standard form.

2. (a) $(2 - 4i)(3 + 3i) = 2(3 + 3i) - 4i(3 + 3i)$ Distributive Property

$\qquad\qquad\qquad\quad = 6 + 6i - 12i - 12i^2$ Distributive Property

$\qquad\qquad\qquad\quad = 6 + 6i - 12i - 12(-1)$ $i^2 = -1$

$\qquad\qquad\qquad\quad = (6 + 12) + (6 - 12)i$ Group like terms.

$\qquad\qquad\qquad\quad = 18 - 6i$ Write in standard form.

(b) $(4 + 5i)(4 - 5i) = 4(4 - 5i) + 5i(4 - 5i)$ Distributive Property

$\qquad\qquad\qquad\quad = 16 - 20i + 20i - 25i^2$ Distributive Property

$\qquad\qquad\qquad\quad = 16 - 20i + 20i - 25(-1)$ $i^2 = -1$

$\qquad\qquad\qquad\quad = 16 + 25$ Simplify.

$\qquad\qquad\qquad\quad = 41$ Write in standard form.

(c) $(4 + 2i)^2 = (4 + 2i)(4 + 2i)$ Square of a binomial

$\qquad\qquad\quad = 4(4 + 2i) + 2i(4 + 2i)$ Distributive Property

$\qquad\qquad\quad = 16 + 8i + 8i + 4i^2$ Distributive Property

$\qquad\qquad\quad = 16 + 8i + 8i + 4(-1)$ $i^2 = -1$

$\qquad\qquad\quad = (16 - 4) + (8i + 8i)$ Group like terms.

$\qquad\qquad\quad = 12 + 16i$ Write in standard form.

3. (a) The complex conjugate of $3 + 6i$ is $3 - 6i$.

$(3 + 6i)(3 - 6i) = (3)^2 - (6i)^2$

$\qquad\qquad\qquad = 9 - 36i^2$

$\qquad\qquad\qquad = 9 - 36(-1)$

$\qquad\qquad\qquad = 45$

(b) The complex conjugate of $2 - 5i$ is $2 + 5i$.

$(2 - 5i)(2 + 5i) = (2)^2 - (5i)^2$

$\qquad\qquad\qquad = 4 - 25i^2$

$\qquad\qquad\qquad = 4 - 25(-1)$

$\qquad\qquad\qquad = 29$

4. $\dfrac{2 + i}{2 - i} = \dfrac{2 + i}{2 - i} \cdot \dfrac{2 + i}{2 + i}$ Multiply numerator and denominator by complex conjugate of the denominator.

$\qquad = \dfrac{4 + 2i + 2i + i^2}{4 - i^2}$ Expand.

$\qquad = \dfrac{4 - 1 + 4i}{4 - (-1)}$ $i^2 = -1$

$\qquad = \dfrac{3 + 4i}{5}$ Simplify.

$\qquad = \dfrac{3}{5} + \dfrac{4}{5}i$ Write in standard form.

5. $\sqrt{-14}\,\sqrt{-2} = \sqrt{14}\,i\sqrt{2}\,i = \sqrt{28}\,i^2 = 2\sqrt{7}(-1) = -2\sqrt{7}$

6. To solve $8x^2 + 14x + 9 = 0$, use the Quadratic formula

$$x = \frac{-b \pm \sqrt{b^2 - 4ac}}{2a}.$$

$$x = \frac{-14 \pm \sqrt{14^2 - 4(8)(9)}}{2(8)} \qquad \text{Substitute } a = 8, b = 14, \text{ and } c = 9.$$

$$= \frac{-14 \pm \sqrt{-92}}{16} \qquad \text{Simplify.}$$

$$= \frac{-14 \pm 2\sqrt{23}i}{16} \qquad \text{Write } \sqrt{-92} \text{ in standard form.}$$

$$= \frac{-14}{16} + \frac{2\sqrt{23}i}{16} \qquad \text{Write in standard form.}$$

$$= \frac{-7}{8} \pm \frac{\sqrt{23}i}{8} \qquad \text{Simplify.}$$

Checkpoints for Section 2.5

1. $f(x) = x^4 - 1 = \left(x^2 + 1\right)\left(x^2 - 1\right)$

$\qquad = \left(x^2 + 1\right)(x + 1)(x - 1)$

$x^2 + 1 \Rightarrow x = \pm i$

$x + 1 \Rightarrow x = -1$

$x - 1 \Rightarrow x = 1$

The fourth-degree polynomial function $f(x) = x^4 - 1$ has exactly four zeros, $x = \pm i$ and $x = \pm 1$

2. (a) Because the leading coefficient is 1, the possible rational zeros are the factors of the constant term

Possible rational zeros: $\pm 1, \pm 2, \pm 4, \pm 8$

By testing these zeros,

$$f(-1) = (-1)^3 - 5(-1)^2 + 2(-1) + 8 = 0$$

$$f(1) = (1)^3 - 5(1)^2 + 2(1) + 8 = 6$$

$$f(-2) = (-2)^3 - 5(-2)^2 + 2(-2) + 8 = -24$$

$$f(2) = (2)^3 - 5(2)^2 + 2(2) + 8 = 0$$

$$f(-4) = (-4)^3 - 5(-4)^2 + 2(-4) + 8 = -144$$

$$f(4) = (4)^3 - 5(4)^3 + 2(4) + 8 = 0$$

$$f(-8) = (-8)^3 - 5(-8) + 2(-8) + 8 = -840$$

$$f(8) = (8)^3 - 5(8)^2 + 2(8) + 8 = 216$$

you can conclude that the polynomial function $f(x) = x^3 - 5x^2 + 2x + 8$ has three rational zeros $x = -1$, $x = 2$, and $x = 4$.

(b) *Possible rational zeros*: $\pm 1 \ \pm 2$ and ± 4

By testing these possible zeros,

$$f(-1) = (-1)^3 + 2(-1)^2 + 6(-1) - 4 = -9$$
$$f(1) = (1)^3 + 2(1)^2 + 6(1) - 4 = 5$$
$$f(-2) = (-2)^3 + 2(-2)^2 + 6(-2) - 4 = -16$$
$$f(2) = (2)^3 + 2(2)^2 + 6(2) - 4 = 24$$
$$f(-4) = (-4)^3 + 2(-4)^2 + 6(-4) - 4 = -60$$
$$f(4) = (4)^3 + 2(4)^2 + 6(4) - 4 = 116$$

you can conclude that the polynomial $f(x) = x^3 + 2x^2 + 6x - 4$ has *no* rational zeros.

(c) *Possible rational zeros*: $\pm 1 \ \pm 2 \ \pm 3$ and ± 6

By testing these possible zeros,

$$f(-1) = (-1)^3 - 3(-1)^2 + 2(-1) - 6 = -12$$
$$f(1) = (1)^3 - 3(1)^2 + 2(1) - 6 = -6$$
$$f(-2) = (-2)^3 - 3(-2)^2 + 2(-2) - 6 = -30$$
$$f(2) = (2)^3 - 3(2)^2 + 2(2) - 6 = -6$$
$$f(-3) = (-3)^3 - 3(-3)^2 + 2(-3) - 6 = -66$$
$$f(3) = (3)^3 - 3(3)^2 + 2(3) - 6 = 0$$
$$f(-6) = (-6)^3 - 3(-6)^2 + 2(-6) - 6 = -342$$
$$f(6) = (6)^3 - 3(6)^2 + 2(6) - 6 = 114$$

you can conclude that the polynomial function $f(x) = x^3 - 3x^2 + 2x - 6$ has one rational zero, $x = 3$.

3. Because the leading coefficient is 1, the possible rational zeros are the factors of the constant term.

Possible rational zeros: $\pm 1, \pm 5, \pm 25, \pm 125$

```
5 | 1   -15    75   -125
  |       5   -50    125
  ---------------------------
    1   -10    25     0    →   0 remainder, so x = 5 is a factor.
```

```
5 | 1   -10    25
  |       5   -25
  ------------------
    1    -5     0    →   0 remainder, so x = 5 is a factor.
```

By applying synthetic division successively, you can determine that $x = 5$ is the only rational zero.

So, $f(x) = x^3 - 15x^2 + 75x - 125$ factors as $f(x) = (x - 5)(x - 5)(x - 5) = (x - 5)^3$.

Because the rational zero $x = 5$ has multiplicity of three, which is odd, the graph of f crosses the x-axis at the x-intercept, $(5, 0)$.

4. The leading coefficient is 2 and the constant term is -30.

$$\textit{Possible rational zeros: } \frac{\text{Factors of } -30}{\text{Factors of 2}} = \frac{\pm 1, \pm 2, \pm 3, \pm 5, \pm 6, \pm 10, \pm 15, \pm 30}{\pm 1, \pm 2}$$

$$= \pm 1, \pm 2, \pm 3, \pm 5, \pm 6, \pm 10, \pm 15, \pm 30, \pm \frac{1}{2}, \pm \frac{3}{2}, \pm \frac{5}{2}, \pm \frac{15}{2}$$

Choose a value of x and use synthetic division.

$x = -3$

$$
\begin{array}{r|rrrrr}
-3 & 2 & -9 & -18 & 71 & -30 \\
   &   & -6 & 45 & -81 & 30 \\
\hline
   & 2 & -15 & 27 & -10 & 0
\end{array}
$$
$\rightarrow$ 0 remainder, so $x + 3$ is a factor.

Choose another value of x and use synthetic division.

$x = 2$

$$
\begin{array}{r|rrrr}
2 & 2 & -15 & 27 & -10 \\
  &   & 4 & -22 & 10 \\
\hline
  & 2 & -11 & 5 & 0
\end{array}
$$
$\rightarrow$ 0 remainder, so $x + 3$ is a factor.

So, $f(x) = 2x^4 - 9x^3 - 18x^2 + 71x - 30$ factors as

$f(x) = (x + 3)(x - 2)(2x^2 - 11x + 5) = (x + 3)(x - 2)(x - 5)(2x - 1)$ and

you can conclude that the rational zeros of f are $x = -3$, $x = \dfrac{1}{2}$, $x = 2$, and $x = 5$.

5. The leading coefficient is 1 and the constant term is -18.

$$\textit{Possible rational zeros: } \frac{\text{Factor of } -18}{\text{Factors of 1}} = \frac{\pm 1, \pm 2, \pm 3, \pm 6, \pm 9, \pm 18}{\pm 1} = \pm 1, \pm 2, \pm 3, \pm 6, \pm 9, \pm 18$$

A graph can assist you to narrow the list to reasonable possibilities.

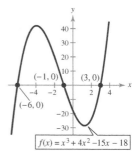

Start by testing $x = -6$, $x = -1$ or $x = 3$.

$$
\begin{array}{r|rrrr}
-1 & 1 & 4 & -15 & -18 \\
   &   & -1 & -3 & 18 \\
\hline
   & 1 & 3 & -18 & 0
\end{array}
$$
$\rightarrow$ 0 remainder, so $x + 1$ is a factor.

Choose another value of x to test.

$$
\begin{array}{r|rrr}
3 & 1 & 3 & -18 \\
  &   & 3 & 18 \\
\hline
  & 1 & 6 & 0
\end{array}
$$
$\rightarrow$ 0 remainder, so $x - 3$ is a factor.

So, $f(x) = x^3 + 4x^2 - 15x - 18$ factors as $f(x) = (x + 1)(x - 3)(x + 6)$ and you can conclude that

the rational zeros of f are $x = -1$, $x = 3$, and $x = -6$.

6. (a) Because $-7i$ is a zero *and* the polynomial is stated to have real coefficients, you know that the conjugate $7i$ must also be a zero.

So, the four zeros are $2, -2, 7i,$ and $-7i$.

Then, using the Linear Factorization Theorem, $f(x)$ can be written as

$$f(x) = a(x - 2)(x + 2)(x - 7i)(x + 7i).$$

For simplicity, let $a = 1$. Then multiply the factors with real coefficients to obtain

$$(x + 2)(x - 2) = x^2 - 4$$

and multiply the complex conjugates to obtain

$$(x - 7i)(x + 7i) = x^2 + 49.$$

So, you obtain the following fourth-degree polynomial function.

$$f(x) = (x^2 - 4)(x^2 + 49) = x^4 + 49x^2 - 4x^2 - 196$$

$$= x^4 + 45x^2 - 196$$

(b) Because $4 - i$ is a zero *and* the polynomial is stated to have real coefficients, you know that the conjugate $4 + i$ must also be a zero.

So, the four zeros are $1, 3, 4 + i,$ and $4 - i$.

Then using the Linear Factorization Theorem, $f(x)$ can be written as

$$f(x) = a(x - 1)(x - 3)(x - 4 - i)(x - 4 + i).$$

For simplicity, let $a = 1$. Then multiply the factors with real coefficients to obtain

$$(x - 1)(x - 3) = x^2 - 4x + 3$$

and multiply the complex conjugates to obtain

$$(x - 4 - i)(x - 4 + i) = x^2 - 4x + xi - 4x + 16 - 4i - xi + 4i - i^2$$

$$= x^2 - 8x + 17.$$

So, you obtain the following fourth-degree polynomial function.

$$f(x) = (x^2 - 4x + 3)(x^2 - 8x + 17)$$

$$= x^4 - 12x^3 + 52x^2 - 92x + 51$$

(c) Because $3 + i$ is a zero *and* the polynomial is stated to have real coefficients, you know that the conjugate $3 - i$ must also be a zero.

So, the four zeros are $-1, 2, 3 + i,$ and $3 - i$.

Then using the Linear Factorization Theorem, $f(x)$ can be written as

$$f(x) = a(x + 1)(x - 2)(x - 3 - i)(x - 3 + i).$$

For simplicity, let $a = 1$. Then multiply the factors with real coefficients to obtain

$$(x + 1)(x - 2) = x^2 - x - 2$$

and multiply the complex conjugates to obtain

$$(x - 3 - i)(x - 3 + i) = x^2 - 3x + xi - 3x + 9 - 3i - xi + 3i - i^2$$

$$= x^2 - 6x + 10.$$

So, you obtain the following fourth-degree polynomial function,

$$f(x) = (x^2 - x - 2)(x^2 - 6x + 10)$$

$$= x^4 - 7x^3 + 14x^2 + 2x - 20$$

7. Because complex zeros occur in conjugate pairs you know that if $4i$ is a zero of f, so is $-4i$.

This means that both $(x - 4i)$ and $(x + 4i)$ are factors of f.

$$(x - 4i)(x + 4i) = x^2 - 16i^2 = x^2 + 16$$

Using long division, you can divide $x^2 + 16$ into $f(x)$ to obtain the following.

$$
\begin{array}{r}
3x - 12 \\
x^2 + 16 \overline{\smash{\big)}\, 3x^3 - 2x^2 + 48x - 32} \\
\underline{3x^3 + 48x } \\
-2x^2 - 32 \\
\underline{-2x^2 - 32} \\
0
\end{array}
$$

So, you have $f(x) = (x^2 + 16)(3x - 2)$ and you can conclude that the real zeros of f are $x = -4i$, $x = 4i$, and $x = \dfrac{2}{3}$.

8. (a) Because the leading coefficient is 1, the possible rational zeros are the factors of the constant term.

Possible rational zeros: $\pm 1, \pm 3$, and ± 9

Synthetic division produces the following.

$$
\begin{array}{r|rrrrr}
1 & 1 & 0 & 8 & 0 & -9 \\
  &   & 1 & 1 & 9 & 9 \\
\hline
  & 1 & 1 & 9 & 9 & 0
\end{array}
$$
$\rightarrow$ 1 is a zero, so $x - 1$ is a factor.

$$
\begin{array}{r|rrrr}
-1 & 1 & 1 & 9 & 9 \\
   &   & -1 & 0 & -9 \\
\hline
   & 1 & 0 & 9 & 0
\end{array}
$$
$\rightarrow$ -1 is a zero, so $x + 1$ is a factor.

So, you have $f(x) = x^4 + 8x^2 - 9 = (x - 1)(x + 1)(x^2 + 9)$.

You can factor $x^2 + 9$ as $x^2 - (-9) = (x + \sqrt{-9})(x - \sqrt{-9}) = (x + 3i)(x - 3i)$.

So, you have $f(x) = (x - 1)(x + 1)(x + 3i)(x - 3i)$ and you can conclude that the real zeros of f are $x = 1$, $x = -1$, $x = 3i$, and $x = -3i$.

(b) *Possible rational zeros*: ± 1 and ± 5

Synthetic division produces the following.

$$
\begin{array}{r|rrrr}
1 & 1 & -3 & 7 & -5 \\
  &   & 1 & -2 & 5 \\
\hline
  & 1 & -2 & 5 & 0
\end{array}
$$
$\rightarrow$ 1 is a zero, so $x - 1$ is a factor.

$$f(x) = x^3 - 3x^2 + 7x - 5 = (x - 1)(x^2 - 2x + 5)$$

You can find the zeros of $x^2 - 2x + 5$ by completing the square.

$$x^2 - 2x = -5$$
$$x^2 - 2x + 1 = -5 + 1$$
$$(x - 1)^2 = -4$$
$$x - 1 = \pm 2i$$
$$x = 1 \pm 2i$$

So, you have $f(x) = (x - 1)(x^2 - 2x + 5) = (x - 1)(x - 1 - 2i)(x - 1 + 2i)$

and you can conclude that the real zeros of f are $x = 1$, $x = 1 + 2i$, and $x = 1 - 2i$.

(c) *Possible rational zeros*: $\pm 1, \pm 3, \pm 17$ and ± 51

Synthetic division produces the following.

$$
\begin{array}{r|rrrr}
3 & 1 & -11 & 41 & -51 \\
  &   & 3 & -24 & 51 \\
\hline
  & 1 & -8 & 17 & 0
\end{array}
\quad \rightarrow \quad 3 \text{ is a zero, so } x - 3 \text{ is a factor.}
$$

$$f(x) = x^3 - 11x^2 + 41x - 51 = (x - 3)(x^2 - 8x + 17)$$

You can find the zeros of $x^2 - 8x + 17$ by completing the square.

$$x^2 - 8x = -17$$
$$x^2 - 8x + 16 = -17 + 16$$
$$(x - 4)^2 = -1$$
$$x - 4 = \pm i$$
$$x = 4 \pm i$$

So, you have $f(x) = (x - 3)(x^2 - 8x + 17) = (x - 3)(x - 4 - i)(x - 4 + i)$

and you can conclude that the real zeros of f are $x = 3, x = 4 + i,$ and $x = 4 - i$.

9. The original polynomial has *three* variations in sign.

$$
\begin{array}{c}
\text{– to +} \qquad \text{– to +} \\
\downarrow \quad \downarrow \qquad \downarrow \qquad \downarrow \\
f(x) = -2x^3 + 5x^2 - x + 8 \\
\qquad \uparrow \qquad \uparrow \\
\qquad \text{+ to –}
\end{array}
$$

The polynomial $f(-x) = -2(-x)^3 + 5(-x)^2 - (-x) + 8 = 2x^3 + 5x + x + 8$ has no variations in sign.

So, from Descartes' Rule of Signs, the polynomial $f(x) = -2x^3 + 5x^2 - x + 8$ has either three positive real zeros or one positive real zero and no negative real zeros.

From the graph, you can see that the function has only one real zero.

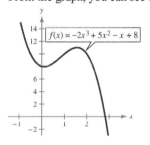

10. The possible real zeros are as follows.

$$\frac{\text{Factors of } -3}{\text{Factors of } 8} = \frac{\pm 1 \ \pm 3}{\pm 1 \ \pm 2 \ \pm 4 \ \pm 8} = \pm\frac{1}{8}, \ \pm\frac{1}{4}, \ \pm\frac{3}{8}, \ \pm\frac{1}{2}, \ \pm\frac{3}{4}, \ \pm 1, \ \pm\frac{3}{2}, \ \pm 3$$

The original polynomial $f(x)$ has three variations in sign. The polynomial

$$f(-x) = 8(-x)^3 - 4(-x)^2 + 6(-x) - 3 = -8x^3 - 4x^2 - 6x - 3$$

has no variations in sign. So, you can apply Descartes' Rule of Signs to conclude that there are either three positive real zeros or one positive real zero, and no negative real zeros.

Using $x = 1$, synthetic division produces the following.

$$\begin{array}{r|rrrr} 1 & 8 & -4 & 6 & -3 \\ & & 8 & 4 & 10 \\ \hline & 8 & 4 & 10 & 7 \end{array} \rightarrow \quad 1 \text{ is not a zero.}$$

So, $x = 1$ is not a zero, but because the last row has all positive entries, you know that $x = 1$ is an upper bound for the real zeros. So, you can restrict the search to real zeros between 0 and 1. Using $x = \dfrac{1}{2}$, synthetic division produces the following.

$$\begin{array}{r|rrrr} \frac{1}{2} & 8 & -4 & 6 & -3 \\ & & 4 & 0 & 3 \\ \hline & 8 & 0 & 6 & 0 \end{array} \rightarrow \quad \frac{1}{2} \text{ is a real zero.}$$

$$\begin{aligned} f(x) &= 8x^3 - 4x^2 + 6x - 3 \\ &= \left(x - \frac{1}{2}\right)\!\left(8x^2 + 6\right) \end{aligned}$$

Because $8x^2 + 6$ has no real zeros, it follows that $x = \dfrac{1}{2}$ is the only real zero.

11. The volume of a pyramid is $V = \frac{1}{3}Bh$, where B is the area of the base and h is the height. The area at the base is x^2 and the height is $x + 2$. So, the volume of the pyramid is $V = \frac{1}{3}x^2(x + 2)$. Substituting 147 for the volume yields the following.

$$147 = \tfrac{1}{3}x^2(x + 2)$$
$$441 = x^3 + 2x^2$$
$$0 = x^3 + 2x^2 - 441$$

The possible rational zeros are $x = \pm 1, \pm 3, \pm 7, \pm 9, \pm 21, \pm 49, \pm 63, \pm 147,$ and ± 441.

Use synthetic division to test some of the possible solutions. So, you can determine that $x = 7$ is a solution.

$$\begin{array}{r|rrrr} 7 & 1 & 2 & 0 & -441 \\ & & 7 & 63 & 441 \\ \hline & 1 & 9 & 63 & 0 \end{array}$$

The other two solutions that satisfy $x^2 + 9x + 63 = 0$ are imaginary and can be discarded. You can conclude that the base of the candle mold should be 7 inches by 7 inches and the height should be $7 + 2 = 9$ inches.

Checkpoints for Section 2.6

1. Because the denominator is zero when $x = 1$, the domain of f is all real numbers except $x = 1$.

To determine the behavior of f, this excluded value, evaluate $f(x)$ to the left and to the right of $x = 1$.

x	0	0.5	0.9	0.99	0.999	$\rightarrow 1$
$f(x)$	0	-3	-27	-297	-2997	$\rightarrow -\infty$

x	$1 \leftarrow$	1.001	1.01	1.1	1.5	2
$f(x)$	$\infty \leftarrow$	3003	303	33	9	6

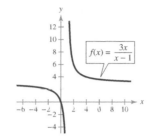

As x approaches 1 from the left, $f(x)$ decreases without bound.

As x approaches 1 from the right, $f(x)$ increases without bound.

2. For this rational function, the degree of the numerator is equal to the degree of the denominator. The leading coefficient of the numerator is 3 and the leading coefficient of the denominator is 1, so the graph of the function has the line $y = \dfrac{3}{1} = 3$ as a horizontal asymptote. To find any vertical asymptotes, first factor the numerator and denominator as follows.

$$f(x) = \frac{3x^2 + 7x - 6}{x^2 + 4x + 3} = \frac{(3x - 2)(x + 3)}{(x + 1)(x + 3)}$$

$$= \frac{3x - 2}{x + 1}, x \neq -3$$

By setting the denominator $x + 1$ (of the simplified function) equal to zero, you can determine that the graph has the line $x = -1$ as a vertical asymptote.

3. *y-intercept*: $\left(0, \frac{1}{3}\right)$, because $f(0) = \frac{1}{3}$

x-intercept: none, because $1 \neq 0$

Vertical asymptote: $x = -3$, zero of denominator

Horizontal asymptote: $y = 0$, because degree of

$$N(x) < \text{degree of } D(x)$$

Additional points:

x	-5	-4	-2	-1	1	2
$f(x)$	$-\frac{1}{2}$	-1	1	$\frac{1}{2}$	$\frac{1}{4}$	$\frac{1}{5}$

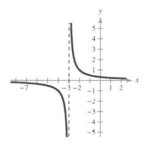

The domain of f is all real numbers except $x = -3$.

4. *y-intercept:* $(0, 3)$, because $C(0) = 3$

x-intercept: $\left(-\frac{3}{2}, 0\right)$, because $C\left(-\frac{3}{2}\right) = 0$

Vertical asymptote: $x = -1$, zero of denominator

Horizontal asymptote: $y = 2$, because degree of
$$N(x) = \text{degree of } D(x)$$

Additional points:

x	-3	-2	1	3
$C(x)$	$\frac{3}{2}$	1	$\frac{5}{2}$	$\frac{9}{4}$

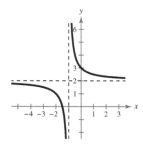

The domain of f is all real number except $x = -1$.

5. $f(x) = -\dfrac{3x}{x^2 + x - 2} = \dfrac{3x}{(x + 2)(x - 1)}$

y-intercept: $(0, 0)$, because $f(0) = 0$

x-intercept: $(0, 0)$, because $f(0) = 0$

Vertical asymptotes: $x = -2$, $x = 1$, zeros of denominator

Horizontal asymptote: $y = 0$, because degree of
$$N(x) < \text{degree of } D(x)$$

Additional points:

x	-3	-1	2	3
$f(x)$	$-\frac{9}{4}$	$\frac{3}{2}$	$\frac{3}{2}$	$\frac{9}{10}$

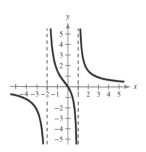

The domain of f is all real numbers except $x = -2$ and $x = 1$.

6. $f(x) = -\dfrac{x^2 - 4}{x^2 - x - 6}$

$ = \dfrac{(x + 2)(x - 2)}{(x - 3)(x + 2)}$

$ = \dfrac{x - 2}{x - 3}, \ x \neq -2$

y-intercept: $\left(0, \dfrac{2}{3}\right)$, because $f(0) = \dfrac{2}{3}$

x-intercept: $(2, 0)$, because $f(2) = 0$

Vertical asymptote: $x = 3$, zero of (simplified) denominator

Horizontal asymptote: $y = 1$, because degree of $N(x)$ = degree of $D(x)$

Additional points:

x	-7	-5	-1	1	4	5
$f(x)$	$\dfrac{9}{10}$	$\dfrac{7}{8}$	$\dfrac{3}{4}$	$\dfrac{1}{2}$	2	$\dfrac{3}{2}$

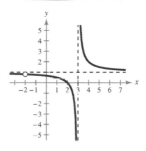

Notice that there is a hole at $x = -2$ because the function is not defined when $x = -2$, the domain is all real number except $x = -2$ and $x = 3$.

7. $f(x) = \dfrac{3x^2 + 1}{x}$

First divide $3x^2 + 1$ by x, either by long division:

$$x \overline{\smash{)}3x^2 + 0x + 1} \quad \text{quotient } 3x$$

$$\underline{3x^2}$$

$$1$$

So $\dfrac{3x^2 + 1}{x} = 3x + \dfrac{1}{x}$

or by separating, the numerator and simplifying:

$$\dfrac{3x^2 + 1}{x} = \dfrac{3x^2}{x} + \dfrac{1}{x} = 3x + \dfrac{1}{x}$$

So, the start asymptote is $y = 3x$, since

$$\dfrac{3x^2 + 1}{x} = 3x + \dfrac{1}{x}.$$

y-intercept: none, since $f(0)$ is undefined.

x-intercept: none, since $3x^2 + 1 \neq 0$ for real numbers.

Vertical asymptote: $x = 0$, zero of denominator

Start asymptote: $y = 3x$

Additional points:

x	-2	-1	-0.5	0.5	1	2
$f(x)$	$-\dfrac{13}{2}$	-4	$-\dfrac{7}{2}$	$\dfrac{7}{2}$	4	$\dfrac{13}{2}$

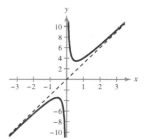

The domain of f is all real numbers except $x = 0$.

8. (a) The cost to remove 20% of the pollutants is

$C = \dfrac{255(20)}{100 - (20)} = \$63.75 \text{ million.}$

The cost to remove 45% of the pollutants is

$C = \dfrac{255(45)}{100 - 45} \approx \$208.64 \text{ million.}$

The cost to remove 80% of the pollutants is

$C = \dfrac{255(80)}{100 - 80} = \$1020 \text{ million.}$

(b) The cost to remove 100% of the pollutants is $C = \dfrac{255(100)}{100 - (100)}$ which is undefined.

So, it would not be possible to remove 100% of the pollutants.

9. Graphical Solution

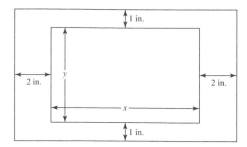

Let A be the area to be minimized.

$$A = (x + 4)(y + 2)$$

The printed area inside the margins is modeled by $40 = xy$ or $y = \dfrac{40}{x}$.

To find the minimum area, rewrite the equation for A in terms of just one variable by substituting $\dfrac{40}{x}$ for y.

$$A = (x + 4)\left(\dfrac{40}{x} + 2\right)$$

$$= (x + 4)\left(\dfrac{40 + 2x}{x}\right)$$

$$= \dfrac{(x + 4)(40 + 2x)}{x}, \; x > 0$$

The graph of this rational function is shown below. Because x represents the width of the printed area, you need to consider only the portion of the graph for which x is positive. Using a graphing utility, you can approximate the minimum value of A to occur when $x \approx 8.9$ inches. The corresponding value of y is $\dfrac{40}{8.9} \approx 4.5$ inches.

So, the dimensions should be $8.9 + 4 = 129$ inches by $4.5 + 2 = 6.5$ inches.

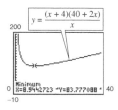

Numerical Solution

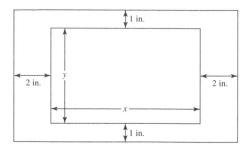

Let A be the area to be minimized.

$$A = (x + 4)(y + z)$$

The printed area inside the margins is modeled by $40 = xy$ or $y = \dfrac{40}{x}$.

To find the minimum area, rewrite the equation for A in terms of just one variable by substituting $\dfrac{40}{x}$ for y.

$$A = (x + 4)\left(\dfrac{40}{x} + 2\right)$$

$$= (x + 4)\left(\dfrac{40 + 2x}{x}\right)$$

$$= \dfrac{(x + 4)(40 + 2x)}{x}, \; x > 0$$

Use the *table* feature of a graphing utility to create a table of values for the function

$$y_1 = \dfrac{(x + 4)(40 + 2x)}{x}, \; x > 0$$

beginning at $x = 6$. From the table, you can see that the minimum value of y_1 occurs when x is somewhere between 8 and 9, as shown.

To approximate the minimum value of y_1 to one decimal place, change the table so that it starts at $x = 8$ and increases by 0.1. The minimum value of y_1 occurs when $x \approx 8.9$ as shown.

The corresponding value of y is $\dfrac{40}{8.9} \approx 4.5$ inches.

So, the dimensions should be $8.9 + 4 = 12.9$ inches by $4.5 + 2 = 6.5$ inches.

x	y_1
6	86.667
7	84.857
8	84
9	83.778
10	84
11	84.545

x	y_1
8.8	83.782
8.9	83.778
9.0	83.778
9.1	83.782

Checkpoints for Section 2.7

1. By factoring the polynomial $x^2 - x - 20 < 0$ as $x^2 - x - 20 = (x + 4)(x - 5)$ you can see that the key numbers are $x = -4$ and $x = 5$. So, the polynomial's test intervals are $(-\infty, -4)$, $(-4, 5)$, and $(5, \infty)$.

In each test interval, choose a representative x-value and evaluate the polynomial.

Test interval	x-value	Polynomial value	Conclusion
$(-\infty, -4)$	$x = -5$	$(-5)^2 - (-5) - 20 = 10$	Positive
$(-4, 5)$	$x = 0$	$(0)^2 - (0) - 20 = -20$	Negative
$(5, \infty)$	$x = 6$	$(6)^2 - (6) - 20 = 10$	Positive

From this, you can conclude that the inequality is satisfied for all x-values in $(-4, 5)$.

This implies that the solution of the inequality $x^2 - x - 20 < 0$ is the interval $(-4, 5)$.

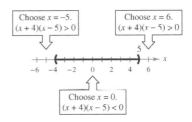

2.

$$3x^3 - x^2 - 12x > -4 \qquad \text{Write original inequality.}$$
$$3x^2 - x^2 - 12x + 4 > 0 \qquad \text{Write in general form.}$$
$$x^2(3x - 1) - 4(3x - 1) > 0 \qquad \text{Factor.}$$
$$(3x - 1)(x^2 - 4) > 0 \qquad \text{Factor.}$$
$$(3x - 1)(x + 2)(x - 2) > 0 \qquad \text{Factor.}$$

The key numbers are $x = -2$, $x = \frac{1}{3}$, and $x = 2$, and the test intervals are $(-\infty, -2)$, $\left(-2, \frac{1}{3}\right)$, $\left(\frac{1}{3}, 2\right)$, and $(2, \infty)$.

Test interval	x-value	Polynomial value	Conclusion
$(-\infty, -2)$	$x = -3$	$3(-3)^3 - (-3)^2 - 12(-3) + 4 = -50$	Negative
$\left(-2, \frac{1}{3}\right)$	$x = 0$	$3(0)^3 - (0)^2 - 12(0) + 4 = 4$	Positive
$\left(\frac{1}{3}, 2\right)$	$x = 1$	$3(1)^3 - (1)^2 - 12(1) + 4 = -6$	Negative
$(2, \infty)$	$x = 3$	$3(3)^3 - (3)^2 - 12(3) + 4 = 40$	Positive

From this, you can conclude that the inequality is satisfied on the open intervals $\left(-2, \frac{1}{3}\right)$ and $(2, \infty)$.

So, the solution set is $\left(-2, \frac{1}{3}\right) \cup (2, \infty)$.

3. (a) Algebraic solution

$$2x^2 + 3x < 5 \qquad \text{Write original inequality.}$$
$$2x^2 + 3x - 5 < 0 \qquad \text{Write in general form.}$$
$$(2x + 5)(x - 1) < 0 \qquad \text{Factor.}$$

Key numbers: $x = -\frac{5}{2}$ and $x = 1$

Test intervals: $\left(-\infty, -\frac{5}{2}\right), \left(-\frac{5}{2}, 1\right), (1, \infty)$

Test: Is $(2x + 5)(x - 1) < 0$?

After testing the intervals, you can see that the polynomial $2x^2 + 3x - 5$ is negative on the open interval $\left(-\frac{5}{2}, 1\right)$.

So, the solution set of the inequality is $\left(-\frac{5}{2}, 1\right)$.

(b) Graphical solution

First write the polynomial inequality $2x^2 + 3x < 5$ as $2x^2 + 3x - 5 > 0$. Then use a graphing utility to graph $y = 2x^2 + 3x - 5$. You can see that the graph is below the x-axis when x is greater than $-\frac{5}{2}$ and when x is less than 1.

So, the solution set is $\left(-\frac{5}{2}, 1\right)$.

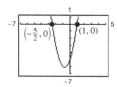

4. (a) The solution set of $x^2 + 6x + 9 < 0$ is empty. In other words, the quadratic $x^2 + 6x + 9$ is not less than 0 for any value of x.

(b) The solution set of $x^2 + 4x + 4 \leq 0$ consists of the single real number $\{-2\}$, because the quadratic $x^2 + 4x + 4$ has only one key number, $x = -2$, and it is the only value that satisfies the inequality.

(c) The solution set of $x^2 - 6x + 970$ consists of all real numbers except $x = 3$. In interval notation, the solution set can be written as $(-\infty, 3) \cup (3, \infty)$.

(d) The solution set of $x^2 - 2x + 1 \geq 0$ consists of the entire set of real numbers $(-\infty, \infty)$. In other words, the value of the quadratic $x^2 - 2x + 1$ is non-negative for every real value of x.

5. (a)

$$\frac{x-2}{x-3} \geq -3 \qquad \text{Write original inequality.}$$

$$\frac{x-2}{x-3} + 3 \geq 0 \qquad \text{Write in general form.}$$

$$\frac{x-2}{x-3} + \frac{3(x-3)}{x-3} \geq 0 \qquad \text{Rewrite fraction using LCD.}$$

$$\frac{x-2+3x-9}{x-3} \geq 0 \qquad \text{Add fractions.}$$

$$\frac{4x-11}{x-3} \geq 0 \qquad \text{Simplify.}$$

Key numbers: $x = \dfrac{11}{4}, x = 3$

Test intervals: $\left(-\infty, \dfrac{11}{4}\right), \left(\dfrac{11}{4}, 3\right), (3, \infty)$

Test: Is $\dfrac{4x-11}{x-3} \geq 0$?

Test interval	x-value	Polynomial value	Conclusion
$\left(-\infty, \dfrac{11}{4}\right)$	$x = 0$	$\dfrac{4(0) - 11}{0 - 3} = \dfrac{11}{3}$	Positive
$\left(\dfrac{11}{4}, 3\right)$	$x = 2.9$	$\dfrac{4(2.9) - 11}{2.9 - 3} = \dfrac{0.6}{-0.1} = -6$	Negative
$(3, \infty)$	$x = 4$	$\dfrac{4(4) - 11}{4 - 3} = \dfrac{5}{1} = 5$	Positive

After testing these intervals, you can see that the inequality is satisfied on the open intervals $\left(-\infty, \dfrac{11}{4}\right)$ and $(3, \infty)$. Moreover, because $\dfrac{4x-11}{x-3} = 0$ when $x = \dfrac{11}{4}$, you can conclude that the solution set consists of all real numbers in the intervals $\left(-\infty, \dfrac{11}{4}\right] \cup (3, \infty)$.

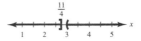

(b)

$$\frac{4x - 1}{x - 6} > 3 \qquad \text{Write original inequality.}$$

$$\frac{4x - 1}{x - 6} - 3 > 0 \qquad \text{Write in general form.}$$

$$\frac{4x - 1 - 3(x - 6)}{x - 6} > 0 \qquad \text{Combine fractions with LCD.}$$

$$\frac{4x - 1 - 3x + 18}{x - 6} > 0 \qquad \text{Simplify.}$$

$$\frac{x + 17}{x - 6} > 0 \qquad \text{Simplify.}$$

Key numbers: $x = -17, x = 6$

Test intervals: $(-\infty, -17), (-17, 6),$ and $(6, \infty)$

Test: Is $\dfrac{x + 17}{x - 6} > 0$?

Test interval	*x*-value	Polynomial value	Conclusion
$(-\infty, -17)$	-20	$\dfrac{(20) + 17}{(20) - 6} = \dfrac{3}{14}$	Positive
$(-17, 6)$	0	$\dfrac{(0) + 17}{(0) - 6} = -\dfrac{17}{6}$	Negative
$(6, \infty)$	8	$\dfrac{(8) + 17}{(8) - 6} = \dfrac{25}{2}$	Positive

After testing these intervals, you can see that the inequality is satisfied on the open intervals $(-\infty, -17)$ and $(6, \infty)$.

So, you can conclude that the solution set consists of all real numbers in the intervals $(-\infty, -17) \cup (6, \infty)$.

6. *Verbal Model:* $\boxed{\text{Profit}} = \boxed{\text{Review}} - \boxed{\text{Cost}}$

Equation:
$$P = R - C$$
$$P = x(60 - 0.0001x) - (12x + 1{,}800{,}000)$$
$$P = -0.0001x^2 + 48x = 1{,}800{,}000$$

To answer the question, solve the inequality as follows.
$$P \geq 3{,}600{,}000$$
$$-0.0001x^2 + 48x - 1{,}800{,}000 \geq 3{,}600{,}000$$
$$-0.0001x^2 + 48x - 5{,}400{,}000 \geq 0$$
$$0.0001x^2 - 48x + 5{,}400{,}000 \leq 0$$
$$x^2 - 480{,}000x + 54{,}000{,}000{,}000 \leq 0$$
$$(x - 180{,}000)(x - 300{,}000) \leq 0$$

After finding the key point and testing the intervals, you can find the solution set is $[180{,}000, \ 300{,}000]$.

So, by selling at least 180,000 units but not more than 300,000 units, the profit is at least $3,600,000.

7. Algebraic solution

Recall that the domain of an expression is the set of all x-values for which the expression is defined. Because $\sqrt{x^2 - 7x + 10}$ is defined only of $x^2 - 7x + 10$ is non-negative, the domain is given by $x^2 - 7x + 10 \geq 0$.

$x^2 - 7x + 10 \geq 0$ Write in general form.

$(x - 2)(x - 5) \geq 0$ Factor.

So, the inequality has two key numbers: $x = 2$ and $x = 5$.

Key numbers: $x = 2, x = 5$

Test intervals: $(-\infty, 2), (2, 5), (5, \infty)$

Test: Is $(x - 2)(x - 5) \geq 0$?

A test shows that the inequality is satisfied in the unbounded half-closed intervals $(-\infty, 2]$ or $[5, \infty)$. So, the domain of the expression $\sqrt{x^2 - 7x + 10}$ is $(-\infty, 2] \cup [5, \infty)$.

Graphical solution

Begin by sketching the graph of the equation $y = \sqrt{x^2 - 7x + 10}$. From the graph, you can determine that the x-values extend up to 2 (including 2) and from 5 and beyond (including 5). So, the domain of the expression $\sqrt{x^2 - 7x + 10}$ is $(-\infty, 2] \cup [5, \infty)$.

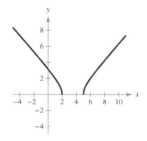

Chapter 3

Checkpoints for Section 3.1

1. Function Value

$$f\left(\sqrt{2}\right) = 8^{-\sqrt{2}}$$

Graphing Calculator Keystrokes

8 ∧ ((−) √ 2) Enter

Display

0.052824803759

2. The table lists some values for each function, and the graph shows a sketch of the two functions. Note that both graphs are increasing and the graph of $g(x) = 9^x$ is increasing more rapidly than the graph of $f(x) = 3^x$.

x	3	−2	−1	0	1	2
3^x	$\frac{1}{27}$	$\frac{1}{9}$	$\frac{1}{3}$	1	3	9
9^x	$\frac{1}{729}$	$\frac{1}{81}$	$\frac{1}{9}$	1	9	81

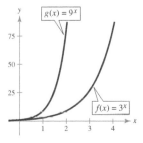

3. The table lists some values for each function and, the graph shows a sketch for each function. Note that both graphs are decreasing and the graph of $g(x) = 9^{-x}$ is decreasing more rapidly than the graph of $f(x) = 3^{-x}$

x	-2	-1	0	1	2	3
9^{-x}	64	8	1	$\frac{1}{8}$	$\frac{1}{64}$	$\frac{1}{512}$
$3^{-x}\ g(x)$	9	3	1	$\frac{1}{3}$	$\frac{1}{9}$	$\frac{1}{27}$

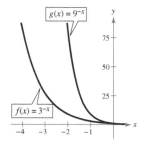

4. (a)

$8 = 2^{2x-1}$	Write Original equation.
$2^3 = 2^{2x-1}$	$8 = 2^3$
$3 = 2x - 1$	One-to-One Property
$4 = 2x$	
$2 = x$	Solve for x.

(b)

$\left(\frac{1}{3}\right)^{-x} = 27$	Write Original equation.
$3^x = 27$	$\left(\frac{1}{3}\right)^{-x} = 3^x$
$3^x = 3^3$	$27 = 3^3$
$x = 3$	One-to-One Property

5. (a) Because $g(x) = 4^{x-2} = f(x-2)$, the graph of g can be obtained by shifting the graph of f two units to the right.

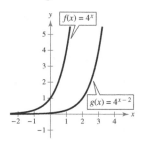

(b) Because $h(x) = 4^x + 3 = f(x) + 3$ the graph of h can be obtained by shifting the graph of f up three units.

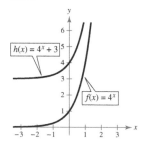

(c) Because $k(x) = 4^{-x} - 3 = f(-x) - 3$, the graph of k can be obtained by reflecting the graph of f in the y-axis and shifting the graph of f down three units.

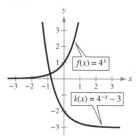

6.

Function Value	Graphing Calculator Keystrokes	Display
(a) $f(0.3) = e^{0.3}$	$\boxed{e^x}$ 0.3 $\boxed{\text{Enter}}$	1.3498588
(b) $f(-1.2) = e^{-1.2}$	$\boxed{e^x}$ $\boxed{(-)}$ 1.2 $\boxed{\text{Enter}}$	6.3011942
(c) $f(6, 2) = e^{6.2}$	$\boxed{e^x}$ 6.2 $\boxed{\text{Enter}}$	492.74904

7. To sketch the graph of $f(x) = 5e^{0.17x}$, use a graphing utility to construct a table of values. After constructing the table, plot the points and draw a smooth curve.

x	-3	-2	-1	0	1	2	3
$f(x)$	3.002	3.559	4.218	5.000	5.927	7.025	8.326

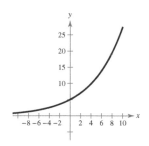

8. (a) For quarterly compounding, you have $n = 4$. So, in 7 years at 4%, the balance is as follows.

$$A = P\left(1 + \frac{r}{n}\right)^{nt} \qquad \text{Formula for compound interest.}$$

$$= 6000\left(1 + \frac{0.04}{4}\right)^{4(7)} \qquad \text{Substitute } P, r, n, \text{ and } t.$$

$$\approx \$7927.75 \qquad \text{Use a calculator.}$$

(b) For monthly compounding, you have $n = 12$. So in 7 years at 4%, the balance is as follows.

$$A = P\left(1 + \frac{r}{n}\right)^{nt} \qquad \text{Formula for compound interest.}$$

$$= 6000\left(1 + \frac{0.04}{12}\right)^{12(7)} \qquad \text{Substitute } P, r, n, \text{ and } t$$

$$\approx \$7935.08 \qquad \text{Use a calculator.}$$

(c) For continuous compounding, the balance is as follows.

$$A = Pe^{rt} \qquad \text{Formula for continuous compounding.}$$

$$= 6000e^{0.04(7)} \qquad \text{Substitute } P, r, \text{ and } t.$$

$$\approx \$7938.78 \qquad \text{Use a calculator.}$$

9. Use the model for the amount of Plutonium that remains from an initial amount of 10 pounds after t years, where $t = 0$ represents the year 1986.

$$P = 10\left(\tfrac{1}{2}\right)^{t/24,100}$$

To find the amount that remains in the year 2089, let $t = 103$.

$$P = 10\left(\tfrac{1}{2}\right)^{t/24,100} \qquad \text{Write original model.}$$

$$P = 10\left(\tfrac{1}{2}\right)^{103/24,100} \qquad \text{Substitute 103 for } t.$$

$$P \approx 9.970 \qquad \text{Use a calculator.}$$

In the year 2089, 9.970 pounds of plutonomium will remain.

To find the amount that remains after 125,000 years, let $t = 125,000$.

$$P = 10\left(\tfrac{1}{2}\right)^{t/24,100} \qquad \text{Write original model.}$$

$$P = 10\left(\tfrac{1}{2}\right)^{125,000/24,100} \qquad \text{Substitute 125,000 for } t.$$

$$P \approx 0.275 \qquad \text{Use a calculator.}$$

After 125,000 years 0.275 pound of plutonium will remain.

Checkpoints for Section 3.2

1. (a) $f(1) = \log_6 1 = 0$ because $6^0 = 1$.

(b) $f\left(\frac{1}{125}\right) = \log_5 \frac{1}{125} = -3$ because $5^{-3} = \frac{1}{125}$.

(c) $f(10,000) = \log_{10} 10,000 = 4$ because $10^4 = 10,000$.

2.

Function Value	Graphing Calculator Keystrokes	Display
(a) $f(275) = \log 275$	LOG 275 ENTER	2.4393327
(b) $f(0.275) = \log 0.275$	LOG 0.275 ENTER	-0.5606673
(c) $f\left(-\frac{1}{2} = \log -\frac{1}{2}\right)$	LOG ((−) (1 ÷ 2)) ENTER	ERROR
(d) $f\left(\frac{1}{2}\right) = \log \frac{1}{2}$	LOG (1 ÷ 2) ENTER	-0.3010300

3. (a) Using Property 2, $\log_9 9 = 1$.

(b) Using Property 3, $20^{\log_{20} 3} = 3$.

(c) Using Property 1, $\log_{\sqrt{3}} 1 = 0$.

4. $\log_5 (x^2 + 3) = \log_5 12$

$x^2 + 3 = 12$

$x^2 = 9$

$x = \pm 3$

5. (a) For $f(x) = 8^x$, construct a table of values. Then plot the points and draw a smooth curve.

x	-2	-1	0	1	2
$f(x) = 8^x$	$\frac{1}{64}$	$\frac{1}{8}$	1	8	64

(b) Because $g(x) = \log_8 x$ is the inverse function of $f(x) = 8^x$, the graph of g is obtained by plotting the points $(f(x), x)$ and connecting them with a smooth curve. The graph of g is a reflection of the graph of f in the line $y = x$.

x	$\frac{1}{64}$	$\frac{1}{8}$	1	8	64
$g(x) = \log_8 x$	-2	-1	0	1	2

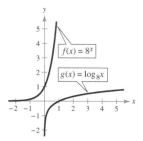

6. Begin by constructing a table of values. Note that some of the values can be obtained without a calculator by using the properties of logarithms. Then plot the points and draw a smooth curve.

x	Without calculator					With calculator					
	$\frac{1}{9}$	$\frac{1}{3}$	1	3	9	2	4	6	8	10	12
$f(x) = \log_9 x$	-1	$-\frac{1}{2}$	0	$\frac{1}{2}$	1	0.315	0.631	0.815	0.946	1.048	1.131

The vertical asymptote is $x = 0$ the y-axis.

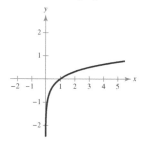

7. (a) Because $g(x) = -1 + \log_3 x = f(x) - 1$, the graph of g can be obtained by shifting the graph of f one unit down.

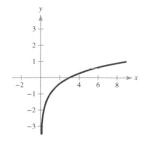

(b) Because $h(x) = \log_3 (x + 3) = f(x + 3)$, the graph of h can be obtained by shifting the graph of f three units to the left.

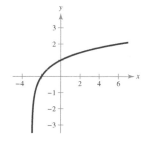

8.

Function Value	Graphing Calculator Keystrokes	Display
$f(0.01) = \ln 0.01$	⎣LN⎦ 0.01 ⎣ENTER⎦	-4.6051702
$f(4) = \ln 4$	⎣LN⎦ 4 ⎣ENTER⎦	1.3862944
$f(\sqrt{3} + 2) = \ln(\sqrt{3} + 2)$	⎣LN⎦ ⎣(⎦ ⎣(⎦ ⎣√⎦ 3 ⎣)⎦ ⎣+⎦ 2 ⎣)⎦ ⎣ENTER⎦	1.3169579
$f(\sqrt{3} - 2) = \ln(\sqrt{3} - 2)$	⎣LN⎦ ⎣(⎦ ⎣(⎦ ⎣√⎦ 3 ⎣)⎦ ⎣−⎦ 2 ⎣)⎦ ⎣ENTER⎦	ERROR

9. (a) $\ln e^{1/3} = \frac{1}{3}$ Inverse Property

    (b) $5 \ln 1 = 5(0) = 0$ Property 1

    (c) $\frac{3}{4} \ln e = \frac{3}{4}(1) = \frac{3}{4}$ Property 2

    (d) $e^{\ln 7} = 7$ Inverse Property

10. Because $\ln(x + 3)$ is defined only when $x + 3 > 0$, it follows that the domain of f is $(-3, \infty)$. The graph of f is shown.

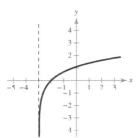

11. (a) After 1 month, the average score was the following.

$$f(1) = 75 - 6 \ln(1 + 1) \quad \text{Substitute 1 for } t.$$
$$= 75 - 6 \ln 2 \quad \text{Simplify.}$$
$$\approx 75 - 6(0.6931) \quad \text{Use a calculator.}$$
$$\approx 70.84 \quad \text{Solution}$$

    (b) After 9 months, the average score was the following.

$$f(9) = 75 - 6 \ln(9 + 1) \quad \text{Substitute 9 for } t.$$
$$= 75 - 6 \ln 10 \quad \text{Simplify.}$$
$$\approx 75 - 6(2.3026) \quad \text{Use a calculator.}$$
$$\approx 61.18 \quad \text{Solution}$$

    (c) After 12 months, the average score was the following.

$$f(12) = 75 - 6 \ln(12 + 1) \quad \text{Substitute 9 for } t.$$
$$= 75 - 6 \ln 13 \quad \text{Simplify.}$$
$$\approx 75 - 6(2.5649) \quad \text{Use a calculator.}$$
$$\approx 59.61 \quad \text{Solution}$$

Checkpoints for Section 3.3

1. $\log_2 12 = \dfrac{\log 12}{\log 2}$ $\log_a x = \dfrac{\log x}{\log a}$

    $\approx \dfrac{1.07918}{0.30103}$ Use a calculator.

    ≈ 3.5850 Simplify.

2. $\log_2 12 = \dfrac{\ln 12}{\ln 2}$ $\log_a x = \dfrac{\ln x}{\ln a}$

    $\approx \dfrac{2.48491}{0.69315}$ Use a calculator.

    ≈ 3.5850 Simplify.

3. (a) $\log 75 = \log(3 \cdot 25)$ Rewrite 75 as $3 \cdot 25$.

        $= \log 3 + \log 25$ Product Property

        $= \log 3 + \log 5^2$ Rewrite 25 as 5^2.

        $= \log 3 + 2 \log 5$ Power Property

    (b) $\log \frac{9}{125} = \log 9 - \log 125$ Quotient Property

        $= \log 3^2 - \log 5^3$ Rewrite 9 as 3^2 and 125 as 5^2.

        $= 2 \log 3 - 3 \log 5$ Power Property

4. $\ln e^6 - \ln e^2 = 6 \ln e - 2 \ln e$

                $= 6(1) - 2(1)$

                $= 4$

5. $\log_3 \dfrac{4x^2}{\sqrt{y}} = \log_3 \dfrac{4x^2}{y^{1/2}}$ Rewrite using rational exponent.

$= \log_3 4x^2 - \log_3 y^{1/2}$ Quotient Property

$= \log_3 4 + \log_3 x^2 - \log_3 y^{1/2}$ Product Property

$= \log_3 4 + 2 \log_3 x - \dfrac{1}{2} \log_3 y$ Power Property

6. $2\Big[\log(x + 3) - 2 \log(x - 2)\Big] = 2\Big[\log(x + 3) - \log(x - 2)^2\Big]$ Power Property

$= 2\left[\log\left(\dfrac{x + 3}{(x - 2)^2}\right)\right]$ Quotient Property

$= \log\left(\dfrac{x + 3}{(x - 2)^2}\right)^2$ Power Property

$= \log\dfrac{(x + 3)^2}{(x - 2)^4}$ Simplify.

7. To solve this problem, take the natural logarithm of each of the *x*- and *y*-values of the ordered pairs.

$(\ln x, \ln y)$: $(-0.994, -0.673)$, $(0.000, 0.000)$, $(1.001, 0.668)$, $(2.000, 1.332)$, $(3.000, 2.000)$

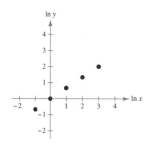

By plotting the ordered pairs, you can see that all five points appear to lie in a line. Choose any two points to determine the slope of the line. Using the points $(0, 0)$ and $(1.001, 0.668)$, the slope of the line is

$m = \dfrac{0.668 - 0}{1 - 0} = 0.668 \approx \dfrac{2}{3}.$

By the point-slope form, the equation of the line is $y = \dfrac{2}{3}x$, where $y = \ln y$ and $x = \ln x$. So, the

logarithmic equation is $\ln y = \dfrac{2}{3} \ln x$.

Checkpoints for Section 3.4

1.

Original Equation	Rewritten Equation	Solution	Property
(a) $2^x = 512$	$2^x = x^9$	$x = 9$	One-to-One
(b) $\log_6 x = 3$	$6^{\log_6 x} = 6^3$	$x = 216$	Inverse
(c) $5 - e^x = 0$ $5 = e^x$	$\ln 5 = \ln e^x$	$\ln 5 = x$	Inverse
(d) $9^x = \dfrac{1}{3}$	$3^{2x} = 3^{-1}$	$2x = -1$ $x = -\dfrac{1}{2}$	One-to-One

2. (a)

$e^{2x} = e^{x^2-8}$	Write original equation.
$2x = x^2 - 8$	One-to-One Property
$0 = x^2 - 2x - 8$	Write in general form.
$0 = (x - 4)(x + 2)$	Factor.
$x - 4 = 0 \Rightarrow x = 4$	Set 1st factor equal to 0.
$x + 2 = 0 \Rightarrow x = -2$	Set 2nd factor equal to 0.

The solutions are $x = 4$ and $x = -2$

Check $x = -2$: $x = 4$:

$e^{2x} = e^{x^2-8}$ $e^{2(4)} \overset{?}{=} e^{(4)^2-8}$

$e^{2(-2)} \overset{?}{=} e^{(-2)^2-8}$ $e^8 \overset{?}{=} e^{16-8}$

$e^{-4} \overset{?}{=} e^{4-8}$ $e^8 = e^8$ ✓

$e^{-4} = e^{-4}$ ✓

(b)

$2(5^x) = 32$	Write original equation.
$5^x = 16$	Divide each side by 2.
$\log_5 5^x = \log_5 16$	Take log(base 5) of each side.
$x = \log_5 16$	Inverse Property
$x = \dfrac{\ln 16}{\ln 5} \approx 1.723$	Change of base formula

The solution is $x = \log_5 16 \approx 1.723$.

Check $x = \log_5 16$:

$2(5^x) = 32$

$2\left[5^{(\log_5 16)}\right] \overset{?}{=} 32$

$2(16) \overset{?}{=} 32$

$32 = 32$ ✓

3.

$e^x - 7 = 23$	Write original equation.
$e^x = 30$	Add 7 to each side.
$\ln e^x = \ln 30$	Take natural log of each side.
$x = \ln 30 \approx 3.401$	Inverse Property

Check $x = \ln 30$:

$e^x - 7 = 23$

$e^{(\ln 30)-7} \overset{?}{=} 23$

$30 - 7 \overset{?}{=} 23$

$23 = 23$ ✓

4.

$6(2^{t+5}) + 4 = 11$	Write original equation.
$6(2^{t+5}) = 7$	Subtract 4 from each side.
$2^{t+5} = \dfrac{7}{6}$	Divide each side by 6.
$\log_2 2^{t+5} = \log_2\left(\dfrac{7}{6}\right)$	Take log (base 2) of each side.
$t + 5 = \log_2\left(\dfrac{7}{6}\right)$	Inverse Property
$t = \log_2\left(\dfrac{7}{6}\right) - 5$	Subtract 5 from each side.
$t = \dfrac{\ln\left(\dfrac{1}{6}\right)}{\ln 2} - 5$	Change of base formula.
$t \approx -4.778$	Use a calculator.

The solution is $t = \log_2\left(\dfrac{7}{6}\right) - 5 \approx -4.778$.

Check $t \approx -4.778$:

$6(2^{t+5}) + 4 = 11$

$6\left[2^{(-4.778+5)}\right] + 4 \overset{?}{=} 11$

$6(1.166) + 4 \overset{?}{=} 11$

$10.998 \approx 11$ ✓

5. **Algebraic Solution**

$$e^{2x} - 7e^x + 12 = 0 \qquad \text{Write original equation.}$$

$$\left(e^x\right)^2 - 7e^x + 12 = 0 \qquad \text{Write in quadratic form.}$$

$$\left(e^x - 3\right)\left(e^x - 4\right) = 0 \qquad \text{Factor.}$$

$$e^x - 3 = 0 \Rightarrow e^x = 3 \qquad \text{Set 1st factor equal to 0.}$$

$$x = \ln 3 \qquad \text{Solution}$$

$$e^x - 4 = 0 \Rightarrow e^x = 4 \qquad \text{Set 2nd factor equal to 0.}$$

$$x = \ln 4 \qquad \text{Solution}$$

The solutions are $x = \ln 3 \approx 1.099$ and $x = \ln 4 \approx 1.386$.

Check $x = \ln 3$: $\qquad\qquad\qquad x = \ln 4$:

$$e^{2x} - 7e^x + 12 = 0 \qquad\qquad e^{2(\ln 4)} - 7e^{(\ln 4)} + 12 = 0$$

$$e^{2(\ln 3)} - 7e^{(\ln 3)} + 12 \overset{?}{=} 0 \qquad\qquad e^{\ln 4^2} - 7e^{\ln 4} + 12 \overset{?}{=} 0$$

$$e^{\ln\left(3^2\right)} - 7e^{\ln 3} + 12 \overset{?}{=} 0 \qquad\qquad 4^2 - 7(4) + 12 \overset{?}{=} 0$$

$$3^2 - 7(3) + 12 \overset{?}{=} 0 \qquad\qquad\qquad 0 = 0 \checkmark$$

$$0 = 0 \checkmark$$

Graphical Solution

Use a graphing utility to graph $y = e^{2x} - 7e^x + 12$ and then find the zeros.

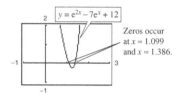

Zeros occur at $x \approx 1.099$ and $x \approx 1.386$.

So, you can conclude that the solutions are $x \approx 1.099$ and $x \approx 1.386$.

6. (a) $\ln x = \dfrac{2}{3} \qquad$ Write original equation.

$$e^{\ln x} = e^{2/3} \qquad \text{Exponentiate each side.}$$

$$x = e^{2/3} \qquad \text{Inverse Property}$$

(b) $\log_2 (2x - 3) = \log_2 (x + 4) \qquad$ Write original equation.

$$2x - 3 = x + 4 \qquad \text{One-to-One Property}$$

$$x = 7 \qquad \text{Solution}$$

(c) $\log 4x - \log(12 + x) = \log 2 \qquad$ Write Original equation.

$$\log\left(\frac{4x}{12 + x}\right) = \log 2 \qquad \text{Quotient Property of Logarithms}$$

$$\frac{4x}{12 + x} = 2 \qquad \text{One-to-One Property}$$

$$4x = 2(12 + x) \qquad \text{Multiply each side by } (12 + x).$$

$$4x = 24 + 2x \qquad \text{Distribute.}$$

$$2x = 24 \qquad \text{Subtract } 2x \text{ from each side.}$$

$$x = 12 \qquad \text{Solution}$$

7. Algebraic Solution

$$7 + 3 \ln x = 5 \qquad \text{Write original equation.}$$

$$3 \ln x = -2 \qquad \text{Subtract 7 from each side.}$$

$$\ln x = -\frac{2}{3} \qquad \text{Divide each side by 3.}$$

$$e^{\ln x} = e^{-2/3} \qquad \text{Exponentiate each side.}$$

$$x = e^{-2/3} \qquad \text{Inverse Property}$$

$$x \approx 0.513 \qquad \text{Use a calculator.}$$

Graphical Solution

Use a graphing utility to graph $y_1 = 7 + 3 \ln x$ and $y_2 = 5$. Then find the intersection point.

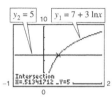

The point of intersection is about $(0.513, 5)$. So, the solution is $x \approx 0.513$.

8.
$$3 \log_4 6x = 9 \qquad \text{Write original equation.}$$

$$\log_4 6x = 3 \qquad \text{Divide each side by 3.}$$

$$4^{\log_4 6x} = 4^3 \qquad \text{Exponentiate each side (base 4).}$$

$$6x = 64 \qquad \text{Inverse Property}$$

$$x = \frac{32}{3} \qquad \text{Divide each side by 6 and simplify.}$$

Check $x = \frac{32}{3}$:

$$3 \log_4 6x = 9$$

$$3 \log_4 6\left(\frac{32}{3}\right) \overset{?}{=} 9$$

$$3 \log_4 64 \overset{?}{=} 9$$

$$3 \log_4 4^3 \overset{?}{=} 9$$

$$3 \cdot 3 \overset{?}{=} 9$$

$$9 = 9 \ \checkmark$$

9. Algebraic Solution

$$\log x + \log(x - 9) = 1 \qquad \text{Write original equation.}$$

$$\log\big[x(x - 9)\big] = 1 \qquad \text{Product Property of Logarithms}$$

$$10^{\log[x(x-9)]} = 10^1 \qquad \text{Exponentiate each side (base 10).}$$

$$x(x - 9) = 10 \qquad \text{Inverse Property}$$

$$x^2 - 9x - 10 = 0 \qquad \text{Write in general form.}$$

$$(x - 10)(x + 1) = 0 \qquad \text{Factor.}$$

$$x - 10 = 0 \Rightarrow x = 10 \qquad \text{Set 1st factor equal to 0.}$$

$$x + 1 = 0 \Rightarrow x = -1 \qquad \text{Set 2nd factor equal to 0.}$$

Check $x = 10$:

$$\log x + \log(x - 9) = 1$$

$$\log(10) + \log(10 - 9) \overset{?}{=} 1$$

$$\log 10 + \log 1 \overset{?}{=} 1$$

$$1 + 0 \overset{?}{=} 1$$

$$1 = 1 \ \checkmark$$

$x = -1$:

$$\log x + \log(x - 9) = 1$$

$$\log(-1) + \log(-1 - 9) \overset{?}{=} 1$$

$$\log(-1) + \log(-10) \overset{?}{=} 1$$

-1 and -10 are not in the domain of $\log x$. So, it does not check.

The solutions appear to be $x = 10$ and $x = -1$. But when you check these in the original equation, you can see that $x = 10$ is the only solution.

Graphical Solution

First, rewrite the original solution as

$$\log x + \log(x - 9) - 1 = 0.$$

Then use a graphing utility to graph the equation $y = \log x + \log(x - 9) - 1$ and find the zeros.

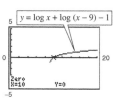

10. Using the formula for continuous compounding, the balance is

$$A = Pe^{rt}$$

$$A = 500e^{0.0525t}.$$

To find the time required for the balance to double, let $A = 1000$ and solve the resulting equation for t

$$500e^{0.0525t} = 1000 \qquad \text{Let } A = 1000.$$

$$e^{0.0525t} = 2 \qquad \text{Divide each side by 500.}$$

$$\ln e^{0.0525t} = \ln 2 \qquad \text{Take natural log of each side.}$$

$$0.0525t = \ln 2 \qquad \text{Inverse Property}$$

$$t = \frac{\ln 2}{0.0525} \qquad \text{Divide each side by 0.0525.}$$

$$t \approx 13.20 \qquad \text{Use a calculator.}$$

The balance in the account will double after approximately 13.20 years.

Because the interest rate is lower than the interest rate in Example 2, it will take more time for the account balance to double.

11. To find when sales reached $80 billion, let $y = 80$ and solve for t.

$-566 + 244.7 \ln t = y$ Write original equation

$-566 + 244.7 \ln t = 80$ Substitute 80 for y.

$244.7 \ln t = 646$ Add 566 to each side.

$\ln t = \dfrac{646}{244.7}$ Divide each side by 244.7.

$e^{\ln t} = e^{646/244.7}$ Exponentiate each side (base e).

$t = e^{646/244.7}$ Inverse Property

$t \approx 14$ Use a calculator.

The solution is $t \approx 14$. Because $t = 12$ represents 2002, it follows that $t = 14$ represents 2004. So, sales reached $80 billion in 2004.

Checkpoints for Section 3.5

1. **Algebraic Solution**

To find when the amount of U.S. online advertising spending will reach $100 billion, let $s = 100$ and solve for t.

$9.30e^{0.1129t} = s$ Write original model.

$9.30e^{0.1129t} = 100$ Substitute 100 for s.

$e^{0.1129t} \approx 10.7527$ Divide each side by 9.30.

$\ln e^{0.1129t} \approx \ln 10.7527$ Take natural log of each side.

$0.1129t \approx 2.3752$ Inverse Property

$t \approx 21.0$ Divide each side by 0.1129.

According to the model, the amount of U.S. online advertising spending will reach $100 million in 2021.

Graphical Solution

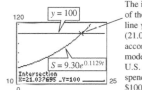

The intersection point of the model and the line $y = 100$ is about (21.0, 100). So, according to the model, the amount of U.S. online advertising spending will reach $100 billion in 2021.

2. Let y be the number of bacteria at time t. From the given information you know that $y = 100$ when $t = 1$ and $y = 200$ when $t = 2$. Substituting this information into the model $y = ae^{bt}$ produces $100 = ae^{(1)b}$ and $200 = ae^{(2)b}$. To solve for b, solve for a in the first equation.

$100 = ae^{b}$ Write first equation.

$\dfrac{100}{e^{b}} = a$ Solve for a.

Then substitute the result into the second equation.

$200 = ae^{2b}$ Write second equation

$200 = \left(\dfrac{100}{e^{b}}\right)e^{2b}$ Substitute $\dfrac{100}{e^{b}}$ for a.

$\dfrac{200}{100} = e^{b}$ Simplify and divide each side by 100.

$2 = e^{b}$ Simplify.

$\ln 2 = \ln e^{b}$ Take natural log of each side

$\ln 2 = b$ Inverse Property

Use $b = \ln 2$ and the equation you found for a.

$a = \dfrac{100}{e^{\ln 2}}$ Substitute $\ln 2$ for b.

$= \dfrac{100}{2}$ Inverse Property

$= 50$ Simplify.

So, with $a = 50$ and $b = \ln 2$, the exponential growth model is $y = 50e^{(\ln 2)t}$.

After 3 hours, the number of bacteria will be $y = 50e^{\ln 2(3)} = 400$ bacteria.

3. Algebraic Solution

In the carbon dating model, substitute the given value of R to obtain the following.

$$\frac{1}{10^{12}}e^{-t/8223} = R \qquad\qquad \text{Write original model.}$$

$$\frac{e^{-t/8223}}{10^{12}} = \frac{1}{10^{14}} \qquad\qquad \text{Substitute } \frac{1}{10^{14}} \text{ for } R.$$

$$e^{-t/8223} = \frac{1}{10^2} \qquad\qquad \text{Multiply each side by } 10^2.$$

$$e^{-t/8223} = \frac{1}{100} \qquad\qquad \text{Simplify.}$$

$$\ln e^{-t/8223} = \ln \frac{1}{100} \qquad\qquad \text{Take natural log of each side.}$$

$$-\frac{t}{8223} \approx -4.6052 \qquad\qquad \text{Inverse Property}$$

$$t \approx 37{,}869 \qquad\qquad \text{Multiply each side by } -8223.$$

So, to the nearest thousand years, the age of the fossil is about 38,000 years.

Graphical Solution

Use a graphing utility to graph the formula for the ratio of carbon 14 to carbon 12 at any time t as

$$y_1 = \frac{1}{10^{12}}e^{-x/8223}.$$

In the same viewing window, graph $y_2 = \frac{1}{10^{14}}$

Use the *intersect* feature to estimate that $x \approx 18{,}934$ when $y = 1/10^{13}$.

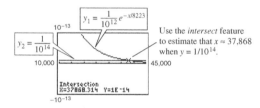

Use the *intersect* feature to estimate that $x \approx 37{,}868$ when $y = 1/10^{14}$.

So, to the nearest thousand years, the age of fossil is about 38,000 years.

4. The graph of the function is shown below. On this bell-shaped curve, the maximum value of the curve represents the average score. From the graph, you can estimate that, the average reading score for high school graduates in 2011 was 497.

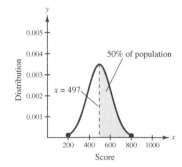

$$y = 0.0035e^{-(x-497)^2/25.992}$$

5. To find the number of days that 250 students are infected, let $y = 250$ and solve for t.

$$\frac{5000}{1 + 4999e^{-0.8t}} = y \qquad \text{Write original model.}$$

$$\frac{5000}{1 + 4999e^{-0.8t}} = 250 \qquad \text{Substitute 250 for } y.$$

$$\frac{5000}{250} = 1 + 4999e^{-0.8t} \qquad \text{Divide each side by 250 and multiply each side by } 1 + 4999e^{-0.8t}.$$

$$20 = 1 + 4999e^{-0.8t} \qquad \text{Simplify.}$$

$$19 = 4999e^{-0.8t} \qquad \text{Subtract 1 from each side.}$$

$$\frac{19}{4999} = e^{-0.8t} \qquad \text{Divide each side by 4999}$$

$$\ln\left(\frac{19}{4999}\right) = \ln e^{-0.8t} \qquad \text{Take natural log of each side.}$$

$$\ln\left(\frac{19}{4999}\right) = -0.8t \qquad \text{Inverse Property}$$

$$-5.5726 \approx -0.8t \qquad \text{Use a calculator.}$$

$$t \approx 6.97 \qquad \text{Divide each side by } -0.8.$$

So, after about 7 days, 250 students will be infected.

Graphical Solution

To find the number of days that 250 students are infected, use a graphing utility to graph.

$$y_1 = \frac{5000}{1 + 4999e^{-0.8x}} \text{ and } y_2 = 250$$

in the same viewing window. Use the *intersect* feature of the graphing utility to find the point of intersection of the graphs.

The point of intersection occurs near $x \approx 6.96$. So, after about 7 days, at least 250 students will be infected.

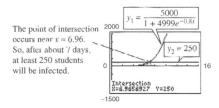

6. (a) Because $I_0 = 1$ and $R = 6.0$, you have the following.

$$R = \log \frac{I}{I_0}$$

$$6.0 = \log \frac{I}{1} \qquad \text{Substitute 1 for } I_0 \text{ and 6.0 for } R.$$

$$10^{6.0} = 10^{\log I} \qquad \text{Exponentiate each side (base 10).}$$

$$10^{6.0} = I \qquad \text{Inverse Property}$$

$$1,000,000 = I \qquad \text{Simplify.}$$

(b) Because $I_0 = 1$ and $R = 7.9$, you have the following.

$$7.9 = \log \frac{I}{1} \qquad \text{Substitute 1 for } I_0 \text{ and 7.9 for } R.$$

$$10^{7.9} = 10^{\log I} \qquad \text{Exponentiate each side (base 10).}$$

$$10^{7.9} = I \qquad \text{Inverse Property}$$

$$79,432,823 \approx I \qquad \text{Simplify.}$$

Chapter 4

Checkpoints for Section 4.1

1. (a) *Sample answers:* $\dfrac{9\pi}{4} + 2\pi = \dfrac{17\pi}{4}$

   $\dfrac{9\pi}{4} - 2\pi = \dfrac{\pi}{4}$

   (b) *Sample answers:* $\dfrac{-\pi}{3} + 2\pi = \dfrac{5\pi}{3}$

   $\dfrac{-\pi}{3} - 2\pi = -\dfrac{7\pi}{3}$

2. (a) $\dfrac{\pi}{2} - \dfrac{\pi}{6} = \dfrac{3\pi}{6} - \dfrac{\pi}{6} = \dfrac{2\pi}{6} = \dfrac{\pi}{3}$

   The complement of $\dfrac{\pi}{6}$ is $\dfrac{\pi}{3}$.

   $\pi - \dfrac{\pi}{6} = \dfrac{6\pi}{6} - \dfrac{\pi}{6} = \dfrac{5\pi}{6}$

   The supplement of $\dfrac{\pi}{6}$ is $\dfrac{5\pi}{6}$.

   (b) Because $\dfrac{5\pi}{6}$ is greater than $\dfrac{\pi}{2}$, it has no complement.

   $\pi - \dfrac{5\pi}{6} = \dfrac{6\pi}{6} - \dfrac{5\pi}{6} = \dfrac{\pi}{6}$

   The supplement of $\dfrac{5\pi}{6}$ is $\dfrac{\pi}{6}$.

3. (a) $60° = \left(60 \ \text{deg}\right)\left(\dfrac{\pi \ \text{rad}}{180 \ \text{deg}}\right) = \dfrac{\pi}{3}$ radians

   (b) $320° = \left(320 \ \text{deg}\right)\left(\dfrac{\pi \ \text{rad}}{180 \ \text{deg}}\right) = \dfrac{16\pi}{9}$ radians

4. (a) $\dfrac{\pi}{6} = \left(\dfrac{\pi}{6} \ \text{rad}\right)\left(\dfrac{180 \ \text{deg}}{\pi \ \text{rad}}\right) = 30°$

   (b) $\dfrac{5\pi}{3} = \left(\dfrac{5\pi}{3} \ \text{rad}\right)\left(\dfrac{180 \ \text{deg}}{\pi \ \text{rad}}\right) = 300°$

5. To use the formula $s = r\theta$ first convert 160° to radian measure.

   $160° = \left(160 \ \text{deg}\right)\left(\dfrac{\pi \ \text{rad}}{180 \ \text{deg}}\right) = \dfrac{8\pi}{9}$ radians

   Then, using a radius of $r = 27$ inches, you can find the arc length to be

   $s = r\theta$

   $\quad = (27)\left(\dfrac{8\pi}{9}\right)$

   $\quad = 24\pi$

   $\quad \approx 75.40$ inches.

6. In one revolution, the arc length traveled is

   $s = 2\pi r$

   $\quad = 2\pi(8)$

   $\quad = 16\pi$ centimeters.

   The time required for the second hand to travel this distance is

   $t = 1$ minute $= 60$ seconds.

   So, the linear speed of the tip of the second hand is

   Linear speed $= \dfrac{s}{t}$

   $\qquad\qquad\quad = \dfrac{16\pi \ \text{centimeters}}{60 \ \text{seconds}}$

   $\qquad\qquad\quad \approx 0.838$ centimeters per second.

7. (a) Because each revolution generates 2π radians, it follows that the saw blade turns $(2400)(2\pi) = 4800\pi$ radians per minute. In other words, the angular speed is

   Angular speed $= \dfrac{\theta}{t} = \dfrac{4800\pi \ \text{radians}}{1 \ \text{minute}} = 80\pi$ radians per minute.

   (b) The radius is $r = 4$. The linear speed is

   Linear speed $= \dfrac{s}{t} = \dfrac{r\theta}{t} = \dfrac{(4)(4800\pi) \ \text{inches}}{60 \ \text{seconds}} = 60{,}319$ inches per minute.

8. First convert 80° to radian measure as follows.

$$\theta = 80° = \left(80 \text{ deg}\right)\left(\frac{\pi \text{ rad}}{180 \text{ deg}}\right) = \frac{4\pi}{9} \text{ radians}$$

Then, using $\theta = \dfrac{4\pi}{9}$ and $r = 40$ feet, the area is

$$A = \frac{1}{2}r^2\theta \qquad\qquad \text{Formula for area of a sector of a circle}$$

$$= \frac{1}{2}(40)^2\left(\frac{4\pi}{9}\right) \qquad \text{Substitute for } r \text{ and } \theta$$

$$= \frac{3200\pi}{9} \qquad\qquad \text{Multiply}$$

$$\approx 1117 \text{ square feet.} \qquad \text{Simplify.}$$

Checkpoints for Section 4.2

1. (a) $t = \dfrac{\pi}{2}$ corresponds to the point $(x, y) = (0, 1)$

$$\sin\frac{\pi}{2} = 1 \qquad\qquad \csc\frac{\pi}{2} = 1$$

$$\cos\frac{\pi}{2} = 0 \qquad\qquad \sec\frac{\pi}{2} \text{ is undefined.}$$

$$\tan\frac{\pi}{2} \text{ is undefined.} \qquad \cot\frac{\pi}{2} = 0$$

(b) $t = 0$ corresponds to the point $(x, y) = (1, 0)$

$$\sin 0 = 0 \qquad\qquad \csc 0 \text{ is undefined.}$$

$$\cos 0 = 1 \qquad\qquad \sec 0 = 1$$

$$\tan 0 = 0 \qquad\qquad \cot 0 \text{ is undefined.}$$

(c) $t = -\dfrac{5\pi}{6}$ corresponds to the point $(x, y) = \left(-\dfrac{\sqrt{3}}{2}, -\dfrac{1}{2}\right)$

$$\sin\left(-\frac{5\pi}{6}\right) = -\frac{1}{2} \qquad \csc\left(-\frac{5\pi}{6}\right) = -2$$

$$\cos\left(-\frac{5\pi}{6}\right) = -\frac{\sqrt{3}}{2} \qquad \sec\left(-\frac{5\pi}{6}\right) = -\frac{2\sqrt{3}}{3}$$

$$\tan\left(-\frac{5\pi}{6}\right) = \frac{\sqrt{3}}{3} \qquad \cot\left(-\frac{5\pi}{6}\right) = \sqrt{3}$$

(d) $t = -\dfrac{3\pi}{4}$ corresponds to the point $(x, y) = \left(-\dfrac{\sqrt{2}}{2}, -\dfrac{\sqrt{2}}{2}\right)$

$$\sin\left(-\frac{3\pi}{4}\right) = -\frac{\sqrt{2}}{2} \qquad \csc\left(-\frac{3\pi}{4}\right) = -\sqrt{2}$$

$$\cos\left(-\frac{3\pi}{4}\right) = -\frac{\sqrt{2}}{2} \qquad \sec\left(-\frac{3\pi}{4}\right) = -\sqrt{2}$$

$$\tan\left(-\frac{3\pi}{4}\right) = 1 \qquad\qquad \cot\left(-\frac{3\pi}{4}\right) = 1$$

2. (a) Because $\dfrac{9\pi}{2} = 4\pi + \dfrac{\pi}{2}$, you have $\cos\dfrac{9\pi}{2} = \cos\left(4\pi + \dfrac{\pi}{2}\right) = \cos\dfrac{\pi}{2} = 0$.

   (b) Because $-\dfrac{7\pi}{3} = -2\pi - \dfrac{\pi}{3}$, you have $\sin-\dfrac{7\pi}{3} = \sin\left(-2\pi - \dfrac{\pi}{3}\right) - \sin-\dfrac{\pi}{3} = -\dfrac{\sqrt{3}}{2}$

   (c) For $\cos(-t) = 0.3$, $\cos t = 0.3$ because the cosine function is even.

3. (a) 0.78183148

   (b) 1.0997502

Checkpoints for Section 4.3

1.

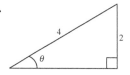

By the Pythagorean Theorem, $(\text{hyp})^2 = (\text{opp})^2 + (\text{adj})^2$, it follows that

$\text{adj} = \sqrt{4^2 - 2^2} = \sqrt{12} = 2\sqrt{3}.$

So, the six trigonometric functions of θ are

$\sin\theta = \dfrac{\text{opp}}{\text{hyp}} = \dfrac{2}{4} = \dfrac{1}{2}$ $\csc\theta = \dfrac{\text{hyp}}{\text{opp}} = \dfrac{4}{2} = 2$

$\cos\theta = \dfrac{\text{adj}}{\text{hyp}} = \dfrac{2\sqrt{3}}{4} = \dfrac{\sqrt{3}}{2}$ $\sec\theta = \dfrac{\text{hyp}}{\text{adj}} = \dfrac{4}{2\sqrt{3}} = \dfrac{2}{\sqrt{3}} = \dfrac{2\sqrt{3}}{3}$

$\tan\theta = \dfrac{\text{opp}}{\text{adj}} = \dfrac{2}{2\sqrt{3}} = \dfrac{1}{\sqrt{3}} = \dfrac{\sqrt{3}}{3}$ $\cot\theta = \dfrac{\text{adj}}{\text{opp}} = \dfrac{2\sqrt{3}}{2} = \sqrt{3}$

2.

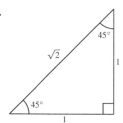

$\sec\theta = \dfrac{\text{hyp}}{\text{adj}} = \dfrac{\sqrt{2}}{1} = \sqrt{2}$

3.

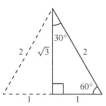

For $\theta = 60°$, you have $\text{adj} = 1$, $\text{opp} = \sqrt{3}$ and $\text{hyp} = 2$.

So, $\tan 60° = \dfrac{\text{opp}}{\text{adj}} = \dfrac{\sqrt{3}}{1} = \sqrt{3}.$

For $\theta = 30°$, you have $\text{adj} = \sqrt{3}$, $\text{opp} = 1$ and $\text{hyp} = 2$.

So, $\tan 30° = \dfrac{\text{opp}}{\text{adj}} = \dfrac{1}{\sqrt{3}} = \dfrac{\sqrt{3}}{3}.$

4. $34° \, 30' \, 36'' = 34° + \left(\dfrac{30}{60}\right)° + \left(\dfrac{36}{3600}\right)° = 34.51°$

$\csc(34° \, 30' \, 36'') = \csc 34.51° = \dfrac{1}{\sin 34.51°} \approx 1.765069$

5. (a) To find the value of $\sin \theta$, use the Pythagorean Identity

$\sin^2 \theta + \cos^2 \theta = 1.$

So, you have

$\sin^2 \theta + (0.25)^2 = 1$

$\qquad \sin^2 \theta = 1 - (0.25)^2$

$\qquad \sin^2 \theta = 0.9375$

$\qquad \sin \theta = \sqrt{0.9375}$

$\qquad\qquad \approx 0.9682.$

(b) Now, knowing the sine and cosine of θ, you can find the tangent of θ to be

$\tan \theta = \dfrac{\sin \theta}{\cos \theta} \approx \dfrac{0.9682}{0.25} = 3.8728.$

6. $\cot \beta = \dfrac{1}{\tan \beta}$ Reciprocal Identity.

$\qquad = \dfrac{1}{2}$

$\sec^2 \beta = 1 + \tan^2 \beta$ Pythagorean identity

$\sec^2 \beta = 1 + (2)^2$

$\sec^2 \beta = 5$

$\sec \beta = \sqrt{5}$

Use the definitions of $\cot \beta$ and $\sec \beta$ and the triangle to check these results.

7. (a) $\tan \theta \, \csc \theta$

$= \left(\dfrac{\cancel{\sin \theta}}{\cos \theta}\right)\left(\dfrac{1}{\cancel{\sin \theta}}\right)$ Use a Quotient Identity and a Reciprocal Identity.

$= \dfrac{1}{\cos \theta}$ Simplify.

$= \sec \theta$ Use a Reciprocal Identity

(b) $(\csc \theta + 1)(\csc \theta - 1) = \csc^2 \theta - \csc \theta + \csc \theta - 1$ FOIL Method.

$\qquad\qquad\qquad\qquad\qquad = \csc^2 \theta - 1$ Simplify.

$\qquad\qquad\qquad\qquad\qquad = \cot^2 \theta$ Pythagorean identity

8. From the figure you can see that

$\tan 64.6° = \dfrac{\text{opp}}{\text{adj}} = \dfrac{y}{x}$

where $x = 19$ and y is the height of the flagpole. So, the height of the flagpole is

$y = 19 \tan 64.6°$

$\quad \approx 19(2.106)$

$\quad \approx 40$ feet.

9. From the figure, you can see that the cosine of the angle θ is

$\cos \theta = \dfrac{\text{adj}}{\text{hyp}} = \dfrac{3}{6} = \dfrac{1}{2}.$

You should recognize that $\theta = 60°$.

10. From the figure, you can see that

$\sin 11.5° = \dfrac{\text{opp}}{\text{hyp}} = \dfrac{3.5}{c}.$

$\sin 11.5° = \dfrac{3.5}{c}$

$c \sin 11.5° = 3.5$

$\qquad c = \dfrac{3.5}{\sin 11.5°}$

So, the length c of the loading ramp is

$c = \dfrac{3.5}{\sin 11.5} \approx \dfrac{3.5}{0.1994} \approx 17.6$ feet.

Also from the figure, you can see that

$\tan 11.5° = \dfrac{\text{opp}}{\text{adj}} = \dfrac{3.5}{a}.$

So, the length a of the ramp is

$a = \dfrac{3.5}{\tan 11.5°} \approx \dfrac{3.5}{0.2034} \approx 17.2$ feet.

Checkpoints for Section 4.4

1. Referring to the figure shown, you can see that $x = -2$, $y = 3$ and

$$r = \sqrt{x^2 + y^2} = \sqrt{(-2)^2 + (3)^2} = \sqrt{13}.$$

So, you have the following.

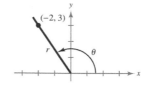

$$\sin \theta = \frac{y}{r} = \frac{3}{\sqrt{13}} = \frac{3\sqrt{13}}{13}$$

$$\cos \theta = \frac{x}{r} = -\frac{2}{\sqrt{13}} = -\frac{2\sqrt{13}}{13}$$

$$\tan \theta = \frac{y}{x} = -\frac{3}{2}$$

2. Note that θ lies in Quadrant II because that is the only quadrant in which the sine is positive and the tangent is negative. Moreover, using

$$\sin \theta = \frac{4}{5} = \frac{y}{r}$$

and the fact that y is positive in Quadrant II, you can let $y = 4$ and $r = 5$.

So,

$$r = \sqrt{x^2 + y^2}$$
$$5 = \sqrt{x^2 + 4^2}$$
$$25 = x^2 + 16$$
$$9 = x^2$$
$$\pm 3 = x$$

Since x is negative in Quadrant II, $x = -3$.

So, $\cos \theta = \frac{x}{r} = -\frac{3}{5}$.

3. To begin, choose a point on the terminal side of the angle $\frac{3\pi}{2}$.

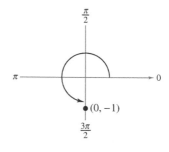

For the point $(0, -1)$, $r = 1$ and you have the following.

$$\sin \frac{3\pi}{2} = \frac{y}{r} = \frac{-1}{1} = -1$$

$$\cot \frac{3\pi}{2} = \frac{x}{y} = \frac{0}{-1} = 0$$

4. (a) Because $213°$ lies in Quadrant III, the angle it makes with the x-axis is $\theta' = 213° - 180° = 33°$.

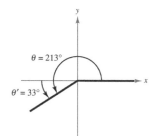

(b) Because $\frac{14\pi}{9}$ lies in Quadrant IV, the angle it makes with the x-axis is

$$\theta' = 2\pi - \frac{14\pi}{9} = \frac{18\pi}{9} - \frac{14\pi}{9} = \frac{4\pi}{9}.$$

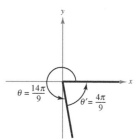

(c) Because $\frac{4\pi}{5}$ lies in Quadrant II, the angle it makes with the x-axis is

$$\theta' = \pi - \frac{4\pi}{5} = \frac{\pi}{5}.$$

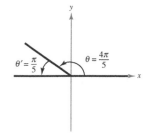

5. (a) Because $\theta = \dfrac{7\pi}{4}$ lies in Quadrant IV, the reference angle is $\theta' = 2\pi - \dfrac{7\pi}{4} = \dfrac{\pi}{4}$ as shown.

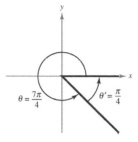

Because the sine is negative in Quadrant IV, you have $\sin \dfrac{7\pi}{4} = (-)\sin \dfrac{\pi}{7}$

$$= -\dfrac{\sqrt{2}}{2}.$$

(b) Because $-120° + 360° = 240°$, it follows that $-120°$ is coterminal with the third-quadrant angle $240°$. So, the reference angle is $\theta' = 240° - 180° = 60°$ as shown.

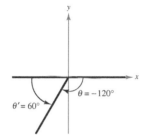

Because the cosine is negative in Quadrant III, you have $\cos(-120°) = (-)\cos 60° = -\dfrac{1}{2}$.

(c) Because $\theta = \dfrac{11\pi}{6}$ lies in Quadrant IV, the reference angle is $\theta' = 2\pi - \dfrac{11\pi}{6} = \dfrac{\pi}{6}$ as shown.

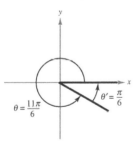

Because the tangent is negative in Quadrant IV, you have

$$\tan \dfrac{11\pi}{6} = (-)\tan \dfrac{\pi}{6} = -\dfrac{\sqrt{3}}{3}.$$

6. (a) Using the Pythagorean Identity $\sin^2 \theta + \cos^2 \theta = 1$, you obtain the following.

$$\sin^2 \theta + \cos^2 \theta = 1 \qquad \text{Write Identity}$$

$$\left(-\frac{4}{5}\right)^2 + \cos^2 \theta = 1 \qquad \text{Substitute } -\frac{4}{5} \text{ for } \sin \theta.$$

$$\frac{16}{25} + \cos^2 \theta = 1 \qquad \text{Simplify.}$$

$$\cos^2 \theta = 1 - \frac{16}{25} \qquad \text{Subtract } \frac{16}{25} \text{ from each side.}$$

$$\cos^2 \theta = \frac{9}{25} \qquad \text{Simplify.}$$

Because $\cos \theta < 0$ in Quadrant III, you can use the negative root to obtain

$$\cos \theta = -\sqrt{\frac{9}{25}} = -\frac{3}{5}.$$

(b) Using the trigonometric identity $\tan \theta = \dfrac{\sin \theta}{\cos \theta}$, you obtain

$$\tan \theta = \frac{-\dfrac{4}{5}}{-\dfrac{3}{5}} \qquad \text{Substitute for } \sin \theta \text{ and } \cos \theta.$$

$$= \frac{4}{3}. \qquad \text{Simplify.}$$

7.

Function	Mode	Calculator Keystrokes	Display
(a) $\tan 119°$	Degree	$\boxed{\tan}$ $\boxed{(}$ 119 $\boxed{)}$ $\boxed{\text{ENTER}}$	-1.8040478
(b) $\csc 5$	Radian	$\boxed{(}$ $\boxed{\sin}$ $\boxed{(}$ 5 $\boxed{)}$ $\boxed{)}$ $\boxed{x^{-1}}$ $\boxed{\text{ENTER}}$	-1.0428352
(c) $\cos \dfrac{\pi}{5}$	Radian	$\boxed{\cos}$ $\boxed{(}$ π $\boxed{\div}$ 5 $\boxed{)}$ $\boxed{\text{ENTER}}$	0.8090170

8. Because $t = \dfrac{7\pi}{3}$ and $t = \dfrac{\pi}{3}$ are coterminal angles, it follows that $f\left(\dfrac{7\pi}{3}\right) = f\left(\dfrac{\pi}{3}\right) = \tan \dfrac{\pi}{3} = \dfrac{y}{x} = \dfrac{\dfrac{\sqrt{3}}{2}}{\dfrac{1}{2}} = \sqrt{3}.$

Checkpoints for Section 4.5

1. Note that $y = 2 \cos x = 2(\cos x)$ indicates that the y-values for the key points will have twice the magnitude of those on the graph of $y = \cos x$. Divide the period 2π into four equal parts to get the key points.

Maximum	Intercept	Minimum	Intercept	Maximum
$(0, 2)$	$\left(\dfrac{\pi}{2}, 0\right)$	$(\pi, -2)$	$\left(\dfrac{3\pi}{2}, 0\right)$	$(2\pi, 2)$

By connecting these key points with a smooth curve and extending the curve in both directions over the interval $\left[-\dfrac{\pi}{2}, \dfrac{9\pi}{2}\right]$, you obtain the graph shown.

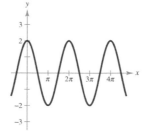

2. (a) Because the amplitude of $y = \dfrac{1}{3} \sin x$ is $\dfrac{1}{3}$, the maximum value is $\dfrac{1}{3}$ and the minimum value is $-\dfrac{1}{3}$.

Divide one cycle, $0 \le x \le 2\pi$, into for equal parts to get the key points.

Intercept	Maximum	Intercept	Minimum	Intercept
$(0, 0)$	$\left(\dfrac{\pi}{2}, \dfrac{1}{3}\right)$	$(\pi, 0)$	$\left(\dfrac{3\pi}{2}, -\dfrac{1}{3}\right)$	$(2\pi, 0)$

(b) A similar analysis shows that the amplitude of $y = 3 \sin x$ is 3, and the key points are as follows.

Intercept	Maximum	Intercept	Minimum	Intercept
$(0, 0)$	$\left(\dfrac{\pi}{2}, 3\right)$	$(\pi, 0)$	$\left(\dfrac{3\pi}{2}, -3\right)$	$(2\pi, 0)$

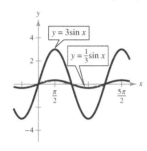

3. The amplitude is 1. Moreover, because $b = \dfrac{1}{3}$, the period is

$$\frac{2\pi}{b} = \frac{2\pi}{\dfrac{1}{3}} = 6\pi. \quad \text{Substitute } \frac{1}{3} \text{ for } b.$$

Now, divide the period-interval $[0, 6\pi]$ into four equal parts using the values $\dfrac{3\pi}{2}$, 3π, and $\dfrac{9\pi}{2}$ to obtain the key points.

Maximum	Intercept	Minimum	Intercept	Maximum
$(0, 1)$	$\left(\dfrac{3\pi}{2}, 0\right)$	$(3\pi, -1)$	$\left(\dfrac{9\pi}{2}, 0\right)$	$(6\pi, 1)$

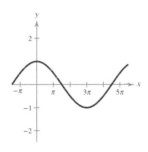

4. Algebraic Solution

The amplitude is 2 and the period is 2π.

By solving the equations

$$x - \frac{\pi}{2} = 0 \Rightarrow x = \frac{\pi}{2}$$

and $\quad x - \frac{\pi}{2} = 2\pi \Rightarrow x = \frac{5\pi}{2}$

you see that the interval $\left[\frac{\pi}{2}, \frac{5\pi}{2}\right]$ corresponds to one cycle of the graph. Dividing this interval into four equal parts produces the key points.

Maximum	Intercept	Minimum	Intercept	Maximum
$\left(\frac{\pi}{2}, 2\right)$	$(\pi, 0)$	$\left(\frac{3\pi}{2}, -2\right)$	$(2\pi, 0)$	$\left(\frac{5\pi}{2}, 2\right)$

Graphical Solution

Use a graphing utility set in *radian* mode to graph $y = 2 \cos\left(x - \frac{\pi}{2}\right)$ as shown.

Use the *minimum*, *maximum*, and *zero* or *root* features of the graphing utility to approximate the key points $(1.57, 2), (3.14, 0), (4.71, -2), (6.28, 0)$ and $(7.85, 2)$.

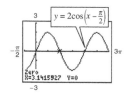

5. The amplitude is $\frac{1}{2}$ and the period is $\frac{2\pi}{b} = \frac{2\pi}{\pi} = 2$.

By solving the equations

$$\pi x + \pi = 0$$
$$\pi x = -\pi$$
$$x = -1$$

and $\quad \pi x + \pi = 2\pi$
$$\pi x = \pi$$
$$x = 1$$

you see that the interval $[-1, 1]$ corresponds to one cycle of the graph. Dividing this into four equal parts produces the key points.

Intercept	Minimum	Intercept	Maximum	Intercept
$(-1, 0)$	$\left(-\frac{1}{2}, -\frac{1}{2}\right)$	$(0, 0)$	$\left(\frac{1}{2}, \frac{1}{2}\right)$	$(1, 0)$

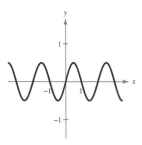

6. The amplitude is 2 and the period is 2π. The key points over the interval $[0, 2\pi]$ are

$$(0, -3), \left(\frac{\pi}{2}, -5\right), (\pi, -7), \left(\frac{3\pi}{2}, -5\right), \text{ and } (2\pi, -3).$$

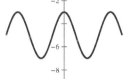

7. Use a sine model of the form $y = a \sin(bt - c) + d$.

The difference between the maximum value and minimum value is twice the amplitude of the function. So, the amplitude is

$$a = \frac{1}{2}\left[(\text{maximum depth}) - (\text{minimum depth})\right]$$

$$= \frac{1}{2}(11.3 - 0.1) = 5.6.$$

The sine function completes one half cycle between the times at which the maximum and minimum depths occur. So, the period p is

$$p = 2\left[(\text{time of min. depth}) - (\text{time of max. depth})\right]$$

$$= 2(10 - 4) = 12$$

which implies that $b = \dfrac{2\pi}{p} \approx 0.524$. Because high tide occurs 4 hours after midnight, consider the maximum to be

$$bt - c = \frac{\pi}{2} \approx 1.571.$$

So, $(0.524)(4) - c \approx 1.571$

$$c \approx 0.525.$$

Because the average depth is $\dfrac{1}{2}(11.3 + 0.1) = 5.7$, it follows that $d = 5.7$. So, you can model the depth with the function

$$y = a \sin(bt - c) + d$$

$$= 5.6 \sin(0.524t - 0.525) + 5.7.$$

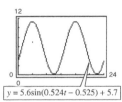

$$y = 5.6\sin(0.524t - 0.525) + 5.7$$

Checkpoints for Section 4.6

1. By solving the equations

$$\frac{x}{4} = -\frac{\pi}{2} \quad \text{and} \quad \frac{x}{4} = \frac{\pi}{2}$$

$$x = -2\pi \qquad x = 2\pi$$

you can see that two consecutive vertical asymptotes occur at $x = -2\pi$ and $x = 2\pi$. Between these two asymptotes, plot a few points including the x-intercept.

x	-2π	$-\pi$	0	π	2π
$f(x)$	Undef.	-1	0	1	Undef.

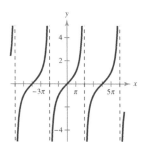

2. By solving the equations

$$2x = -\frac{\pi}{2} \quad \text{and} \quad 2x = \frac{\pi}{2}$$

$$x = -\frac{\pi}{4} \qquad x = \frac{\pi}{4}$$

you can see that two consecutive vertical asymptotes occur at $x = -\frac{\pi}{4}$ and $x = \frac{\pi}{4}$. Between these two asymptotes, plot a few points including the x-intercept.

x	$-\frac{\pi}{4}$	$-\frac{\pi}{8}$	0	$\frac{\pi}{8}$	$\frac{\pi}{4}$
$\tan 2x$	Undef.	-1	0	1	Undef.

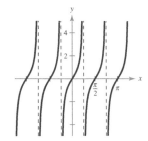

3. By solving the equations

$$\frac{x}{4} = 0 \quad \text{and} \quad \frac{x}{4} = \pi$$

$$x = 0 \qquad x = 4\pi$$

you can see that two consecutive vertical asymptotes occur at $x = 0$ and $x = 4\pi$. Between these two asymptotes, plot a few points, including the x-intercept.

x	0	π	2π	3π	4π
$\cot \frac{x}{4}$	Undef.	1	0	-1	Undef.

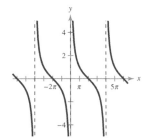

4. Begin by sketching the graph of $y = 2 \sin\left(x + \frac{\pi}{2}\right)$. For this function, the amplitude is 2 and the period is 2π. By solving the equations

$$x + \frac{\pi}{2} = 0 \quad \text{and} \quad x + \frac{\pi}{2} = 2\pi$$

$$x = -\frac{\pi}{2} \qquad x = \frac{3\pi}{2}$$

you can see that one cycle of the sine function corresponds to the interval from $x = -\frac{\pi}{2}$ to $x = \frac{3\pi}{2}$. The graph of this sine function is represented by the gray curve. Because the sine function is zero at the midpoint and endpoints of this interval, the corresponding cosecant function

$$y = 2 \csc\left(x + \frac{\pi}{2}\right)$$

$$= 2\left(\frac{1}{\sin\left(x + \frac{\pi}{2}\right)}\right)$$

has vertical asymptotes at

$$x = -\frac{\pi}{2}, x = \frac{\pi}{2}, x = \frac{3\pi}{2},$$

and so on. The graph of the cosecant curve is represented by the black curve.

5. Begin by sketching the graph of $y = \cos \dfrac{x}{2}$ as indicated

by the gray curve. Then, form the graph of $y = \sec \dfrac{x}{2}$ as

the black curve. Note that the x-intercepts of

$y = \cos \dfrac{x}{2}$, $(\pi, 0), (3\pi, 0), (5\pi, 0), \ldots$ correspond to the

vertical asymptotes $x = \pi, x = 3\pi, x = 5\pi, \ldots$ of the

graph of $y = \sec \dfrac{x}{2}$. Moreover, notice that the period of

$y = \cos \dfrac{x}{2}$ and $y = \sec \dfrac{x}{2}$ is $\dfrac{2\pi}{\frac{1}{2}} = 4\pi$.

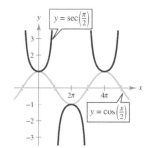

6. Consider $f(x)$ as the product of these two functions

$y = e^x$ and $y = \sin 4x$

each of which has a set of real numbers as its domain. For any real number x, you know that $e^x |\sin 4x| \le e^x$

which means that $-e^x \le e^x \sin 4x \le e^x$.

Furthermore, because

$f(x) = e^x \sin 4x = \pm e^x$ at $x = \dfrac{\pi}{8} \pm \dfrac{n\pi}{4}$ since

$\sin 4x = \pm 1$ at $4x = \dfrac{\pi}{2} + n\pi$

and

$f(x) = e^x \sin 4x = 0$ at $x = \dfrac{n\pi}{4}$ since $\sin 4x = 0$ at

$4x = n\pi$

the graph of f touches the curve $y = -e^x$ or $y = e^x$ at

$x = \dfrac{\pi}{8} + \dfrac{n\pi}{4}$ and has x-intercepts at $x = \dfrac{n\pi}{4}$.

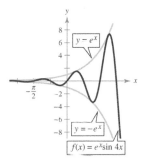

Checkpoints for Section 4.7

1. (a) Because $\sin \dfrac{\pi}{2} = 1$, and $\dfrac{\pi}{2}$ lies in $\left[-\dfrac{\pi}{2}, \dfrac{\pi}{2} \right]$, it follows that $\arcsin 1 = \dfrac{\pi}{2}$.

(b) It is not possible to evaluate $y = \sin^{-1} x$ when $x = -2$ because there is no angle whose sine is -2. Remember that the domain of the inverse sine function is $[-1, 1]$.

2. Using a graphing utility you can graph the three functions with the following keystrokes

Function	Keystroke	Display
$y = \sin x$	$\boxed{y=}\;\boxed{\text{SIN}}\;\boxed{(}\;\boxed{x}\;\boxed{)}$	$y_1 = \sin(x)$
$y = \arcsin x$	$\boxed{y=}\;\boxed{\text{2ND}}\;\boxed{\text{SIN}}\;\boxed{(}\;\boxed{x}\;\boxed{)}$	$y_2 = \sin^{-1}(x)$
$y = x$	$\boxed{y=}\;\boxed{x}$	$y_3 = x$

Remember to check the mode to make sure the angle measure is set to radian mode. Although the graphing utility will

graph the sine function for all real values of x, restrict the viewing window to values of x to be the interval $\left[-\dfrac{\pi}{2}, \dfrac{\pi}{2} \right]$.

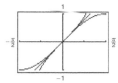

Notice that the graphs of $y_1 = \sin x$, $\left(-\dfrac{\pi}{2}, \dfrac{\pi}{2} \right)$ and $y_2 = \sin^{-1} x$ are

reflections of each other in the line $y_3 = x$. So, g is the inverse of f.

3. Because $\cos \pi = -1$ and π lies in $[0, \pi]$, it follows that $\arccos(-1) = \cos^{-1}(-1) = \pi$.

4.

Function	Mode	Calculator Keystrokes
(a) arctan 4.84	Radian	TAN^{-1} (4.84) ENTER

From the display, it follows that arctan $4.84 \approx 1.3670516$.

| (b) arcsin (-1.1) | Radian | SIN^{-1} ((–) 1.1) ENTER |

In radian mode the calculator should display an *error* message because the domain of the inverse sine function is $[-1, 1]$.

| (c) arccos (-0.349) | Radian | COS^{-1} ((–) 0.349) ENTER |

From the display, it follows that arccos $(-0.349) \approx 1.9273001$.

5. (a) Because -14 lies in the domain of the arctangent function, the inverse property applies, and you have

$$\tan\left[\tan^{-1}(-14)\right] = -14.$$

(b) In this case, $\dfrac{7\pi}{4}$ does not lie in the range of the arcsine function, $-\dfrac{\pi}{2} \le y \le \dfrac{\pi}{2}$.

However, $\dfrac{7\pi}{4}$ is coterminal with $\dfrac{7\pi}{4} - 2\pi = -\dfrac{\pi}{4}$ which does lie in the range of the arcsine function, and you have

$$\sin^{-1}\left(\sin \frac{7\pi}{4}\right) = \sin^{-1}\left[\sin\left(-\frac{\pi}{4}\right)\right]$$

$$= -\frac{\pi}{4}.$$

(c) Because 0.54 lies in the domain of the arccosine function, the inverse property applies and you have

$$\cos(\arccos 0.54) = 0.54.$$

6. If you let $u = \arctan\left(-\dfrac{3}{4}\right)$, then $\tan u = -\dfrac{3}{4}$. Because the range of the inverse tangent function is the first and fourth quadrants and $\tan u$ is negative, u is a fourth-quadrant angle. You can sketch and label angle u.

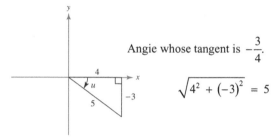

Angie whose tangent is $-\dfrac{3}{4}$.

$$\sqrt{4^2 + (-3)^2} = 5$$

So, $\cos\left[\arctan\left(-\dfrac{3}{4}\right)\right] = \cos u = \dfrac{4}{5}$.

7. If you let $u = \arctan x$, then $\tan u = x$, where x is any real number. Because $\tan u = \dfrac{\text{opp}}{\text{adj}} = \dfrac{x}{1}$, you can sketch a right triangle with acute angle u as shown. From this triangle, you can convert to algebraic form.

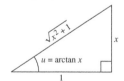

$$\sec(\arctan x) = \sec u$$

$$= \frac{\sqrt{x^2 + 1}}{1}$$

$$= \sqrt{x^2 + 1}$$

Checkpoints for Section 4.8

1. Because $c = 90°$, it follows that $A + B = 90°$ and $B° = 90° - 20° = 70°$.

To solve for a, use the fact that

$$\tan A = \frac{\text{opp}}{\text{adj}} = \frac{a}{b} \Rightarrow a = b \tan A.$$

So, $a = 15 \tan 20° \approx 5.46$. Similarly, to solve for c, use the fact that $\cos A = \dfrac{\text{adj}}{\text{hyp}} = \dfrac{b}{c} \Rightarrow c = \dfrac{b}{\cos A}$

So, $c = \dfrac{15}{\cos 20°} \approx 15.96$.

2.

From the equation $\sin A = \dfrac{a}{c}$, it follows that

$a = c \sin A$

$\quad = 16 \sin 80°$

$\quad \approx 15.8.$

So, the height from the top of the ladder to the ground is about 15.8 feet.

3.

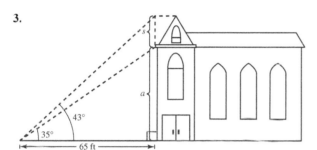

Note that this problem involves two right triangles. For the smaller right triangle, use the fact that

$\tan 35° = \dfrac{a}{65}$ to conclude that the height of the church is $a = 65 \tan 35°$.

For the larger right triangle use the equation

$\tan 43° = \dfrac{a + s}{65}$ to conclude that $a + s = 65 \tan 43°$.

So, the height of the steeple is

$s = 65 \tan 43° - a$

$\quad = 65 \tan 43° - \left(65 \tan 35°\right)$

$\quad \approx 15.1$ feet.

4.

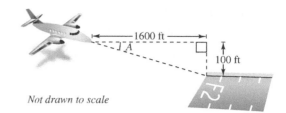

Not drawn to scale

Using the tangent function, you can see that

$\tan A = \dfrac{\text{opp}}{\text{adj}} = \dfrac{100}{1600} = 0.0625$

So, the angle of depression is

$A = \arctan\left(0.0625\right)$ radian

$\quad \approx 0.06242$ radian

$\quad \approx 3.58°.$

5.

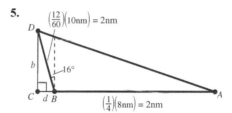

For triangle BCD, you have $B = 90° - 16° = 74°$.

The two sides of this triangle can be determined to be

$b = 2 \sin 74°$ and $d = 2 \cos 74°$.

For triangle ACD, you can find angle A as follows.

$\tan A = \dfrac{b}{d + 2} = \dfrac{2 \sin 74°}{2 \cos 74° + 2} \approx 0.7535541$

$A = \arctan A \approx \arctan 0.7535541$ radian $\approx 37°$

The angle with the north south line is $90° - 37° = 53°$.

So, the bearing of the ship is N 53° W.

Finally, from triangle ACD you have

$\sin A = \dfrac{b}{c}$, which yields

$c = \dfrac{b}{\sin A} = \dfrac{2 \sin 74°}{\sin 37°} \approx 3.2$ nautical miles.

6. Because the spring is at equilibrium $\left(d = 0\right)$ when $t = 0$, use the equation $d = a \sin wt$.

Because the maximum displacement from zero is 6 and the period is 3, you have the following.

Amplitude $= \left|a\right| = 6$

Period $= \dfrac{2\pi}{w} = 3 \Rightarrow w = \dfrac{2\pi}{3}$

So, an equation of motion is $d = 6 \sin \dfrac{2\pi}{3} t.$

The frequency is

Frequency $= \dfrac{w}{2\pi} = \dfrac{\dfrac{2\pi}{3}}{2\pi} = \dfrac{1}{3}$ cycle per second.

7. Algebraic Solution

The given equation has the form $d = 4 \cos 6\pi t$, with $a \approx 4$ and $w = 6\pi$.

(a) The maximum displacement is given by the amplitude. So, the maximum displacement is 4.

(b) Frequency $= \dfrac{w}{2\pi} = \dfrac{6\pi}{2\pi} = 3$ cycles per unit of time

(c) $d = 4 \cos\left[6\pi(4)\right] = 4 \cos 24\pi = 4(1) = 4$

(d) To find the least positive value of t, for which $d = 0$, solve the equation $4 \cos 6\pi t = 0$.

First divide each side by 4 to obtain $\cos 6\pi t = 0$.

This equation is satisfied when $6\pi t = \dfrac{\pi}{2}, \dfrac{3\pi}{2}, \dfrac{5\pi}{2}, \dots$.

Divide each of these values by 6π to obtain $t = \dfrac{1}{12}, \dfrac{1}{4}, \dfrac{5}{12}, \dots$.

So, the least positive value of t is $t = \dfrac{1}{12}$.

Graphical Solution

(a) Use a graphing utility set in radian mode.

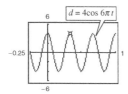

The maximum displacement is from the point of equilibrium $\left(d = 0\right)$ is 4.

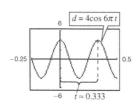

(b) The period is the time for the graph to complete one cycle, which is $t \approx 0.333$. So, the frequency is about $\dfrac{1}{0.333} \approx 3$ per unit of time.

(c)

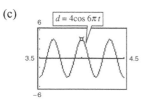

The value of d when $t = 4$ is $d = 4$

(d)

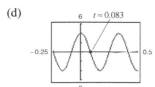

The least positive value of t for which $d = 0$ is $t \approx 0.083$.

Chapter 5

Checkpoints for Section 5.1

1. Using a reciprocal identity, you have $\cot x = \dfrac{1}{\tan x} = \dfrac{1}{\frac{1}{3}} = 3$.

   Using a Pythagorean identity, you have

   $$\sec^2 x = 1 + \tan^2 x = 1 + \left(\frac{1}{3}\right)^2 = 1 + \frac{1}{9} = \frac{10}{9}.$$

   Because $\tan x > 0$ and $\cos x < 0$, you know that the angle x lies in Quadrant III.

   Moreover, because $\sec x$ is negative when x is in Quadrant III, choose the negative root and obtain

   $$\sec x = -\sqrt{\frac{10}{9}} = -\frac{\sqrt{10}}{3}.$$

   Using a reciprocal identity, you have

   $$\cos x = \frac{1}{\sec x} = -\frac{1}{\sqrt{10}/3} = -\frac{3}{\sqrt{10}} = -\frac{3\sqrt{10}}{10}.$$

   Using a quotient identity, you have

   $$\tan x = \frac{\sin x}{\cos x} \Rightarrow \sin x = \cos x \tan x = \left(-\frac{3\sqrt{10}}{10}\right)\left(\frac{1}{3}\right) = -\frac{\sqrt{10}}{10}.$$

   Using a reciprocal identity, you have

   $$\csc x = \frac{1}{\sin x} = -\frac{1}{\sqrt{10}/10} = -\frac{10}{\sqrt{10}} = -\sqrt{10}.$$

   $\sin x = -\dfrac{\sqrt{10}}{10}$ $\qquad$ $\csc x = -\sqrt{10}$

   $\cos x = -\dfrac{3\sqrt{10}}{10}$ $\qquad$ $\sec x = -\dfrac{\sqrt{10}}{3}$

   $\tan x = \dfrac{1}{3}$ $\qquad$ $\cot x = 3$

2. First factor out a common monomial factor then use a fundamental identity.

   $\cos^2 x \csc x - \csc x = \csc x\left(\cos^2 x - 1\right)$ $\qquad$ Factor out a common monomial factor.

   $ = -\csc x\left(1 - \cos^2 x\right)$ $\qquad$ Factor out -1.

   $ = -\csc x \sin^2 x$ $\qquad$ Pythagorean identity

   $ = -\left(\dfrac{1}{\sin x}\right)\sin^2 x$ $\qquad$ Reciprocal identity

   $ = -\sin x$ $\qquad$ Multiply.

3. (a) This expression has the form $u^2 - v^2$, which is the difference of two squares. It factors as

   $$1 - \cos^2 \theta = \left(1 - \cos \theta\right)\left(1 + \cos \theta\right).$$

   (b) This expression has the polynomial form $ax^2 + bx + c$, and it factors as

   $$2\csc^2 \theta - 7\csc \theta + 6 = \left(2\csc \theta - 3\right)\left(\csc \theta - 2\right).$$

4. Use the identity $\sec^2 x = 1 + \tan^2 x$ to rewrite the expression.

$$\sec^2 x + 3\tan x + 1 = \left(1 + \tan^2 x\right) + 3\tan x + 1 \qquad \text{Pythagorean identity}$$

$$= \tan^2 x + 3\tan x + 2 \qquad \text{Combine like terms.}$$

$$= (\tan x + 2)(\tan x + 1) \qquad \text{Factor.}$$

5. $\csc x - \cos x \cot x = \dfrac{1}{\sin x} - \cos x\left(\dfrac{\cos x}{\sin x}\right) \qquad$ Quotient and reciprocal identities

$$= \dfrac{1}{\sin x} - \dfrac{\cos^2 x}{\sin x} \qquad \text{Multiply.}$$

$$= \dfrac{1 - \cos^2 x}{\sin x} \qquad \text{Add fractions.}$$

$$= \dfrac{\sin^2 x}{\sin x} \qquad \text{Pythagorean identity.}$$

$$= \sin x \qquad \text{Simplify.}$$

6. $\dfrac{1}{1 + \sin \theta} + \dfrac{1}{1 - \sin \theta} = \dfrac{1 - \sin \theta + 1 + \sin \theta}{(1 + \sin \theta)(1 - \sin \theta)} \qquad$ Add fractions.

$$= \dfrac{2}{1 - \sin^2 \theta} \qquad \text{Combine like terms in numerator}$$

$$\text{and multiply factors in denominator.}$$

$$= \dfrac{2}{\cos^2 \theta} \qquad \text{Pythagorean identity}$$

$$= 2\sec^2 \theta \qquad \text{Reciprocal identity}$$

7. $\dfrac{\cos^2 \theta}{1 - \sin \theta} = \dfrac{1 - \sin^2 \theta}{1 - \sin \theta} \qquad$ Pythagorean identity

$$= \dfrac{(1 + \sin \theta)(1 - \sin \theta)}{1 - \sin \theta} \qquad \text{Factor the numerator as the difference of squares.}$$

$$= 1 + \sin \theta \qquad \text{Simplify.}$$

8. Begin by letting $x = 3\sin x$, then you obtain the following

$$\sqrt{9 - x^2} = \sqrt{9 - \left(3\sin \theta\right)^2} \qquad \text{Substitute } 3\sin \theta \text{ for } x.$$

$$= \sqrt{9 - 9\sin^2 \theta} \qquad \text{Rule of exponents.}$$

$$= \sqrt{9\left(1 - \sin^2 \theta\right)} \qquad \text{Factor.}$$

$$= \sqrt{9\cos^2 \theta} \qquad \text{Pythagorean identity}$$

$$= 3\cos \theta \qquad \cos \theta > 0 \text{ for } 0 < \theta = \dfrac{\pi}{2}$$

9. $\ln|\sec x| + \ln|\sin x| = \ln|\sec x \sin x| \qquad$ Product Property of Logarithms

$$= \ln\left|\dfrac{1}{\cos s} \cdot \sin x\right| \qquad \text{Reciprocal identity}$$

$$= \ln\left|\dfrac{\sin x}{\cos x}\right| \qquad \text{Simplify.}$$

$$= \ln|\tan x| \qquad \text{Quotient identity}$$

Checkpoints for Section 5.2

1. Start with the left side because it is more complicated.

$$\frac{\sin^2 \theta + \cos^2 \theta}{\cos^2 \theta \sec^2 \theta} = \frac{1}{\cos^2 \theta \sec^2 \theta} \qquad \text{Pythagorean identity}$$

$$= \frac{1}{\cos^2 \theta \left(\dfrac{1}{\cos^2 \theta}\right)} \qquad \text{Reciprocal identity}$$

$$= 1 \qquad \text{Simplify.}$$

2. Algebraic Solution:

Start with the right side because it is more complicated.

$$\frac{1}{1 - \cos \beta} + \frac{1}{1 + \cos \beta} = \frac{1 + \cos \beta + 1 - \cos \beta}{(1 - \cos \beta)(1 + \cos \beta)} \qquad \text{Add fractions.}$$

$$= \frac{2}{1 - \cos^2 \beta} \qquad \text{Simplify.}$$

$$= \frac{2}{\sin^2 \beta} \qquad \text{Pythagorean identity}$$

$$= 2\csc^2 \beta \qquad \text{Reciprocal identity}$$

Numerical Solution:

Use a graphing utility to create a table that shows the values of

$$y_1 = 2\csc^2 x \text{ and } y_2 = \frac{1}{1 - \cos x} + \frac{1}{1 + \cos x} \text{ for different values of } x.$$

X	Y1	Y2
-3	100.43	100.43
-2	2.4189	2.4189
-1	2.8246	2.8246
0	ERROR	ERROR
1	2.8246	2.8246
2	2.4189	2.4189
3	100.43	100.42

X=-3

The values for y_1 and y_2 appear to be identical, so the equation appears to be an identity.

3. Algebraic Solution:

By applying identities before multiplying, you obtain the following.

$$\left(\sec^2 x - 1\right)\left(\sin^2 x - 1\right) = \left(\tan^2 x\right)\left(-\cos^2 x\right) \qquad \text{Pythagorean identities}$$

$$= \left(\frac{\sin x}{\cos x}\right)^2 \left(-\cos^2 x\right) \qquad \text{Quotient identity}$$

$$= \left(\frac{\sin^2 x}{\cos^2 x}\right)\left(-\cos^2 x\right) \qquad \text{Property of exponents}$$

$$= -\sin^2 x \qquad \text{Multiply.}$$

Graphical Solution:

Using a graphing utility, let $y_1 = \left(\sec^2 x - 1\right)\left(\sin^2 x - 1\right)$ and $y_2 = -\sin^2 x$.

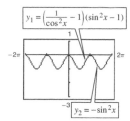

Because the graphs appear to coincide the given equation, $\left(\sec^2 x - 1\right)\left(\sin^2 x - 1\right) = -\sin^2 x$ appears to be an identity.

4. Convert the left into sines and cosines.

$$\csc x - \sin x = \frac{1}{\sin x} - \sin x$$

$$= \frac{1 - \sin^2 x}{\sin x} \qquad \text{Add fractions.}$$

$$= \frac{\cos^2 x}{\sin x} \qquad \text{Pythagorean identity}$$

$$= \left(\frac{\cos x}{1}\right)\left(\frac{\cos x}{\sin x}\right) \quad \text{Product of fractions}$$

$$= \cos x \cot x \qquad \text{Quotient identity}$$

5. Algebraic Solution:

Begin with the right side and create a monomial denominator by multiplying the numerator and denominator by $1 + \cos x$.

$$\frac{\sin x}{1 - \cos x} = \frac{\sin x}{1 - \cos x}\left(\frac{1 + \cos x}{1 + \cos x}\right) \qquad \text{Multiply numerator and denomintor by } 1 + \cos x.$$

$$= \frac{\sin x + \sin x \cos x}{1 - \cos^2 x} \qquad \text{Multiply.}$$

$$= \frac{\sin x + \sin x \cos x}{\sin^2 x} \qquad \text{Pythagorean identity}$$

$$= \frac{\sin x}{\sin^2 x} + \frac{\sin x \cos x}{\sin^2 x} \qquad \text{Write as separate functions.}$$

$$= \frac{1}{\sin x} + \frac{\cos x}{\sin x} \qquad \text{Simplify.}$$

$$= \csc x + \cot x \qquad \text{Identities}$$

Graphical Solution:

Using a graphing utility, let $y_1 = \csc x + \cot x$ and $y_2 = \dfrac{\sin x}{1 - \cos x}$.

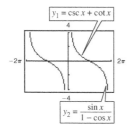

Because the graphs appear to coincide, the given equation appear to be an identity.

6. Algebraic Solution:

Working with the left side, you have the following.

$$\frac{\tan^2 \theta}{1 + \sec \theta} = \frac{\sec^2 \theta - 1}{\sec \theta + 1} \qquad \text{Pythagorean identity}$$

$$= \frac{(\sec \theta + 1)(\sec \theta - 1)}{\sec \theta + 1} \qquad \text{Factor.}$$

$$= \sec \theta - 1 \qquad \text{Simplify.}$$

Now, working with the right side, you have the following.

$$\frac{1 - \cos \theta}{\cos \theta} = \frac{1}{\cos \theta} - \frac{\cos \theta}{\cos \theta} \qquad \text{Write as separate fractions.}$$

$$= \sec \theta - 1 \qquad \text{Identity and simplify.}$$

This verifies the identity because both sides are equal to $\sec \theta - 1$.

Numerical Solution:

Use a graphing utility to create a table that shows the values of

$$y_1 = \frac{\tan^2 x}{1 + \sec x} \quad \text{and} \quad y_2 = \frac{1 - \cos x}{\cos x} \quad \text{for different values of } x.$$

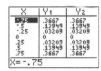

X	Y₁	Y₂
-.75	.3667	.3667
-.5	.12949	.13949
-.25	.03209	.03209
0	0	0
.25	.03209	.03209
.5	.13949	.13949
.75	.3667	.3667
X=-.75		

The values of y_1 and y_2 appear to be identical, so the equation appears to be an identity.

7. (a) $\tan x \sec^2 x - \tan x = \tan x(\sec^2 x - 1) \qquad$ Factor.

$$= \tan x \tan^2 x \qquad \text{Pythagorean identity}$$

$$= \tan^3 x \qquad \text{Multiply.}$$

(b) $(\cos^4 x - \cos^6 x)\sin x = \cos^4 x(1 - \cos^2 x)\sin x \qquad$ Factor.

$$= \cos^4 x \left(\sin^2 x\right)\sin x \qquad \text{Pythagorean identity}$$

$$= \sin^3 x \cos^4 x \qquad \text{Multiply.}$$

Checkpoints for Section 5.3

1. Begin by isolating $\sin x$ on one side of the equation.

$$\sin x - \sqrt{2} = -\sin x \qquad \text{Write original equation.}$$

$$\sin x + \sin x - \sqrt{2} = 0 \qquad \text{Add } \sin x \text{ to each side.}$$

$$\sin x + \sin x = \sqrt{2} \qquad \text{Add } \sqrt{2} \text{ to each side.}$$

$$2\sin x = \sqrt{2} \qquad \text{Combine like terms.}$$

$$\sin x = \frac{\sqrt{2}}{2} \qquad \text{Divide each side by 2.}$$

Because $\sin x$ has a period of 2π, first find all solutions in the interval $[0, 2\pi)$. These solutions are $x = \dfrac{\pi}{4}$ and $x = \dfrac{3\pi}{4}$.

Finally, add multiples of 2π to each of these solutions to obtain the general form

$$x = \frac{\pi}{4} + 2n\pi \text{ and } x = \frac{3\pi}{4} + 2n\pi \text{ where } n \text{ is an integer.}$$

2. Begin by isolating $\sin x$ on one side of the equation.

$$4\sin^2 x - 3 = 0 \qquad \text{Write original equation.}$$

$$4\sin^2 x = 3 \qquad \text{Add 3 to each side.}$$

$$\sin^2 x = \frac{3}{4} \qquad \text{Divide each side by 4.}$$

$$\sin x = \pm\sqrt{\frac{3}{4}} \qquad \text{Extract square roots.}$$

$$\sin x = \pm\frac{\sqrt{3}}{2} \qquad \text{Simplify.}$$

Because $\sin x$ has a period of 2π, first find all solutions in the interval $[0, 2\pi)$. These solutions are $x = \dfrac{\pi}{3}$, $x = \dfrac{2\pi}{3}$,

$x = \dfrac{4\pi}{3}$, and $x = \dfrac{5\pi}{3}$.

Finally, add multiples of 2π to each of these solutions to obtain the general form.

$$x = \frac{\pi}{3} + 2n\pi, \ x = \frac{2\pi}{3} + 2n\pi, \ x = \frac{4\pi}{3} + 2n\pi, \text{ and } x = \frac{5\pi}{3} + 2n\pi \text{ where } n \text{ is an integer.}$$

3. Begin by collecting all terms on one side of the equation and factoring.

$$\sin^2 x = 2\sin x \qquad \text{Write original equation.}$$

$$\sin^2 x - 2\sin x = 0 \qquad \text{Subtract } 2\sin x \text{ from each side.}$$

$$\sin x(\sin x - 2) = 0 \qquad \text{Factor.}$$

By setting each of these factors equal to zero, you obtain

$$\sin x = 0 \text{ and } \sin x - 2 = 0$$

$$\sin x = 2.$$

In the interval $[0, 2\pi)$, the equation $\sin x = 0$ has solutions $x = 0$ and $x = \pi$. Because $\sin x$ has a period of 2π, you would obtain the general forms $x = 0 + 2n\pi$ and $x = \pi + 2n\pi$ where n is an integer by adding multiples of 2π.

No solution exists for $\sin x = 2$ because 2 is outside the range of the sine function, $[-1, 1]$. Confirm this graphically by graphing $y = \sin^2 x - 2\sin x$.

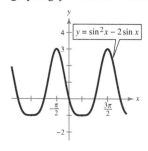

Notice that the x-intercepts occur at $-2\pi, -\pi, 0, \pi, 2\pi$ and so on.

These x-intercepts correspond to the solutions of $\sin^2 x - 2\sin x = 0$.

4. Algebraic Solution:

Treat the equation as a quadratic in $\sin x$ and factor.

$$2\sin^2 x - 3\sin x + 1 = 0 \quad \text{Write original equation.}$$

$$(2\sin x - 1)(\sin x - 1) = 0 \quad \text{Factor.}$$

Setting each factor equal to zero, you obtain the following solutions in the interval $[0, 2\pi)$.

$$2\sin x - 1 = 0 \qquad \text{and} \qquad \sin x - 1 = 0$$

$$\sin x = \frac{1}{2} \qquad\qquad \sin x = 1$$

$$x = \frac{\pi}{6}, \frac{5\pi}{6} \qquad\qquad x = \frac{\pi}{2}$$

Graphical Solution:

The x-intercepts are $x \approx 0.524$, $x = 2.618$, and $x = 1.571$.

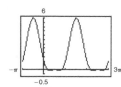

From the graph, you can conclude that the approximate solutions of $2\sin^2 x - 3\sin x + 1 = 0$ in the interval

$[0, 2\pi)$ are $x \approx 0.524 = \dfrac{\pi}{6}$, $x \approx 2.618 = \dfrac{5\pi}{6}$, and

$$x \approx 1.571 = \frac{\pi}{2}.$$

5. This equation contains both tangent and secant functions. You can rewrite the equation so that it has only tangent functions by using the identity $\sec^2 x = \tan^2 x + 1$.

$$3\sec^2 x - 2\tan^2 x - 4 = 0 \qquad \text{Write original equation.}$$
$$3\left(\tan^2 x + 1\right) - 2\tan^2 x - 4 = 0 \qquad \text{Pythagorean identity}$$
$$3\tan^2 x + 3 - 2\tan^2 x - 4 = 0 \qquad \text{Distributive property}$$
$$\tan^2 x - 1 = 0 \qquad \text{Simplify.}$$
$$\tan^2 x = 1 \qquad \text{Add 1 to each side.}$$
$$\tan x = \pm 1 \qquad \text{Extract square roots.}$$

Because $\tan x$ has a period of π, you can find the solutions in the interval $[0, \pi)$ to be $x = \dfrac{\pi}{4}$ and $x = \dfrac{3\pi}{4}$.

The general solution is $x = \dfrac{\pi}{4} + n\pi$ and $x = \dfrac{3\pi}{4} + n\pi$ where n is an integer.

6. **Solution** It is not clear how to rewrite this equation in terms of a single trigonometric function. Notice what happens when you square each side of the equation.

$$\sin x + 1 = \cos x \qquad \text{Write original equation.}$$
$$\sin^2 x + 2\sin x + 1 = \cos^2 x \qquad \text{Square each side.}$$
$$\sin^2 x + 2\sin x + 1 = 1 - \sin^2 x \qquad \text{Pythagorean identity}$$
$$\sin^2 x + \sin^2 x + 2\sin x + 1 - 1 = 0 \qquad \text{Rewrite equation.}$$
$$2\sin^2 x + 2\sin x = 0 \qquad \text{Combine like terms.}$$
$$2\sin x\left(\sin x + 1\right) = 0 \qquad \text{Factor.}$$

Setting each factor equal to zero produces the following.

$$2\sin x = 0 \qquad \text{and} \qquad \sin x + 1 = 0$$
$$\sin x = 0 \qquad\qquad\qquad \sin x = -1$$
$$x = 0, \pi \qquad\qquad\qquad x = \dfrac{3\pi}{2}$$

Because you squared the original equation, check for extraneous solutions.

check $x = 0 \qquad \sin 0 + 1 \overset{?}{=} \cos 0 \qquad$ Substitute 0 for x.
$$0 + 1 = 1 \qquad \text{Solution checks. } \checkmark$$

check $x = \pi \qquad \sin \pi + 1 \overset{?}{=} \cos \pi \qquad$ Substitute π for x.
$$0 + 1 \neq -1 \qquad \text{Solution does not check.}$$

check $x = \dfrac{3\pi}{2} \qquad \sin \dfrac{3\pi}{2} + 1 \overset{?}{=} \cos \dfrac{3\pi}{2} \qquad$ Substitute $\dfrac{3\pi}{2}$ for x.
$$-1 + 1 = 0 \qquad \text{Solution checks. } \checkmark$$

of the three possible solutions, $x = \pi$ is extraneous. So, in the interval $[0, 2\pi)$, the two solutions are $x = 0$ and $x = \dfrac{3\pi}{2}$.

7. $2\sin 2t - \sqrt{3} = 0$ Write original equation.

$2\sin 2t = \sqrt{3}$ Add $\sqrt{3}$ to each side.

$\sin 2t = \dfrac{\sqrt{3}}{2}$ Divide each side by 2.

In the interval $[0, 2\pi)$, you know that

$2t = \dfrac{\pi}{3}$ and $2t = \dfrac{2\pi}{3}$ are the only solutions.

So, in general you have

$2t = \dfrac{\pi}{3} + 2n\pi$ and $2t = \dfrac{2\pi}{3} + 2n\pi.$

Dividing these results by 2, you obtain the general solution

$t = \dfrac{\pi}{6} + n\pi$ and $t = \dfrac{\pi}{3} + n\pi.$

8. $2\tan \dfrac{x}{2} - 2 = 0$ Write original equation.

$2\tan \dfrac{x}{2} = 2$ Add 2 to each side.

$\tan \dfrac{x}{2} = 1$ Divide each side by 2.

In the interval $[0, \pi)$, you know that $\dfrac{x}{2} = \dfrac{\pi}{4}$ is the only solution. So, in general, you have

$\dfrac{x}{2} = \dfrac{\pi}{4} + n\pi.$

Multiplying this result by 2, you obtain the general solution

$x = \dfrac{\pi}{2} + 2n\pi$

Where n is an integer.

9. $4\tan^2 x + 5\tan x - 6 = 0$ Write original equation.

$(4\tan x - 3)(\tan x + 2) = 0$ Factor.

$4\tan x - 3 = 0$ and $\tan x + 2 = 0$ Set each factor equal to zero.

$\tan x = \dfrac{3}{4}$ $\tan x = -2$

$x = \arctan\left(\dfrac{3}{4}\right)$ $x = \arctan(-2)$ Use inverse tangent function to solve for x.

These two solutions are in the interval $\left(-\dfrac{\pi}{2}, \dfrac{\pi}{2}\right)$. Recall that the range of the inverse tangent function is $\left(-\dfrac{\pi}{2}, \dfrac{\pi}{2}\right)$.

Finally, because $\tan x$ has a period of π, you add multiples of π to obtain

$x = \arctan\left(\dfrac{3}{4}\right) + n\pi$ and $x = \arctan(-2) + n\pi$

where n is an integer.

You can use a calculator to approximate the values of $x = \arctan\left(\dfrac{3}{4}\right) \approx 0.6435$ and $x = \arctan(-2) \approx -1.1071$.

10. Graph the function $S = 10.8 + 0.84375\left[\left(\sqrt{3} - \cos\theta\right)/\sin\theta\right]$ using a graphing utility.

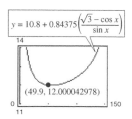

Use the *trace* feature to find the values of θ when $y = 12$. So, when $\theta \approx 49.9°$ and $\theta \approx 59.9°$, the surface area is 12 square inches. The exact values are $\theta \approx \arccos(0.644228) \approx 49.9°$ and $\theta \approx \arccos(0.50180) \approx 59.9°$.

Checkpoints for Section 5.4

1. To find the exact value of $\cos \dfrac{\pi}{12}$, use the fact that

$$\frac{\pi}{12} = \frac{\pi}{3} - \frac{\pi}{4}.$$

The formula for $\cos(u - v)$ yields the following.

$$\cos \frac{\pi}{12} = \cos\left(\frac{\pi}{3} - \frac{\pi}{4}\right)$$

$$= \cos\frac{\pi}{3}\cos\frac{\pi}{4} + \sin\frac{\pi}{3}\sin\frac{\pi}{4}$$

$$= \left(\frac{1}{2}\right)\left(\frac{\sqrt{2}}{2}\right) + \left(\frac{\sqrt{3}}{2}\right)\left(\frac{\sqrt{2}}{2}\right)$$

$$= \frac{\sqrt{2}}{4} + \frac{\sqrt{6}}{4}$$

$$= \frac{\sqrt{2} + \sqrt{6}}{4}$$

2. Using the fact that $75° = 30° + 45°$, together with the formula for $\sin(u + v)$, you obtain the following.

$$\sin 75° = \sin(30° + 45°)$$

$$= \sin 30° \cos 45° + \cos 30° \sin 45°$$

$$= \left(\frac{1}{2}\right)\left(\frac{\sqrt{2}}{2}\right) + \left(\frac{\sqrt{3}}{2}\right)\left(\frac{\sqrt{2}}{2}\right)$$

$$= \frac{\sqrt{2}}{4} + \frac{\sqrt{6}}{4}$$

$$= \frac{\sqrt{2} + \sqrt{6}}{4}$$

3. Because $\sin u = \dfrac{12}{13}$ and u is in Quadrant I,

$\cos u = \dfrac{5}{13}$ as shown.

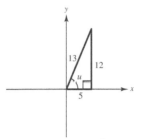

Because $\cos v = -\dfrac{3}{5}$ and v is in Quadrant II,

$\sin v = \dfrac{4}{5}$ as shown.

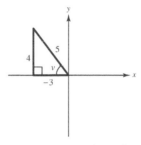

You can find $\cos(u + v)$ as follows.

$$\cos(u + v) = \cos u \cos v - \sin u \sin v$$

$$= \left(\frac{5}{13}\right)\left(-\frac{3}{5}\right) - \left(\frac{12}{13}\right)\left(\frac{4}{5}\right)$$

$$= -\frac{63}{65}$$

4. This expression fits the formula for $\sin(u + v)$. The figures show the angles $u = \arctan 1$ and $v = \arccos x$.

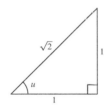   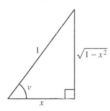

$$\sin(u + v) = \sin u \cos v + \cos u \sin v$$

$$= \sin(\arctan 1)\cos(\arccos x) + \cos(\arctan 1)\sin(\arccos x)$$

$$= \left(\frac{1}{\sqrt{2}}\right)(x) + \left(\frac{1}{\sqrt{2}}\right)\left(\sqrt{1 - x^2}\right)$$

$$= \frac{x}{\sqrt{2}} + \frac{\sqrt{1 - x^2}}{\sqrt{2}}$$

$$= \frac{x + \sqrt{1 - x^2}}{\sqrt{2}}$$

5. Using the formula for $\sin(u - v)$, you have

$$\sin\left(x - \frac{\pi}{2}\right) = \sin x \cos \frac{\pi}{2} - \cos x \sin \frac{\pi}{2}$$

$$= (\sin x)(0) - (\cos x)(1)$$

$$= -\cos x.$$

6. (a) Using the formula for $\sin(u - v)$, you have

$$\sin\left(3\frac{\pi}{2} - \theta\right) = \sin 3\frac{\pi}{2} \cos \theta - \cos 3\frac{\pi}{2} \sin\theta$$

$$= (-1)(\cos \theta) - (0)(\sin \theta)$$

$$= -\cos \theta.$$

(b) Using the formula for $\tan(u - v)$, you have

$$\tan\left(\theta - \frac{\pi}{4}\right) = \frac{\tan \theta - \tan \frac{\pi}{4}}{1 + \tan \theta \tan \frac{\pi}{4}}$$

$$= \frac{\tan \theta - 1}{1 + (\tan \theta)(1)}$$

$$= \frac{\tan \theta - 1}{1 + \tan \theta}.$$

7. Algebraic Solution

Using sum and difference formulas, rewrite the equation.

$$\sin\left(x + \frac{\pi}{2}\right) + \sin\left(x - \frac{3\pi}{2}\right) = 1$$

$$\sin x \cos \frac{\pi}{2} + \cos x \sin \frac{\pi}{2} + \sin x \cos \frac{3\pi}{2} - \cos x \sin \frac{3\pi}{2} = 1$$

$$(\sin x)(0) + (\cos x)(1) + (\sin x)(0) - (\cos x)(1) = 1$$

$$\cos x + \cos x = 1$$

$$2\cos x = 1$$

$$\cos x = \frac{1}{2}$$

So, the only solutions in the interval $[0, 2\pi)$ are $x = \frac{\pi}{3}$ and $x = \frac{5\pi}{3}$.

Graphical Solution

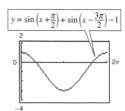

The x-intercepts are $x \approx 1.047198$ and $x \approx 5.235988$.

From the above figure, you can conclude that the approximate solutions in the interval $[0, 2\pi)$ are

$$x \approx 1.047198 = \frac{\pi}{3} \text{ and } x \approx 5.235988 = \frac{5\pi}{3}.$$

8. Using the formula for $\cos(x + h)$, you have the following.

$$\frac{\cos(x + h) - \cos x}{h} = \frac{\cos x \cos h - \sin x \sin h - \cos x}{h}$$

$$= \frac{\cos x \cos h - \cos x - \sin x \sin h}{h}$$

$$= \frac{\cos x(\cos h - 1) - \sin x \sin h}{h}$$

$$= \cos x\left(\frac{\cos h - 1}{h}\right) - \sin x\left(\frac{\sin h}{h}\right)$$

Checkpoints for Section 5.5

1. Begin by rewriting the equation so that it involves functions of x (rather than $2x$). Then factor and solve.

$\cos 2x + \cos x = 0$	Write original equation.
$2\cos^2 x - 1 + \cos x = 0$	Double-angle formula
$2\cos^2 x + \cos x - 1 = 0$	Rearrange terms
$(2\cos x - 1)(\cos x + 1) = 0$	Factor.
$2\cos x - 1 = 0 \qquad \cos x + 1 = 0$	Set factors equal to zero.
$\cos x = \dfrac{1}{2} \qquad\quad \cos x = -1$	Solve by $\cos x$.
$x = \dfrac{\pi}{3}, \dfrac{5\pi}{3} \qquad\quad x = \pi$	Solutions in $[0, 2\pi)$.

So, the general solution is $x = \dfrac{\pi}{3} + 2n\pi$, $x = \dfrac{5\pi}{3} + 2n\pi$, and $x = \pi + 2n\pi$ where n is an integer.

2. Begin by drawing the angle θ, $0 < \theta < \dfrac{\pi}{2}$ given $\sin \theta = \dfrac{3}{5}$.

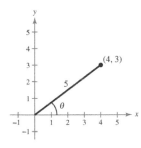

From the sketch, you know that $\sin \theta = \dfrac{y}{r} = \dfrac{3}{5}$.

Because $x = 4$, you know $\sin \theta = \dfrac{3}{5}$, $\cos \theta = \dfrac{4}{5}$, and $\tan \theta = \dfrac{3}{4}$.

Using the double angle formulas, you have the following.

$$\sin 2\theta = 2\sin \theta \cos \theta = 2\left(\frac{3}{5}\right)\left(\frac{4}{5}\right) = \frac{24}{25}$$

$$\cos 2\theta = \cos^2 \theta - \sin^2 \theta = \left(\frac{4}{5}\right)^2 - \left(\frac{3}{5}\right)^2 = \frac{7}{25}$$

$$\tan 2\theta = \frac{2\tan \theta}{1 - \tan^2 \theta} = \frac{2\left(\frac{3}{4}\right)}{1 - \left(\frac{3}{4}\right)^2} = \frac{\frac{3}{2}}{\frac{7}{16}} = \frac{24}{7}$$

3. $\cos 3x = \cos(2x + x)$ Rewrite $3x$ as sum of $2x$ and x.

$\quad\quad\quad = \cos 2x \cos x - \sin 2x \sin x$ Sum formula

$\quad\quad\quad = \left(2\cos^2 x - 1\right)(\cos x) - (2\sin x \cos x)(\sin x)$ Double-angle formulas

$\quad\quad\quad = 2\cos^3 x - \cos x - 2\sin^2 x \cos x$ Distribute property and simplify.

$\quad\quad\quad = 2\cos^3 x - \cos x - 2\left(1 - \cos^2 x\right)(\cos x)$ Pythagorean identity

$\quad\quad\quad = 2\cos^3 x - \cos x - 2\cos x + 2\cos^3 x$ Distribute property

$\quad\quad\quad = 4\cos^3 x - 3\cos x$ Simplify.

4. You can make repeated use of power-reducing formulas.

$\tan^4 x = \left(\tan^2 x\right)^2$ Property of exponets.

$\quad\quad = \left(\dfrac{1 - \cos 2x}{1 + \cos 2x}\right)^2$ Power-reducing formula

$\quad\quad = \dfrac{1 - 2\cos 2x + \cos^2 2x}{1 + 2\cos 2x + \cos^2 2x}$ Expand.

$\quad\quad = \dfrac{1 - 2\cos 2x + \left(\dfrac{1 + \cos 4x}{2}\right)}{1 + 2\cos 2x + \left(\dfrac{1 + \cos 4x}{2}\right)}$ Power-reducing formula

$\quad\quad = \dfrac{\dfrac{2 - 4\cos 2x + 1 + \cos 4x}{2}}{\dfrac{2 + 4\cos 2x + 1 + \cos 4x}{2}}$ Simplify.

$\quad\quad = \dfrac{3 - 4\cos 2x + \cos 4x}{3 + 4\cos 2x + \cos 4x}$ Collect like terms, invert, and multiply.

You can use a graphing utility to check this result. Notice that the graphs coincide.

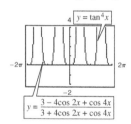

5. Begin by noting $105°$ is one half of $210°$. Then using the half-angle formula for $\cos\left(\dfrac{u}{2}\right)$ and the fact that $105°$ lies in Quadrant II, you have the following.

$\cos 105° = -\sqrt{\dfrac{1 + \cos 210°}{2}} = -\sqrt{\dfrac{1 + \left(-\dfrac{\sqrt{3}}{2}\right)}{2}} = -\sqrt{\dfrac{\dfrac{2 - \sqrt{3}}{2}}{2}} = -\sqrt{\dfrac{2 - \sqrt{3}}{4}} = -\dfrac{\sqrt{2 - \sqrt{3}}}{2}$

The negative square root is chosen because $\cos\theta$ is negative in Quadrant II.

6. Algebraic Solution

$$\cos^2 x = \sin^2 \frac{x}{2}$$ Write original equation.

$$\cos^2 x = \left(\pm\sqrt{\frac{1 - \cos x}{2}}\right)^2$$ Half-angle formula

$$\cos^2 x = \frac{1 - \cos x}{2}$$ Simplify.

$$2\cos^2 x = 1 - \cos x$$ Multiply each side by 2.

$$2\cos^2 x + \cos x - 1 = 0$$ Simplify.

$$(2\cos x - 1)(\cos x + 1) = 0$$ Factor.

$$2\cos x - 1 = 0 \qquad \cos x + 1 = 0$$ Set each factor equal to zero.

$$\cos x = \frac{1}{2} \qquad \cos x = -1$$ Solve each equation for $\cos x$.

$$x = \frac{\pi}{3}, \frac{5\pi}{3} \qquad x = \pi$$ Solutions in $[0, 2\pi)$.

The solutions in the interval $[0, 2\pi)$ are $x = \frac{\pi}{3}$, $x = \pi$, and $x = \frac{5\pi}{3}$.

Graphical Solution

Use a graphing utility to graph $y = \cos^2 x - \sin^2 \frac{x}{2}$ in the interval $[0, 2\pi)$. Determine the approximate value of the x-intercepts.

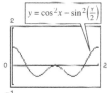

The x-intercepts are $x \approx 1.04720$, $x \approx 3.14159$, and $x \approx 5.23599$.

From the graph, you can conclude that the approximate solutions of $\cos^2 x = \sin^2 \frac{2x}{2}$ in the interval $[0, 2\pi)$ are

$$x \approx 1.04720 = \frac{\pi}{3}, x \approx 3.14159 = \pi, \text{ and } x \approx 5.23599 = \frac{5\pi}{3}.$$

7. Using the appropriate product-to-sum formula

$$\sin u \cos v = \frac{1}{2}[\sin(u + v) + \sin(u - v)], \text{ you obtain the following.}$$

$$\sin 5x \cos 3x = \frac{1}{2}[\sin(5x + 3x) + \sin(5x - 3x)]$$

$$= \frac{1}{2}(\sin 8x + \sin 2x)$$

$$= \frac{1}{2}\sin 8x + \frac{1}{2}\sin 2x$$

8. Using the appropriate sum-to-product formula,

$$\sin u + \sin v = 2\sin\left(\frac{u+v}{2}\right)\cos\left(\frac{u-v}{2}\right), \text{ you obtain the following.}$$

$$\sin 195° + \sin 105° = 2\sin\left(\frac{195° + 105°}{2}\right)\cos\left(\frac{195° - 105°}{2}\right)$$

$$= 2\sin 150° \cos 45°$$

$$= 2\left(\frac{1}{2}\right)\left(\frac{\sqrt{2}}{2}\right)$$

$$= \frac{\sqrt{2}}{2}$$

9.

$$\sin 4x - \sin 2x = 0 \quad \text{Write orignal equation.}$$

$$2\cos\left(\frac{4x+2x}{2}\right)\sin\left(\frac{4x-2x}{2}\right) = 0 \quad \text{Sum-to-product formula}$$

$$2\cos 3x \sin x = 0 \quad \text{Simplify.}$$

$$\cos 3x \sin x = 0 \quad \text{Divide each side by 2.}$$

$$\cos 3x = 0 \qquad \sin x = 0 \quad \text{Set each factor equal to zero.}$$

The solutions in the interval $[0, 2\pi)$ are $3x = \dfrac{\pi}{2}, \dfrac{3\pi}{2}$ and $x = 0, \pi$.

The general solutions for the equation $\cos 3x = 0$ are $3x = \dfrac{\pi}{2} + 2n\pi$ and $3x = \dfrac{3\pi}{2} + 2n\pi$.

So, by solving these equations for x, you have $x = \dfrac{\pi}{6} + \dfrac{2n\pi}{3}$ and $x = \dfrac{\pi}{2} + \dfrac{2n\pi}{3}$.

The general solution for the equation $\sin x = 0$ is $x = 0 + 2n\pi$ and $x = \pi + 2n\pi$.

These can be combined as $x = n\pi$.

So, the general solutions to the equation, $\sin 4x - \sin 2x = 0$ are

$$x = \frac{\pi}{6} + \frac{2n\pi}{3}, x = \frac{\pi}{2} + \frac{2n\pi}{3}, \text{ and } x = n\pi \text{ where } n \text{ is an integer.}$$

To verify these solutions you can graph $y = \sin 4x - \sin 2x$ and approximate the x-intercepts.

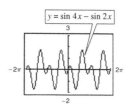

The x-intercepts occur at $0, \dfrac{\pi}{6}, \dfrac{\pi}{2}, \dfrac{5\pi}{6}, \pi, \dfrac{7\pi}{6}, \ldots$

10. Given that a football player can kick a football from ground level with an initial velocity of 80 feet per second, you have the following

$$r = \tfrac{1}{32}v_0^2 \sin 2\theta \qquad \text{Write projectile motion model.}$$

$$r = \tfrac{1}{32}(80)^2 \sin 2\theta \qquad \text{Substitute 80 for } v_0.$$

$$r = 200 \sin 2\theta \qquad \text{Simplify.}$$

Use a graphing utility to graph the model, $r = 200 \sin 2\theta$.

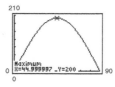

The maximum point on the graph over the interval $(0°, 90°)$ occurs at $\theta = 45°$.

So, the player must kick the football at an angle of $45°$ to yield the maximum horizontal distance of 200 feet.

Appendix

Checkpoints for Appendix A.1

1. (a) Natural numbers: $\left\{\frac{6}{3}, 8\right\}$

(b) Whole numbers: $\left\{\frac{6}{3}, 8\right\}$

(c) Integers: $\left\{-22, -1, \frac{6}{3}, 8\right\}$

(d) Rational numbers: $\left\{-22, -7.5, -1 - \frac{1}{4}, \frac{6}{3}, 8\right\}$

(e) Irrational numbers: $\left\{-\pi, \frac{1}{2}\sqrt{2}\right\}$

2.

$-1.6 \quad -\frac{3}{4} \quad 0.7 \quad \frac{5}{2}$

(a) The point representing the real number $\frac{5}{2} = 2.5$ lies halfway between 2 and 3, on the real number line.

(b) The point representing the real number -1.6 lies between -2 and -1 but closer to -2, on the real number line.

(c) The point representing the real number $-\frac{3}{4}$ lies between -1 and 0 but closer to -1, on the real number line.

(d) The point representing the real number 0.7 lies between 0 and 1 but closer to 1, on the real number line.

3. (a) Because -5 lies to the left of 1 on the real number line, you can say that -5 is *less than* 1, and write $-5 < 1$.

(b) Because $\frac{3}{2}$ lies to the left of 7 on the real number line, you can say that $\frac{3}{2}$ is *less than* 7, and write $\frac{3}{2} < 7$.

(c) Because $-\frac{2}{3}$ lies to the right of $-\frac{3}{4}$ on the real number line, you can say that $-\frac{2}{3}$ is *greater than* $-\frac{3}{4}$, and write $-\frac{2}{3} > -\frac{3}{4}$.

(d) Because -3.5 lies to the left of 1 on the real number line, you can say that -3.5 is *less than* 1, and write $-3.5 < 1$.

4. (a) The inequality $x > -3$ denotes all real numbers greater than -3.

(b) The inequality $0 < x \le 4$ means that $x > 0$ and $x \le 4$. This double inequality denotes all real numbers between 0 and 4, including 4 but not including 0.

5. The interval consists of real numbers greater than or equal to -2 and less than 5.

6. The inequality $-2 < x \le 4$ can represent the statement "x is greater than -2 and at most 4."

7. (a) $|1| = 1$

(b) $-\left|\frac{3}{4}\right| = -\left(\frac{3}{4}\right) = -\frac{3}{4}$

(c) $\frac{2}{|-3|} = \frac{2}{3}$

(d) $-|0.7| = -(0.7) = -0.7$

8. (a) If $x > -3$, then $\dfrac{|x + 3|}{x + 3} = \dfrac{x + 3}{x + 3} = 1$.

(b) If $x < -3$, then $\dfrac{|x + 3|}{x + 3} = \dfrac{-(x + 3)}{x + 3} = -1$.

9. (a) $|-3| < |4|$ because $|-3| = 3$ and $|4| = 4$, and 3 is less than 4.

(b) $-|-4| = -|-4|$ because $-|-4| = -4$ and $-|4| = -4$.

(c) $|-3| > -|-3|$ because $|-3| = 3$ and $-|-3| = -3$, and 3 is greater than -3.

10. (a) The distance between 35 and -23 is
$$|35 - (-23)| = |58| = 58.$$

(b) The distance between -35 and -23 is
$$|-35 - (-23)| = |-12| = 12.$$

(c) The distance between 35 and 23 is
$$|35 - 23| = |12| = 12.$$

11.

Algebraic Expression	Terms	Coefficients
$-2x + 4$	$-2x, 4$	$-2, 4$

12.

Expression	Value of Variable	Substitute	Value of Expression
$4x - 5$	$x - 0$	$4(0) - 5$	$0 - 5 = -5$

13. (a) $x + 9 = 9 + x$: This statement illustrates the Commutative Property of Addition. In other words, you obtain the same result whether you add x and 9, or 9 and x.

(b) $5(x^3 \cdot 2) = (5x^3)2$: This statement illustrates the Associative Property of Multiplication. In other words, to form the product $5 \cdot x^3 \cdot 2$, it does not matter whether 5 and $(x^3 \cdot 2)$, or $5x^3$ and 2 are multiplied first.

(c) $(2 + 5x^2)y^2 = 2y^2 + 5x^2 \cdot y^2$: This statement illustrates the Distributive Property. In other words, the terms 2 and $5x^2$ are multiplied by y^2.

14. (a) $\dfrac{3}{5} \cdot \dfrac{x}{6} = \dfrac{3x}{30} = \dfrac{3x \div 3}{30 \div 3} = \dfrac{x}{10}$

(b) $\dfrac{x}{10} + \dfrac{2x}{5} = \dfrac{x}{10} + \dfrac{2x}{5} \cdot \dfrac{2}{2}$

$= \dfrac{x}{10} + \dfrac{2x}{5} = \dfrac{x}{10} + \dfrac{2x}{5} \cdot \dfrac{2}{2}$

$= \dfrac{x}{10} + \dfrac{4x}{10}$

$= \dfrac{x + 4x}{10}$

$= \dfrac{5x \div 5}{10 \div 5}$

$= \dfrac{x}{2}$

Checkpoints for Appendix A.2

1. (a) $-3^4 = -(3)(3)(3)(3) = -81$

(b) $(-3)^4 = (-3)(-3)(-3)(-3) = 81$

(c) $3^2 \cdot 3 = 3^{2+1} = 3^3 = (3)(3)(3) = 27$

(d) $\dfrac{3^5}{3^8} = 3^{5-8} = 3^{-3} = \dfrac{1}{3^3} = \dfrac{1}{27}$

2. (a) When $x = 4$, the expression $-x^{-2}$ has a value of

$-x^{-2} = -(4)^{-2} = -\dfrac{1}{4^2} = -\dfrac{1}{16}.$

(b) When $x = 4$, the expression $\dfrac{1}{4}(-x)^4$ has a value of

$\dfrac{1}{4}(-x)^4 = \dfrac{1}{4}(-4)^4 = \dfrac{1}{4}(256) = 64.$

3. (a) $(2x^{-2}y^3)(-x^4y) = (2)(-1)(x^{-2})(x^4)(y^3)(y)$

$= -2x^2y^4$

(b) $(4a^2b^3)^0 = 1,\ a \neq 0,\ b \neq 0$

(c) $(-5z)^3(z^2) = (-5)^3(z)^3z^2$

$= -125z^5$

(d) $\left(\dfrac{3x^4}{x^2y^2}\right)^2 = \left(\dfrac{3x^2}{4^2}\right)^2 = \dfrac{3^2(x^2)^2}{(y^2)^2}$

$= \dfrac{9x^4}{y^4},\ x \neq 0$

4. (a) $2a^{-2} = \dfrac{2}{a^2}$ Property 3

(b) $\dfrac{3a^{-3}b^4}{15ab^{-1}} = \dfrac{3b^4 \cdot b}{15a \cdot a^3}$ Property 3

$= \dfrac{b^5}{5a^4}$ Property 1

(c) $\left(\dfrac{x}{10}\right)^{-1} = \dfrac{x^{-1}}{10^{-1}}$ Property 7

$= \dfrac{10}{x}$ Property 3

(d) $(-2x^2)^3(4x^3)^{-1} = (-2)^3(x^2)^3 \cdot 4^{-1} \cdot (x^3)^{-1}$ Property 5

$= \dfrac{-8x^6}{4x^3}$ Properties 3 and 6

$= -2x^3$ Property 2

5. $45,850 = 4.585 \times 10^4$

6. $-2.718 \times 10^{-3} = -0.002718$

7. $(24,000,000,000)(0.00000012)(300,000)$

$= (2.4 \times 10^{10})(1.2 \times 10^{-7})(3.0 \times 10^5)$

$= (2.4)(1.2)(3.0)(10^8)$

$= 8.64 \times 10^8$

$= 864,000,000$

8. (a) $-\sqrt{144} = -12$ because $-\left(\sqrt{144}\right) = \left(\sqrt{12^2}\right) = -(12) = -12$.

(b) $\sqrt{-144}$ is not a real number because no real number raised to the second power produces -144.

(c) $\sqrt{\dfrac{25}{64}} = \dfrac{5}{8}$ because $\left(\dfrac{5}{8}\right)^2 = \dfrac{5^2}{8^2} = \dfrac{25}{64}$.

(d) $-\sqrt[3]{\dfrac{8}{27}} = -\dfrac{2}{3}$ because $-\left(\sqrt[3]{\dfrac{8}{27}}\right) = -\left(\dfrac{\sqrt[3]{8}}{\sqrt[3]{27}}\right) = -\left(\dfrac{2}{3}\right)$.

9. (a) $\dfrac{\sqrt{125}}{\sqrt{5}} = \sqrt{\dfrac{125}{5}}$ Property 3

$\qquad = \sqrt{25}$ Simplify.

$\qquad = 5$ Simplify.

(b) $\sqrt[3]{125^2} = \left(\sqrt[3]{125}\right)^2$ Property 1

$\qquad = (5)^2$ Simplify.

$\qquad = 25$ Simplify.

(c) $\sqrt[3]{x^2} \cdot \sqrt[3]{x} = \sqrt[3]{x^2 \cdot x}$ Property 2

$\qquad = \sqrt[3]{x^3}$ Simplify.

$\qquad = x$ Property

(d) $\sqrt{\sqrt{x}} = \sqrt[2 \cdot 2]{x}$ Property 4

$\qquad = \sqrt[4]{x}$ Simplify.

10. (a) $\sqrt{32} = \sqrt{16 \cdot 2} = \sqrt{4^2 \cdot 2} = 4\sqrt{2}$

(b) $\sqrt[3]{250} = \sqrt[3]{125 \cdot 2} = \sqrt[3]{5^3 \cdot 2} = 5\sqrt[3]{2}$

(c) $\sqrt{24a^5} = \sqrt{4 \cdot 6 \cdot a^4 \cdot a} = \sqrt{4a^4 \cdot 6a}$

$\qquad = \sqrt{\left(2a^2\right)^2 \cdot 6a}$

$\qquad = 2a^2\sqrt{6a}$

(d) $\sqrt[3]{-135x^3} = \sqrt[3]{(-27) \cdot 5 \cdot x^3}$

$\qquad = \sqrt[3]{(-3x)^3 \cdot 5}$

$\qquad = -3x\sqrt[3]{5}$

11. (a) $3\sqrt{8} + \sqrt{18} = 3\sqrt{4 \cdot 2} + \sqrt{9 \cdot 2}$ Find square factors.

$\qquad = 3 \cdot 2\sqrt{2} + 3\sqrt{2}$ Find square roots.

$\qquad = 6\sqrt{2} + 3\sqrt{2}$ Multiply.

$\qquad = (6 + 3)\sqrt{2}$ Combine like radicals.

$\qquad = 9\sqrt{2}$ Simplify.

(b) $\sqrt[3]{81x^5} - \sqrt[3]{24x^2} = \sqrt[3]{27x^3 \cdot 3x^2} - \sqrt[3]{8 \cdot 3x^2}$ Find cube factors.

$\qquad = 3x\sqrt[3]{3x^2} - 2\sqrt[3]{3x^2}$ Find cube roots.

$\qquad = (3x - 2)\sqrt[3]{3x^2}$ Combine like radicals.

12. (a) $\dfrac{5}{3\sqrt{2}} = \dfrac{5}{3\sqrt{2}} \cdot \dfrac{\sqrt{2}}{\sqrt{2}}$ $\sqrt{2}$ is rationalizing factor.

$\qquad = \dfrac{5\sqrt{2}}{3(2)}$ Multiply.

$\qquad = \dfrac{5\sqrt{2}}{6}$ Simplify.

(b) $\dfrac{1}{\sqrt[3]{25}} = \dfrac{1}{\sqrt[3]{25}} \cdot \dfrac{\sqrt[3]{5}}{\sqrt[3]{5}}$ $\sqrt[3]{5}$ is rationalizing factor.

$\qquad = \dfrac{\sqrt[3]{5}}{\sqrt[3]{125}}$ Multiply.

$\qquad = \dfrac{\sqrt[3]{5}}{5}$ Simplify.

13. $\dfrac{8}{\sqrt{6} - \sqrt{2}} = \dfrac{8}{\sqrt{6} - \sqrt{2}} \cdot \dfrac{\sqrt{6} + \sqrt{2}}{\sqrt{6} + \sqrt{2}}$ Multiply numerator and denominator by conjugate of denominator.

$= \dfrac{8\left(\sqrt{6} + \sqrt{2}\right)}{6 + \sqrt{12} - \sqrt{12} - 2}$ Use Distributive Property.

$= \dfrac{8\left(\sqrt{6} + \sqrt{2}\right)}{4}$ Simplify.

$= 2\left(\sqrt{6} + \sqrt{2}\right)$ Simplify.

14. $\dfrac{2 - \sqrt{2}}{3} = \dfrac{2 - \sqrt{2}}{3} \cdot \dfrac{2 + \sqrt{2}}{2 + \sqrt{2}}$ Multiply numerator and denominator by conjugate of numerator.

$= \dfrac{4 + 2\sqrt{2} - 2\sqrt{2} - 2}{3\left(2 + \sqrt{2}\right)}$ Multiply.

$= \dfrac{2}{3\left(2 + \sqrt{2}\right)}$ Simplify.

15. (a) $\sqrt[3]{27} = 27^{1/3}$

(b) $\sqrt{x^3 y^5 z} = \left(x^3 y^5 z\right)^{1/2}$

$= x^{3 \cdot 1/2} y^{5 \cdot 1/2} z^{1/2}$

$= x^{3/2} y^{5/2} z^{1/2}$

(c) $3x\sqrt[3]{x^2} = 3x\left(x^2\right)^{1/3}$

$= 3x \cdot x^{2/3}$

$= 3x^{1 + 2/3}$

$= 3x^{5/3}$

16. (a) $\left(x^2 - 7\right)^{-1/2} = \dfrac{1}{\left(x^2 - 7\right)^{1/2}} = \dfrac{1}{\sqrt{x^2 - 7}}$

(b) $-3b^{1/3} c^{2/3} = -3\left(bc^2\right)^{1/3} = -3\sqrt[3]{bc^2}$

(c) $a^{0.75} = a^{3/4} = \sqrt[4]{a^3}$

(d) $\left(x^2\right)^{2/5} = x^{4/5} = \sqrt[5]{x^4}$

17. (a) $(-125)^{-2/3} = \left(\sqrt[3]{-125}\right)^{-2} = (-5)^{-2} = \dfrac{1}{(-5)^2} = \dfrac{1}{25}$

(b) $\left(4x^2 y^{3/2}\right)\left(-3x^{-1/3}\right)\left(y^{-3/5}\right) = -12x^{(2) - (1/3)} y^{(3/2) - (3/5)} = -12x^{5/3} y^{9/10}, x \ne 0, y \ne 0$

(c) $\sqrt[3]{\sqrt[4]{27}} = \sqrt[12]{27} = \sqrt[12]{(3)^3} = 3^{3/12} = 3^{1/4} = \sqrt[4]{3}$

(d) $(3x + 2)^{5/2} (3x + 2)^{-1/2} = (3x + 2)^{(5/2) - (1/2)} = (3x + 2)^2, x \ne -2/3$

Checkpoints for Appendix A.3

1.

Polynomial	Standard Form	Degree	Leading Coefficient
$6 - 7x^3 + 2x$	$-7x^3 + 2x + 6$	3	-7

3.

$$\overset{\text{F}\quad\text{O}\quad\text{I}\quad\text{L}}{(3x - 1)(x - 5) = 3x^2 - 15x - x + 5}$$

$$= 3x^2 - 16x + 5$$

2. $\left(2x^3 - x + 3\right) - \left(x^2 - 2x - 3\right)$

$= 2x^3 - x + 3 - x^2 + 2x + 3$

$= 2x^3 - x^2 + (-x + 2x) + (3 + 3)$

$= 2x^3 - x^2 + x + 6$

4. This product has the form $(u + v)(u - v) = u^2 - v^2$.

$$(x - 2 + 3y)(x - 2 - 3y) = [(x - 2) + 3y][(x - 2) - 3y]$$
$$= (x - 2)^2 - (3y)^2$$
$$= x^2 - 4x + 4 - 9y^2$$
$$= x^2 - 9y^2 - 4x + 4$$

5. (a) $5x^3 - 15x^2 = 5x^2(x) - 5x^2(3)$ $\quad 5x^2$ is a common factor.
$$= 5x^2(x - 3)$$

(b) $-3 + 6x - 12x^3 = -12x^3 + 6x - 3$
$$= -3(4x^3) + (-3)(-2x) + (-3)(1) \quad -3 \text{ is a common factor.}$$
$$= -3(4x^3 - 2x + 1)$$

(c) $(x + 1)(x^2) - (x + 1)(2) = (x + 1)(x^2 - 2)$ $\quad (x + 1)$ is a common factor.

6. $100 - 4y^2 = 4(25 - y^2)$ $\quad 4$ is a common factor.
$$= 4[(5)^2 - (y)^2]$$
$$= 4(5 + y)(5 - y) \quad \text{Difference of two squares.}$$

7. $(x - 1)^2 - 9y^4 = (x - 1)^2 - (3y^2)^2$
$$= [(x - 1) + 3y^2][(x - 1) - 3y^2]$$
$$= (x - 1 + 3y^2)(x - 1 - 3y^2)$$

8. $9x^2 - 30x + 25 = (3x)^2 - 2(3x)(5) + 5^2$
$$= (3x - 5)^2$$

9. $64x^3 - 1 = (4x)^3 - (1)^3$
$$= (4x - 1)(16x^2 - 4x + 1)$$

10. (a) $x^3 + 216 = (x)^3 + (6)^3$
$$= (x + 6)(x^2 - 6x + 36)$$

(b) $5y^3 + 135 = 5(y^3 + 27)$
$$= 5[(y)^3 + (3)^3]$$
$$= 5(y + 3)(y^2 - 3y + 9)$$

11. For the trinomial $x^2 + x - 6$, you have $a = 1$, $b = 1$, and $c = -6$. Because b is positive and c is negative, one factor of -6 is positive and one is negative. So, the possible factorizations of $x^2 + x - 6$ are

$(x - 3)(x + 2)$,

$(x + 3)(x - 2)$,

$(x + 6)(x - 1)$, and

$(x - 6)(x + 1)$.

Testing the middle term, you will find the correct factorization to be $(x^2 + x - 6) = (x + 3)(x - 2)$.

12. (a) For the trinomial $2x^2 - 5x + 3$, you have $a = 2$ and $c = 3$, which means that the factors of 3 must have like signs. The possible factorizations are

$(2x + 1)(x + 3)$,

$(2x - 1)(x - 3)$,

$(2x + 3)(x + 1)$, and

$(2x - 3)(x - 1)$.

Testing the middle term, you will find the correct factorization to be $2x^2 - 5x + 3 = (2x - 3)(x - 1)$.

(b) For the trinomial $12x^2 + 7x + 1$, you have $a = 12$, $b = 7$, and $c = 1$. Because a, b, and c are all positive, the factors of a and c are positive.

So, the possible factorizations are

$(12x + 1)(x + 1)$,

$(6x + 1)(2x + 1)$, and

$(4x + 1)(3x + 1)$.

Testing the middle term, you will find the correct factorization to be $12x^2 + 7x + 1 = (4x + 1)(3x + 1)$.

13. $\begin{aligned} x^3 + x^2 - 5x - 5 &= (x^3 + x^2) - (5x + 5) && \text{Group terms.} \\ &= x^2(x + 1) - 5(x + 1) && \text{Factor each group.} \\ &= (x + 1)(x^2 - 5) && \text{Distributive Property} \end{aligned}$

14. $\begin{aligned} 2x^2 + 5x - 12 &= 2x^2 + 8x - 3x - 12 && \text{Rewrite middle term.} \\ &= (2x^2 + 8x) - (3x + 12) && \text{Group terms.} \\ &= 2x(x + 4) - 3(x + 4) && \text{Factor groups.} \\ &= (x + 4)(2x - 3) && \text{Distributive Property} \end{aligned}$

Checkpoints for Appendix A.4

1. (a) The domain of the polynomial $4x^2 + 3$, $x \geq 0$ is the set of all real numbers that are greater than or equal to 0. The domain is specifically restricted.

(b) The domain of the radical expression $\sqrt{x + 7}$ is the set of all real numbers greater than or equal to -7, because the square root of a negative number is not a real number.

(c) The domain of the rational expression $\dfrac{1 - x}{x}$ is the set of all real number except $x = 0$, which would

result in division by zero, which is undefined.

2. $\begin{aligned} \dfrac{4x + 12}{x^2 - 3x - 18} &= \dfrac{4(x + 3)}{(x - 6)(x + 3)} && \text{Factor completely.} \\ &= \dfrac{4}{x - 6}, x \neq -3 && \text{Divide out common factor.} \end{aligned}$

3. $\begin{aligned} \dfrac{3x^2 - x - 2}{5 - 4x - x^2} &= \dfrac{3x^2 - x - 2}{-x^2 - 4x + 5} = \dfrac{(3x + 2)(x - 1)}{-(x + 5)(x - 1)} && \text{Write in standard form.} \\ &= -\dfrac{3x + 2}{x + 5}, x \neq 1 && \text{Divide out common factor.} \end{aligned}$

4. $\dfrac{15x^2 + 5x}{x^3 - 3x^2 - 18x} \cdot \dfrac{x^2 - 2x - 15}{3x^2 - 8x - 3} = \dfrac{5\cancel{x}\,\cancel{(3x+1)}}{\cancel{x}(x - 6)\cancel{(x+3)}} \cdot \dfrac{(x - 5)\cancel{(x+3)}}{\cancel{(3x+1)}(x - 3)}$

$$= \dfrac{5(x - 5)}{(x - 6)(x - 3)}, \, x \neq -3, \, x \neq -\dfrac{1}{3}, \, x \neq 0$$

5. $\dfrac{x^3 - 1}{x^2 - 1} \div \dfrac{x^2 + x + 1}{x^2 + 2x + 1} = \dfrac{x^3 - 1}{x^2 - 1} \cdot \dfrac{x^2 + 2x + 1}{x^2 + x + 1}$ Invert and multiply.

$$= \dfrac{\cancel{(x-1)}\,\cancel{(x^2 + x + 1)}}{\cancel{(x+1)}\,\cancel{(x-1)}} \cdot \dfrac{\cancel{(x+1)}(x + 1)}{\cancel{x^2 + x + 1}}$$ Factor completely.

$$= x + 1, \, x \neq \pm1$$ Divide out common factors.

6. $\dfrac{x}{2x - 1} - \dfrac{1}{x + 2} = \dfrac{x(x + 2) - (2x - 1)}{(2x - 1)(x + 2)}$ Basic definition

$$= \dfrac{x^2 + 2x - 2x + 1}{(2x - 1)(x + 2)}$$ Distributive Property

$$= \dfrac{x^2 + 1}{(2x - 1)(x + 2)}$$ Combine like terms.

7. The LCD of the ration expression $\dfrac{4}{x} - \dfrac{x + 5}{x^2 - 4} + \dfrac{4}{x + 2}$ is $x(x + 2)(x - 2)$.

$\dfrac{4}{x} - \dfrac{x + 5}{(x + 2)(x - 2)} + \dfrac{4}{x + 2} = \dfrac{4(x + 2)(x - 2)}{x(x + 2)(x - 2)} - \dfrac{x(x + 5)}{x(x + 2)(x - 2)} + \dfrac{4x(x - 2)}{x(x + 2)(x - 2)}$ Rewrite using the LCD.

$$= \dfrac{4(x + 2)(x - 2) - x(x + 5) + 4x(x - 2)}{x(x + 2)(x - 2)}$$ Distributive Property

$$= \dfrac{4x^2 - 16 - x^2 - 5x + 4x^2 - 8x}{x(x + 2)(x - 2)}$$

$$= \dfrac{7x^2 - 13x - 16}{x(x + 2)(x - 2)}$$

8. $\dfrac{\left(\dfrac{1}{x + 2} + 1\right)}{\left(\dfrac{x}{3} - 1\right)} = \dfrac{\left(\dfrac{1 + 1(x + 2)}{x + 2}\right)}{\left(\dfrac{x - 1(3)}{3}\right)}$ Combine fractions.

$$= \dfrac{\left(\dfrac{x + 3}{x + 2}\right)}{\left(\dfrac{x - 3}{3}\right)}$$ Simplify.

$$= \dfrac{x + 3}{x + 2} \cdot \dfrac{3}{x - 3}$$ Invert and multiply.

$$= \dfrac{3(x + 3)}{(x + 2)(x - 3)}$$

9. $(x - 1)^{-1/3} - x(x - 1)^{-4/3} = (x - 1)^{-4/3}\left[(x - 1)^{(-1/3) - (-4/3)} - x\right]$

$$= (x - 1)^{-4/3}\left[(x - 1)^1 - x\right]$$

$$= -\dfrac{1}{(x - 1)^{4/3}}$$

10. $\dfrac{x^2(x^2-2)^{-1/2} + (x^2-2)^{1/2}}{x^2-2} = \dfrac{x^2(x^2-2)^{-1/2} + (x^2-2)^{1/2}}{x^2-2} \cdot \dfrac{(x^2-2)^{1/2}}{(x^2-2)^{1/2}}$

$$= \dfrac{x^2(x^2-2)^{0} + (x^2-2)^{1}}{(x^2-2)^{3/2}}$$

$$= \dfrac{x^2 + x^2 - 2}{(x^2-2)^{3/2}}$$

$$= \dfrac{2x^2 - 2}{(x^2-2)^{3/2}}$$

$$= \dfrac{2(x+1)(x-1)}{(x^2-2)^{3/2}}$$

11. $\dfrac{\sqrt{9+h}-3}{h} = \dfrac{\sqrt{9+h}-3}{h} \cdot \dfrac{\sqrt{9+h}+3}{\sqrt{9+h}+3}$

$$= \dfrac{\left(\sqrt{9+h}\right)^2 - (3)^2}{h\left(\sqrt{9+h}+3\right)}$$

$$= \dfrac{(9+h)-9}{h\left(\sqrt{9+h}+3\right)}$$

$$= \dfrac{h}{h\left(\sqrt{9+h}+3\right)}$$

$$= \dfrac{1}{\sqrt{9+h}+3}, h \ne 0$$

Checkpoints for Appendix A.5

1. (a)

$7 - 2x = 15$	Write original equation.
$-2x = 8$	Subtract 7 from each side.
$x = -4$	Divide each side by -2.

Check: $7 - 2x = 15$

$7 - 2(-4) \overset{?}{=} 15$

$7 + 8 \overset{?}{=} 15$

$15 = 15$

(b)

$7x - 9 = 5x + 7$	Write original equation.
$2x - 9 = 7$	Subtract $5x$ from each side.
$2x = 16$	Add 9 from each side.
$x = 8$	Divide each side by 2.

Check: $7x - 9 = 5x + 7$

$7(8) - 9 = 5(8 + 7)$

$56 - 9 = 40 + 7$

$47 = 47$ ✓

2.

$\dfrac{4x}{9} - \dfrac{1}{3} = x + \dfrac{5}{3}$	Write original equation.
$(9)\left(\dfrac{4x}{9}\right) - (9)\left(\dfrac{1}{3}\right) = (9)x + 9\left(\dfrac{5}{3}\right)$	Multiply each term by the LCD.
$4x - 3 = 9x + 15$	Simplify.
$-5x = 18$	Combine like terms.
$x = -\dfrac{18}{5}$	Divide each side by -5.

3.
$$\frac{3x}{x-4} = 5 + \frac{12}{x-4}$$ Write original equation.

$$(x-4)\left(\frac{3x}{x-4}\right) = (x-4)5 + (x-4)\left(\frac{12}{x-4}\right)$$ Multiply each term by LCD.

$$3x = 5x - 20 + 12, \ x \neq 4$$ Simplify.

$$-2x = -8$$ Divide each side by -2.

$$x = 4$$ Extraneous solution

In the original equation, $x = 4$ yields a denominator of zero. So, $x = 4$ is an extraneous solution, and the original equation has no solution.

4.
$$2x^2 - 3x + 1 = 6$$ Write original equation.

$$2x^2 - 3x - 5 = 0$$ Write in general form.

$$(2x - 5)(x + 1) = 0$$ Factor.

$$2x - 5 = 0 \Rightarrow x = \frac{5}{2}$$ Set 1st factor equal to 0.

$$x + 1 = 0 \Rightarrow x = -1$$ Set 2nd factor equal to 0.

The solutions are $x = -1$ and $x = \frac{5}{2}$.

Check: $x = -1$

$$2x^2 - 3x + 1 = 6$$

$$2(-1)^2 - 3(-1) + 1 \overset{?}{=} 6$$

$$2(1) + 3 + 1 \overset{?}{=} 6$$

$$6 = 6 \ \checkmark$$

$$x = \frac{5}{2}$$

$$2x^2 - 3x + 1 = 6$$

$$2\left(\frac{5}{2}\right)^2 - 3\left(\frac{5}{2}\right) + 1 \overset{?}{=} 6$$

$$2\left(\frac{25}{4}\right) - \frac{15}{2} + 1 \overset{?}{=} 6$$

$$6 = 6 \ \checkmark$$

5. (a)
$$3x^2 = 36$$ Write original equation.

$$x^2 = 12$$ Divide each side by 3.

$$x = \pm\sqrt{12}$$ Extract square roots.

$$x = \pm 2\sqrt{3}$$

The solutions are $x = \pm 2\sqrt{3}$.

Check: $x = -2\sqrt{3}$

$$3x^2 = 36$$

$$3\left(-2\sqrt{3}\right)^2 \overset{?}{=} 36$$

$$3(12) \overset{?}{=} 36$$

$$36 = 36 \ \checkmark$$

$$x = 2\sqrt{3}$$

$$3x^2 = 36$$

$$3\left(2\sqrt{3}\right)^2 \overset{?}{=} 36$$

$$3(12) \overset{?}{=} 36$$

$$36 = 36 \ \checkmark$$

(b)
$$(x - 1)^2 = 10$$

$$x - 1 = \pm\sqrt{10}$$

$$x = 1 \pm \sqrt{10}$$

The solutions are $x = 1 \pm \sqrt{10}$.

Check: $x = 1 - \sqrt{10}$

$$(x - 1)^2 = 10$$

$$\left[\left(1 - \sqrt{10}\right) - 1\right]^2 \overset{?}{=} 10$$

$$\left(-\sqrt{10}\right)^2 \overset{?}{=} 10$$

$$10 = 10 \ \checkmark$$

$$x = 1 + \sqrt{10}$$

$$(x - 1)^2 = 10$$

$$\left[\left(1 + \sqrt{10}\right) - 1\right]^2 \overset{?}{=} 10$$

$$\left(\sqrt{10}\right)^2 \overset{?}{=} 10$$

$$10 = 10 \ \checkmark$$

6. $x^2 - 4x - 1 = 0$ Write original equation.

         $x^2 - 4x = 1$ Add 1 to each side.

   $x^2 - 4x + (2)^2 = 1 + (2)^2$ Add 2^2 to each side.

$$\underbrace{\qquad\qquad}_{\left(\text{half of 4}\right)^2}$$

         $(x - 2)^2 = 5$ Simplify.

         $x - 2 = \pm\sqrt{5}$ Extract square roots.

         $x = 2 \pm \sqrt{5}$ Add 2 to each side.

The solutions are $x = 2 \pm \sqrt{5}$.

Check: $x = 2 - \sqrt{5}$

$$x^2 - 4x - 1 = 0$$

$$\left(2 - \sqrt{5}\right)^2 - 4\left(2 - \sqrt{5}\right) - 1 \overset{?}{=} 0$$

$$\left(4 - 4\sqrt{5} + 5\right) - 8 + 4\sqrt{5} - 1 \overset{?}{=} 0$$

$$4 + 5 - 8 - 1 \overset{?}{=} 0$$

$$0 = 0 \checkmark$$

    $x = 2 + \sqrt{5}$ also checks. $\checkmark$

7. $3x^2 - 10x - 2 = 0$ Original equation

         $3x^2 - 10x = 2$ Add 2 to each side.

         $x^2 - \dfrac{10}{3}x = \dfrac{2}{3}$ Divide each side by 3.

   $x^2 - \dfrac{10}{3}x + \left(\dfrac{5}{3}\right)^2 = \dfrac{2}{3} + \left(\dfrac{5}{3}\right)^2$ Add $\left(\dfrac{5}{3}\right)^2$ to each side.

         $\left(x - \dfrac{5}{3}\right)^2 = \dfrac{31}{9}$ Simplify.

         $x - \dfrac{5}{3} = \pm\dfrac{\sqrt{31}}{3}$ Extract square roots.

         $x = \dfrac{5}{3} \pm \dfrac{\sqrt{31}}{3}$ Add $\dfrac{5}{3}$ to each side.

The solutions are $\dfrac{5}{3} \pm \dfrac{\sqrt{31}}{3}$.

8. $3x^2 + 2x - 10 = 0$ Write original equation.

$$x = \frac{-6 \pm \sqrt{6^2 - 4ac}}{2a}$$ Quadratic Formula

$$x = \frac{-2 \pm \sqrt{(2)^2 - 4(3)(-10)}}{2(3)}$$ Substitute $a = 3$, $b = 2$ and $c = -10$.

$$x = \frac{-2 \pm \sqrt{4 + 120}}{6}$$ Simplify.

$$x = \frac{-2 \pm \sqrt{124}}{6}$$ Simplify.

$$x = \frac{-2 \pm 2\sqrt{31}}{6}$$ Simplify.

$$x = \frac{2(-1 \pm \sqrt{31})}{6}$$ Factor our common factor.

$$x = \frac{-1 \pm \sqrt{31}}{3}$$ Simplify.

The solutions are $\dfrac{-1 \pm \sqrt{31}}{3}$.

Check: $x = \dfrac{-1 \pm \sqrt{31}}{3}$

$$3x^2 + 2x - 10 = 0$$

$$3\left(\frac{-1 + \sqrt{31}}{3}\right)^2 + 2\left(\frac{-1 + \sqrt{31}}{3}\right) - 10 \overset{?}{=} 0$$

$$\frac{1}{3} + \frac{2\sqrt{31}}{3} + \frac{31}{3} + \frac{2\sqrt{31}}{3} - 10 \overset{?}{=} 0$$

$$10 - 10 \overset{?}{=} 0$$

$$0 = 0 \checkmark$$

The solution $x = \dfrac{-1 - \sqrt{31}}{3}$ also checks. $\checkmark$

9. $18x^2 - 48x + 32 = 0$

$9x^2 - 24x + 16 = 0$

$$x = \frac{-b \pm \sqrt{b^2 - 4ac}}{2a}$$

$$x = \frac{-(-24) \pm \sqrt{(-24)^2 - 4(9)(16)}}{2(9)}$$

$$x = \frac{24 \pm \sqrt{0}}{18}$$

$$x = \frac{4}{3}$$

The quadratic equation has only one solution: $x = \dfrac{4}{3}$.

10.

$$9x^4 - 12x^2 = 0 \qquad \text{Write original equation.}$$

$$3x^2(3x^2 - 4) = 0 \qquad \text{Factor out common factor.}$$

$$3x^2 = 0 \implies x = 0 \qquad \text{Set 1st factor equal to 0.}$$

$$3x^2 - 4 = 0 \implies 3x^2 = 4 \qquad \text{Set 2nd factor equal to 0.}$$

$$x^2 = \frac{4}{3}$$

$$x = \pm\sqrt{\frac{4}{3}}$$

$$x = \frac{\pm 2\sqrt{3}}{3}$$

Check: $x = 0$

$$9x^4 - 12x^2 = 0$$

$$9(0)^4 - 12(0)^2 \overset{?}{=} 0$$

$$0 = 0 \checkmark$$

$$x = \frac{2\sqrt{3}}{3}$$

$$9x^4 - 12x^2 = 0$$

$$9\left(\frac{2\sqrt{3}}{3}\right)^4 - 12\left(\frac{2\sqrt{3}}{3}\right)^2 \overset{?}{=} 0$$

$$9\left(\frac{16}{9}\right) - 12\left(\frac{4}{3}\right) \overset{?}{=} 0$$

$$16 - 16 \overset{?}{=} 0$$

$$0 = 0 \checkmark$$

The solution $x = -\sqrt{2}$ also checks. $\checkmark$

11. (a)

$x^3 - 5x^2 - 2x + 10 = 0$	Write original equation.
$x^2(x - 5) - 2(x - 5) = 0$	Factor by grouping.
$(x - 5)(x^2 - 2) = 0$	Distributive Property
$x - 5 = 0 \Rightarrow x = 5$	Set 1st factor equal to 0.
$x^2 - 2 = 0 \Rightarrow x^2 = 2$	Set 2nd factor equal to 0.
$\quad = \pm\sqrt{2}$	

Check: $x = 5$

$$x^3 - 5x^2 - 2x + 10 = 0$$

$$(5)^3 - 5(5)^2 - 2(5) + 10 \stackrel{?}{=} 0$$

$$125 - 125 - 10 + 10 \stackrel{?}{=} 0$$

$$0 = 0 \checkmark$$

$x = \sqrt{2}$

$$x^3 - 5x^2 - 2x + 10 = 0$$

$$(\sqrt{2})^3 - 5(\sqrt{2})^2 - 2(\sqrt{2}) + 10 \stackrel{?}{=} 0$$

$$2\sqrt{2} - 10 - 2\sqrt{2} + 10 \stackrel{?}{=} 0$$

$$0 = 0 \checkmark$$

The solution $x = -\sqrt{2}$ also checks. $\checkmark$

(b) $6x^3 - 27x^2 - 54x = 0$

$3x(2x^2 - 9x - 18) = 0$	Factor out common factor.
$3x(2x + 3)(x - 6) = 0$	Factor quadratic factor.
$3x = 0 \Rightarrow x = 0$	Set 1st factor equal to 0.
$2x + 3 = 0 \Rightarrow x = -\frac{3}{2}$	Set 2nd factor equal to 0.
$x - 6 = 0 \Rightarrow x = 6$	Set 3rd factor equal to 0.

Check: $x = 0$

$$6x^3 - 27x^2 - 54x = 0$$

$$6(0)^3 - 27(0)^2 - 54(0) \stackrel{?}{=} 0$$

$$0 = 0 \checkmark$$

$x = -\frac{3}{2}$

$$6x^3 - 27x^2 - 54x = 0$$

$$6\left(-\frac{3}{2}\right)^3 - 27\left(-\frac{3}{2}\right)^2 - 54\left(-\frac{3}{2}\right) \stackrel{?}{=} 0$$

$$6\left(-\frac{27}{8}\right)^3 - 27\left(\frac{9}{4}\right)^2 + 27(3) \stackrel{?}{=} 0$$

$$-\frac{81}{4} - \frac{243}{4} + 81 \stackrel{?}{=} 0$$

$$0 = 0 \checkmark$$

$x = 6$

$$6x^3 - 27x^2 - 54x = 0$$

$$6(6)^3 - 27(6)^2 - 54(6) \stackrel{?}{=} 0$$

$$6(216) - 27(36) - 324 \stackrel{?}{=} 0$$

$$0 = 0 \checkmark$$

12.

$-\sqrt{40 - 9x} + 2 = x$ Write original equation.

$-\sqrt{40 - 9x} = x - 2$ Isolated radical.

$\left(-\sqrt{40 - 9x}\right)^2 = (x - 2)^2$ Square each side.

$40 - 9x = x^2 - 4x + 4$ Simplify.

$0 = x^2 + 5x - 36$ Write in general form.

$0 = (x - 4)(x + 9)$ Factor.

$x - 4 = 0 \Rightarrow x = 4$ Set 1st factor equal to 0.

$x + 9 = 0 \Rightarrow x = -9$ Set 2nd factor equal to 0.

Check: $x = 4$

$$-\sqrt{40 - 9x} + 2 = x$$

$$-\sqrt{40 - 9(4)} + 2 \overset{?}{=} 4$$

$$-\sqrt{4} + 2 \overset{?}{=} 4$$

$$-2 + 2 \overset{?}{=} 4$$

$$0 \neq 4 \; ✗$$

$x = 4$ is an extraneous solution.

$x = -9$

$$-\sqrt{40 - 9(-9)} + 2 \overset{?}{=} -9$$

$$-\sqrt{121} + 2 \overset{?}{=} -9$$

$$-11 + 2 \overset{?}{=} -9$$

$$-9 \overset{?}{=} -9 \; ✓$$

The only solution is $x = -9$.

13. $(x - 5)^{2/3} = 16$ Write original equation.

$\sqrt[3]{(x - 5)^2} = 16$ Rewrite in radical form.

$(x - 5)^2 = 4096$ Cube each side.

$x - 5 = \pm 64$ Extract square roots.

$x = 5 \pm 64$ Add 5 to each side.

$x = -59, x = 69$

Check: $x = -59$ $x = 69$

$(x - 5)^{2/3} = 16$ $(x - 5)^{2/3} = 16$

$(-59 - 5)^{2/3} \overset{?}{=} 16$ $(69 - 5)^{2/3} \overset{?}{=} 16$

$(-64)^{2/3} \overset{?}{=} 16$ $(64)^{2/3} \overset{?}{=} 16$

$(-4)^2 \overset{?}{=} 16$ $(4)^2 \overset{?}{=} 16$

$16 = 16 \checkmark$ $16 = 16 \checkmark$

The solutions are $x = -59$ and $x = 64$.

14. $\left| x^2 + 4x \right| = 5x + 12$

First Equation

$x^2 + 4x = 5x + 12$ Use positive expression.

$x^2 - x - 12 = 0$ Write in general form.

$(x + 3)(x - 4) = 0$ Factor.

$x + 3 = 0 \Rightarrow x = -3$ Set 1st factor equal to 0.

$x - 4 = 0 \Rightarrow x = 4$ Set 2nd factor equal to 0.

Second Equation

$-(x^2 + 4x) = 5x + 12$ Use negative expression.

$-x^2 - 4x = 5x + 12$ Distributive Property

$0 = x^2 + 9x + 12$ Write in general form.

Use the Quadratic equation to solve the equation $0 = x^2 + 9x + 12$.

$x = \dfrac{-b \pm \sqrt{b^2 - 4ac}}{2a}$

$x = \dfrac{-9 \pm \sqrt{9^2 - 4(1)(12)}}{2(1)}$

$x = \dfrac{-9 \pm \sqrt{33}}{2}$

The possible solutions are $x = -3$, $x = 4$, and $x = \dfrac{-9 \pm \sqrt{33}}{2}$.

Check: $x = -3$

$$\left|x^2 + 4x\right| = 5x + 12$$

$$\left|(-3)^2 + 4(-3)\right| \overset{?}{=} 5(-3) + 12$$

$$\left|-3\right| \overset{?}{=} -15 + 12$$

$$3 \overset{\times}{=} -3$$

$x = -3$ does not check.

$x = 4$

$$\left|(4)^2 + 4(4)\right| \overset{?}{=} 5(4) + 12$$

$$\left|32\right| \overset{?}{=} 32$$

$$32 = 32 \checkmark$$

$x = 4$ checks.

$$x = \frac{-9 \pm \sqrt{33}}{2}$$

$$\left|\frac{\left(-9 + \sqrt{33}\right)^2}{2} + 4\left(\frac{-9 + \sqrt{33}}{2}\right)\right| \overset{?}{=} 5\left(\frac{-9 + \sqrt{33}}{2}\right) + 12$$

$$\left|\frac{21}{2} - \frac{5\sqrt{33}}{2}\right| \overset{?}{=} \frac{-45}{2} + \frac{5\sqrt{33}}{2} + 12$$

$$\frac{5\sqrt{33}}{2} - \frac{21}{2} = \frac{-21}{2} + \frac{5\sqrt{33}}{2} \checkmark$$

$x = \dfrac{-9 + \sqrt{33}}{2}$ checks.

$$x = \frac{-9 \pm \sqrt{33}}{2}$$

$$\left|\frac{\left(-9 - \sqrt{33}\right)^2}{2} + 4\left(\frac{-9 - \sqrt{33}}{2}\right)\right| \overset{?}{=} 5\left(\frac{-9 - \sqrt{33}}{2}\right) + 12$$

$$\left|\frac{21}{2} + \frac{5\sqrt{33}}{2}\right| \overset{?}{=} \frac{-21}{2} - \frac{5\sqrt{33}}{2}$$

$$\frac{21}{2} + \frac{5\sqrt{33}}{2} \overset{\times}{=} -\frac{21}{2} - \frac{5\sqrt{33}}{2}$$

$x = \dfrac{-9 - \sqrt{33}}{2}$ does not check.

$x = -3$ and $x = \dfrac{-9 - \sqrt{33}}{2}$ are extraneous solutions. So, the solutions are $x = 4$ and $x = \dfrac{-9 + \sqrt{33}}{2}$.

15. The formula for the volume of a cylindrical container is $V = \pi r^2 h$. To find the height of the container, solve for h.

$$h = \frac{V}{\pi r^2}$$

Then, using $V = 84$ and $r = 3$, find the height.

$$h = \frac{84}{\pi(3)^2}$$

$$h = \frac{84}{9\pi}$$

$$h \approx 2.97$$

So, the height of the container is about 2.97 inches. You can use unit analysis to check that your answer is reasonable.

$$\frac{84 \text{ in.}^3}{9\pi \text{ in.}^2} = \frac{84 \text{ in.} \cdot \cancel{\text{in.}} \cdot \cancel{\text{in.}}}{9\pi \; \cancel{\text{in.}} \cdot \cancel{\text{in.}}} = \frac{84}{9\pi} \text{ in.} \approx 2.97 \text{ in.}$$

Checkpoints for Appendix A.6

1. (a) $[-1, 3]$ corresponds to $-1 \le x \le 3$. The interval is bounded.

(b) $(-1, 6)$ corresponds to $-1 < x < 6$. The interval is bounded.

(c) $(-\infty, 4)$ corresponds to $x < 4$. The interval is unbounded.

(d) $[0, \infty)$ corresponds to $x \ge 0$. The interval is unbounded.

2.

$7x - 3 \le 2x + 7$	Write original inequality.
$5x \le 10$	Subtract $2x$ and add 3 to each side.
$x \le 2$	Divide each side by 5.

The solution set is all real numbers less than or equal to 2.

3. (a) **Algebraic solution**

$2 - \frac{5}{3}x > x - 6$	Write original inequality.
$6 - 5x > 3x - 18$	Multiply each side by 3.
$-8x > -24$	Subtract $3x$ and subtract 6 from each side.
$x < 3$	Divide each side by -8 reverse the inequality symbol.

The solution set is all real numbers that are less than 3.

(b) **Graphical solution**

Use a graphing utility to graph $y_1 = 2 - \frac{5}{3}x$ and $y_2 = x - 6$ in the same viewing window. Use the *intersect* feature to determine that the graphs intersect at $(3, -3)$. The graph of y_1 lies above the graph of y_2 to the left of their point of intersection, which implies that $y_1 > y_2$ for all $x < 3$.

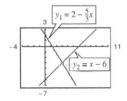

4.

$1 < 2x + 7 < 11$	Write original inequality.
$1 - 7 < 2x + 7 - 7 < 11 - 7$	Subtract 7 from each part.
$-6 < 2x < 4$	Simplify.
$-\dfrac{6}{2} < \dfrac{2x}{2} < \dfrac{4}{2}$	Divide each part by 2.
$-3 < x < 2$	Simplify.

The solution set is all real numbers greater than -3 and less than 2, which is denoted by $(-3, 2)$.

5.

$\left| x - 20 \right| \le 4$	Write original inequality.
$-4 \le x - 20 \le 4$	Write equivalent inequalities.
$-4 + 20 \le x - 20 + 20 \le 4 = 20$	Add 20 to each part.
$16 \le x \le 24$	Simplify.

The solution set is all real numbers that are greater than or equal to 16 and less than or equal to 24, which is denoted by $[16, 24]$.

6. Let m represent your additional minutes in one month. Write and solve an inequality.

$$0.45m + 45.99 > 0.35m + 54.99$$
$$0.10m > 9$$
$$m > 90$$

Plan B costs more when you use more than 90 additional minutes in one month.

7. Let x represent the actual weight of your bag. The difference of the actual weight and the weight on the scale is at most $\frac{1}{64}$ pound. That is, $\left| x - \frac{1}{2} \right| \le -\frac{1}{64}$.

You can solve the inequality as follows.

$$-\tfrac{1}{64} \le x - \tfrac{1}{2} \le \tfrac{1}{64}$$
$$\tfrac{31}{64} \le x \le \tfrac{33}{64}$$

The least your bag can weigh is $\frac{31}{64}$ pound, which would have cost $\left(\frac{31}{64} \text{ pound} \right) \times (\$9.89 \text{ per pound}) = \$4.79$.

The most your bag can weigh is $\frac{33}{64}$ pound, which would have cost $\left(\frac{33}{64} \text{ pound} \right) \times (\$9.89 \text{ per pound}) = \$5.10$.

So, you might have been under charged by as much as $\$5.10 - \$4.95 = \$0.15$ or over charged as much as $\$4.95 - \$4.79 = \$0.16$.

Checkpoints for Appendix A.7

1. Do not apply radicals term-by-term when adding terms.

   Leave as $\sqrt{x^2 + 4}$.

2. $x(x - 2)^{-1/2} + 3(x - 2)^{1/2} = (x - 2)^{-1/2}\left[x(x - 2)^0 + 3(x - 2)^1\right]$

   $= (x - 2)^{-1/2}[x + 3x - 6]$

   $= (x - 2)^{-1/2}(4x - 6)$

3. The expression on the left side of the equation is three times the expression on the right side. To make both sides equal, insert a factor of 3.

   $$\dfrac{6x - 3}{\left(x^2 - x + 4\right)^2} = (3)\dfrac{1}{\left(x^2 - x + 4\right)^2}(2x - 1)$$

4. To write the expression on the left side of the equation in the form given on the right side, first multiply the numerator and denominator of the first term by $\dfrac{1}{9}$. Then multiply the numerator and denominator of the second term by $\dfrac{1}{25}$.

   $$\dfrac{9x^2}{16} + 25y^2 = \dfrac{9x^2}{16}\left(\dfrac{1/9}{1/9}\right) + \dfrac{25y^2}{1}\left(\dfrac{1/25}{1/25}\right) = \dfrac{x^2}{16/25} + \dfrac{y^2}{1/25}$$

5. $\dfrac{-6x}{\left(1 - 3x^2\right)^2} + \dfrac{1}{3\sqrt{x}} = -x\left(1 - 3x^2\right)^{-2} + x^{-1/3}$

6. $\dfrac{x^4 - 2x^3 + 5}{x^3} = \dfrac{x^4}{x^3} - \dfrac{2x^3}{x^3} + \dfrac{5}{x^3} = x - 2 + \dfrac{5}{x^3}$

Chapter 1   Practice Test Solutions

1. (a) Midpoint: $\left(\dfrac{-3+5}{2}, \dfrac{4+(-6)}{2}\right) = (1,-1)$

(b) Distance: $d = \sqrt{\left[5-(-3)\right]^2 + (-6-4)^2}$

$\qquad\qquad\ = \sqrt{(8)^2 + (-10)^2}$

$\qquad\qquad\ = \sqrt{164}$

$\qquad\qquad\ = 2\sqrt{41}$

2. $y = \sqrt{7-x}$

Domain: $x \le 7$

x	7	6	3	-2
y	0	1	2	3

3. $\left[x-(-3)\right]^2 + (y-5)^2 = 6^2$

$\quad (x+3)^2 + (y-5)^2 = 36$

4. $\quad m = \dfrac{-1-4}{3-2} = -5$

$\quad y-4 = -5(x-2)$

$\quad y-4 = -5x+10$

$\qquad y = -5x+14$

5. $y = \frac{4}{3}x - 3$

6. $2x + 3y = 0$

$\qquad y = -\frac{2}{3}x$

$\qquad m_1 = -\frac{2}{3}$

$\perp m_2 = \frac{3}{2}$ through $(4,1)$

$\quad y-1 = \frac{3}{2}(x-4)$

$\quad y-1 = \frac{3}{2}x - 6$

$\qquad y = \frac{3}{2}x - 5$

7. $(5, 32)$ and $(9, 44)$

$\quad m = \dfrac{44-32}{9-5} = \dfrac{12}{4} = 3$

$\quad y - 32 = 3(x-5)$

$\quad y - 32 = 3x - 15$

$\qquad y = 3x + 17$

When $x = 20$, $y = 3(20) + 17$

$\qquad\qquad\quad y = \$77.$

8. $f(x-3) = (x-3)^2 - 2(x-3) + 1$

$\qquad\qquad\ = x^2 - 6x + 9 - 2x + 6 + 1$

$\qquad\qquad\ = x^2 - 8x + 16$

9. $\qquad f(3) = 12 - 11 = 1$

$\dfrac{f(x) - f(3)}{x-3} = \dfrac{(4x-11)-1}{x-3}$

$\qquad\qquad\quad = \dfrac{4x-12}{x-3}$

$\qquad\qquad\quad = \dfrac{4(x-3)}{x-3}$

$\qquad\qquad\quad = 4, \ x \ne 3$

10. $f(x) = \sqrt{36 - x^2} = \sqrt{(6+x)(6-x)}$

Domain: $[-6, 6]$, because $(6+x)(6-x) \ge 0$ on this interval.

Range: $[0, 6]$, because $0 \le (6+x)(6-x) \le 36$ on this interval.

11. (a) $6x - 5y + 4 = 0$

$\qquad y = \dfrac{6x+4}{5}$ is a function of x.

(b) $x^2 + y^2 = 9$

$\qquad y = \pm\sqrt{9 - x^2}$ is not a function of x.

(c) $y^3 = x^2 + 6$

$\qquad y = \sqrt[3]{x^2 + 6}$ is a function of x.

12. Parabola

Vertex: $(0, -5)$

Intercepts: $(0, -5), \left(\pm\sqrt{5}, 0\right)$

y-axis symmetry

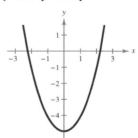

13. Intercepts: $(0, 3), (-3, 0)$

x	-4	-3	-2	-1	0	1	2
y	1	0	1	2	3	4	5

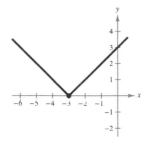

14.

x	-3	-2	-1	0	1	2	3
y	12	6	2	1	3	5	7

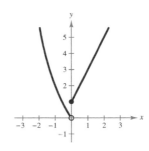

15. (a) $f(x + 2)$

Horizontal shift two units to the left

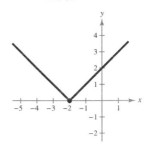

(b) $-f(x) + 2$

Reflection in the x-axis and a vertical shift two units upward

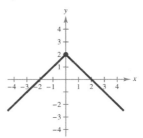

16. (a) $(g - f)(x) = g(x) - f(x)$

$$= (2x^2 - 5) - (3x + 7)$$

$$= 2x^2 - 3x - 12$$

(b) $(fg)(x) = f(x)g(x)$

$$= (3x + 7)(2x^2 - 5)$$

$$= 6x^3 + 14x^2 - 15x - 35$$

17. $f(g(x)) = f(2x + 3)$

$$= (2x + 3)^2 - 2(2x + 3) + 16$$

$$= 4x^2 + 12x + 9 - 4x - 6 + 16$$

$$= 4x^2 + 8x + 19$$

18. $f(x) = x^3 + 7$

$$y = x^3 + 7$$

$$x = y^3 + 7$$

$$x - 7 = y^3$$

$$\sqrt[3]{x - 7} = y$$

$$f^{-1}(x) = \sqrt[3]{x - 7}$$

19. (a) $f(x) = |x - 6|$ does not have an inverse.

Its graph does not pass the horizontal line test.

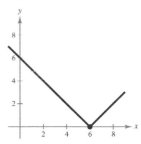

(b) $f(x) = ax + b, a \neq 0$ does have an inverse.

$$y = ax + b$$

$$x = ay + b$$

$$\frac{x - b}{a} = y$$

$$f^{-1}(x) = \frac{x - b}{a}$$

(c) $f(x) = x^3 - 19$ does have an inverse.

$$y = x^3 - 19$$

$$x = y^3 - 19$$

$$x + 19 = y^3$$

$$\sqrt[3]{x + 19} = y$$

$$f^{-1}(x) = \sqrt[3]{x + 19}$$

© 2014 Cengage Learning. All Rights Reserved. May not be scanned, copied or duplicated, or posted to a publicly accessible website, in whole or in part.

20. $f(x) = \sqrt{\dfrac{3 - x}{x}}, \ 0 < x \le 3, \ y \ge 0$

$y = \sqrt{\dfrac{3 - x}{x}}$

$x = \sqrt{\dfrac{3 - y}{y}}$

$x^2 = \dfrac{3 - y}{y}$

$x^2 y = 3 - y$

$x^2 y + y = 3$

$y(x^2 + 1) = 3$

$y = \dfrac{3}{x^2 + 1}$

$f^{-1}(x) = \dfrac{3}{x^2 + 1}, \ x \ge 0$

21. False. The slopes of 3 and $\frac{1}{3}$ are not negative reciprocals.

22. True. Let $y = (f \circ g)(x)$. Then $x = (f \circ g)^{-1}(y)$.

Also, $(f \circ g)(x) = y$

$f(g(x)) = y$

$g(x) = f^{-1}(y)$

$x = g^{-1}(f^{-1}(y))$

$x = (g^{-1} \circ f^{-1})(y)$

Because $x = x$, we have

$(f \circ g)^{-1}(y) = (g^{-1} \circ f^{-1})(y).$

23. True. It must pass the vertical line test to be a function and it must pass the horizontal line test to have an inverse.

24. $z = \dfrac{cx^3}{\sqrt{y}}$

$-1 = \dfrac{c(-1)^3}{\sqrt{25}}$

$-1 = \dfrac{-c}{5}$

$5 = c$

$z = \dfrac{5x^3}{\sqrt{y}}$

25. $y \approx 0.669x + 2.669$

Chapter 2 Practice Test Solutions

1. x-intercepts: $(1, 0), (5, 0)$

y-intercept: $(0, 5)$

Vertex: $(3, -4)$

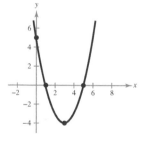

2. $a = 0.01, \ b = -90$

$\dfrac{-b}{2a} = \dfrac{90}{2(0.01)} = 4500$ units

3. Vertex: $(1, 7)$ opening downward through $(2, 5)$

$y = a(x - 1)^2 + 7$ Standard form

$5 = a(2 - 1)^2 + 7$

$5 = a + 7$

$a = -2$

$y = -2(x - 1)^2 + 7$

$\quad = -2(x^2 - 2x + 1) + 7$

$\quad = -2x^2 + 4x + 5$

4. $y = \pm a(x - 2)(3x - 4)$ where a is any real number

$y = \pm(3x^2 - 10x + 8)$

5. Leading coefficient: -3

Degree: 5

Moves down to the right and up to the left

6. $0 = x^5 - 5x^3 + 4x$

$\quad = x(x^4 - 5x^2 + 4)$

$\quad = x(x^2 - 1)(x^2 - 4)$

$\quad = x(x + 1)(x - 1)(x + 2)(x - 2)$

$x = 0, \ x = \pm 1, \ x = \pm 2$

7. $f(x) = x(x - 3)(x + 2)$

$\quad = x(x^2 - x - 6)$

$\quad = x^3 - x^2 - 6x$

8. Intercepts: $(0, 0), (\pm 2\sqrt{3}, 0)$

Moves up to the right

Moves down to the left

Origin symmetry

x	-2	-1	0	1	2
y	16	11	0	-11	-16

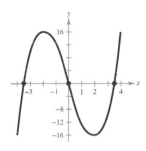

9.
$$
x - 3 \overline{) 3x^4 + 0x^3 - 7x^2 + 2x - 10}
$$

quotient: $3x^3 + 9x^2 + 20x + 62 + \dfrac{176}{x - 3}$

$\underline{3x^4 - 9x^3}$

$9x^3 - 7x^2$

$\underline{9x^3 - 27x^2}$

$20x^2 + 2x$

$\underline{20x^2 - 60x}$

$62x - 10$

$\underline{62x - 186}$

176

10.
$$
x^2 + 2x - 1 \overline{) x^3 + 0x^2 + 0x - 11}
$$

quotient: $x - 2 + \dfrac{5x - 13}{x^2 + 2x - 1}$

$\underline{x^3 + 2x^2 - x}$

$-2x^2 + x - 11$

$\underline{-2x^2 - 4x + 2}$

$5x - 13$

11.

$$
\begin{array}{r|rrrrrr}
-5 & 3 & 13 & 0 & 0 & 12 & -1 \\
   &   & -15 & 10 & -50 & 250 & -1310 \\
\hline
   & 3 & -2 & 10 & -50 & 262 & -1311
\end{array}
$$

$$
\frac{3x^5 + 13x^4 + 12x - 1}{x + 5} = 3x^4 - 2x^3 + 10x^2 - 50x + 262 - \frac{1311}{x + 5}
$$

12.

$$
\begin{array}{r|rrrr}
-6 & 7 & 40 & -12 & 15 \\
   &   & -42 & 12 & 0 \\
\hline
   & 7 & -2 & 0 & 15
\end{array}
$$

$f(-6) = 15$

13. $0 = x^3 - 19x - 30$

Possible rational roots:
$\pm 1, \pm 2, \pm 3, \pm 5, \pm 6, \pm 10, \pm 15, \pm 30$

$$
\begin{array}{r|rrrr}
-2 & 1 & 0 & -19 & -30 \\
   &   & -2 & 4 & 30 \\
\hline
   & 1 & -2 & -15 & 0
\end{array}
$$

$x = -2$ is a zero.

$0 = (x + 2)(x^2 - 2x - 15)$

$0 = (x + 2)(x + 3)(x - 5)$

Zeros: $x = -2, x = -3, x = 5$

14. $0 = x^4 + x^3 - 8x^2 - 9x - 9$

Possible rational roots: $\pm 1, \pm 3, \pm 9$

$$
\begin{array}{r|rrrrr}
3 & 1 & 1 & -8 & -9 & -9 \\
  &   & 3 & 12 & 12 & 9 \\
\hline
  & 1 & 4 & 4 & 3 & 0
\end{array}
$$

$x = 3$ is a zero.

$0 = (x - 3)(x^3 + 4x^2 + 4x + 3)$

Possible rational roots of $x^3 + 4x^2 + 4x + 3$: $\pm 1, \pm 3$

$$
\begin{array}{r|rrrr}
-3 & 1 & 4 & 4 & 3 \\
   &   & -3 & -3 & -3 \\
\hline
   & 1 & 1 & 1 & 0
\end{array}
$$

$x = -3$ is a zero.

$0 = (x - 3)(x + 3)(x^2 + x + 1)$

The zeros of $x^2 + x + 1$ are $x = \dfrac{-1 \pm \sqrt{3}i}{2}$

(by the Quadratic Formula).

Zeros:

$$x = 3, \; x = -3, \; x = -\frac{1}{2} + \frac{\sqrt{3}}{2}i, \; x = -\frac{1}{2} - \frac{\sqrt{3}}{2}i$$

15. $0 = 6x^3 - 5x^2 + 4x - 15$

Possible rational roots:

$\pm 1, \pm 3, \pm 5, \pm 15, \pm\frac{1}{2}, \pm\frac{3}{2}, \pm\frac{5}{2}, \pm\frac{15}{2}, \pm\frac{1}{3}, \pm\frac{5}{3}, \pm\frac{1}{6}, \pm\frac{5}{6}$

16. $0 = x^3 - \frac{20}{3}x^2 + 9x - \frac{10}{3}$

$0 = 3x^3 - 20x^2 + 27x - 10$

Possible rational roots:

$\pm 1, \pm 2, \pm 5, \pm 10, \pm\frac{1}{3}, \pm\frac{2}{3}, \pm\frac{5}{3}, \pm\frac{10}{3}$

$$\begin{array}{r|rrrr} 1 & 3 & -20 & 27 & -10 \\ & & 3 & -17 & 10 \\ \hline & 3 & -17 & 10 & 0 \end{array}$$

$0 = (x - 1)(3x^2 - 17x + 10)$

$0 = (x - 1)(3x - 2)(x - 5)$

Zeros: $x = 1, x = \frac{2}{3}, x = 5$

17. Possible rational roots: $\pm 1, \pm 2, \pm 5, \pm 10$

$$\begin{array}{r|rrrrr} 1 & 1 & 1 & 3 & 5 & -10 \\ & & 1 & 2 & 5 & 10 \\ \hline & 1 & 2 & 5 & 10 & 0 \end{array}$$

$x = 1$ is a zero.

$$\begin{array}{r|rrrr} -2 & 1 & 2 & 5 & 10 \\ & & -2 & 0 & -10 \\ \hline & 1 & 0 & 5 & 0 \end{array}$$

$x = -2$ is a zero.

$f(x) = (x - 1)(x + 2)(x^2 + 5)$

$\quad = (x - 1)(x + 2)(x + \sqrt{5}i)(x - \sqrt{5}i)$

18. $f(x) = (x - 2)\left[x - (3 + i)\right]\left[x - (3 - i)\right]$

$\quad = (x - 2)\left[(x - 3) - i\right]\left[(x - 3) + i\right]$

$\quad = (x - 2)\left[(x - 3)^2 - i^2\right]$

$\quad = (x - 2)\left[x^2 - 6x + 10\right]$

$\quad = x^3 - 8x^2 + 22x - 20$

19.

$$\begin{array}{r|rrrr} 3i & 1 & 4 & 9 & 36 \\ & & 3i & 12i - 9 & -36 \\ \hline & 1 & 4 + 3i & 12i & 0 \end{array}$$

20. Vertical asymptote: $x = 0$

Horizontal asymptote: $y = \frac{1}{2}$

x-intercept: $(1, 0)$

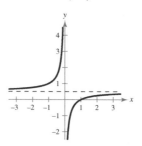

21. $y = 8$ is a horizontal asymptote because the degree of the numerator equals the degree of the denominator. There are no vertical asymptotes.

22. $x = 1$ is a vertical asymptote.

$$\frac{4x^2 - 2x + 7}{x - 1} = 4x + 2 + \frac{9}{x - 1}$$

Thus, $y = 4x + 2$ is a slant asymptote.

23. (a) $(4 - 3i) - (-2 + i) = 4 - 3i + 2 - i = 6 - 4i$

(b) $(4 - 3i)(-2 + i) = -8 + 4i + 6i - 3i^2 = -8 + 10i + 3 = -5 + 10i$

(c) $\dfrac{4 - 3i}{-2 + i} = \dfrac{4 - 3i}{-2 + i} \cdot \dfrac{-2 - i}{-2 - i} = \dfrac{-8 - 4i + 6i + 3i^2}{4 + 1}$

$\quad = \dfrac{-11 + 2i}{5} = -\dfrac{11}{5} + \dfrac{2}{5}i$

24. $x^2 - 49 \leq 0$

$(x + 7)(x - 7) \leq 0$

Critical numbers: $x = -7$ and $x = 7$

Test intervals: $(-\infty, -7), (-7, 7), (7, \infty)$

Test: Is $x^2 - 49 \leq 0$?

Solution set: $[-7, 7]$

25. $\dfrac{x + 3}{x - 7} \geq 0$

Critical numbers: $x = -3$ and $x = 7$

Test intervals: $(-\infty, -3), (-3, 7), (7, \infty)$

Test: Is $\dfrac{x + 3}{x - 7} \geq 0$?

Solution set: $(-\infty, -3] \cup [7, \infty)$

Chapter 3   Practice Test Solutions

1. $x^{3/5} = 8$

$x = 8^{5/3} = \left(\sqrt[3]{8}\right)^5 = 2^5 = 32$

2. $3^{x-1} = \frac{1}{81}$

$3^{x-1} = 3^{-4}$

$x - 1 = -4$

$x = -3$

3. $f(x) = 2^{-x} = \left(\frac{1}{2}\right)^x$

x	-2	-1	0	1	2
$f(x)$	4	2	1	$\frac{1}{2}$	$\frac{1}{4}$

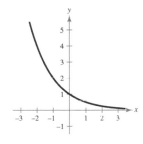

4. $g(x) = e^x + 1$

x	-2	-1	0	1	2
$g(x)$	1.14	1.37	2	3.72	8.39

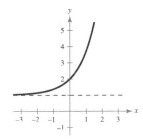

5. (a) $A = P\left(1 + \frac{r}{n}\right)^{nt}$

$A = 5000\left(1 + \frac{0.09}{12}\right)^{12(3)} \approx \$6543.23$

(b) $A = P\left(1 + \frac{r}{n}\right)^{nt}$

$A = 5000\left(1 + \frac{0.09}{4}\right)^{4(3)} \approx \$6530.25$

(c) $A = Pe^{rt}$

$A = 5000e^{(0.09)(3)} \approx \$6549.82$

6. $7^{-2} = \frac{1}{49}$

$\log_7 \frac{1}{49} = -2$

7. $x - 4 = \log_2 \frac{1}{64}$

$2^{x-4} = \frac{1}{64}$

$2^{x-4} = 2^{-6}$

$x - 4 = -6$

$x = -2$

8. $\log_b \sqrt[4]{\frac{8}{25}} = \frac{1}{4} \log_b \frac{8}{25}$

$= \frac{1}{4}\left[\log_b 8 - \log_b 25\right]$

$= \frac{1}{4}\left[\log_b 2^3 - \log_b 5^2\right]$

$= \frac{1}{4}\left[3 \log_b 2 - 2 \log_b 5\right]$

$= \frac{1}{4}\left[3(0.3562) - 2(0.8271)\right]$

$= -0.1464$

9. $5 \ln x - \frac{1}{2} \ln y + 6 \ln z = \ln x^5 - \ln \sqrt{y} + \ln z^6$

$= \ln\left(\frac{x^5 z^6}{\sqrt{y}}\right), z > 0$

10. $\log_9 28 = \frac{\log 28}{\log 9} \approx 1.5166$

11. $\log N = 0.6646$

$N = 10^{0.6646} \approx 4.62$

12.

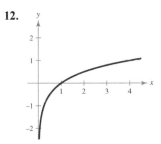

13. Domain:

$x^2 - 9 > 0$

$(x + 3)(x - 3) > 0$

$x < -3 \text{ or } x > 3$

14.

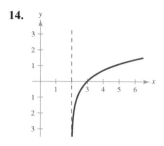

15. False. $\dfrac{\ln x}{\ln y} \neq \ln(x - y)$ because $\dfrac{\ln x}{\ln y} = \log_y x$.

16. $5^3 = 41$

$$x = \log_5 41 = \dfrac{\ln 41}{\ln 5} \approx 2.3074$$

17. $x - x^2 = \log_5 \frac{1}{25}$

$$5^{x - x^2} = \tfrac{1}{25}$$

$$5^{x - x^2} = 5^{-2}$$

$$x - x^2 = -2$$

$$0 = x^2 - x - 2$$

$$0 = (x + 1)(x - 2)$$

$$x = -1 \text{ or } x = 2$$

18. $\log_2 x + \log_2(x - 3) = 2$

$$\log_2[x(x - 3)] = 2$$

$$x(x - 3) = 2^2$$

$$x^2 - 3x = 4$$

$$x^2 - 3x - 4 = 0$$

$$(x + 1)(x - 4) = 0$$

$$x = 4$$

$$x = -1 \ (\text{extraneous})$$

$x = 4$ is the only solution.

19. $\dfrac{e^x + e^{-x}}{3} = 4$

$$e^x(e^x + e^{-x}) = 12e^x$$

$$e^{2x} + 1 = 12e^x$$

$$e^{2x} - 12e^x + 1 = 0$$

$$e^x = \dfrac{12 \pm \sqrt{144 - 4}}{2}$$

$e^x \approx 11.9161$	or	$e^x \approx 0.0839$
$x = \ln 11.9161$		$x = \ln 0.0839$
$x \approx 2.478$		$x \approx -2.478$

20. $A = Pe^{rt}$

$$12{,}000 = 6000e^{0.13t}$$

$$2 = e^{0.13t}$$

$$0.13t = \ln 2$$

$$t = \dfrac{\ln 2}{0.13}$$

$$t \approx 5.3319 \text{ years or 5 years 4 months}$$

Chapter 4   Practice Test Solutions

1. $350° = 350\left(\dfrac{\pi}{180}\right) = \dfrac{35\pi}{18}$

2. $\dfrac{5\pi}{9} = \dfrac{5\pi}{9} \cdot \dfrac{180}{\pi} = 100°$

3. $135° \, 14' \, 12'' = \left(135 + \frac{14}{60} + \frac{12}{3600}\right)°$

$$\approx 135.2367°$$

4. $-22.569° = -\left(22° + 0.569(60)'\right)$

$$= -22° \, 34.14'$$

$$= -\left(22° \, 34' + 0.14(60)''\right)$$

$$\approx -22° \, 34' \, 8''$$

5. $\cos\theta = \dfrac{2}{3}$

$$x = 2, r = 3, y = \pm\sqrt{9 - 4} = \pm\sqrt{5}$$

$$\tan\theta = \dfrac{y}{x} = \pm\dfrac{\sqrt{5}}{2}$$

6. $\sin \theta = 0.9063$

$\theta = \arcsin(0.9063)$

$\theta = 65° = \dfrac{13\pi}{36}$ or $\theta = 180° - 65° = 115° = \dfrac{23\pi}{36}$

7. $\tan 20° = \dfrac{35}{x}$

$x = \dfrac{35}{\tan 20°}$

≈ 96.1617

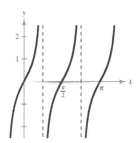

8. $\theta = \dfrac{6\pi}{5}$, θ is in Quadrant III.

Reference angle: $\dfrac{6\pi}{5} - \pi = \dfrac{\pi}{5}$ or $36°$

9. $\csc 3.92 = \dfrac{1}{\sin 3.92} \approx -1.4242$

10. $\tan \theta = 6 = \dfrac{6}{1}$, θ lies in Quandrant III.

$y = -6, x = -1, r = \sqrt{36 + 1} = \sqrt{37}$, so

$\sec \theta = \dfrac{\sqrt{37}}{-1} \approx -6.0828.$

11. Period: 4π

Amplitude: 3

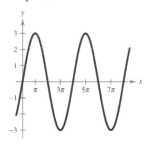

12. Period: 2π

Amplitude: 2

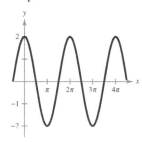

13. Period: $\dfrac{\pi}{2}$

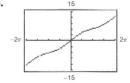

14. Period: 2π

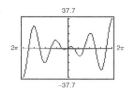

15.

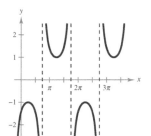

16.

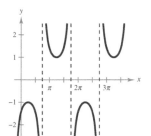

17. $\theta = \arcsin 1$

$\sin \theta = 1$

$\theta = \dfrac{\pi}{2} = 90°$

18. $\theta = \arctan(-3)$

$\tan \theta = -3$

$\theta \approx -1.249 \approx -71.565°$

19. $\sin\left(\arccos\dfrac{4}{\sqrt{35}}\right)$

$\sin\theta = \dfrac{\sqrt{19}}{\sqrt{35}} \approx 0.7368$

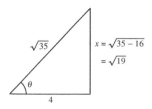

$x = \sqrt{35-16}$
$= \sqrt{19}$

20. $\cos\left(\arcsin\dfrac{x}{4}\right)$

$\cos\theta = \dfrac{\sqrt{16-x^2}}{4}$

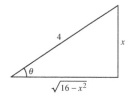

21. Given $A = 40°, c = 12$

$B = 90° - 40° = 50°$

$\sin 40° = \dfrac{a}{12}$

$a = 12\sin 40° \approx 7.713$

$\cos 40° = \dfrac{b}{12}$

$b = 12\cos 40° \approx 9.193$

22. Given $B = 6.84°, a = 21.3$

$A = 90° - 6.84° = 83.16°$

$\sin 83.16° = \dfrac{21.3}{c}$

$c = \dfrac{21.3}{\sin 83.16°} \approx 21.453$

$\tan 83.16° = \dfrac{21.3}{b}$

$b = \dfrac{21.3}{\tan 83.16°} \approx 2.555$

23. Given $a = 5, b = 9$

$c = \sqrt{25+81} = \sqrt{106} \approx 10.296$

$\tan A = \dfrac{5}{9}$

$A = \arctan\dfrac{5}{9} \approx 29.055°$

$B \approx 90° - 29.055° = 60.945°$

24. $\sin 67° = \dfrac{x}{20}$

$x = 20\sin 67° \approx 18.41$ feet

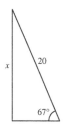

25. $\tan 5° = \dfrac{250}{x}$

$x = \dfrac{250}{\tan 5°}$

≈ 2857.513 feet

≈ 0.541 mi

Chapter 5   Practice Test Solutions

1. $\tan x = \dfrac{4}{11}, \sec x < 0 \Rightarrow x$ is in Quadrant III.

$y = -4, x = -11, r = \sqrt{16+121} = \sqrt{137}$

$\sin x = -\dfrac{4}{\sqrt{137}} = -\dfrac{4\sqrt{137}}{137}$ $\csc x = -\dfrac{\sqrt{137}}{4}$

$\cos x = -\dfrac{11}{\sqrt{137}} = -\dfrac{11\sqrt{137}}{137}$ $\sec x = -\dfrac{\sqrt{137}}{11}$

$\tan x = \dfrac{4}{11}$ $\cot x = \dfrac{11}{4}$

2. $\dfrac{\sec^2 x + \csc^2 x}{\csc^2 x\left(1+\tan^2 x\right)} = \dfrac{\sec^2 x + \csc^2 x}{\csc^2 x + \left(\csc^2 x\right)\tan^2 x}$

$= \dfrac{\sec^2 x + \csc^2 x}{\csc^2 x + \dfrac{1}{\sin^2 x}\cdot\dfrac{\sin^2 x}{\cos^2 x}}$

$= \dfrac{\sec^2 x + \csc^2 x}{\csc^2 x + \dfrac{1}{\cos^2 x}}$

$= \dfrac{\sec^2 x + \csc^2 x}{\csc^2 x + \sec^2 x} = 1$

3. $\ln|\tan\theta| - \ln|\cot\theta| = \ln\left|\dfrac{\tan\theta}{\cot\theta}\right| = \ln\left|\dfrac{\sin\theta/\cos\theta}{\cos\theta/\sin\theta}\right| = \ln\left|\dfrac{\sin^2\theta}{\cos^2\theta}\right| = \ln\left|\tan^2\theta\right| = 2\ln|\tan\theta|$

4. $\cos\left(\dfrac{\pi}{2} - x\right) = \dfrac{1}{\csc x}$ is true since $\cos\left(\dfrac{\pi}{2} - x\right) = \sin x = \dfrac{1}{\csc x}$.

5. $\sin^4 x + \left(\sin^2 x\right)\cos^2 x = \sin^2 x\left(\sin^2 x + \cos^2 x\right)$ **6.** $\left(\csc x + 1\right)\left(\csc x - 1\right) = \csc^2 x - 1 = \cot^2 x$
$$= \sin^2 x(1) = \sin^2 x$$

7. $\dfrac{\cos^2 x}{1 - \sin x} \cdot \dfrac{1 + \sin x}{1 + \sin x} = \dfrac{\cos^2 x(1 + \sin x)}{1 - \sin^2 x} = \dfrac{\cos^2 x(1 + \sin x)}{\cos^2 x} = 1 + \sin x$

8. $\dfrac{1 + \cos\theta}{\sin\theta} + \dfrac{\sin\theta}{1 + \cos\theta} = \dfrac{\left(1 + \cos\theta\right)^2 + \sin^2\theta}{\sin\theta(1 + \cos\theta)}$

$$= \dfrac{1 + 2\cos\theta + \cos^2\theta + \sin^2\theta}{\sin\theta(1 + \cos\theta)} = \dfrac{2 + 2\cos\theta}{\sin\theta(1 + \cos\theta)} = \dfrac{2}{\sin\theta} = 2\csc\theta$$

9. $\tan^4 x + 2\tan^2 x + 1 = \left(\tan^2 x + 1\right)^2 = \left(\sec^2 x\right)^2 = \sec^4 x$

10. (a) $\sin 105° = \sin\left(60° + 45°\right) = \sin 60° \cos 45° + \cos 60° \sin 45°$

$$= \dfrac{\sqrt{3}}{2} \cdot \dfrac{\sqrt{2}}{2} + \dfrac{1}{2} \cdot \dfrac{\sqrt{2}}{2} = \dfrac{\sqrt{2}}{4}\left(\sqrt{3} + 1\right)$$

   (b) $\tan 15° = \tan\left(60° - 45°\right) = \dfrac{\tan 60° - \tan 45°}{1 + \tan 60° \tan 45°}$

$$= \dfrac{\sqrt{3} - 1}{1 + \sqrt{3}} \cdot \dfrac{1 - \sqrt{3}}{1 - \sqrt{3}} = \dfrac{2\sqrt{3} - 1 - 3}{1 - 3} = \dfrac{2\sqrt{3} - 4}{-2} = 2 - \sqrt{3}$$

11. $\left(\sin 42°\right)\cos 38° - \left(\cos 42°\right)\sin 38° - \sin\left(42° - 38°\right) = \sin 4°$

12. $\tan\left(\theta + \dfrac{\pi}{4}\right) = \dfrac{\tan\theta + \tan\left(\dfrac{\pi}{4}\right)}{1 - \left(\tan\theta\right)\tan\left(\dfrac{\pi}{4}\right)} = \dfrac{\tan\theta + 1}{1 - \tan\theta(1)} = \dfrac{1 + \tan\theta}{1 - \tan\theta}$

13. $\sin\left(\arcsin x - \arccos x\right) = \sin\left(\arcsin x\right)\cos\left(\arccos x\right) - \cos\left(\arcsin x\right)\sin\left(\arccos x\right)$

$$= (x)(x) - \left(\sqrt{1 - x^2}\right)\left(\sqrt{1 - x^2}\right) = x^2 - \left(1 - x^2\right) = 2x^2 - 1$$

14. (a) $\cos\left(120°\right) = \cos\left[2\left(60°\right)\right] = 2\cos^2 60° - 1 = 2\left(\dfrac{1}{2}\right)^2 - 1 = -\dfrac{1}{2}$

   (b) $\tan\left(300°\right) = \tan\left[2\left(150°\right)\right] = \dfrac{2\tan 150°}{1 - \tan^2 150°} = \dfrac{-\dfrac{2\sqrt{3}}{3}}{1 - \left(\dfrac{1}{3}\right)} = -\sqrt{3}$

15. (a) $\sin 22.5° = \sin\dfrac{45°}{2} = \sqrt{\dfrac{1 - \cos 45°}{2}} = \sqrt{\dfrac{1 - \dfrac{\sqrt{2}}{2}}{2}} = \dfrac{\sqrt{2 - \sqrt{2}}}{2}$

   (b) $\tan\dfrac{\pi}{12} = \tan\dfrac{\dfrac{\pi}{6}}{2} = \dfrac{\sin\dfrac{\pi}{6}}{1 + \cos\left(\dfrac{\pi}{6}\right)} = \dfrac{\dfrac{1}{2}}{1 + \dfrac{\sqrt{3}}{2}} = \dfrac{1}{2 + \sqrt{3}} = 2 - \sqrt{3}$

16. $\sin \theta = \dfrac{4}{5}, \theta$ lies in Quadrant II $\Rightarrow \cos \theta = -\dfrac{3}{5}$.

$$\cos \dfrac{\theta}{2} = \sqrt{\dfrac{1 + \cos \theta}{2}} = \sqrt{\dfrac{1 - \dfrac{3}{5}}{2}} = \sqrt{\dfrac{2}{10}} = \dfrac{1}{\sqrt{5}} = \dfrac{\sqrt{5}}{5}$$

17. $\left(\sin^2 x\right) \cos^2 x = \dfrac{1 - \cos 2x}{2} \cdot \dfrac{1 + \cos 2x}{2} = \dfrac{1}{4}\left[1 - \cos^2 2x\right] = \dfrac{1}{4}\left[1 - \dfrac{1 + \cos 4x}{2}\right]$

$$= \dfrac{1}{8}\left[2 - (1 + \cos 4x)\right] = \dfrac{1}{8}\left[1 - \cos 4x\right]$$

18. $6\left(\sin 5\theta\right) \cos 2\theta = 6\left\{\dfrac{1}{2}\left[\sin(5\theta + 2\theta) + \sin(5\theta - 2\theta)\right]\right\} = 3\left[\sin 7\theta + \sin 3\theta\right]$

19. $\sin(x + \pi) + \sin(x - \pi) = 2\left(\sin \dfrac{\left[(x + \pi) + (x - \pi)\right]}{2}\right) \cos \dfrac{\left[(x + \pi) - (x - \pi)\right]}{2}$

$$= 2 \sin x \cos \pi = -2 \sin x$$

20. $\dfrac{\sin 9x + \sin 5x}{\cos 9x - \cos 5x} = \dfrac{2 \sin 7x \cos 2x}{-2 \sin 7x \sin 2x} = -\dfrac{\cos 2x}{\sin 2x} = -\cot 2x$

21. $\dfrac{1}{2}\left[\sin(u + v) - \sin(u - v)\right] = \dfrac{1}{2}\left\{(\sin u) \cos v + (\cos u) \sin v - \left[(\sin u) \cos v - (\cos u) \sin v\right]\right\}$

$$= \dfrac{1}{2}\left[2(\cos u) \sin v\right] = (\cos u) \sin v$$

22. $4 \sin^2 x = 1$

$$\sin^2 x = \dfrac{1}{4}$$

$$\sin x = \pm\dfrac{1}{2}$$

$\sin x = \dfrac{1}{2} \qquad$ or $\sin x = -\dfrac{1}{2}$

$x = \dfrac{\pi}{6}$ or $\dfrac{5\pi}{6} \qquad x = \dfrac{7\pi}{6}$ or $\dfrac{11\pi}{6}$

23. $\tan^2 \theta + \left(\sqrt{3} - 1\right) \tan \theta - \sqrt{3} = 0$

$$\left(\tan \theta - 1\right)\left(\tan \theta + \sqrt{3}\right) = 0$$

$\tan \theta = 1 \qquad$ or $\tan \theta = -\sqrt{3}$

$\theta = \dfrac{\pi}{4}$ or $\dfrac{5\pi}{4} \qquad \theta = \dfrac{2\pi}{3}$ or $\dfrac{5\pi}{3}$

24.
$$\sin 2x = \cos x$$

$$2(\sin x) \cos x - \cos x = 0$$

$$\cos x(2 \sin x - 1) = 0$$

$\cos x = 0 \qquad$ or $\qquad \sin x = \dfrac{1}{2}$

$x = \dfrac{\pi}{2}$ or $\dfrac{3\pi}{2} \qquad\qquad x = \dfrac{\pi}{6}$ or $\dfrac{5\pi}{6}$

25. $\tan^2 x - 6 \tan x + 4 = 0$

$$\tan x = \dfrac{-(-6) \pm \sqrt{(-6)^2 - 4(1)(4)}}{2(1)}$$

$$\tan x = \dfrac{6 \pm \sqrt{20}}{2} = 3 \pm \sqrt{5}$$

$\tan x = 3 + \sqrt{5} \qquad$ or $\tan x = 3 - \sqrt{5}$

$x \approx 1.3821$ or $4.5237 \qquad x \approx 0.6524$ or 3.7940